Organic Reactions

Organic Reactions

VOLUME IV

NEW YORK

JOHN WILEY & SONS, INC.

LONDON: CHAPMAN & HALL, LIMITED

PRINTED IN THE UNITED STATES OF AMERICA

PREFACE TO THE SERIES

In the course of nearly every program of research in organic chemistry the investigator finds it necessary to use several of the better-known synthetic reactions. To discover the optimum conditions for the application of even the most familiar one to a compound not previously subjected to the reaction often requires an extensive search of the literature; even then a series of experiments may be necessary. When the results of the investigation are published, the synthesis, which may have required months of work, is usually described without comment. The background of knowledge and experience gained in the literature search and experimentation is thus lost to those who subsequently have occasion to apply the general method. The student of preparative organic chemistry faces similar difficulties. The textbooks and laboratory manuals furnish numerous examples of the application of various syntheses, but only rarely do they convey an accurate conception of the scope and usefulness of the processes.

For many years American organic chemists have discussed these problems. The plan of compiling critical discussions of the more important reactions thus was evolved. The volumes of *Organic Reactions* are collections of about twelve chapters, each devoted to a single reaction, or a definite phase of a reaction, of wide applicability. The authors have had experience with the processes surveyed. The subjects are presented from the preparative viewpoint, and particular attention is given to limitations, interfering influences, effects of structure, and the selection of experimental techniques. Each chapter includes several detailed procedures illustrating the significant modifications of the method. Most of these procedures have been found satisfactory by the author or one of the editors, but unlike those in *Organic Syntheses* they have not been subjected to careful testing in two or more laboratories. When all known examples of the reaction are not mentioned in the text, tables are given to list compounds which have been prepared by or subjected to the reaction. Every effort has been made to include in the tables all such compounds and references; however, because of the very nature of the reactions discussed and their frequent use as one of the several steps of syntheses in which not all of the intermediates have been isolated, some instances may well have been missed. Never-

v

theless, the investigator will be able to use the tables and their accompanying bibliographies in place of most or all of the literature search so often required.

Because of the systematic arrangement of the material in the chapters and the entries in the tables, users of the books will be able to find information desired by reference to the table of contents of the appropriate chapter. In the interest of economy the entries in the indices have been kept to a minimum, and, in particular, the compounds listed in the tables are not repeated in the indices.

The success of this publication, which will appear periodically in volumes of about twelve chapters, depends upon the cooperation of organic chemists and their willingness to devote time and effort to the preparation of the chapters. They have manifested their interest already by the almost unanimous acceptance of invitations to contribute to the work. The editors will welcome their continued interest and their suggestions for improvements in *Organic Reactions*.

CONTENTS

vii

SUBJECTS OF PREVIOUS VOLUMES

CHAPTER 1

THE DIELS-ALDER REACTION WITH MALEIC ANHYDRIDE

MILTON C. KLOETZEL

DePauw University *

CONTENTS

* Present address, University of Southern California, Los Angeles, California.

1

NATURE OF THE REACTION

The Diels-Alder reaction (diene synthesis) consists in the addition of a compound containing a double or triple bond (usually activated by additional unsaturation in the α,β-position) to the 1,4-positions of a conjugated diene system, with the formation of a six-membered hydroaromatic ring. The following additions of various diene systems to dienophiles are typical examples of the Diels-Alder reaction.

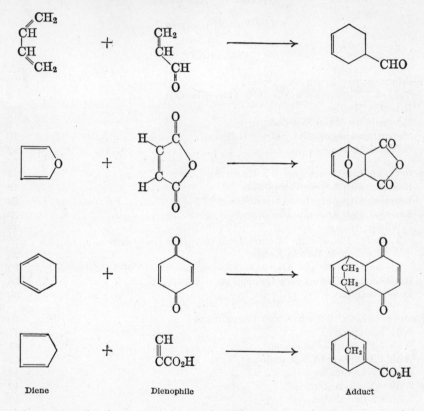

Diene   Dienophile   Adduct

A noteworthy feature of the Diels-Alder reaction is the great variety of the compounds which may serve as the dienophile. With a few exceptions, the compounds that have been employed as dienophiles fall into one of the following categories.

1. $CH_2{=}CHA$.

A = CHO, CO_2H, CO_2CH_3, $CO_2C_2H_5$, $COCl$, $COCH_3$, COC_6H_5, CN, NO_2, C_6H_5, CH_2OH, CH_2X, CH_2NH_2, CH_2CN, CH_2CO_2H, CH_2NCS, $OCOCH_3$, $SC_6H_4CH_3$, SO_2R, X, H.

2. $C_6H_5CH=CHA$.

   $A = CHO, CO_2H, CO_2CH_3, CO_2C_2H_5, COCH_3, COC_6H_5$.

3. $CH_2=CA_2$.

   $A = CO_2C_2H_5, CN, COCH_3, X$.

4. $ACH=CHA$.

   $A = CO_2H, COCl, CO_2CH_3, CO_2C_2H_5, COCH_3, COC_6H_5, X$.

5. Quinones.

6. $AC\equiv CA$.

   $A = CO_2H, CO_2CH_3, CO_2C_2H_5, COC_6H_5, C_6H_5, H$.

The more reactive dienophiles usually contain the $C=C—C=O$ or the $C\equiv C—C=O$ system. Other unsaturated groups, such as CN, NO_2, or SO_2, promote the addition. In some instances even substances with isolated double bonds have been found to add dienes, but these substances usually require more drastic reaction conditions. Ketenes do not react with dienes in the Diels-Alder fashion.[1-4]

Among those substances that have been employed most frequently as dienophiles are maleic anhydride and other closely related dicarboxylic acid derivatives (which are discussed in this chapter), α,β-unsaturated carbonyl compounds and acetylenic compounds (which are discussed in Chapter 2), and quinones and other cyclic ketones (which will be discussed in Volume V). In Table I are listed some other compounds which have been employed successfully as dienophiles.

[1] Allen and Sheps, *Can. J Research*, **11**, 171 (1934).
[2] Farmer and Farooq, *J. Chem. Soc.*, **1938**, 1925.
[3] Smith, Agre, Leekley, and Prichard, *J. Am. Chem. Soc.*, **61, 7** (1939).
[4] Brooks and Wilbert, *J. Am. Chem. Soc.*, **63**, 870 (1941).

TABLE I

Dienophiles in the Diels-Alder Reaction

Dienophile	Reference	Dienophile	Reference
Acrolein	5–21	Ethylenetetracarboxylic acid	
Crotonaldehyde	6, 12, 15, 16,	and ester	51
	20–23	Azodicarboxylic ester	52, 53
Cinnamaldehyde	6, 24	Acrylonitrile	54
Acetylethylene (methyl			
vinyl ketone)	25	β-Naphthol (keto tautomer)	55
Ethylideneacetone	9	Nitroalkenes	29, 56–59
Benzoylethylene (vinyl			
phenyl ketone)	26	α,β-Unsaturated sulfones	56
Benzalacetone and		Cyclopentadiene	60–63
benzalacetophenone	27, 28	1,3-Cyclohexadiene	64
Dibenzalacetone	29	Styrene	58, 65
1-Cyclopenten-3-one and		Indenes	44, 65–69
derivatives	30–33	Acenaphthylene	69
1-Cyclohexen-3-one	34	Allyl compounds	70
sym-Diacetylethylene	35, 36	Vinyl halides, esters, and	
sym-Diaroylethylenes	27, 29, 37–41	sulfides	56, 71, 72
Acrylic acids	8, 10, 18, 42	Di- and poly-chloroethylenes	71, 73
Crotonic acid and crotonyl		4-Vinyl-1-cyclohexene	74
chloride	8, 43	1-Methyl-1-cyclopentene	66
Cinnamic acids and esters	24, 27, 44–47	Unsaturated bicyclic com-	
3,4-Dihydro-1-naphthoic		pounds (such as dicyclo-	
acids and esters	48, 49	pentadiene)	75, 76
Coumarin	46	Ethylene	77, 78
β-Aroylacrylic acids	27, 50		
Alkylidene-malonic,			
-acetoacetic, and			
-cyanoacetic esters	51		

[5] Diels and Alder, *Ann.*, **460**, 98 (1928).

[6] Diels, Alder, Lübbert, Naujoks, Querberitz, Röhl, and Segeberg, *Ann.*, **470**, 62 (1929).

[7] Diels, Alder, Petersen, and Querberitz, *Ann.*, **478**, 137 (1930).

[8] Alder, Stein, Liebmann, and Rolland, *Ann.*, **514**, 197 (1934).

[9] Diels and Alder, U. S. pats. 1,944,731–2 [*C. A.*, **28**, 2016 (1934)].

[10] Lehmann and Paasche, *Ber.*, **68**, 1146 (1935).

[11] Kasansky and Plate, *Ber.*, **68**, 1259 (1935).

[12] Arbuzov, *Ber.*, **68**, 1435 (1935).

[13] Lehmann, *Ber.*, **69**, 631 (1936).

[14] Dupont and Dulou, *Compt. rend.*, **202**, 1861 (1936).

[15] Arbuzov, Zinov'eva, and Fink, *J. Gen. Chem. U.S.S.R.*, **7**, 2278 (1937) [*C. A.*, **32**, 507 (1938)].

[16] Chayanov and Grishin, *Colloid J. U.S.S.R.*, **3**, 461 (1937) [*C. A.*, **32**, 6226 (1938)].

[17] Chayanov, *J. Gen. Chem. U.S.S.R.*, **8**, 460 (1938) [*C. A.*, **32**, 7905 (1938)].

[18] Lehmann, *Ber.*, **71**, 1874 (1938).

[19] Dupont, Dulou, Desreux, and Picoux, *Bull. soc. chim. France*, [5] **5**, 322 (1938).

[20] Langenbeck, Gödde, Weschky, and Schaller, *Ber.*, **75**, 232 (1942) [*C. A.*, **37**, 3746 (1943)].

[21] Fiesselmann, *Ber.*, **75**, 881 (1942) [*C. A.*, **37**, 3417 (1943)].

[22] Shorygin and Guseva, *J. Gen. Chem. U.S.S.R.*, **6**, 1569 (1936) [*C. A.*, **31**, 2184 (1937)].

[23] Clar, *Ber.*, **72**, 1817 (1939).

[24] Fujise, Horiuti, and Takahashi, *Ber.*, **69**, 2102 (1936).

[25] Petrov, *J. Gen. Chem. U.S.S.R.*, **11**, 309 (1941) [*C. A.*, **35**, 5873 (1941)].

[26] Allen, Bell, Bell, and Van Allan, *J. Am. Chem. Soc.*, **62**, 656 (1940).

[27] Bergmann and Eschinazi, *J. Am. Chem. Soc.*, **65**, 1405 (1943).

[28] Natsinskaya and Petrov, *J. Gen. Chem. U.S.S.R.*, **11**, 665 (1941) [*C. A.*, **35**, 6934 (1941)].

[29] Bergmann, Eschinazi, and Neeman, *J. Org. Chem.*, **8**, 179 (1943)

[30] Dane, Schmitt, and Rautenstrauch, *Ann.*, **532**, 29 (1937).

[31] Dane and Schmitt, *Ann.*, **536**, 196 (1938).

[32] Dane and Schmitt, *Ann.*, **537**, 246 (1939).

[33] Dane and Eder, *Ann.*, **539**, 207 (1939).

[34] Bartlett and Woods, *J. Am. Chem. Soc.*, **62**, 2933 (1940).

[35] Goldberg and Müller, *Helv. Chim. Acta*, **21**, 1699 (1938).

[36] Goldberg and Müller, *Helv. Chim. Acta*, **23**, 831 (1940).

[37] Adams and Geissman, *J. Am. Chem. Soc.*, **61**, 2083 (1939).

[38] Adams and Gold, *J. Am. Chem. Soc.*, **62**, 56 (1940).

[39] Adams and Wearn, *J. Am. Chem. Soc.*, **62**, 1233 (1940).

[40] Adams and Gold, *J. Am. Chem. Soc.*, **62**, 2038 (1940).

[41] Adams, U. S. pat. 2,341,850 [*C. A.*, **38**, 4270 (1944)].

[42] Komppa and Komppa, *Ber.*, **69**, 2606 (1936).

[43] Komppa and Beckmann, *Ann.*, **523**, 68 (1936).

[44] Weiss and Beller, *Monatsh.*, **61**, 143 (1932).

[45] Weizmann, Bergmann, and Berlin, *J. Am. Chem. Soc.*, **60**, 1331 (1938).

[46] Adams, McPhee, Carlin, and Wicks, *J. Am. Chem. Soc.*, **65**, 356 (1943).

[47] Adams and Carlin, *J. Am. Chem. Soc.*, **65**, 360 (1943).

[48] Fieser and Holmes, *J. Am. Chem. Soc.*, **58**, 2319 (1936).

[49] Fieser and Holmes, *J. Am. Chem. Soc.*, **60**, 2548 (1938).

[50] Fieser and Fieser, *J. Am. Chem. Soc.*, **57**, 1679 (1935).

[51] Alder and Rickert, *Ber.*, **72**, 1983 (1939).

[52] Diels, Blom, and Koll, *Ann.*, **443**, 242 (1925).

[53] Diels, Schmidt, and Witte, *Ber.*, **71**, 1186 (1938).

[54] Wolfe, U. S. pat. 2,217,632 [*C. A.*, **35**, 1069 (1941)].

[55] Salfeld, *Ber.*, **73**, 376 (1940).

[56] Alder, Rickert, and Windemuth, *Ber.*, **71**, 2451 (1938).

[57] Allen and Bell, *J. Am. Chem. Soc.*, **61**, 521 (1939).

[58] Allen, Bell, and Gates, *J. Org. Chem.*, **8**, 373 (1943).

[59] Nightingale and Janes, *J. Am. Chem. Soc.*, **66**, 352 (1944).

[60] Alder, Stein, and Finzenhagen, *Ann.*, **485**, 223 (1931).

[61] Alder, Stein, Eckardt, Buddenbrock, and Schneider, *Ann.*, **504**, 216 (1933).

[62] Alder and Stein, *Angew. Chem.*, **47**, 837 (1934).

[63] Grummitt, Klopper, and Blenkhorn, *J. Am. Chem. Soc.*, **64**, 604 (1942).

[64] Alder and Stein, *Ann.*, **496**, 197 (1932).

[65] Alder and Rickert, *Ber.*, **71**, 379 (1938).

[66] Bergmann and Weizmann, *J. Org. Chem.*, **9**, 352 (1944).

[67] Swain and Todd, *J. Chem. Soc.*, **1942**, 626.

[68] Mameli, Pancotto, and Crestani, *Gazz. chim. ital.*, **67**, 669 (1937).

[69] Dilthey, Henkels, and Schaefer, *Ber.*, **71**, 974 (1938).

[70] Alder and Windemuth, *Ber.*, **71**, 1939 (1938).

[71] Alder and Rickert, *Ann.*, **543**, 1 (1940).

The types of conjugated systems capable of undergoing the Diels-Alder reaction are equally diverse. These may be classified conveniently in the following manner.

1. Acyclic conjugates (butadiene, alkylbutadienes, arylbutadienes, conjugated polyenes, etc.).
2. Alicyclic conjugates.
   a. Wholly alicyclic systems (cyclopentadiene, 1,3-cyclohexadiene, fulvenes).
   b. Bicyclic systems (1,1'-bicyclohexenyl, etc.).
   c. Alicyclic-acyclic systems (1-vinyl-1-cyclohexene, 1-vinyl-3,4-dihydronaphthalene).
3. Aromatic conjugates.
   a. Wholly aromatic systems (anthracene, 9,10-dialkylanthracenes, pentacene, etc.).
   b. Aromatic-acyclic systems (isosafrole, 1-vinylnaphthalene, 9-vinylphenanthrene, etc.).
   c. Aromatic-alicyclic systems (1-α-naphthyl-1-cyclopentene, etc.).
4. Heterocyclic compounds (furan, isobenzofurans, α-pyrone).

The versatility of the Diels-Alder reaction was recognized primarily through the work of Diels and Alder, whose series of papers on this subject began to appear in 1928.[5] Isolated instances of the reaction were discovered, however, as early as 1893[79] and 1897[80] by Zincke,[81, 82] who subsequently formulated the reactions as additions which conform to the general scheme of the diene synthesis.

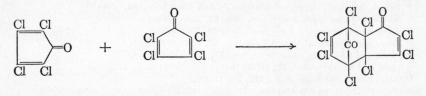

In 1906, Albrecht[83] described the addition products of p-benzoquinone with one and two molecules of cyclopentadiene, for which he suggested the erroneous formulas I and II. Staudinger[84] suggested formulas III

[72] Alder and Windemuth, Ann., **543**, 41 (1940).
[73] Alder and Rickert, U. S. pat. 2,351,311 [C. A., **38**, 5222 (1944)].
[74] Alder and Rickert, Ber., **71**, 373 (1938).
[75] Alder, Stein, Reese, and Grassmann, Ann., **496**, 204 (1932).
[76] Alder and Windemuth, Ber., **71**, 2409 (1938).
[77] Joshel and Butz, J. Am. Chem. Soc., **63**, 3350 (1941).
[78] Nudenberg and Butz, J. Am. Chem. Soc., **66**, 307 (1944).
[79] Zincke and Günther, Ann., **272**, 243 (1893).
[80] Zincke, Bergmann, Francke, and Prenntzell, Ann., **296**, 135 (1897).
[81] Zincke and Meyer, Ann., **367**, 1 (1909).
[82] Zincke and Pfaffendorf, Ann., **394**, 3 (1912).
[83] Albrecht, Ann., **348**, 31 (1906).
[84] Staudinger, Die Ketene, p. 59, F. Enke, Stuttgart, 1912.

and IV for these compounds. That Albrecht's addition compounds

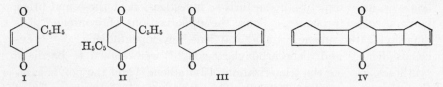

were actually the result (V and VI) of a typical diene synthesis was shown later by Diels and Alder.[5, 85] During the controversy concerning

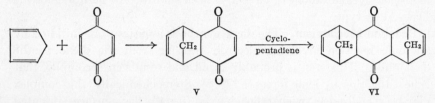

the quinone-cyclopentadiene reaction, Euler and Josephson [86] reported that isoprene could be made to react with 1,4-benzoquinone to yield VII. Diels and Alder subsequently showed that this reaction product was actually a mixture of VII and VIII.

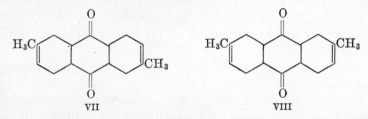

An indication of the generality of these addition reactions was given by the work of Diels, Blom, and Koll [52] on the reaction of azodicarboxylic ester with cyclopentadiene. The remarkably broad scope of the diene synthesis was then established by the papers of Diels and Alder, which appeared in rapid succession.

The development of the Diels-Alder reaction has been of inestimable value not only in synthesis but also for the light it has cast upon the mechanism of polymerization. Indeed, the discovery of certain dimerization processes that conform to the general scheme of the diene synthesis preceded the work of Diels and Alder. Among these may be mentioned the dimerization of butadiene to 4-vinyl-1-cyclohexene [87, 88]

[85] Diels, Alder, Stein, Pries, and Winckler, *Ber.*, **62**, 2337 (1929).

[86] Euler and Josephson, *Ber.*, **53**, 822 (1920).

[87] Lebedev, *J. Russ. Phys. Chem. Soc.*, **42**, 949 (1910) [*C. A.*, **6**, 2009 (1912)].

[88] Lebedev and Skavronskaya, *J. Russ. Phys. Chem. Soc.*, **43**, 1124 (1911) [*C. A.*, **6**, 855 (1912)].

and of isoprene to dipentene.[89]   Discovery of the Diels-Alder reaction, however, gave impetus to the further investigation of these and other polymerization processes.   Thus, the dimerizations of isoprene,[90] 3,4-dimethyl-2,4-hexadiene,[91] 1,3,5-hexatriene,[92] cyclopentadiene,[60-62,93,94] cyclohexadiene,[64] and dienecarboxylic acids [95,96] were shown to be diene syntheses, as were the trimerization of butadiene [74] and the polymerization of cyclopentadiene.[60,61,75,93]   The dimerizations of such carbonyl compounds as acetylketene,[97] acrolein,[98] methyl vinyl ketone,[99] and o-methylenecyclohexanone [100] have also been shown to be additions of the Diels-Alder type.

Reaction Mechanism.   The diene synthesis appears to be initiated by an ionic reaction involving electron transfer from the diene to the dienophile.   This step is probably rapid and results in a complex that is held together by ionic forces.[27,29,101-103]   Stereochemically, this complex may be visualized as two parallel charged (usually flat) surfaces, oriented in such a way as to take maximum advantage of electrostatic attractive forces.[102,103]   It has been postulated that this intermediate complex is in some instances an open-chain diradical, although kinetic studies of the association of butadiene and of other diene syntheses are not in harmony with this view.[104-106]   The second, and probably rate-controlling, step in the reaction is a rearrangement of the ionic complex to yield the stabilized adduct.

Certain characteristics of the Diels-Alder reaction appear to support this mechanism.

1. The reaction usually (though not necessarily) is accompanied by the production of a transient color, which has been attributed to forma-

[89] Wallach, *Ann.*, **227**, 277 (1885).
[90] Wagner-Jauregg, *Ann.*, **488**, 176 (1931).
[91] vonRomburgh and vonRomburgh, *Proc. Acad. Sci. Amsterdam*, **34**, 224 (1931) [*C. A.*, **25**, 3309 (1931)].
[92] Kharasch and Sternfeld, *J. Am. Chem. Soc.*, **61**, 2318 (1939)
[93] Alder, Stein, and Grassmann, *Ann.*, **504**, 205 (1933).
[94] Pirsch, *Ber.*, **67**, 101 (1934).
[95] Kuhn and Deutsch, *Ber.*, **65**, 43 (1932).
[96] Farmer, *Trans. Faraday Soc.*, **35**, 1034 (1939).
[97] Hurd, Roe, and Williams, *J. Org. Chem.*, **2**, 314 (1937).
[98] Alder and Rüden, *Ber.*, **74**, 920 (1941).
[99] Alder, Offermanns, and Rüden, *Ber.*, **74**, 905 (1941).
[100] Mannich, *Ber.*, **74**, 557 (1941).
[101] Hudson and Robinson, *J. Chem. Soc.*, **1941**, 715.
[102] Woodward, *J. Am. Chem. Soc.*, **64**, 3058 (1942).
[103] Woodward and Baer, *J. Am. Chem. Soc.*, **66**, 645 (1944).
[104] Wassermann, *J. Chem. Soc.*, **1935**, 828.
[105] Benford and Wassermann, *J. Chem. Soc.*, **1939**, 362.
[106] Wassermann, *J. Chem. Soc.*, **1942**, 612.

tion of the complex.[107-110] Production of a color with maleic anhydride, however, should not be construed as a reliable test for a diene or a guarantee that a normal Diels-Alder reaction will ensue. Stilbene, for example, when mixed with maleic anhydride gives first a yellow color and then an amorphous substance having a high molecular weight.[108] In other instances a colored complex is formed, but no further reaction takes place.[110]

2. Ionic compounds actually have been isolated from the reaction of dimethyl acetylenedicarboxylate with such heterocyclic substances as pyridine, α-picoline, quinoline, isoquinoline, and quinaldine.[111-115] Furthermore, the nature of the solvent affects not only the rate of reaction [116-118] but also in some instances (the aforementioned nitrogen heterocycles) the nature of the product.

3. The course of the reaction is sterically specific (see p. 10).

4. The tendency of a styrene to react with maleic anhydride is enhanced by an alkoxyl group *para* to the unsaturated side chain, but a similar group in the *meta* position has no such effect.[101]

5. Certain substances which may act as donor or acceptor molecules, but which cannot themselves take part in the diene reaction, have been found to catalyze diene syntheses. Among these are trichloroacetic acid, trimethylamine,[118-120] and possibly dimethylaniline and *sym*-trinitrobenzene.[102]

Reversibility of the Reaction. It has been observed repeatedly that adducts from the Diels-Alder reaction are thermally unstable. Dissociation takes place with varying facility, depending upon the nature of the adducts. Those which have an *endo* bridge, such as XXXIII, XLI, LXXXVII, and XCIII (pp. 22, 24, 35, 38), generally show a pronounced tendency to revert to their components.[121] The adduct from furan and maleic anhydride, for example, decomposes at its melting point (125°). When the adduct from cyclopentadiene and maleic anhydride is warmed,

[107] Kuhn and Wagner-Jauregg, *Helv. Chim. Acta*, **13**, 9 (1930).
[108] Kuhn and Wagner-Jauregg, *Ber.*, **63**, 2662 (1930).
[109] Littmann, *J. Am. Chem. Soc.*, **58**, 1316 (1936).
[110] Sandermann, *Seifensieder-Ztg.*, **65**, 553 (1938) [*C. A.*, **32**, 8698 (1938)].
[111] Diels, Alder, Friedrichsen, Klare, Winckler, and Schrum, *Ann.*, **505**, 103 (1933).
[112] Diels, Alder, Friedrichsen, Petersen, Brodersen, and Kech, *Ann.*, **510**, 87 (1934).
[113] Diels and Meyer, *Ann.*, **513**, 129 (1934).
[114] Diels and Pistor, *Ann.*, **530**, 87 (1937).
[115] Diels and Harms, *Ann.*, **525**, 73 (1936).
[116] Wassermann, *Ber.*, **66**, 1392 (1933).
[117] Wassermann, *J. Chem. Soc.*, **1936**, 1028.
[118] Wassermann, *J. Chem. Soc.*, **1942**, 623.
[119] Wassermann, Fr. pat. 838,454 (1939) [*C. A.*, **33**, 7818 (1939)].
[120] Wassermann, *J. Chem. Soc.*, **1942**, 618.
[121] Diels, Alder, and Naujoks, *Ber.*, **62**, 554 (1929).

it likewise dissociates into its components.   On the other hand, the adducts from cyclohexadiene and its derivatives are much more thermostable.   Indeed, this difference in properties has been suggested as a means of differentiating between five- and six-carbon cyclic dienes [122] (compare Chapter 2).

The reactions between maleic anhydride and a number of polycyclic hydrocarbons containing the anthracene nucleus are truly reversible.[123] Identical mixtures of hydrocarbon, maleic anhydride, and adduct were obtained by heating xylene solutions of either the pure adduct or the components in equimolecular proportion.   The quantitative results of this investigation are discussed in a later section (p. 28).

The course taken by dissociation of maleic anhydride adducts is in keeping with the thermal decomposition of other bicyclic compounds. It has been observed [124-126] that the bonds that undergo pyrolytic rupture are those once removed from unsaturation rather than those adjacent to unsaturation (the double bond rule).   In a typical maleic anhydride

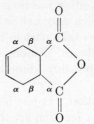

adduct the α-bonds are strong, whereas the β-bonds are weak and subject to thermal cleavage.

Stereochemical Selectivity of the Reaction.   The Diels-Alder reaction exhibits pronounced stereochemical selectivity.   The configuration of a given adduct conforms to the following general principles,[27, 127] commonly known as the Alder rules.

1. The addition of a dienophile to a diene is a purely *cis* addition. The relative positions of substituents in the dienophile are retained in the adduct.   For example, maleic anhydride reacts with anthracene to yield the *cis*-anhydride adduct IX, while fumaric acid yields the *trans*-dicarboxylic acid adduct X.[128a]

[122] Alder and Rickert, *Ann.*, **524**, 180 (1936).

[123] Bachmann and Kloetzel, *J. Am. Chem. Soc.*, **60**, 481 (1938).

[124] Littmann, *J. Am. Chem. Soc.*, **57**, 586 (1935).

[125] Norton, *Chem. Revs.*, **31**, 387, 469 (1942).

[126] Allen and Van Allan, *J. Am. Chem. Soc.*, **65**, 1384 (1943).

[127] Alder and Stein, *Angew. Chem.*, **50**, 510 (1937).

[128] (*a*) Bachmann and Scott, *J. Am. Chem. Soc.*, **70**, 1458, 1462 (1948); (*b*) Bachmann and Chemerda, *J. Am. Chem. Soc.*, **70**, 1468 (1948).

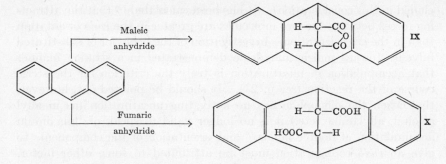

2. In the reaction of maleic anhydride with a cyclic diene, such as cyclopentadiene, two modes of addition are theoretically possible, leading to the formation of an *"endo"* configuration (XI) or an *"exo"* configuration (XII) respectively. Actually, the *endo* configuration (XI) is produced exclusively.[127, 129] This "one-sided" addition indicates that immediately before combination the components must always be oriented in exactly the same manner with respect to each other; that is, of the two possible orientations, A and B, A is favored.

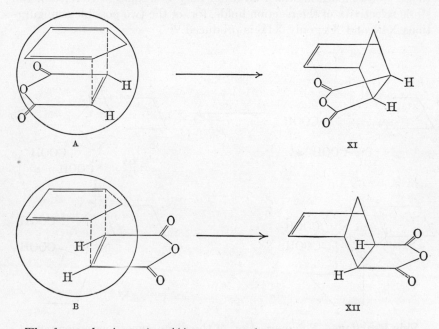

The favored orientation (A) corresponds to the maximum accumulation of double bonds (the double bonds of the carbonyl groups are in-

[129] Alder, Stein, Buddenbrock, Eckardt, Frercks, and Schneider, *Ann.*, **514**, 1 (1934).

cluded in this consideration). It has been calculated [130] that the attract-
ing forces between the two molecules are greater in the *endo* orientation
than in the *exo* orientation. Investigation of the behavior of substituted
fulvenes toward maleic anhydride demonstrated in a striking manner
that accumulation of unsaturation is truly the criterion for the steric
course of the reaction (see p. 24). It should be pointed out, however,
that when the dienophile has no activating unsaturation (as in allyl
alcohol, allylamine, etc.) it is no longer valid to speak of "maximum
accumulation of double bonds," and orientation of the components to
give an *endo* configuration must be attributed to some other factor.
According to Alder [70] the unshared electrons on an oxygen, nitrogen, or
halogen atom may be considered equivalent to unsaturation, and in a
broader sense the presence of unshared electrons governs the spatial
arrangement of the components before addition.

3. The steric course of most Diels-Alder reactions is controlled by
the aforementioned generalizations. When, however, the dienophile is
an asymmetrically substituted maleic acid, such as 3,6-*endo*methylene-
3,4,5,6-tetrahydrophthalic acid (XIII), there are theoretically two additional steric modes in which addition may take place. Here, too, the
steric selectivity of the reaction holds, for, of the two possible configurations XIV and XV, only XIV is produced.[127]

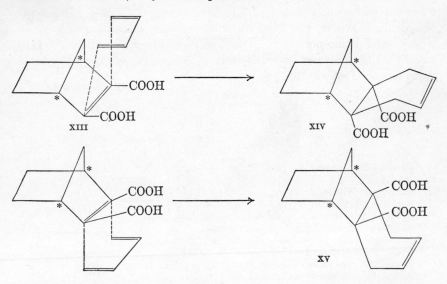

Side Reactions. Polymerization of the diene sometimes accompanies,
or takes place to the exclusion of, the Diels-Alder reaction. Dienes with
doubly substituted carbon atoms in the terminal positions of the con-

[130] Wassermann, *J. Chem. Soc.*, **1935**, 1511.

jugated system generally tend to produce polymers rather than normal adducts. Thus, 4-methyl-1,3-pentadiene,[131-133] 2-methyl-2,4-hexadiene,[134,135] 4-methyl-1,3-hexadiene, 2,5-dimethyl-2,4-hexadiene,[135] 4-methyl-6-phenyl-1,3-hexadiene, 4-methyl-6-*m*-methoxyphenyl-1,3-hexadiene,[136] and 4-*n*-propyl-1,3-heptadiene [137] give, with maleic anhydride, polymeric products exclusively. *cis*-1,3-Pentadiene likewise yields only polymeric material, though the *trans* isomer readily adds maleic anhydride in the normal fashion.[131,138-140]

Conjugated aromatic-acyclic systems, such as styrene,[141] *p*-methoxystyrene, 3,4-methylenedioxystyrene, anethole,* *trans*-isoeugenol ethyl ether,[101] stilbene, benzalfluorene, 1,4-diphenyl-1-butene,[108,141] 5-vinylhydrindene, 5-isopropenylhydrindene,[142] 1-vinylnaphthalene, 1-vinyl-6-methoxynaphthalene,[128a] and 6-isopropenylchrysene [143] also appear to be particularly sensitive to the polymerizing influence of maleic anhydride. With certain other dienes (for example, 2-methyl-1,3-pentadiene,[132] 3-methyl-1,3-pentadiene,[131] 1,10-diphenyldecapentaene,[108,141] α-phellandrene, and α-terpinene [144]) the normal addition of maleic anhydride, even under mild conditions, is accompanied by polymer formation.

Relatively few polymers have been studied carefully to determine the nature of the polymerization involved. Heteropolymerization appears to occur most frequently, since most of the polymers have been observed to be alkali-soluble. The product from styrene and maleic anhydride, however, has been reported [141] to be a complex mixture of hetero- and homo-polymers. Oxidation experiments [132,133] have indicated that the polymer from maleic anhydride and 4-methyl-1,3-pentadiene has the following structure.

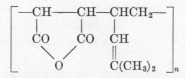

* Compare Tamayo and Ayestaran, *Anales soc. españ. fís. quím.*, **36**, 44 (1940) [*C. A.*, **34**, 7288 (1940)].

[131] Farmer and Warren, *J. Chem. Soc.*, **1931**, 3221.
[132] Bachman and Goebel, *J. Am. Chem. Soc.*, **64**, 787 (1942).
[133] Bachman and Hatton, *J. Am. Chem. Soc.*, **66**, 1513 (1944).
[134] Bacon and Farmer, *J. Chem. Soc.*, **1937**, 1065.
[135] Henne and Turk, *J. Am. Chem. Soc.*, **64**, 826 (1942).
[136] Cohen, *J. Chem. Soc.*, **1935**, 429.
[137] Slobodin, *J. Gen. Chem. U.S.S.R.*, **8**, 241 (1938) [*C. A.*, **32**, 5371 (1938)].
[138] Robey, Morrell, and Wiese, *J. Am. Chem. Soc.*, **63**, 627 (1941).
[139] Norton, *Chem. Revs.*, **31**, 349 (1942).
[140] Craig, *J. Am. Chem. Soc.*, **65**, 1006 (1943).
[141] Wagner-Jauregg, *Ber.*, **63**, 3213 (1930).
[142] Arnold, *J. Am. Chem. Soc.*, **61**, 1405 (1939).
[143] Bergmann and Eschinazi, *J. Am. Chem. Soc.*, **65**, 1413 (1943).
[144] Littmann, *Ind. Eng. Chem.*, **28**, 1150 (1936).

In other polymers, only the ratio of maleic anhydride to diene has been determined.   In the product from maleic anhydride and 1,10-diphenyl-decapentaene this ratio is 3:1; from α-phellandrene, 4:3 or 5:4; from α-terpinene, 2:1 or 3:2; from p-methoxystyrene, 3:2; from benzal-fluorene, 1:1.

The complexity of the polymer obtained is dependent both upon the nature of the reactants and upon the conditions employed.   With maleic anhydride under comparable conditions, α-phellandrene and α-terpinene yield polymers of molecular weight 1220 and 350, respectively. 3,4-Methylenedioxystyrene yields a relatively simple heteropolymer with a molecular weight of 482.   Stilbene and benzalfluorene yield poly-mers with very high molecular weights.   Anethole gives a relatively simple polymer with maleic anhydride if reaction is effected in the cold; application of heat yields a more complex product.   The use of poly-merization inhibitors (hydroquinone), low reaction temperatures, and suitable solvents is sometimes effective in suppressing polymerization of the diene.[131,132]   It has also been observed [128a] that the addition of trans-dienophiles (fumaric or mesaconic acids) to 1-vinylnaphthalene or 1-vinyl-6-methoxynaphthalene is accompanied by less polymer for-mation than the addition of cis-dienophiles (maleic or citraconic an-hydrides).

The use of purified maleic anhydride in the Diels-Alder reaction is to be recommended.   Free maleic acid in the maleic anhydride may cause isomerization of the diene with which the anhydride is to react, thus altering the course of the subsequent condensation,[145] or it may initiate polymerization of the diene.[146]   Maleic anhydride is not, however, without polymerizing influence of its own, for a mixture of 2-methyl-1,3-pentadiene and 4-methyl-1,3-pentadiene does not polymerize readily with either styrene or vinyl acetate unless maleic anhydride is present.[132]

SCOPE AND LIMITATIONS OF THE REACTION

In this discussion consideration will be given those Diels-Alder reac-tions which involve the following dienophiles:

Maleic anhydride.
Maleic acid and its esters.
Fumaric acid and its esters.
Fumaryl chloride.
Fumaronitrile.
Citraconic (methylmaleic) anhydride.
Pyrocinchonic (dimethylmaleic) anhydride.

[145] Hultzsch, Ber., **72**, 1173 (1939).
[146] Butz, Gaddis, Butz, and Davis, J. Org. Chem., **5**, 379 (1940).

Mesaconic (methylfumaric) acid.
Itaconic anhydride.
Di- and tetra-hydrophthalic anhydrides.
Dihydronaphthalenedicarboxylic anhydrides.
Dihydrophenanthrenedicarboxylic anhydrides.
3,4-Dihydro-8,9-acephenanthrene-1,2-dicarboxylic anhydride.

Reaction with Acyclic Compounds. Butadiene reacts with maleic anhydride in benzene solution at 100° to give a quantitative yield of cis-1,2,3,6-tetrahydrophthalic anhydride (XVI).[5, 147, 148] Mono-, di-, and tri-alkylbutadienes, as well as 2-acetoxybutadiene, 2-formoxybutadiene

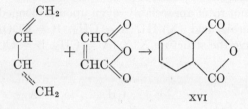

(formoprene), 2,3-dimethoxybutadiene, butadienyl thioethers, chloroprene, and bromoprene react in a similar manner (see Table III). The reaction usually proceeds readily at room temperature when the components are mixed in equivalent proportions, and a quantitative yield of the corresponding adduct is often obtained. Fatty acids containing conjugated systems likewise add maleic anhydride readily.* Certain halogenated dienes are, however, inert toward maleic anhydride. Thus, 2,3-dichloro-1,3-butadiene, 1,3,4,6-tetrachloro-2,4-hexadiene, 3,6-dichloro-1,3,4-hexatriene, 3,4,6-trichloro-1,2,4-hexatriene, 4-chloro-1,2,3,5-hexatetraene, and 3,4-dichloro-1,2,4,5-hexatetraene fail to react, though it has been shown that 1,4-addition to a conjugated system terminating in a series of contiguous double bonds is possible.[149, 150]

The Diels-Alder reaction provides a convenient route for the synthesis of biphenyl, terphenyl, and quaterphenyl derivatives. 1,4-Diphenyl-1,3-butadiene, for example, reacts readily with maleic anhydride to give the hydroterphenyl derivative XVII.[151] Hydrobiphenyl systems have also been prepared successfully by the addition of butadienes to cinnamaldehyde,[6] benzylidenemalonic ester,[51] or styrene,[65] and by the thermal polymerization of butadiene itself.[74] An adduct of type XVII may be

---

* This reaction sometimes yields elastic or resinous condensation products of industrial value. See C. A., **27**, 4890 (1933); C. A., **29**, 5953 (1935); C. A., **30**, 6848 (1936); C. A., **32**, 2248 (1938).

[147] Diels and Alder, Ber., **62**, 2087 (1929).
[148] Farmer and Warren, J. Chem. Soc., **1929**, 897.
[149] Berchet and Carothers, J. Am. Chem. Soc., **55**, 2004 (1933).
[150] Coffman and Carothers, J. Am. Chem. Soc., **55**, 2040 (1933).
[151] Diels, Alder, and Pries, Ber., **62**, 2081 (1929).

aromatized and decarboxylated simultaneously by distilling with a mixture of lime and zinc dust [151] or may be aromatized by treating with potassium ferricyanide or sulfur and then decarboxylated by distilling with soda-lime [108] or heating with basic copper carbonate in quinoline.[152] In this manner, XVII yields terphenyl.

When a diene carrying an unsaturated substituent is employed in the Diels-Alder reaction, stabilization of the adduct may occur through spontaneous migration of the double bond to afford a conjugated system. In this way, ethyl *trans-trans*-muconate (XVIII, A = B = $COOC_2H_5$) reacts with maleic anhydride to give 3,6-dicarbethoxy-1,2,5,6-tetra-hydrophthalic anhydride (XIX, A = B = $COOC_2H_5$).[148] Ethyl *cis-cis*-muconate does not react appreciably, even upon prolonged boiling. The adduct from sorbic acid (XVIII, A = CH_3, B = COOH) likewise is presumed to have the structure XIX (A = CH_3, B = COOH).

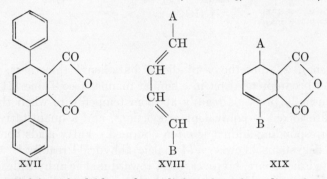

XVII   XVIII   XIX

When maleic anhydride and 1,4-diphenyl-1,3-butadiene interact, the product is not homogeneous but consists of two isomers (XX and XXI) which are assumed to differ by the position of unsaturation in the central ring.[108] Maleic anhydride failed to react with 1,4-di-*p*-anisyl-1,3-butadiene,[153] 1,2,3,4-tetraphenyl-1,3-butadiene,* or 1,4-dibiphenylene-1,3-butadiene.[154]

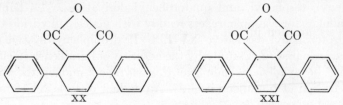

XX   XXI

* Tetraphenylcyclopentadienone, however, reacts readily.[1, 155, 156]

[152] Bergmann and Weizman, *J. Org. Chem.*, **9**, 415 (1944).
[153] Weizmann, Bergmann, and Haskelberg, *J. Chem. Soc.*, **1939**, 391.
[154] Wagner-Jauregg, *Ann.*, **491**, 1 (1931).
[155] Dilthey, Schommer, and Trösken, *Ber.*, **66**, 1627 (1933).
[156] Dilthey, Thewalt, and Trösken, *Ber.*, **67**, 1959 (1934).

An interesting variation of the aforementioned Diels-Alder reaction consists in the replacement of maleic anhydride by fumaryl chloride.[108] Whereas maleic acid gives rise to a *cis* acid, fumaryl chloride leads to the corresponding *trans* acid. The addition of fumaryl chloride to other dienes is limited, however, by the polymerizing action of this reagent. Butadiene, for example, is polymerized even when the reaction mixture is cooled in an acetone-Dry Ice bath.

The following examples illustrate the use of substituted maleic anhydrides in the synthesis of complex molecules by the Diels-Alder reaction.

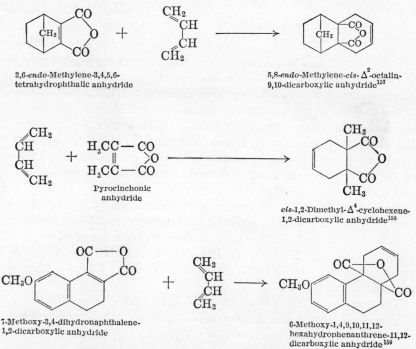

3,6-*endo*-Methylene-3,4,5,6-tetrahydrophthalic anhydride

5,8-*endo*-Methylene-*cis*-Δ^2-octalin-9,10-dicarboxylic anhydride[157]

Pyrocinchonic anhydride

cis-1,2-Dimethyl-Δ^4-cyclohexene-1,2-dicarboxylic anhydride[158]

7-Methoxy-3,4-dihydronaphthalene-1,2-dicarboxylic anhydride

6-Methoxy-1,4,9,10,11,12-hexahydrophenanthrene-11,12-dicarboxylic anhydride[159]

A novel variation in the Diels-Alder reaction is the substitution of two molecules of ketene diethylacetal for one of a conjugated diene. The reaction with maleic anhydride (pyrocinchonic anhydride does not react) presumably proceeds in the following manner.[160]

[157] Alder and Backendorf, *Ber.*, **71**, 2199 (1938).
[158] Woodward and Loftfield, *J. Am. Chem. Soc.*, **63**, 3167 (1941).
[159] Fieser and Hershberg, *J. Am. Chem. Soc.*, **58**, 2314 (1936).
[160] McElvain and Cohen, *J. Am. Chem. Soc.*, **64**, 260 (1942).

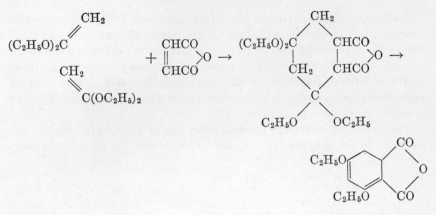

Extension of the Diels-Alder reaction to a series of conjugated polyenes disclosed that these compounds react in the normal way to give six-membered rings.[108] Addition of maleic anhydride is initiated at the ends of the conjugated polyene system and takes place in such a manner that the double bonds are saturated in pairs. This behavior is in accord with the observed manner of hydrogen addition to conjugated systems.[161] Addition of one molecule of maleic anhydride at the terminal carbons of the polyene system is not observed. Allenes and cumulenes fail to add maleic anhydride.[162-167]

Hexatriene itself reacts readily with maleic anhydride to give an adduct which is probably 3-vinyl-1,2,3,6-tetrahydrophthalic anhydride (XXII),[92, 168] though Farmer and Warren[148] have ascribed to it the isomeric structure XXIII. 2,5-Dimethyl-1,3,5-hexatriene reacts in a similar manner to give 5-methyl-3-isopropenyl-1,2,3,6-tetrahydrophthalic anhydride.[168]

The structure of the adduct obtained from maleic anhydride and 1,6-diphenyl-1,3,5-hexatriene depends upon the reaction conditions. Fusion of the components in the absence of a solvent yields one product (possibly XXIV); refluxing in xylene yields a different isomer.[108, 151] These adducts are presumed to differ in the position of the double bond in the cyclohexene ring.

[161] Kuhn and Winterstein, *Helv. Chim. Acta*, **11**, 123 (1928).
[162] Kuhn and Wallenfels, *Ber.*, **71**, 783 (1938).
[163] Gulyaeva and Dauguleva, *Caoutchouc and Rubber U.S.S.R.*, No. 1, 53 (1937) [*C. A.*, **32**, 3754 (1938)].
[164] Acree and LaForge, *J. Org. Chem.*, **4**, 569 (1939).
[165] Carothers, Berchet, and Collins, *J. Am. Chem. Soc.*, **54**, 4066 (1932).
[166] Dykstra, *J. Am. Chem. Soc.*, **58**, 1747 (1936).
[167] Acree and LaForge, *J. Org. Chem.*, **5**, 48 (1940).
[168] Kharasch, Nudenberg, and Sternfeld, *J. Am. Chem. Soc.*, **62**, 2034 (1940).

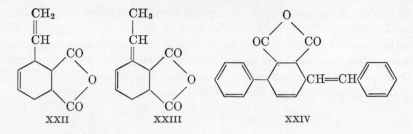

1,8-Diphenyloctatetraene adds two molecules of maleic anhydride smoothly to give a homogeneous adduct (probably XXV). The position of the double bonds in the central rings was not ascertained. When reaction is effected in boiling xylene or tetralin a mixture of isomeric adducts is obtained. Even if only one mole of anhydride is employed, XXV still is obtained, and unreacted 1,8-diphenyloctatetraene may be recovered. This would indicate that the monoaddition adduct is more reactive toward maleic anhydride than is the tetraene itself. The adducts from 1,4-diphenylbutadiene or 1,8-diphenyloctatetraene are decomposed into their components upon distillation in vacuum, whereas the adduct from 1,6-diphenylhexatriene does not dissociate under these conditions.

Reaction of 1,10-diphenyldecapentaene with maleic anhydride in boiling xylene yields two isomeric adducts (XXVI, position of double bonds in cyclohexene rings uncertain) and an amorphous substance. 1,12-Diphenyldodecahexaene combines with three molecules of maleic anhydride to give an adduct whose structure was not determined conclusively. Reaction took place similarly with 1,14-diphenyltetradecaheptaene but no homogeneous adduct was obtained in this instance.

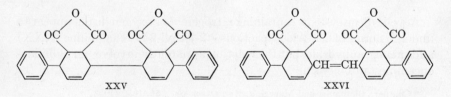

All the natural polyene pigments are decolorized by addition of maleic anhydride. The acetate of vitamin A reacts smoothly to give an adduct (probably XXVII).[169, 170] Carotene also reacts with maleic anhydride

[169] Hamano, *Sci. Papers Inst. Phys. Chem. Research Tokyo*, **26**, 87 (1935) [*C. A.*, **29**, 2545 (1935)].

[170] Kawakami, *Sci. Papers Inst. Phys. Chem. Research Tokyo*, **26**, 77 (1935) [*C. A.*, **29**, 2545 (1935)].

but yields an adduct whose absorption spectrum shows no remaining double linkings.[171]   An addition product of maleic anhydride with the methyl ester of bixin has been isolated as a crystalline sodium salt, but its structure has not been ascertained.[108]   The extension of the Diels-Alder reaction to the natural carotenoids apparently is rendered difficult by the multiplicity of possible stereoisomers.

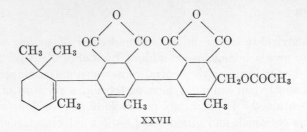

XXVII

Conjugated systems containing a triple bond as well as double bonds have been made to undergo the Diels-Alder reaction.   2,5-Dimethyl-1,5-hexadien-3-yne (XXVIII) adds two molecules of maleic anhydride to yield the hydronaphthalene derivative XXIX.[146, *]   Similar reactions have provided syntheses of phenanthrene,[172, 173] chrysene,[174, 175] and 1,2-cyclopentenophenanthrene [175, 176] nuclei.

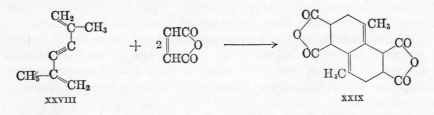

Acyclic diene systems containing nitrogen [177] or oxygen do not appear to undergo normal Diels-Alder reactions.   2-Ethyl-2-hexenalaniline (XXX) adds maleic anhydride, but the reaction apparently involves an aldimine-eneamine tautomerism.[178, 179]

* Compare Blomquist and Marvel, *J. Am. Chem. Soc.*, **55**, 1655 (1933).
[171] Nakamiya, *Bull. Inst. Phys. Chem. Research Tokyo*, **15**, 286 (1936) [*C. A.*, **31**, 4984 (1937)].
[172] Dane, Höss, Bindseil, and Schmitt, *Ann.*, **532**, 39 (1937).
[173] Dane, Höss, Eder, Schmitt, and Schön, *Ann.*, **536**, 183 (1938).
[174] Joshel, Butz, and Feldman, *J. Am. Chem. Soc.*, **63**, 3348 (1941).
[175] Butz and Joshel, *J. Am. Chem. Soc.*, **64**, 1311 (1942).
[176] Butz and Joshel, *J. Am. Chem. Soc.*, **63**, 3344 (1941).
[177] van Alphen, *Rec. trav. chim.*, **61**, 895 (1942) [*C. A.*, **38**, 5824 (1944)].
[178] Snyder, Hasbrouck, and Richardson, *J. Am. Chem. Soc.*, **61**, 3558 (1939).
[179] Snyder and Robinson, *J. Am. Chem. Soc.*, **63**, 3279 (1941).

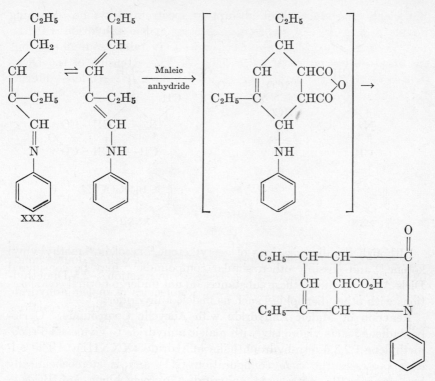

Cinnamalaniline fails to undergo a similar condensation because the initial tautomerism cannot take place. If moisture is present, cinnamaldehyde and maleanilic acid are obtained; [180,181] under anhydrous conditions the reaction does not proceed.[178] Benzalmaleinhydrazine and benzaldehyde are similarly obtained when maleic anhydride reacts with benzalazine (XXXI).[182] Under more drastic conditions, benzalazine reacts with two molecules of maleic anhydride to give a bispyrazolidine derivative (XXXII).[141,183]

[180] Bergmann, *J. Am. Chem. Soc.*, **60**, 2811 (1938).

[181] LaParola, *Gazz. chim. ital.*, **64**, 919 (1934).

[182] Snyder, Levin, and Wiley, *J. Am. Chem. Soc.*, **60**, 2025 (1938).

[183] van Alphen, *Rec. trav. chim.*, **61**, 892 (1942) [*C. A.*, **38**, 5824 (1944)].

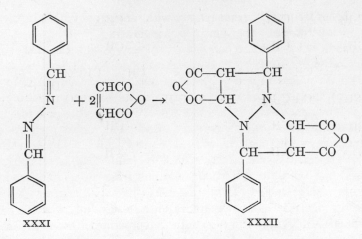

XXXI   XXXII

Although the dimerizations of acetylketene,[97] acrolein,[98] methyl vinyl ketone,[99] and possibly other, similar compounds [184] may be considered Diels-Alder reactions, these substances do not undergo normal condensations with other dienophiles such as maleic anhydride.

Reaction of Maleic Anhydride with Alicyclic Compounds. Cyclopentadiene reacts vigorously with maleic anhydride to give *cis*-3,6-*endo*-methylene-1,2,3,6-tetrahydrophthalic anhydride (XXXIII).[5] The adduct possesses the *endo* configuration (XI) and is stereochemically homogeneous.[129]   Citraconic anhydride,[5] pyrocinchonic anhydride,[121] itaconic anhydride,[5] dibromomaleic anhydride,[7] and acetoxymaleic anhydride [185] react similarly with cyclopentadiene to give the expected adducts.

XXXIII

Cyclic dienes carrying alkyl, aryl, methoxyl, ethoxyl, and carbomethoxyl groups as substituents have been employed successfully in the Diels-Alder reaction. Although these dienes appear to differ somewhat in degree of reactivity, sufficient investigation has not been carried out to indicate the relative hindrance afforded by the individual groups. Ease of condensation also depends to some extent upon the size of the ring containing the conjugated system. Five- and six-membered carbo-

[184] Alder, Offermanns, and Rüden, *Ber.*, **74**, 926 (1941).
[185] Nylen and Olsen, *Kgl. Norske Videnskab. Selskabs, Forh.*, **11**, 229 (1938) [*C. A.*, **33**, 5361 (1939)].

cyclic dienes frequently react readily with maleic anhydride in the cold; seven-membered rings apparently require heating.[186-188]

Terpenes which contain conjugated systems within the ring, such as α-phellandrene (XXXIV) and α-terpinene (XXXV), generally react readily with maleic anhydride in the usual manner. Even under mild conditions, however, the reaction is accompanied by the production of some polymeric material.[144] Certain bicyclic terpenes are able to undergo the Diels-Alder reaction by virtue of a fused cyclopropane or cyclobutane ring acting in conjugation with a double bond. Thus, α-thujene (XXXVI) yields two products (XXXVII and XXXVIII) which are identical with the adducts normally obtained from α-phellandrene and α-terpinene respectively.[189] In like manner, 4-methyl-4-nopinol (XXXIX) yields, through intermediate dehydration and cleavage of the 3-7 bond, an adduct (XXXVIII) identical with that obtained from α-terpinene.[190]

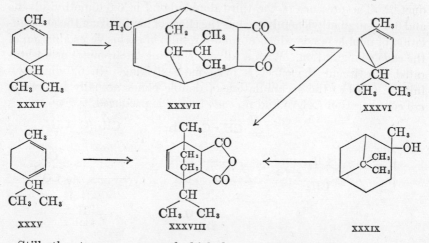

Still other terpenes, some of which do not contain a conjugated system (notably caryophyllene,[191-196] α-pinene, limonene, terpinolene, and carene [145,197,198]) are capable of reacting with maleic anhydride at some-

[186] West, *J. Chem. Soc.*, **1940**, 1162.
[187] Alder, Stein, Friedrichsen, and Hornung, *Ann.*, **515**, 165 (1935).
[188] Kohler, Tishler, Potter, and Thompson, *J. Am. Chem. Soc.*, **61**, 1057 (1939).
[189] Gascoigne, *J. Proc. Roy. Soc. N. S. Wales*, **74**, 359 (1941) [*C. A.*, **35**, 2876 (1941)].
[190] Lipp and Steinbrink, *J. prakt. Chem.*, (2) **149**, 107 (1937).
[191] Ruzicka and Zimmermann, *Helv. Chim. Acta*, **18**, 219 (1935).
[192] Ruzicka, Zimmermann, and Huber, *Helv. Chim. Acta*, **19**, 343 (1936).
[193] Rydon, *J. Chem. Soc.*, **1939**, 537.
[194] Goodway and West, *J. Chem. Soc.*, **1939**, 1853.
[195] Ruzicka, Plattner, and Balla, *Helv. Chim. Acta*, **24**, 1219 (1941).
[196] Ruzicka, Plattner, and Werner, *Helv. Chim. Acta*, **26**, 966 (1943).
[197] Hultzsch, *Angew. Chem.*, **51**, 920 (1938).
[198] Diels, Koch, and Frost, *Ber.*, **71**, 1163 (1938).

what elevated temperatures. The crystalline products obtained under these "forced" conditions are regarded as terpenylsuccinic anhydrides. If maleic acid is employed instead of the anhydride, α-pinene, limonene, terpinolene, and carene are all first isomerized to α-terpinene, which then yields the normal adduct (XXXVIII).

An interesting feature in the fulvene series is the presence of a third double bond which does not take part in the Diels-Alder reaction, but which vitally influences the steric course of the addition process. Addition of maleic anhydride to 6,6-dimethylfulvene (XL) no longer takes place selectively; *endo* and *exo* adducts (XLI and XLII respectively) are produced concurrently in nearly equal quantities.[127, 151] 6,6-Pentamethylenefulvene (XLIII) with maleic anhydride at room temperature yields first the *endo* adduct and, upon longer standing, the *exo* isomer. Elevated reaction temperatures favor formation of the *exo* adduct.[103] The presence of the third double bond in 6,6-dimethylfulvene and 6,6-pentamethylenefulvene has the effect of neutralizing the accumulation of double bonds which normally results in exclusive production of the *endo* configuration. With a fulvene carrying an aromatic or unsaturated substituent the effect is even more striking. In 6,6-diphenylfulvene (XLIV) the accumulation of double bonds actually favors the *exo* configuration (XLV) and no *endo* isomer is produced.[127, 151]

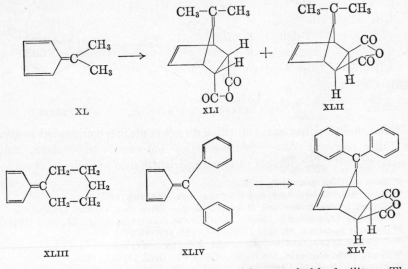

Fulvene adducts generally dissociate with remarkable facility. The *endo* adduct of maleic anhydride and 6,6-pentamethylenefulvene dissociates readily, whereas the *exo* isomer is stable.[103, 199]

[199] Kohler and Kable, *J. Am. Chem. Soc.*, **57**, 917 (1935).

Although 1,2,3,4-tetraphenylbutadiene does not react with maleic anhydride,[153] tetraphenylcyclopentadienone (tetracyclone) reacts readily,[1,155,156] as do other highly arylated cyclopentadienones.[200,201] The dimer of 2,5-dimethyl-3,4-diphenylcyclopentadienone behaves in its reactions as if it were dissociated into the monomer and affords an excellent yield of Diels-Alder adduct (XLVI) with maleic anhydride.[202]

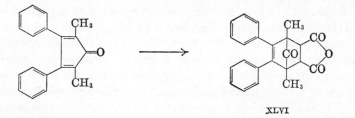

XLVI

Adducts of type XLVI sometimes lose carbon monoxide upon being heated and may eliminate hydrogen at elevated temperatures to become fully aromatic.[1]

In the polycyclic series, the Diels-Alder reaction has provided a convenient diagnostic method for determining whether a conjugated system lies wholly within one ring.[203] Compounds of type A which have the diene system in one ring (*cis* configuration) form normal adducts with maleic anhydride. Such compounds include 2,4-cholestadiene,[204] ergosteryl acetate,[205] 7-dehydrocholesteryl acetate,[206] isodehydrocholesteryl acetate,[207] 7-dehydrositosteryl acetate,[208] and levopimaric acid.[209-211] Compounds of type B, in which the diene system extends over two rings (*trans* configuration), react with maleic anhydride if "forced" but give amorphous products of unknown composition. Among such compounds are 3,5-cholestadiene,[212] cholestenone-enol acetate,[213] and 3,5-solatubiene.[214] This rule has been employed repeatedly in the steroid series

[200] Dilthey, ter Horst, and Schaefer, *J. prakt. Chem.*, **148**, 53 (1937).
[201] Dilthey and Henkels, *J. prakt. Chem.*, **149**, 85 (1937).
[202] Allen and Van Allan, *J. Am. Chem. Soc.*, **64**, 1260 (1942).
[203] Bergmann and Hirschmann, *J. Org. Chem.*, **4**, 40 (1939).
[204] Stavely and Bergmann, *J. Org. Chem.*, **1**, 575 (1936).
[205] Inhoffen, *Ann.*, **508**, 81 (1934).
[206] Schenck, Buchholz, and Wiese, *Ber.*, **69**, 2696 (1936).
[207] Windaus, Linsert, and Eckhardt, *Ann.*, **534**, 22 (1938).
[208] Wunderlich, *Z. physiol. Chem.*, **241**, 116 (1936).
[209] Bacon and Ruzicka, *Chemistry & Industry*, 546 (1936) [*C. A.*, **30**, 6357 (1936)].
[210] Wienhaus and Sandermann, *Ber.*, **69**, 2202 (1936).
[211] Ruzicka, Bacon, and Kuiper, *Helv. Chim. Acta*, **20**, 1542 (1937).
[212] Stavely and Bergmann, *J. Org. Chem.*, **1**, 567 (1936).
[213] Westphal, *Ber.*, **70**, 2128 (1937).
[214] Rochelmeyer, *Ber.*, **71**, 226 (1938).

and has been particularly useful in the elucidation of the structures of the products of irradiation of ergosterol.[215-223]

Type A   Type B

A few compounds of type B have been observed to yield the usual type of adduct. Thus, abietic acid (XLVII) and levopimaric acid (XLVIII) yield the identical adduct (XLIX), though the latter acid reacts much more readily.[210, 211, 224-226] To account for this behavior it has been assumed that abietic acid is in equilibrium with levopimaric acid under the "forced" conditions required for reaction.[209, 227] A similar phenomenon is encountered with β-phellandrene (L), which yields the same adduct as does α-phellandrene (XXXIV).[228, 229] Menogene (LI) has been reported to react readily with maleic anhydride in warm benzene solution, but the structure of the adduct is not certain.[230]

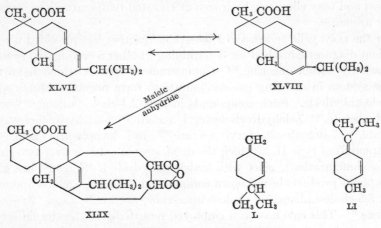

[215] Windaus, Werder, and Lüttringhaus, *Ann.*, **499**, 188 (1932).
[216] Windaus, Gaede, Köser, and Stein, *Ann.*, **483**, 17 (1930).
[217] Windaus, Dithmar, Murke, and Suckfül, *Ann.*, **488**, 91 (1931).
[218] Windaus and Lüttringhaus, *Ber.*, **64**, 850 (1931).
[219] Windaus, Lüttringhaus, and Deppe, *Ann.*, **489**, 252 (1931).
[220] Windaus, Linsert, Lüttringhaus, and Weidlich, *Ann.*, **492**, 226 (1932).
[221] Lettré, *Ann.*, **511**, 280 (1934).
[222] Müller, *Z. physiol. Chem.*, **233**, 223 (1935).
[223] Windaus and Güntzel, *Ann.*, **538**, 120 (1939).
[224] Ruzicka, Ankersmit, and Frank, *Helv. Chim. Acta*, **15**, 1289 (1932).
[225] Arbuzov, *J. Gen. Chem. U.S.S.R.*, **2**, 806 (1932) [*C. A.*, **27**, 2688 (1933)].
[226] Ruzicka and Kaufmann, *Helv. Chim. Acta*, **23**, 1346 (1940).
[227] Fieser and Campbell, *J. Am. Chem. Soc.*, **60**, 159 (1938).
[228] Goodway and West, *Nature*, **140**, 934 (1937).
[229] Goodway and West, *J. Chem. Soc.*, **1938**, 2028.
[230] Horiuti, Otsuki, and Okuda, *Bull. Chem. Soc. Japan*, **14**, 501 (1939) [*C. A.*, **34**, 1983 (1940)].

Certain types of dienes which have the conjugated system extending over two non-fused rings are able to undergo normal Diels-Alder condensation. Thus, 1,1'-bicyclopentenyl (LII) and 1,1'-bicyclohexenyl (LIII) yield the adducts LIV and LV respectively.[231, 232] 3,3'-Bi-indenyl,[233] 3,4,3',4'-tetrahydro-7,7'-dimethyl-1,1'-binaphthyl,[234] 3,4,3',4'-tetrahydro-1,1'-binaphthyl, and 3,4,3',4'-tetrahydro-2,2'-binaphthyl[235] react with maleic anhydride in a similar manner.

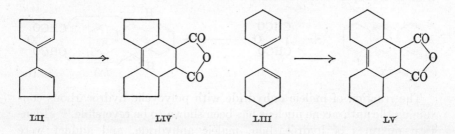

LII   LIV   LIII   LV

Addition of dienophiles to compounds containing a conjugated alicyclic-acyclic system has afforded polycyclic compounds, some of which simulate the steroid nucleus. Condensation of dimethyl fumarate with 4-methoxy-1-cyclohexenyl-1'-cyclopentenylacetylene (LVI), for example, yields LVII,[175] while addition of maleic anhydride to 6-methoxy-1-vinyl-3,4-dihydronaphthalene (LVIII) yields LIX.[172]

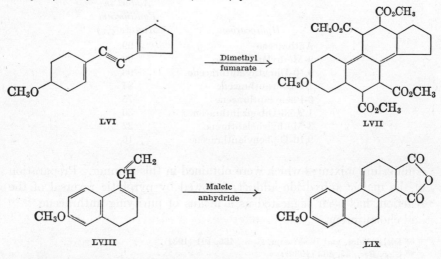

LVI   LVII

LVIII   LIX

[231] Barnett and Lawrence, *J. Chem. Soc.*, **1935**, 1104.
[232] Gruber and Adams, *J. Am. Chem. Soc.*, **57**, 2555 (1935).
[233] Straus, Kühnel, and Haensel, *Ber.*, **66**, 1847 (1933).
[234] Newman, *J. Am. Chem. Soc.*, **62**, 1683 (1940).
[235] Weidlich, *Ber.*, **71**, 1203 (1938).

Reaction of Maleic Anhydride with Aromatic Compounds. 1. *Wholly Aromatic Systems.* The central ring of the anthracene nucleus contains a characteristic diene system, for the hydrocarbon forms stable adducts with maleic anhydride, maleic acid, dimethyl maleate, fumaric acid, dimethyl fumarate, citraconic anhydride, mesaconic acid, crotonic acid, and dibromomaleic anhydride.[128, 236] 9,10-Dihydroanthracene-9,10-*endo*-α,β-succinic anhydride (LXI) shows unmistakably the absorption spectrum of a simple benzene derivative.[237]

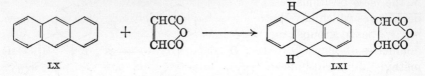

The reaction of maleic anhydride with polycyclic hydrocarbons containing the anthracene nucleus has been shown to be reversible.[123] Identical mixtures of hydrocarbon, maleic anhydride, and adduct were obtained by heating xylene solutions of either the pure adduct or the components in equimolecular proportion. In Table II are indicated the

TABLE II

EQUILIBRIUM MIXTURES FROM POLYCYCLIC HYDROCARBONS AND MALEIC ANHYDRIDE IN BOILING XYLENE

Hydrocarbon	Adduct in Equilibrium Mixture (%)
Anthracene	99
9-Methylanthracene	99
9,10-Dimethylanthracene	98
1,2-Benzanthracene	84
9-Phenylanthracene	75
1,2,5,6-Dibenzanthracene	30
3-Methylcholanthrene	22
9,10-Diphenylanthracene	16

equilibrium mixtures which were obtained in this manner. Preparation of the maleic anhydride adduct, followed by pyrolytic reversal of the reaction, has been suggested as a means of purifying anthracene [238-240] and cholanthrene.[241]

[236] Diels, Alder, and Beckmann, *Ann.*, **486**, 191 (1931).
[237] Clar, *Ber.*, **65**, 503 (1932).
[238] Polyakova, *Org. Chem. Ind. U.S.S.R.*, **7**, 305 (1940) [*C. A.*, **35**, 4008 (1941)].
[239] Dermer and King, *J. Am. Chem. Soc.*, **63**, 3232 (1941).
[240] Winans, U. S. pat. 2,347,228 [*C. A.*, **39**, 92 (1945)].
[241] Bachmann, *J. Org. Chem.*, **3**, 434 (1938).

Hydrocarbons containing the anthracene nucleus differ widely in the rates at which they react with maleic anhydride. This cannot be attributed merely to the steric hindrance offered by substituent groups on the anthracene nucleus, for the presence of methyl groups in the *meso* positions actually facilitates the reaction. 9-Methylanthracene, for example, reacts much faster than anthracene, and reaction between 9,10-dimethylanthracene and maleic anhydride takes place rapidly at room temperature. On the other hand, the presence of phenyl groups in the *meso* positions retards the reaction enormously. In anthracene derivatives which have both activating *meso* methyl groups and inhibiting 1,2-benzo groups, the activating effect of the methyl groups predominates. Thus, 9,10-dimethyl-1,2-benzanthracene and 5,9,10-trimethyl-1,2-benzanthracene react rapidly with maleic anhydride.[242] Ethyl groups in the *meso* positions of anthracene have very little activating effect, for 9,10-diethyl-1,2-benzanthracene reacts slowly with maleic anhydride (though more rapidly than does 1,2-benzanthracene itself).

Adducts of maleic anhydride with the carcinogenic hydrocarbons 1,2,5,6-dibenzanthracene, cholanthrene, and 3-methylcholanthrene have been converted to water-soluble salts by reaction with potassium or sodium hydroxide.[123, 241] Similar water-soluble salts have been prepared from substituted imides, such as 9,10-dihydro-1,2,5,6-dibenzanthracene-9,10-*endo*-α,β-succinoglycine (LXII), which, in turn, can be prepared from glycine and the corresponding maleic anhydride adducts. These salts have proved useful in conducting tests for carcinogenic activity in mice by subcutaneous injection.[243, 244]

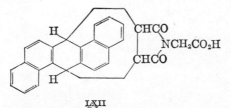

LXII

The Diels-Alder reaction has been employed in the diagnosis of fine structure of numerous polycyclic hydrocarbons. The fact that anthracene will add maleic anhydride is accepted by Diels and Alder[236] as evidence for the validity of the conventional (Armstrong-Hinsberg) anthracene formula, LX. Clar, on the other hand, considers that the course of the Diels-Alder reaction can be explained best by assuming

[242] Bachmann and Chemerda, *J. Am. Chem. Soc.*, **60**, 1023 (1938).

[243] Barry, Cook, Haslewood, Hewett, Hieger, and Kennaway, *Proc. Roy. Soc. London*, **B117**, 318 (1935) [*C. A.*, **29**, 5187 (1935)].

[244] Bachmann and Cole, *J. Org. Chem.*, **4**, 60 (1939).

that the Armstrong-Hinsberg structure is in equilibrium with a diradical form. The colored hydrocarbons 2,3,6,7-dibenzanthracene (pentacene, LXIII), heptacene, and 1,9,5,10-di-(*peri*-naphthylene)-anthracene react (with simultaneous decolorization) more rapidly with maleic anhydride than does anthracene itself. In view of the facility with which the free triphenylmethyl radical combines with maleic anhydride,[245] it is suggested that these hydrocarbons react through diradical intermediates (such as LXIV).[23, 246, 247]   Allen and Bell, however, were able to isolate a mono- and a di-addition product from the reaction of maleic anhydride with 6,13-diphenylpentacene (LXV).[248]

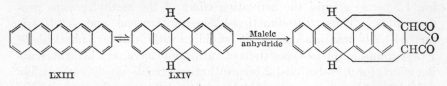

It has been postulated that in 9,10-diphenylanthracene the equilibrium LXVI ⇌ LXVII is displaced in favor of the diradical form (LXVII) to a greater extent than in anthracene itself.[247, 249] 9,10-Diphenylanthracene, however, reacts much more slowly with maleic anhydride than does anthracene.[123, 246] This behavior has been attributed to the protection afforded the trivalent carbon atoms by the compact arrangement of the benzene nuclei.[247]

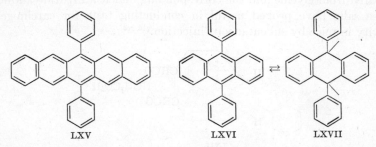

Perylene (LXVIII) reacts with only one molecule of maleic anhydride in boiling nitrobenzene to give LXX.[250] There is little doubt that a normal adduct (LXIX) is first produced and that this is oxidized to LXX by nitrobenzene. Of the various bond structures which may be written for perylene only LXVIII suffices to explain the course of the

[245] Conant and Chow, *J. Am. Chem. Soc.*, **55**, 3475 (1933).
[246] Clar, *Ber.*, **64**, 2194 (1931).
[247] Clar and Guzzi, *Ber.*, **65**, 1521 (1932).
[248] Allen and Bell, *J. Am. Chem. Soc.*, **64**, 1253 (1942).
[249] Ingold and Marshall, *J. Chem. Soc.*, **1926**, 3080.
[250] Clar, *Ber.*, **65**, 846 (1932).

Diels-Alder reaction. 2,3,10,11-Dibenzoperylene, 12,6′-oxido-1,2-benzo-perylene,[251] 3,9-dichloroperylene, 3,9-dibenzoylperylene, and 1,2-di-phenylaceperylene [252] likewise condense with maleic anhydride, whereas 1,12-benzoperylene,[251] 3,4,9,10-tetrachloroperylene, 3,4,9,10-tetranitro-perylene,[252] and periflanthene [253] fail to react.

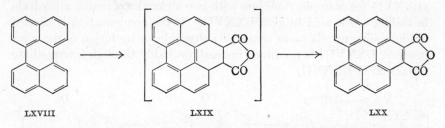

LXVIII   LXIX   LXX

When benzanthrone (LXXI) * is reduced with phosphorus and hy-drogen iodide, a hydrocarbon (LXXII) is obtained which cannot be an anthracene derivative, for it fails to react with maleic anhydride.[254] The compound shows a pronounced phenanthrene extinction curve, and its behavior is in harmony with the observation that phenanthrene itself is inert toward maleic anhydride.[250, 255] When benzanthrone is distilled with zinc dust, benzanthrene is produced. This hydrocarbon probably has the structure LXXIII because of the manner in which it condenses with maleic anhydride to give LXXIV, which subsequently rearranges to LXXV.[254, 256]

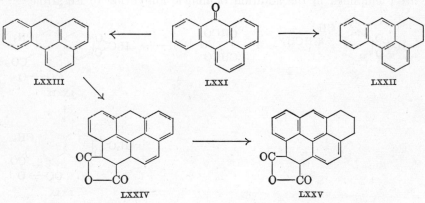

LXXIII   LXXI   LXXII

LXXIV   LXXV

* The structure shown is that employed by Clar. See, however, Gilman, *Organic Chemistry*, I, p. 172, John Wiley & Sons, New York, 1943.

[251] Clar, *Ber.*, **73**, 351 (1940).

[252] Zinke, Noculak, Skrabal, and Troger, *Ber.*, **73**, 1187 (1940).

[253] von Braun and Manz, *Ber.*, **70**, 1603 (1937).

[254] Clar and Furnari, *Ber.*, **65**, 1420 (1932).

[255] Cook and Hewett, *J. Chem. Soc.*, **1933**, 398.

[256] Clar, *Ber.*, **65**, 1425 (1932).

Anthrones do not undergo the normal Diels-Alder reaction but react in the ketonic form to give anthronylsuccinic anhydrides.[257] Methylene-anthrone and its substitution derivatives, however, react readily with maleic anhydride, cinnamic acid, or quinones to give adducts which are converted readily to benzanthrone derivatives.[258] Methyleneanthrone (LXXVI), for example, combines with two molecules of maleic anhydride in boiling acetic acid to give LXXVII. If the condensation is carried out in boiling nitrobenzene or acetic anhydride, or by fusion of the components, LXXVIII is produced instead, probably through intermediate formation of LXXVII.

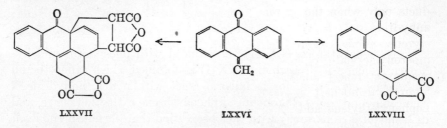

LXXVII   LXXVI   LXXVIII

2. *Aromatic-acyclic and Aromatic-alicyclic Systems.* An aromatic double bond in conjugation with extranuclear unsaturation frequently has been observed to produce an active diene system capable of undergoing the Diels-Alder reaction. The essential features of this reaction are exemplified in the addition of maleic anhydride to isosafrole.[101, 259]

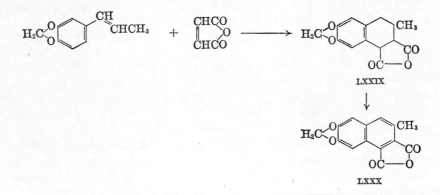

LXXIX

LXXX

A normal adduct is probably the initial product and subsequently rearranges to give the more stable aromatic isomer (LXXIX). Continued heating of the reaction mixture results in dehydrogenation of LXXIX to

[257] Barnett, Goodway, Higgins, and Lawrence, *J. Chem. Soc.*, **1934**, 1224.
[258] Clar, *Ber.*, **69**, 1686 (1936).
[259] Bruckner, *Ber.*, **75**, 2034 (1942) [*C. A.*, **38**, 1228 (1944)].

give LXXX. If the side chain contains a triple bond, a completely
aromatic adduct may be obtained directly.

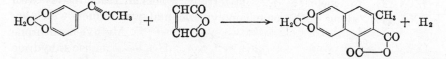

Investigation of a series of styrenes [101] revealed that an alkoxyl group
in the *p*-position to the unsaturated side chain enhances the tendency to
unite with maleic anhydride. An alkoxyl group in the *m*-position has no
such effect. Tetrahydronaphthalene derivatives are obtained as adducts only when the styrene is alkylated in the β-position.* Maleic
anhydride fails to give adducts with *m*-hydroxystyrene, *m*-methoxy-
styrene, *m*-methoxypropenylbenzene, β-bromopiperonylethylene, ethyl
piperonylacrylate, piperonylacetylene, *p*-methoxystyrene,† 3,4-methyl-
enedioxystyrene,† anethole,†‡ styrene,† stilbene,† benzalfluorene,[141] †
5-vinylhydrindene,‡ 5-isopropenylhydrindene,[142] ‡ or biphenyl.[260] *as*-
Diphenylethylene adds two molecules of maleic anhydride to give a
crystalline adduct. The following mechanism has been suggested for
this double addition.[154]

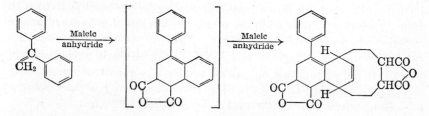

Under relatively drastic conditions, indene undergoes a Diels-Alder
reaction with maleic anhydride to give *endo-cis*-3,4-benzo-3,6-*endo*-
methylene-1,2,3,6-tetrahydrophthalic anhydride. Under similar conditions, hydrindene and fluorene react to give 1-hydrindylsuccinic anhydride and 9-fluorenylsuccinic anhydride respectively.[261]

Extranuclear unsaturation in conjugation with the naphthalene or
phenanthrene nucleus frequently produces a diene system which is
reactive toward maleic anhydride. The reaction affords a convenient

* Compare Tomayo and Viguera, *Anales fís. quím. Spain,* **38,** 184 (1942) [*C. A.,* **37,**
5034 (1943)].

† Gives a copolymer.

‡ Compare Tamayo and Ayestaran, *Anales soc. español. fís. quím.,* **36,** 44 (1940) [*C. A.,*
34, 7288 (1940)].

[260] Arbuzov, Salmina, and Shapshinskaya, *Trans. Butlerov Inst. Chem. Tech. Kazan,*
No. 2, 9 (1934) [*C. A.,* **29,** 3672 (1935)].

[261] Alder, Pascher, and Vagt, *Ber.,* **75,** 1501 (1942) [*C. A.,* **38,** 1227 (1944)].

route to certain complex polycyclic systems. In boiling toluene or xylene, for example, maleic anhydride reacts with 1-vinylnaphthalene (LXXXI) to yield a 1,2,3,11-tetrahydrophenanthrene derivative (LXXXII), along with some copolymeric material.[128, 262, 263] * If the

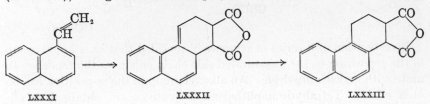

LXXXI   LXXXII   LXXXIII

reaction is effected in boiling acetic acid, the aromatic isomer (LXXXIII) is obtained.[128] Adduct LXXXII may also be isomerized to LXXXIII by refluxing with an acetic acid solution of hydrogen chloride.[263] Esterification of the aromatic product (LXXXIII) obtained in this manner yields both *cis*- and *trans*-esters.[128] Attempts to add citraconic anhydride to 1-vinylnaphthalene in benzene, toluene, xylene, or excess citraconic anhydride yielded only copolymers. The use of acetic and propionic acids as solvents gave mixtures of aromatized adduct and copolymers. The addition of *trans*-dienophiles (fumaric and mesaconic acids) to 1-vinylnaphthalene or 6-methoxy-1-vinylnaphthalene was found to be more satisfactory than addition of *cis*-dienophiles, for less polymeric material was produced.[128]

1-α-Naphthyl-1-cyclopentene (LXXXIV) can be made to react nearly quantitatively with maleic anhydride to give a tetrahydrophenanthrene derivative (probably LXXXV). The calcium salt of 3,4-cyclopentano-1,2,3,11-tetrahydrophenanthrene-1,2-dicarboxylic acid (from LXXXV) was dehydrogenated and decarboxylated concurrently upon distillation with a mixture of calcium oxide and zinc dust, to give 3,4-cyclopenteno-phenanthrene (LXXXVI). In like manner, the addition of maleic anhydride to 1-β-naphthyl-1-cyclopentene, followed by oxidative decarbox-ylation of the resulting adduct, afforded 1,2-cyclopentenophenanthrene in excellent yield.[264]

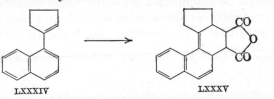

LXXXIV   LXXXV   LXXXVI

---

* Compare Robinson and Walker, *J. Chem. Soc.*, **1935**, 1530.
[262] Cohen, *Nature*, **136**, 869 (1935).
[263] Cohen and Warren, *J. Chem. Soc.*, **1937**, 1315.
[264] Bachmann and Kloetzel, *J. Am. Chem. Soc.*, **60**, 2204 (1938).

Numerous other α- and β-naphthyl and 9-phenanthryl derivatives react with maleic anhydride in a similar manner (see Table V). The following, however, fail to react: [66, 265, 266] 1-α-naphthyl-1-cyclohexene (though 1-β-naphthyl-1-cyclohexene reacts); α-9-phenanthrylstilbene; 9-cyclohexenylphenanthrene (though 9-cyclopentenylphenanthrene reacts); 1'-(9-phenanthryl)-1'-phenylethylene [though 1'-(9-phenanthryl)-2'-phenylethylene reacts]; and 9,9'-biphenanthryl.

There appears to be some correlation between the absorption spectrum of a phenanthrene derivative and its ability to undergo the Diels-Alder reaction. Thus, 9-cyclopentenylphenanthrene exhibits the washed-out spectrum associated with conjugated resonance states, and it also reacts with maleic anhydride. 9-Cyclohexenylphenanthrene and 9,9'-biphenanthryl, on the other hand, fail to react, and their absorption spectra are close to those of their components.[267]

The reaction of maleic anhydride with aromatic-aliphatic dienes has been employed for the synthesis of compounds containing an angular methyl group.[128a, 264, 268, 269]

Reaction of Maleic Anhydride with Heterocyclic Compounds. The furan nucleus undergoes the Diels-Alder reaction with extraordinary facility to yield an adduct which has an oxygen bridge (LXXXVII).

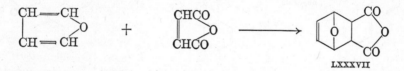

This type of adduct gives the corresponding phthalic anhydride when heated with hydrogen bromide in acetic acid.[270] Furfuryl derivatives,[270, 271] as well as substituted furans carrying alkyl groups [121, 272-276] or halogen,[270] yield normal adducts, but furans with a carbethoxyl, cyano, or nitro group directly attached to the ring have not yielded addition products.[270] Although β-hydroxyfuran gives an adduct, α-

[265] Bergmann and Bergmann, *J. Am. Chem. Soc.*, **59**, 1443 (1937).
[266] Bergmann and Bergmann, *J. Am. Chem. Soc.*, **62**, 1699 (1940).
[267] Calvin, *J. Org. Chem.*, **4**, 256 (1939).
[268] Meggy and Robinson, *Nature*, **140**, 282 (1937).
[269] Koebner and Robinson, *J. Chem. Soc.*, **1941**, 566.
[270] Van Campen and Johnson, *J. Am. Chem. Soc.*, **55**, 430 (1933).
[271] Diels, Alder, Nienburg, and Schmalbeck, *Ann.*, **490**, 243 (1931).
[272] Butz, *J. Am. Chem. Soc.*, **57**, 1314 (1935).
[273] Alder and Backendorf, *Ann.*, **535**, 101 (1938).
[274] Woodward, *J. Am. Chem. Soc.*, **62**, 1478 (1940).
[275] Diels and Olsen, *J. prakt. Chem.*, (2) **156**, 285 (1940).
[276] Paul, *Bull. soc. chim. France*, [5] **10**, 163 (1943) [*C. A.*, **38**, 3978 (1944)].

hydroxyfuran has not yielded satisfactory results.[277] α-Vinylfuran reacts readily with maleic anhydride to give an adduct lacking an oxygen

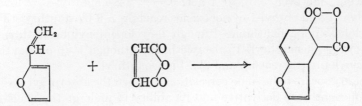

bridge.[276, 278] Maleic acid reacts with furan in the same manner as maleic anhydride,[271] but pyrocinchonic anhydride (dimethylmaleic anhydride) does not yield the expected adduct.[275]

Isobenzofurans, which themselves may be synthesized by means of a Diels-Alder reaction,[33] react rapidly with maleic anhydride at room temperature to yield adducts which may be converted easily to naphthalene derivatives.[38, 279-281]

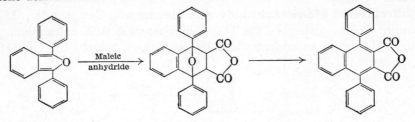

Anthranil also reacts with maleic anhydride, but the structure of the adduct has not been ascertained.[282]

In harmony with its greater degree of resonance stabilization, thiophene is less reactive than furan in the Diels-Alder reaction.[283] Thiophene does not react with maleic anhydride.[284] 2,3,4,5-Di-(1′,8′-naphthylene)-thiophene (LXXXVIII), however, does react with maleic anhydride.[285]

[277] Hodgson and Davies, *J. Chem. Soc.*, **1939**, 806.
[278] Paul, *Compt. rend.*, **208**, 1028 (1939).
[279] Weiss, Abeles, and Knapp, *Monatsh.*, **61**, 162 (1932).
[280] Weiss and Mayer, *Monatsh.*, **71**, 6 (1937).
[281] Bergmann, *J. Chem. Soc.*, **1938**, 1147.
[282] Schönberg and Mostafa, *J. Chem. Soc.*, **1943**, 654.
[283] Schomaker and Pauling, *J. Am. Chem. Soc.*, **61**, 1769 (1939).
[284] Diels, *Ber.*, **69A**, 195 (1936).
[285] Clapp, *J. Am. Chem. Soc.*, **61**, 2733 (1939).

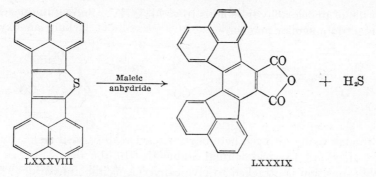

LXXXVIII   LXXXIX

The sulfur atom is lost as hydrogen sulfide during the reaction, and an aromatic adduct (LXXXIX) is formed.

It has been reported [286] that 1,3-diphenylisobenzothiophene does not react with maleic anhydride. 1,3,5,6-Tetraphenylisobenzothiophene (XC), on the other hand, reacts to yield an adduct which contains a sulfur bridge.[287] This adduct (XCI) can be aromatized by treatment with ethanolic hydrogen chloride.

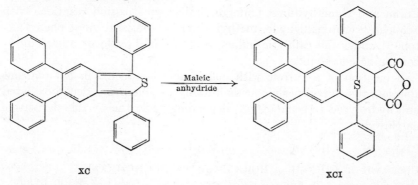

XC   XCI

The facile dissociation of isobenzofuran and isobenzothiophene adducts is remarkable because such dissociation must disturb an aromatic structure.[38, 287, 288]

The α-pyrone (coumalin) nucleus has been observed to yield a normal adduct with maleic anhydride.[289, 290] In boiling toluene, coumalin (XCII) reacts to give the adduct XCIII. If the reaction is effected at 150°, carbon dioxide is eliminated from the initial adduct and a second

[286] Dufraisse and Daniel, *Bull. soc. chim. France*, [5] **4**, 2063 (1937).
[287] Allen and Gates, *J. Am. Chem. Soc.*, **65**, 1283 (1943).
[288] Barnett, *J. Chem. Soc.*, **1935**, 1326.
[289] Diels, Alder, and Mueller, *Ann.*, **490**, 257 (1931).
[290] Fried and Elderfield, *J. Org. Chem.*, **6**, 566 (1941).

molecule of maleic anhydride adds to yield XCIV. Substituted couma-
lins react in a similar manner.

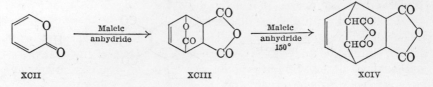

XCII   XCIII   XCIV

Although many nitrogen heterocycles react readily with maleic anhydride, they fail to yield normal adducts.* In the pyrrole series the
active α-position is attacked to give α-pyrrylsuccinic anhydrides.[6, 291, 292]

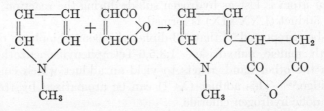

Furan and α-methylfuran undergo similar substitution reactions with
acrolein,[293] crotonaldehyde, methyl vinyl ketone, and vinyl phenyl ketone[294] under the catalytic influence of sulfur dioxide or other sulfur-
containing compounds.

If reaction of a pyrrole with maleic acid is effected in hot aqueous
solution, the pyrrylsuccinic acids initially produced are decarboxylated
and hydrolyzed to some extent, depending upon the pyrrole derivative
employed.

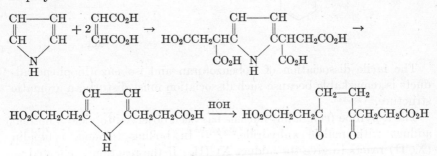

* Hopff and Rautenstrauch, U. S. pat. 2,262,002 [C. A., **36**, 1046 (1942)], have reported,
without citing evidence, that N-isobutylmaleimide reacts with pyrrole to yield a tetra-
hydro-endo-N-phthalimide.

[291] Diels, Alder, and Winter, Ann., **486**, 211 (1931).
[292] Diels, Alder, Winckler, and Petersen, Ann., **498**, 1 (1932).
[293] Sherlin, Berlin, Serebrennikova, and Rabinovich, J. Gen. Chem. U.S.S.R., **8**, 7 (1938)
[C. A., **32**, 5397 (1938)].
[294] Alder and Schmidt, Ber., **76**, 183 (1943).

Indole derivatives which have an α-substituent are attacked in the β-position.[295] An indole nucleus carrying no α-substituent is first dimerized by the action of maleic anhydride, and the resulting dimer then condenses with maleic anhydride.

2,3-Dimethylquinoxaline, in the tautomeric form XCV, reacts with maleic anhydride to yield XCVI or XCVII. Quinoxaline, 2-methylquinoxaline, 2-methyl-3-phenylquinoxaline, and 2,3-diphenylquinoxaline do not react with maleic anhydride.[282]

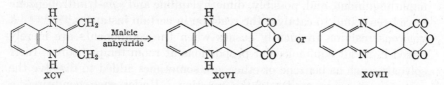

2-Styrylquinoline with maleic anhydride yields 2-styrylquinolinium maleate instead of the expected adduct.[180] The addition of maleic anhydride to the *meso* positions of anthracene is not paralleled by other heterocyclic compounds of apparently similar structure. Thus, acridine, 1,2,3,4-dibenzphenazine, the azine of indanthrone,[257] and dehydroindigo[296] all fail to give adducts. 2,4,10-Trimethylbenzo[g]quinoline (XCVIII), however, yields an adduct (probably XCIX) with maleic anhydride.[297]

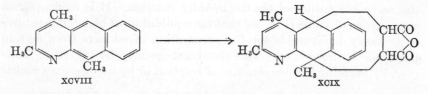

Diene Analysis. The Diels-Alder condensation with maleic anhydride has been adapted to numerous analytical procedures, including a rapid method for the determination of butadiene in complex gas mixtures[298] and methods for the estimation of diolefins in gasoline,[299] levopimaric acid in rosin acid mixtures,[300] and α-terpinene[301] or α-phellandrene[302] in oils. In addition, the reaction has been extended to the determination of "diene number" or "maleic value," constants indicative of unsatu-

[295] Diels, Alder, and Lübbert, *Ann.*, **490**, 277 (1931).
[296] Pummerer, Fiesselmann, and Müller, *Ann.*, **544**, 206 (1940).
[297] Johnson and Mathews, *J. Am. Chem. Soc.*, **66**, 210 (1944).
[298] Tropsch and Mattox, *Ind. Eng. Chem., Anal. Ed.*, **6**, 104 (1934).
[299] Birch and Scott, *Ind. Eng. Chem.*, **24**, 49 (1932).
[300] Sandermann, *Ber.*, **71**, 2005 (1938).
[301] Gascoigne, *J. Proc. Roy. Soc. N. S. Wales*, **74**, 353 (1941) [*C. A.*, **35**, 2877 (1941)].
[302] Birch, *J. Proc. Roy. Soc. N. S. Wales*, **71**, 54 (1937) [*C. A.*, **31**, 8109 (1937)].

rated linkages in oils and fats.[303-314] The determination of these constants is subject, however, to certain inherent errors.[315-319]

EXPERIMENTAL CONDITIONS AND PROCEDURES

Perhaps the most striking characteristic of the Diels-Alder reaction is the ease and rapidity with which it may take place. No condensing agents are required, although trichloroacetic acid, trimethylamine, α-naphthoquinone, and, possibly, dimethylaniline and *sym*-trinitrobenzene have been found to catalyze the reaction in certain instances.[102, 118-120] A vigorous reaction frequently ensues when the components are merely mixed in about equimolecular proportions at room temperature. Inert solvents, such as benzene or ether, are sometimes added to dissolve the components or to moderate the reaction. Under such conditions a quantitative yield of adduct often separates from solution in nearly pure form. Heat of reaction can also be dissipated effectively in certain instances by allowing the reaction to proceed with emulsified dienes in an aqueous medium.[320]

Less reactive dienes form adducts when solutions of the components are refluxed at appropriate temperatures. Although high-boiling solvents, such as anisole, *o*-dichlorobenzene, and nitrobenzene, have been used for some reactions, this procedure is often of no avail because of the reversible nature of the Diels-Alder reaction. It is evident from examination of Table II (p. 28) that the equilibrium at high temperatures is decidedly unfavorable for the preparation of adducts from certain polycyclic hydrocarbons. This disadvantage may be overcome, however, by lowering the temperature of reaction or by use of excess maleic

[303] Kaufmann and Baltes, *Fette u. Seifen*, **43**, 93 (1936) [*C. A.*, **30**, 7885 (1936)].
[304] Kaufmann and Baltes, *Ber.*, **69**, 2676 (1936).
[305] Kaufmann and Baltes, *Ber.*, **69**, 2679 (1936).
[306] Kaufmann, *Ber.*, **70**, 900 (1937).
[307] Kaufmann, Baltes, and Büter, *Ber.*, **70**, 903 (1937).
[308] Kaufmann, Baltes, and Josephs, *Ber.*, **70**, 908 (1937).
[309] Kaufmann, Baltes, and Büter, *Ber.*, **70**, 2535 (1937).
[310] Kaufmann and Hartweg, *Ber.*, **70**, 2554 (1937).
[311] Kaufmann, Baltes, and Hartweg, *Ber.*, **70**, 2559 (1937).
[312] Ellis, *Analyst*, **61**, 812 (1936).
[313] Dyachkov and Ermolova, *Caoutchouc and Rubber U.S.S.R.*, No. 3, 24 (1937) [*C. A.*, **31**, 6138 (1937)].
[314] Grosse-Oetringhaus, *Petroleum Z.*, **35**, 567 (1939) [*C. A.*, **34**, 975 (1940)].
[315] Sabetay and Naves, *Bull. soc. chim. France*, [5] **4**, 2105 (1937).
[316] Bruce and Denley, *Chemistry & Industry*, 937 (1937).
[317] Bickford, Dollear, and Markley, *J. Am. Chem. Soc.*, **59**, 2744 (1937).
[318] Bickford, Dollear, and Markley, *Oil & Soap*, **15**, 256 (1938) [*C. A.*, **33**, 421 (1939)].
[319] Norris, Kass, and Burr, *Oil & Soap*, **18**, 29 (1941) [*C. A.*, **35**, 2351 (1941)].
[320] Hopff and Rautenstrauch, U. S. pat. 2,262,002 [*C. A.*, **36**, 1046 (1942)].

anhydride. In boiling benzene, for example, the equilibrium mixture obtained from equimolecular proportions of 20-methylcholanthrene and maleic anhydride contained 94% of the adduct, compared with 22% present in boiling xylene. By the use of thirty moles of maleic anhydride in boiling xylene, on the other hand, the following yields of adducts were obtained: [123] from 9-phenylanthracene, 97%; 9,10-diphenylanthracene, 78%; 1,2-benzanthracene, 99%; 1,2,5,6-dibenzanthracene, 91%; 20-methylcholanthrene, 83%.

The nature of the product obtained from a Diels-Alder reaction is dependent in some instances upon the solvent employed. Such variations, however, are generally due to secondary changes in the adduct initially formed. When fused with maleic anhydride, 1,6-diphenyl-hexatriene, for example, yields an adduct which is different from that obtained when the reaction is effected in boiling xylene. The adducts are isomers, and the difference is attributed to migration of one double bond. 1,8-Diphenyloctatetraene exhibits a similar phenomenon in its reaction with maleic anhydride.[108, 151] When a Diels-Alder reaction is effected in boiling nitrobenzene, dehydrogenation of the primary hydroaromatic adduct frequently occurs with simultaneous reduction of nitrobenzene to aniline.[29, 250, 258, 321, 322] This transformation generally occurs when maleic anhydride or a quinone is employed as the dienophile.*

Reaction of Maleic Anhydride with Butadiene.[323] A mixture of 50 g. of maleic anhydride and 80 ml. of benzene in a soda bottle is chilled to 0°. The bottle is tared, charged with 32 g. of butadiene by distillation, capped, and placed in an autoclave along with 100 ml. of benzene (to equalize the pressure on both sides of the reaction bottle). The reaction mixture is allowed to stand at room temperature for twelve hours and is then heated at 100° for five hours. Crystallization of the 1,2,3,6-tetrahydrophthalic anhydride from benzene-ligroin yields 69.9 g. (90%) of long, colorless needles, m.p. 101–103°.

Reaction of Maleic Anhydride with 1-Phenyl-1,3-butadiene.[151] Maleic anhydride (7.5 g.) and 1-phenyl-1,3-butadiene (10 g.) are carefully heated on a water bath until vigorous boiling indicates that reaction has started. Heating is then discontinued. When the vigorous reaction has subsided, a small amount of benzene is added and the mixture is

---

* See, however, Weidlich, *Ber.*, **71**, 1203 (1938); Bergmann and Weizman, *J. Org. Chem.*, **9**, 415 (1944).

[321] Bergmann, Haskelberg, and Bergmann, *J. Org. Chem.*, **7**, 303 (1942).

[322] Bergmann, *J. Am. Chem. Soc.*, **64**, 176 (1942).

[323] Fieser and Novello, *J. Am. Chem. Soc.*, **64**, 802 (1942).

again heated on a water bath for about ten minutes to complete the reaction. The addition product begins to separate from the warm mixture as a mass of colorless crystals, and, upon cooling, the mixture sets to a thick paste. The 3-phenyl-*cis*-1,2,3,6-tetrahydrophthalic anhydride is crystallized from benzene-ligroin; colorless needles, m.p. 120°.

Reaction of Maleic Anhydride with 1,2-Diphenyl-1,3-pentadiene.[321] 1,2-Diphenyl-1,3-pentadiene (5 g.) and maleic anhydride (3 g.) are heated for three hours in boiling nitrobenzene (15 ml.). The 3,4-diphenyl-6-methylphthalic anhydride begins to separate during the heating. After standing for forty-eight hours the product is collected and recrystallized from petroleum ether (b.p. 130°); m.p. 161°.

Reaction of Citraconic Anhydride with Cyclopentadiene.[5] Citraconic anhydride (5 g.) dissolved in benzene (5 ml.) is treated with cyclopentadiene (3 g.). Vigorous evolution of heat takes place after a short time. After standing for several hours the solvent is evaporated at room temperature. The product is obtained as a faintly colored, viscous oil which changes to a compact mass of colorless crystals upon standing in a desiccator for two or three days. Two crystallizations from petroleum ether yield pure 1-methyl-3,6-endomethylene-1,2,3,6-tetrahydrophthalic anhydride, m.p. 138°.

Reaction of Maleic Anhydride with 9-Methylanthracene.[123] 9-Methyl-9,10-dihydroanthracene-9,10-*endo*-α,β-succinic anhydride crystallizes in 95% yield as colorless needles from a solution of 0.5 g. of 9-methylanthracene and 0.25 g. of maleic anhydride in 10 ml. of benzene which has been refluxed for two hours; m.p. 264–266°.

Reaction of Maleic Anhydride with 1,2-Benzanthracene.[123] 9,10-Dihydro-1,2-benzanthracene-9,10-*endo*-α,β-succinic anhydride is isolated by heating a mixture of 0.4 g. of 1,2-benzanthracene and 5 g. of maleic anhydride in 8 ml. of boiling benzene for three hours, evaporating the solvent, and distilling the excess maleic anhydride from the mixture at 80° at 0.4 mm. The residue is washed with benzene; yield, 0.26 g. (46%).

Reaction of Maleic Anhydride with Isoeugenol Methyl Ether.[101] A mixture of 24 g. of isoeugenol methyl ether, 18 g. of maleic anhydride, and 50 ml. of xylene is refluxed for five hours and then allowed to stand for two days; 45 ml. of xylene is then distilled. The residual orange-red, glassy mass is boiled with 200 ml. of ethanol, whereupon 30 g. of a solid separates (m.p. 101–103°). This is dissolved in chloroform, and a little petroleum ether is added to precipitate a small quantity of polymeric material. The adduct is recovered from the filtrate and recrystallized from acetic anhydride or from a relatively large volume of petroleum ether (b.p. 80–100°). 6,7-Dimethoxy-3-methyl-1,2,3,4-

tetrahydronaphthalene-1,2-dicarboxylic anhydride forms short, pale yellow prisms, m.p. 107°.

Reaction of Maleic Anhydride with Furan.[121] When the calculated quantity of furan is added to 2 g. of maleic anhydride suspended in ether, a reaction accompanied by a mild evolution of heat gradually ensues. The reaction mixture is allowed to stand for several hours in the cold in order to complete the reaction, during which time the addition product separates for the most part in the form of hard, colorless crystals. By working up the mother liquor the 3,6-endoxo-1,2,3,6-tetrahydrophthalic anhydride is obtained in quantitative yield; m.p. 125° dec.

SURVEY OF THE DIELS-ALDER REACTION
INVOLVING MALEIC ANHYDRIDE

The following tables include most instances reported before January, 1945, in which maleic anhydride and closely related dicarboxylic acid derivatives have been made to react with dienes of known structure. Unless otherwise indicated, the product isolated is assumed to be the normal hydroaromatic adduct of the type formulated in the introduction.

TABLE III

ADDUCTS FROM MALEIC ANHYDRIDE WITH ACYCLIC COMPOUNDS

Diene	Moles Anhydride per Mole Diene	Solvent	Reaction Temperature and Time	Yield %	Ref.*
Butadiene	0.88–1.1	Benzene	Room temp. (12 hr.); 100° (5 hr.)	Quant.	5
Butadiene	1	Benzene	Room temp. (24 hr.)	Quant.	148
Butadiene	0.86	Benzene	Room temp. (12 hr.); 100° (5 hr.)	90	323
Butadiene	—	Benzene	Room temp. (2 days); 100° (8 hr.)	—	324
trans-1,3-Pentadiene (trans-piperylene)	1	Benzene	0° (5 days)	95	131
trans-Piperylene	1.2	None	100° (2.5 hr.)	97	140
Piperylene	—	Benzene	Room temp.	—	6
2-Methyl-1,3-butadiene (isoprene)	—	Benzene	Room temp.	—	6
Isoprene	1	Benzene	Gentle heat	—	324
Isoprene	1	Benzene	0° (12 hr.); 100° (several hours)	Quant.	131
1,3-Hexadiene	—	—	—	—	135
2,4-Hexadiene	1	Benzene	Room temp. (24 hr.)	—	6
2,4-Hexadiene	—	Benzene	—	—	135
2,4-Hexadiene	—	—	—	—	325
2,4-Hexadiene	1	Benzene	0° (12 hr.); 100° (several hours)	Quant.	131
2-Methyl-1,3-pentadiene	1	Benzene	Room temp.	—	6
2-Methyl-1,3-pentadiene	1	Dioxane	4°	77	132
2-Methyl-1,3-pentadiene	1	Benzene	Room temp. (1 week)	—	134
2-Methyl-1,3-pentadiene	1	Benzene	0° (12 hr.); 100° (several hours)	Quant.	131
3-Methyl-1,3-pentadiene	1	Benzene	0° (12 hr.); 100° (several hours)	96	131
4-Methyl-1,3-pentadiene	—	—	—	—	137
2,3-Dimethyl-1,3-butadiene	1	Benzene	0° (12 hr.); 100 (several hours)	Quant.	131
2,3-Dimethyl-1,3-butadiene	—	Benzene	Room temp.	—	6
2,3-Dimethyl-1,3-butadiene	1	Dry benzene	Room temp. (24 hr.)	Quant.	148
2,3-Dimethyl-1,3-butadiene	1	Benzene	Heated	—	324
2,3-Dimethyl-1,3-butadiene	1	Water (emulsion)	40° (12 hr.)	Good	320
2,4-Heptadiene	—	—	—	—	135
5-Methyl-1,3-hexadiene	—	Benzene	Room temp. (>1 week)	—	134
3-Methyl-2,4-hexadiene	—	—	—	—	135
2,4-Dimethyl-1,3-pentadiene	—	—	—	—	326
2,4-Dimethyl-1,3-pentadiene	—	Benzene	Room temp. (2–3 days)	—	6
4-Ethyl-1,3-hexadiene	—	—	—	—	137
2-Cyclopropyl-1,3-butadiene	—	Benzene	—	—	327
2,6-Dimethyl-3,5-octadiene	—	—	—	—	19
7-Methyl-3-methylene-1,6-octadiene (myrcene)	1	None	Warm	Quant.	6, 328
Myrcene	1	None	Warm gently	Quant.	329
Myrcene	1	None	Fuse	—	330
5-Methyl-4-isopropyl-1,3-hexadiene	—	—	—	—	137
1-Phenyl-1,3-butadiene	1	None	Warm	—	151
1-Phenyl-1,3-butadiene	1	—	Heat	—	331
1-Phenyl-1,3-pentadiene	1	None	Warm	—	151
4-Phenyl-1,3-pentadiene	0.66	Benzene	100–105° (2 hr.)	6	18
1-(3′,4′-Methylenedioxyphenyl)-1,3-butadiene †	2	Xylene	Reflux (3 hr.)	Quant.	333
2-Methyl-1-phenyl-1,3-butadiene	1	Dry benzene	100° (6 hr.)	—	331
6-Phenyl-1,3-hexadiene	1	Xylene	Room temp. (4 days)	20	136
4-p-Tolyl-1,3-pentadiene	0.5	Benzene	105–110° (2 hr.)	14	18
1-(3′,4′-Dimethoxyphenyl)-1,3-butadiene ‡	1.5	Xylene	Reflux (7.5 hr.)	55	333

* References 324–434 are listed on pp. 57–59.
† Piperonylallylcarbinol which was dehydrated under the reaction conditions was employed.
‡ 3,4-Dimethoxyphenylallylcarbinol which was dehydrated under the reaction conditions was employed.

TABLE III—*Continued*

ADDUCTS FROM MALEIC ANHYDRIDE WITH ACYCLIC COMPOUNDS

Diene	Moles Anhydride per Mole Diene	Solvent	Reaction Temperature and Time	Yield %	Ref.*
4-(2′,4′-Dimethylphenyl)-1,3-pentadiene	1.1	Benzene	105–110° (2 hr.)	53	18
1-Butadienyl-2-vinyl-3-cyclohexene	—	Benzene	90–100°	—	92
1-α-Naphthyl-1,3-butadiene †	1.5	Xylene	Reflux (6 hr.)	38	333
1-α-Naphthyl-1,3-butadiene	1	None	145–155° (45 min.)	50	333
3-tert-Butyl-1-phenyl-1,3-butadiene	—	None	100° (30 min.)	—	332
trans-trans-1,4-Diphenyl-1,3-butadiene	1	None	Fuse	—	151
1,4-Diphenyl-1,3-butadiene	0.94	Xylene	Reflux (7 hr.)	77	108
2,3-Diphenyl-1,3-butadiene	1.25	Benzene	Reflux (overnight)	94	334
1-p-Nitrophenyl-4-phenyl-1,3-butadiene	6	None	110° (2 hr.)	Quant.	335
1-o-Chlorophenyl-4-phenyl-1,3-butadiene	1	None	Water bath (1 hr.)	48	336
1-m-Chlorophenyl-4-phenyl-1,3-butadiene	7	None	Water bath (12 hr.)	61	336
1-p-Chlorophenyl-4-phenyl-1,3-butadiene	6.1	None	Water bath (5 hr.)	71	336
1-p-Bromophenyl-4-phenyl-1,3-butadiene	1	Dry benzene	Reflux (8 hr.)	91	337
1,2-Diphenyl-1,3-pentadiene	0.94	Xylene	Reflux (3 hr.)	—	266
1,2-Diphenyl-1,3-pentadiene	—	Nitrobenzene	Reflux	—‡	321
1,2,4-Triphenyl-1,3-butadiene	1.1	Xylene	Reflux (2 hr.)	22	266
1,2,4-Triphenyl-1,3-butadiene	—	Nitrobenzene	100°	—‡	321
1-p-Biphenyl-4-phenyl-1,3-butadiene	10	None	140–150° (1 hr.)	80	152
Spilanthol	1.1	None	Cool (ice); warm (50–60°); room temp. (overnight)	5.8	338
2-Chloro-1,3-butadiene (chloroprene)	0.83	None	Warm	77	340
1-Chloro-3-methyl-1,3-pentadiene	—	—	—	—	341
2-Bromo-1,3-butadiene (bromoprene)	0.81	None	Room temp. (3–4 hr.)	—	342
1-Bromo-3-methyl-1,3-butadiene	—	—	—	—	343
5,6-Dibromo-1,3-hexadiene	1	Benzene	Room temp. (12 hr.); 100° (5 hr.)	§	148
1,6-Dibromo-2,4-hexadiene	1	Dry benzene	100° (5.5 hr.)	67	148
2,3-Dimethoxy-1,3-butadiene	—	—	—	—	344
3-Chloro-5-methoxy-1,3-pentadiene	1	Acetone	50° (2 hr.)	—	166
2-(3-Methyl-1,3-butadienyl) methyl thioether	—	—	Heat	54	345
2-(3-Methyl-1,3-butadienyl) ethyl thioether	Excess	—	Heat	42	345
2-(3-Methyl-1,3-butadienyl) n-propyl thioether	Excess	None	150°	—	345
2-(3-Methyl-1,3-butadienyl) isopropyl thioether	—	Ether	Reflux	—	345
2-(3-Methyl-1,3-butadienyl) tert-butyl thioether ‖	—	None	160–165°	—	345
2-(3-Methyl-1,3-butadienyl) phenyl thioether ‖	—	None	160–165°	—	345
2-Formoxy-1,3-butadiene (formoprene)	—	—	—	—	346
2-Acetoxy-1,3-butadiene	—	—	—	—	346
cis-1,3,5-Hexatriene	1	Dry benzene	Room temp. (12 hr.); 100° (5 hr.)	83	148

* References 324–434 are listed on pp. 57–59.

† α-Naphthylallylcarbinol which was dehydrated under the reaction conditions was employed.

‡ Adduct dehydrogenated under these conditions.

§ A pure product could not be isolated.

‖ The corresponding sulfone which probably yielded the diene under the reaction conditions was employed.

TABLE III—*Continued*

ADDUCTS FROM MALEIC ANHYDRIDE WITH ACYCLIC COMPOUNDS

Diene	Moles Anhydride per Mole Diene	Solvent	Reaction Temperature and Time	Yield %	Ref.*
trans-1,3,5-Hexatriene	1	Dry benzene	Room temp. (14 hr.); 100° (5 hr.)	Quant.	148
1,3,5-Hexatriene	1	Benzene	90–100° (3 hr.)	—	92
2,5-Dimethyl-1,3,5-hexatriene	1	Dry benzene	80° (7 hr.)	—	168
2,6-Dimethyl-2,4,6-octatriene (allo-ocimene)	0.95	None	Below 100°	—	145
Allo-ocimene	—	None	100° (1 hr.)	—	329
Allo-ocimene	—	—	—	—	19
Allo-ocimene	1	None	Fuse	—	349
4-Phenyl-1,3,6-heptatriene	1.15	Benzene	105–110° (1 hr.)	—	350
4-*o*-Tolyl-1,3,6-heptatriene	—	Benzene	105–110°	—	350
1-(2′,6′,6′-Trimethylcyclohexenyl)-3-methyl-1,3-butadiene	1	Dry benzene	Room temp. (2 days)	—	347
2-Methylenedicyclohexylideneethane	Excess	Benzene	Room temp. (48 hr.)	70	348
1,6-Diphenyl-1,3,5-hexatriene	—	None	Fuse	—	108
1,6-Diphenyl-1,3,5-hexatriene	1	Xylene	Reflux (7 hr.)	54–72	108
1,6-Diphenyl-1,3,5-hexatriene	1.2	None	Fuse	—	151
α-(1-Δ¹-Octahydronaphthyl)-β-(2′-methylenecyclohexylidene)-ethane	2.05	Dry benzene	Reflux (3 hr.)	52	351
Calciferol acetate	1.6	Benzene	Reflux (4 hr.)	†	352
1,8-Diphenyl-1,3,5,7-octatetraene	16.8	None	Fuse	—	108
1,8-Diphenyl-1,3,5,7-octatetraene	2.2	Xylene or tetralin	Reflux (10 hr.)	70	108
Vitamin A	—	—	—	—	353
Acetyl vitamin A	—	—	80° (2–3 days in CO₂)	—	169, 170
Benzoyl vitamin A	—	—	80° (2–3 days in CO₂)	—	170
Biosterol	—	—	—	—	354, 355
Biosteryl acetate	—	—	—	—	170, 356
Biosteryl palmitate	—	—	90–100° (in CO₂)	—	169, 357
1,10-Diphenyl-1,3,5,7,9-decapentaene	4	Xylene	Reflux (8 hr.)	74 †	108
Carotene	—	Benzene	—	—	171
Sorbic acid	1	Dry benzene	100° (18–38 hr.)	80	148
Sorbic acid	1.1	None	Warm	—	6
Ethyl sorbate	0.71	None	Warm	—	6
β-Chloroethyl sorbate	1.05	Xylene	Reflux (2–3 hr.)	58	358
Ethyl *trans-trans*-muconate	1	Dry benzene	100° (18 hr.)	50	148
9,11-Octadecadienoic acid	Excess	Benzene	90–100° (5 hr.)	—	303
9,11-Octadecadienoic acid	Excess	Acetone	100° (18 hr.)	Quant.	303
9,11-Octadecadienoic acid	—	—	Heat	—	359
Ethyl 9,11-octadecadienoate	—	—	—	—	359
9,11,13-Octadecatrienoic acid (α-eleostearic acid)	1	None	Heat in N₂	—	360–364
α-Eleostearic acid	1	None	70° (1.5 hr. in N₂)	—	365
β-Eleostearic acid	1	None	Heat in N₂	—	360–364
β-Eleostearic acid	1	None	70° (1.5 hr. in N₂)	—	365
β-Eleostearic acid	—	—	—	—	303
β-Eleostearin	Excess	Acetone	100° (10–15 hr.)	Quant.	303
4-Keto-9,11,13-octadecatrienoic acid (α-licanic acid)	1.1	Benzene	Room temp. (overnight); Reflux (10 hr. in N₂)	Quant.	305
α-Licanic acid	Slight excess	None	85° (in dry CO₂)	—	366
β-Licanic acid	Slight excess	None	85° (in dry CO₂)	—	366
Triacetyl-leuco-muscarufin	1.5	Benzene	100° (0.5 hr.); reflux (1 hr.)	72	339
1,3-Hexadien-5-yne	1	None	75° (4 hr.)	37	367
2,5-Dimethyl-1,5-hexadien-3-yne	0.66	None	130° (2 hr. in CO₂)	24	146
2-Ethyl-2-hexenalaniline	1	Dry benzene	Room temp. (2 hr.); reflux (3 hr.)	75–80 ‡	178, 179

* References 324–434 are listed on pp. 57–59. ‡ For structure of this adduct, see p. 21.
† Product consists of two isomeric adducts.

TABLE IV

Adducts from Maleic Anhydride with Alicyclic Compounds

Diene	Moles Anhydride per Mole Diene	Solvent	Reaction Temperature and Time	Yield %	Ref.*
Cyclopentadiene	1	Benzene	Room temp.	Quant.	5
1,5,5-Trimethyl-1,3-cyclopentadiene	1.65	Ether	Room temp. (overnight)	—	368
1-Benzyl-1,3-cyclopentadiene	—	Ether	Room temp. (24 hr.)	—	369
2-Benzyl-1,3-cyclopentadiene	—	Ether	Room temp. (24 hr.)	—	369
1,4-Diphenyl-1,3-cyclopentadiene	1.1	Benzene	Reflux (1 hr.)	—	370
1-Phenyl-4-p-tolyl-1,3-cyclopentadiene	—	—	—	—	370
6,6-Dimethylfulvene	1.1	Benzene	Room temp.	—	151
6,6-Pentamethylenefulvene	1	Benzene	Cool	—	199
6,6-Pentamethylenefulvene	—	Benzene	50–60°	—	127
6,6-Pentamethylenefulvene	1	Benzene	Room temp. –60°	†	103
6-Styrylfulvene	1	Benzene	Room temp.	—	151
6,6-Diphenylfulvene	1	Benzene	Reflux (0.5 hr.)	—	151
1-Carbomethoxy-1,3-cyclopentadiene	—	Benzene	Room temp. (several days)	—	129
1-Carbomethoxy-4,5,5-trimethyl-1,3-cyclopentadiene (methyl α-camphylate)	1	Benzene	Reflux (6 hr.)	—	368
2-Carbomethoxy-1,5,5-trimethyl-1,3-cyclopentadiene (methyl β-camphylate)	1.7	Benzene	120° (8 hr.)	—	368
Pentaphenylcyclopentadienol	5	None	Heat	—	126
2,5-Dimethyl-3,4-diphenyl-1,3-cyclopentadienone	Slight excess	Benzene	Reflux	99	202
3,4-Diphenyl-1,3-cyclopentadienone ‡	2.55	None	131° (3–5 hr.)	61–65	1, 371
Tetraphenylcyclopentadienone (tetracyclone)	1	Benzene	Reflux (7 hr.)	80	155, 156
Tetracyclone	3.9	None	155–160° (5 min.)	96	1
2,5-Diphenyl-3,4-(o,o′-biphenylene)-1,3-cyclopentadienone (phencyclone)	—	Chlorobenzene	Reflux	—	200
2,5-Diphenyl-3,4-(1′,8′-naphthylene)-1,3-cyclopentadienone (acecyclone)	18	None	Heat	95 §	201
Acecyclone	5.5	Chlorobenzene	Heat (2 hr.)	94	201
3a,7a-Dihydro-3,3a,5,6-tetraphenylinden-1-one	—	—	—	—	371
3a,7a-Dihydro-3,3a,5,6-tetraphenylinden-1-one ‖	4.7	None	Boil (15 min.)	70	371
1,3-Cyclohexadiene	1	Benzene	Warm	Quant.	5
1,3-Cyclohexadiene	—	Benzene	Room temp.	—	148
1,3,5,5-Tetramethyl-1,3-cyclohexadiene	1	Benzene	Reflux (0.5 hr.)	77	372
1,5,5,6-Tetramethyl-1,3-cyclohexadiene (α-pyronene)	—	—	—	—	145
α-Pyronene	—	—	—	—	14, 373
1,2,6,6-Tetramethyl-1,3-cyclohexadiene (β-pyronene)	—	—	—	—	145
β-Pyronene	—	—	—	—	14, 373
β-Pyronene	—	None	100° (1 hr.)	—	329
l-5-Isopropyl-1,3-cyclohexadiene	0.62	Ether	Reflux	—	374

* References 324–434 are listed on pp. 57–59.
† Product is a mixture of isomeric endo and exo adducts.
‡ Anhydracetonebenzil which dehydrated under the reaction conditions was employed.
§ Adduct lost carbon monoxide and hydrogen under these conditions.
‖ The dimer of 3,4-diphenyl-1,3-cyclopentadienone which lost carbon monoxide under the reaction conditions was employed.

TABLE IV—*Continued*

ADDUCTS FROM MALEIC ANHYDRIDE WITH ALICYCLIC COMPOUNDS

Diene	Moles Anhydride per Mole Diene	Solvent	Reaction Temperature and Time	Yield %	Ref.*
d-α-Phellandrene	0.69	Ether	Reflux (0.5 hr.)	—	375
l-α-Phellandrene	0.69	Ether	Reflux (0.5 hr.)	—	375
α-Phellandrene	1	Benzene	Room temp.	—	5
α-Phellandrene	—	—	—	—	190
l-β-Phellandrene	0.97	Benzene	Reflux (18 hr.)	7.8†	228, 229
Menogene	1	Benzene	—	—	230
α-Terpinene (1,3-menthadiene)	1	None	Reflux (6 hr.)	—	198 ‡
α-Terpinene	—	—	Room temp.	Quant.	301
α-Terpinene	—	—	—	—	381
3,5-Diethoxy-1,6-dihydrophthalic anhydride	2	Dry benzene	Heat (4 hr.)	60	160
4,5-Diphenyl-1,2-dihydrophthalic acid	—	None	200°	—	1
Thebaine	1.3	Benzene	Reflux	61	379
Thebaine	1.1	Dry benzene	Reflux (1 hr.)	91	380
Levopimaric acid	1	Benzene	Room temp. (12 hr.)	Quant.	209, 211
Levopimaric acid	1	Benzene or ether	20°	45–50	210
Abietic acid	—	Dry benzene	170° (4 hr.)	—	225
Abietic acid	1.1	Xylene	130–140° (several hours)	—	210
Methyl abietate	—	—	—	—	224, 382
Rosin	—	—	—	—	383
2,4-Cholestadiene	1.7	Dry benzene	Reflux (8 hr.)	15	204
2,4-Cholestadiene	1.7	Xylene	135° (18 hr.)	43	204
7,14-Cholestadiene	2.25	Toluene	Reflux (10 hr.)	—	384
$\Delta^{6,8}$-Coprostadienol acetate	19	Dry xylene	135° (15 hr.)	—	385
5-Methyl-$\Delta^{8(14),9(11)}$-norcholestadien-3,6-diol diacetate	5	Xylene	135° (14 hr.)	—	386
5-Methyl-$\Delta^{1(10),9(11)}$-norcholestadien-3,6-diol acetate	5	Benzene	80° (14 hr.)	—	386
Ergosterol acetate	1.9	Xylene	135° (8 hr.)	—	218
Ergosterol acetate	1.7	Dry xylene	135° (8 hr.)	16–20	205
22,23-Dihydroergosterol acetate	—	Xylene	135° (4 hr.)	—	387, 388
Dehydroergosterol acetate	2.2	Benzene	Reflux (4 hr.)	—	218
Dehydroergosterol acetate	—	Benzene	Reflux (4 hr.)	87.5	389
7-Dehydrocholesterol acetate	2.2	Xylene	135° (8 hr.)	—	206
iso-Dehydrocholesterol acetate	2.2	Xylene	135° (8 hr.)	13	207
7-Dehydrositosterol acetate	2.8	Xylene	135°	—	208
Ergosterol-B₃ acetate	Excess	Benzene	Reflux (7 hr.)	—	217
Dehydrocholesterol-B₃ benzoate	2	Dry benzene	Reflux (4 hr.)	—	206
Pyrocalciferol	—	—	—	—	222
Isopyrovitamin D	—	—	—	—	222
Lumisterol acetate	2.7	None	170–180° (0.5 hr.)	—	390
Isocafesterol	2.5	Benzene	Room temp. (overnight)	95	391
Cafesterol acetate	2.56	Benzene	Room temp. (4 days)	60–70	392
ox-Norcafestadienone	—	—	—	—	392
1,3-Cycloheptadiene	Slight excess	Xylene	Reflux (5 hr.)	—	188

* References 324–434 are listed on pp. 57–59.
† Same adduct as that obtained from l-α-phellandrene.
‡ Compare references 145, 376, 377, and 378.

TABLE IV—*Continued*

ADDUCTS FROM MALEIC ANHYDRIDE WITH ALICYCLIC COMPOUNDS

Diene	Moles Anhydride per Mole Diene	Solvent	Reaction Temperature and Time	Yield %	Ref.*
Cycloheptatriene	Slight excess	Xylene	Reflux (5 hr.)	84	188
Eucarvone	1.5	None	150° (4 hr.)	—	187
Eucarvone	0.91	Benzene	Reflux (6 hr.)	43	186
1,1'-Bicyclopentenyl	1.1	None	Warm	—	231
1,1'-Bicyclohexenyl	1.1	None	Heat (2 min.)	—	231
1,1'-Bicyclohexenyl	1	Benzene	4 hr.	34	232
1,1'-Bicyclohexenyl	1	Benzene	4 hr.	36	45
3,4,3',4'-Tetrahydro-1,1'-binaphthyl	2.1	Nitrobenzene	Reflux (3 hr.)	87	29, 235
3,4,3',4'-Tetrahydro-1,1'-binaphthyl	10	None	Water bath (4 hr.)	95 †	29
3,4,3',4'-Tetrahydro-2,2'-binaphthyl	2.6	Xylene	Reflux (1.5 hr.)	89	235
3,4,3',4'-Tetrahydro-7,7'-dimethyl-1,1'-binaphthyl	3	Xylene	Reflux (3 hr.)	73 ‡	234
3,3'-Biindenyl	1.25	Xylene	Reflux (1 hr.)	—§	233
1-Vinyl-1-cyclohexene	0.78	Xylene	Warm; room temp. (overnight)	63	393
2-Methyl-1-vinyl-1-cyclohexene	—	Benzene	—	—	268
2-Methyl-1-vinyl-1-cyclohexene	1	Xylene	100° (30 min.); room temp. (overnight)	—	393
2-Methyl-1-vinyl-1-cyclohexene	1	Benzene	Room temp. (48 hr.)	—	393
1-Vinyl-3,4-dihydronaphthalene	—	Cyclohexane	100° (15 min.)	—	172
1-Vinyl-6-methoxy-3,4-dihydronaphthalene	1	Cyclohexane	Room temp. (several hours)	39	172
1-Ethynyl-6-methoxy-3,4-dihydronaphthalene	3	Ether	Room temp. (overnight)	40–57	172, 173
2-Acetoxy-10-methyl-8-vinyl-5,8,9,10-tetrahydro-1,4-naphthoquinone	—	Benzene	150–160°	25	394
1-Cyclopentenylisopropenylacetylene	1.75	None	110–120° (2 hr.); 150–160° (30 min.)	13	395
1-Cyclohexenyl-1'-cyclopentenylacetylene	3	None	150° (3 hr. in N_2)	15–17	176
1-Cyclohexenyl-1'-cyclopentenylacetylene	1	None	130°	—	396
Di-1-cyclohexenylacetylene	3.9	None	150° (3 hr. in CO_2)	19	174, 175
2-Methyl-di-1-cyclohexenylacetylene	5.1	None	150° (4 hr. in CO_2)	1.9	174, 175

* References 324–434 are listed on pp. 57–59.
† Product consists of two isomeric adducts.
‡ Product consists of two stereoisomers, one of which is polymorphic.
§ Product consists of three isomeric adducts.

TABLE V

ADDUCTS FROM MALEIC ANHYDRIDE WITH AROMATIC COMPOUNDS

Diene	Moles Anhydride per Mole Diene	Solvent	Reaction Temperature and Time	Yield %	Ref.*
Anthracene	1.2	None	<260° (15–20 min.)	—	236
Anthracene	5	Benzene	Reflux (3 hr.)	96	123
Anthracene	1	Xylene	Reflux (10 min.)	Quant.	246
Anthracene	1	Xylene	Reflux (15 min.)	80	397
Anthracene	Excess	Acetone	100° (26 hr.)	Quant.	303
Anthracene	1.15	None	140–150° (4 hr.)	—	398
Anthracene	—	Xylene	150° (15 min.)	—	240
9-Methylanthracene	1	Benzene	Reflux (2 hr.)	95	123
2-Isopropenylanthracene	1.7	Xylene	Reflux (1 hr.)	34	266
9-Phenylanthracene	Excess	o-Dichlorobenzene	Reflux (1 hr.)	—	257
9-Phenylanthracene	1	Xylene	Reflux (30 min.)	75	397
9-Phenylanthracene	30	Xylene	Reflux (2 hr.)	97	123
9-Benzylanthracene	Excess	o-Dichlorobenzene	Reflux (1 hr.)	—	257
2-Chloroanthracene	1	Xylene	Reflux	—	246
9-Bromoanthracene	1	Dry xylene	Reflux (2.5 hr.)	94	399
9-Bromoanthracene	Excess	o-Dichlorobenzene	Reflux (1 hr.)	—	257
9-Nitroanthracene	1.5	Xylene	Reflux (2 hr.)	56	399
9-Acetoxyanthracene	Excess	o-Dichlorobenzene	Reflux (1 hr.)	—	257
9-Anthrylacetamide	1.6	Xylene	Reflux (4.5 hr.)	91	399
Ethyl 9-anthrylcarbamate	9.7	Dry xylene	Reflux (2.75 hr.)	95	399
9,9′-Bianthryl	3.6	Xylene	Reflux (1 hr.)	0	400
9,9′-Bianthryl	14.4	None	Fuse	0	400
9,10-Dimethylanthracene	1	Benzene	Reflux (20 min.)	96	123
9,10-Diphenylanthracene	30	Xylene	Reflux (2 hr.)	78	123
9,10-Diphenylanthracene	3.4	None	Fuse	10	397
10,10′-Diphenyl-9,9′-bianthryl	3.6	Xylene	Reflux (1 hr.)	0	400
10,10′-Diphenyl-9,9′-bianthryl	14.4	None	Fuse	0	400
9,10-Dichloromethylanthracene	—	Xylene	—	—	401
9,10-Anthracenedipropionic acid	—	Nitrobenzene	—	—	401
9,10-Anthracenedi-n-butyric acid	1.3	None	260° (15 min.)	67	402
9,10-Dichloroanthracene	1	Nitrobenzene	Reflux (15 min.)	50	246
9,10-Dibromoanthracene	1	None	200–210°	—	236
9,10-Dibromoanthracene	—	None	Fuse	—	403
10-Bromo-9-anthroic acid	1.5	None	220° (10 min.)	—	404
9,10-Dimethoxyanthracene	Excess	o-Dichlorobenzene	Reflux (1 hr.)	—	257
1,5-Dichloro-9-acetoxyanthracene	Excess	o-Dichlorobenzene	Reflux (1 hr.)	—	257
1,8-Dichloro-9-acetoxyanthracene	Excess	o-Dichlorobenzene	Reflux (1 hr.)	—	257
4,5-Dichloro-9-acetoxyanthracene	Excess	o-Dichlorobenzene	Reflux (1 hr.)	—	257
1,2-Benzanthracene	1.2	Xylene	Reflux	—	237
1,2-Benzanthracene	30	Xylene	Reflux (2 hr.)	Quant.	123
1,2-Benzanthracene	—	Xylene	Reflux	—	255
9,10-Dimethyl-1,2-benzanthracene	1.3	Benzene	Reflux (1 hr.)	94	242
9,10-Diethyl-1,2-benzanthracene	2.9	Xylene	Reflux (2 hr.)	84	242
Cholanthrene	2.7	Benzene	Reflux (2 days)	92	241
5,9,10-Trimethyl-1,2-benzanthracene	2.75	Benzene	Reflux (0.5 hr.)	Quant.	242
3-Methylcholanthrene	30	Xylene	Reflux (15 min.)	83	123
2,3-Benzanthracene (naphthacene)	1.2	Xylene	Reflux (5 min.)	—	237
Naphthacene	—	—	—	—	248
1,4-Diphenyl-2,3-benzanthracene (5,12-diphenylnaphthacene)	—	—	—	—	248

* References 324–434 are listed on pp. 57–59.

TABLE V—*Continued*

ADDUCTS FROM MALEIC ANHYDRIDE WITH AROMATIC COMPOUNDS

Diene	Moles Anhydride per Mole Diene	Solvent	Reaction Temperature and Time	Yield %	Ref.*
Benzanthrene	2	Xylene	Reflux (5 hr.)	—†	256
1,2,3,4-Dibenzanthracene	5.7	Xylene	Reflux (3 hr.)	—‡	405
1,2,5,6-Dibenzanthracene	1.3	None	250–260° (20 min.)	—	406
1,2,5,6-Dibenzanthracene	30	Xylene	Reflux (1 hr.)	90	123
3,3',7,3''-*bis*-Trimethylene-1,2,5,6-dibenzanthracene	—	Xylene	Reflux	—	407
1,2,6,7-Dibenzanthracene	2.85	Xylene	Reflux	—	405
1,2,6,7-Dibenzanthracene	—	Xylene	Reflux (45 min.)	—	408
2,3,6,6-Dibenzanthracene (pentacene)	1	Xylene	Reflux	—	246
9,10-Diphenyl-2,3,6,7-dibenzanthracene (6,13-diphenylpentacene)	3.3	Xylene	Reflux (1 hr.)	§	248
1,4-Dihydro-9,10-diphenyl-2,3,6,7-dibenzanthracene	4.4	Xylene	Reflux (1 hr.)	—	248
9,10-Dichloro-2,3,6,7-dibenzanthracene	—	—	—	—	237
1,2,6,7-Dibenzphenanthrene	2.85	Xylene	Reflux	—	405
2,3,6,7-Dibenzphenanthrene	1.5	Nitrobenzene	Reflux (10–15 min.)	Quant.	246
Perylene	3.1	Nitrobenzene	Reflux (1–1.5 hr.)	—‖	250
3,9-Dichloroperylene	6.6	Nitrobenzene	Reflux (2 hr.)	—‖	252
3,9-Dibenzoylperylene	14.15	Nitrobenzene	Reflux (1.5 hr.)	—‖	252
1,2-Diphenylaceperylene	8.8	Nitrobenzene	Reflux (1.5 hr.)	—‖	252
Hexacene	—	—	—	—	23
5,16-Dihydrohexacene	—	—	—	—	409
1,2,7,8-Dibenztetracene	Excess	Pseudocumene	—	—	410
3,4,8,9-Dibenztetraphene	Excess	Pseudocumene	Reflux (1 hr.)	—	410
1,2-(2',3'-Naphtho)-pyrene	—	Xylene	Reflux	—	411
1,2-(2',3'-Naphtho)-pyrene	3	Xylene	Reflux (45 min.)	—	255
5,18-Dihydroheptacene	—	—	—	—	412
6,17-Dihydroheptacene	—	Xylene	—	—	409
1,2,8,9-Dibenzpentacene	Excess	Pseudocumene	Reflux	—	413
2,3,10,11-Dibenzperylene	5.65	Nitrobenzene	Reflux (3 hr.)	—‖	250
1,9,5,10-Di-perinaphthyleneanthracene	1	Xylene	—	—	247
Methyleneanthrone	2	Acetic acid	Reflux (0.5 hr.)	—¶	258
Methyleneanthrone	1.05	Acetic anhydride	Reflux	—¶	258
Methyleneanthrone	1	Nitrobenzene	Reflux (45 min.)	—¶	258
Methyleneanthrone	1.05	None	Fuse	52¶	258
Benzylideneanthrone	1	Nitrobenzene	Reflux (4 hr.)	—¶	258
β-Anthraquinonylmethyleneanthrone	1.5	Nitrobenzene	Reflux (5 hr.)	—¶	258
Anethole **	1	—	Distilled	10.5 ‖	259
Anethole **	2	Toluene	Reflux (12 hr.)	—	414
Isosafrole	0.87	None	Water bath (3 hr.)	25	259
Isosafrole	1.3	Xylene	Reflux (3 hr.)	40–50	101
Isosafrole	0.83	None	Water bath (24 hr.)	34 ‖	259
Isoeugenol methyl ether	1.4	Xylene	Reflux (5 hr.)	80	101
Isoeugenol methyl ether	0.89	None	Water bath (3 hr.)	40	259

* References 324–434 are listed on pp. 57–59.
† See p. 31 for structure of this adduct.
‡ Product is probably a mixture of two stereoisomers.
§ Two adducts are obtained.
‖ Adduct dehydrogenated under reaction conditions.
¶ See p. 32 for structure of this adduct.
** See, however, Hudson and Robinson, *J. Chem. Soc.*, **1941**, 715.

TABLE V—*Continued*

Adducts from Maleic Anhydride with Aromatic Compounds

Diene	Moles Anhydride per Mole Diene	Solvent	Reaction Temperature and Time	Yield %	Ref.*
cis-Isoeugenol ethyl ether	1.25	Xylene	Reflux (5 hr.)	40–50	101
2,3-Dimethoxy-1-propenylbenzene	1.1	Xylene	Reflux (5 hr.)	4	101
1-(3′,4′-Methylenedioxyphenyl)-1-pentene	—	—	—	10	101
Methyl-3,4-methylenedioxyphenyl-acetylene (piperonylallylene)	1.2	Xylene	150° (2 hr.)	—†	101
as-Diphenylethylene	2	Benzene	Reflux (20 hr.)	—‡	141, 154
Indene	0.71	Benzene	250° (5 hr.)	22	261
1-Vinylnaphthalene	1	Xylene	100° (20 min.); room temp. (3 days)	32	262, 263
1-Vinylnaphthalene	1.2	Dry toluene	92° (3 hr.)	§	128ᵃ
1-Vinylnaphthalene	1.1	Dry xylene	100° (3 hr.)		264
2-Vinylnaphthalene	1.05	Xylene	100° (10 min.); room temp. (7 days)	6	263
1-Propenylnaphthalene	4.3	None	100° (5 hr.)	77.5	415
1-Vinyl-6-methoxynaphthalene	1.1	Xylene	100° (15 min.)	30	262, 263
1-Vinyl-6-methoxynaphthalene	2.1	Acetic acid	Reflux (2.5 hr.)	‖	128ᵃ
1-(α-Naphthyl)-1-cyclopentene	1.05	Dry xylene	Reflux (2 hr.)	20–22	264
1-(β-Naphthyl)-1-cyclopentene	10	None	100° (20 hr.)		264
2-Methyl-1-(α-naphthyl)-1-cyclopentene	10	None	100° (20 hr.)	—	264
2-Methyl-1-(β-naphthyl)-1-cyclopentene	10	None	100° (20 hr.)	—	264
1-(6′-Methoxy-2′-naphthyl)-1-cyclopentene	10	None	100° (20 hr.)	—	264
1-(6′-Methoxy-2′-naphthyl)-2-methyl-1-cyclopentene	10	None	100° (20 hr.)	—	264
3-(5′-Bromo-6′-methoxy-2′-naphthyl)-2-methyl-2-cyclopenten-1-one	10	Xylene	Reflux (5 hr.)	29	269
1-(β-Naphthyl)-1-cyclohexene	10	None	100° (12 hr.)	41	266
9-Vinylphenanthrene	1.3	Xylene	Reflux (5 hr.)	—	265
9-Propenylphenanthrene	1.1	Xylene	Reflux (4 hr.)	10	265
9-Isopropenylphenanthrene	1.1	Xylene	Reflux (4 hr.)	14	265
9-Cyclopentenylphenanthrene	1.8	Xylene	Reflux	58	265
9-Cyclopentenylphenanthrene	—	Nitrobenzene	Reflux	—†	321
9-Styrylphenanthrene	1.1	Xylene	Reflux (4 hr.)	27	265
6-Isopropenylchrysene ¶	5	Acetic anhydride	Reflux (2 hr.)	92.5	143

* References 324–434 are listed on pp. 57–59.
† Adduct dehydrogenated under reaction conditions.
‡ Adduct is a dianhydride.
§ A 95% yield of monomeric and copolymeric product was obtained. A 57% yield of pure, aromatized *cis*-dimethyl ester was obtained by alkaline hydrolysis, treatment with diazomethane, and evaporative distillation.
‖ A 39% yield of aromatized monomeric and copolymeric product was obtained. A 30% overall yield of pure, aromatized *cis*-dimethyl ester was obtained by alkaline hydrolysis, treatment with diazomethane and evaporative distillation.
¶ Dimethyl-6-chrysenylcarbinol which was dehydrated to give 6-isopropenylchrysene under the reaction conditions was employed.

TABLE VI

ADDUCTS FROM MALEIC ANHYDRIDE WITH HETEROCYCLIC COMPOUNDS

Diene	Moles Anhydride per Mole Diene	Solvent	Reaction Temperature and Time	Yield %	Ref.*
Furan	1	Ether	Gentle heat	Quant.	121
Furan	—	Dioxane	—	—	275
2-Methylfuran (sylvan)	1	Ether	Room temp. (2 days)	Quant.	273
2-Ethylfuran	1	Ether	Room temp. (48 hr.)	83	276
2-(β-Phenylethyl)-furan	1	Dry ether	Room temp. (few days)	Quant.	274
2-(β-m-Methoxyphenylethyl)-furan	1	Dry ether	Room temp. (3 days)	Quant.	274
2-Vinylfuran	—	Ether	—	80 †	278
Furfurylacetone	—	—	—	—	270
2-Bromofuran	—	—	—	—	270
3-Bromofuran	—	—	—	—	270
3-Hydroxyfuran	1	Dry ether	Room temp. (48 hr.)	60	277
Furfuryl acetate	1.1	Ether	Room temp. (several days)	—	271
Furfural diacetate	—	—	—	—	270
Furfuryl methyl ether	—	—	—	—	270
2,5-Dimethylfuran	1	Dry ether	Room temp. (24 hr.)	Quant.	121, 275
2-Methyl-5-isopropylfuran	0.8	Dry ether	0–8°	—	272
2-sec-Butyl-5-methylfuran	1.04	Ether	Room temp. (24 hr.)	—	294
5-Methylfurfurylacetone	1	Ether	Room temp. (24 hr.)	—	294
5-Methylfurfurylacetophenone	1.1	Ether	Room temp. (1.5 days)	—	294
2,5-bis-(γ-Ketobutyl)-furan	1	Ether	Room temp. (2 days)	—	294
β-(5-Methyl-2-furyl)-n-butyraldehyde	1	Ether	Room temp. (3 days)	—	294
1,3-Diphenylisobenzofuran	—	Xylene	Warm (0.5–1 hr.)	95	279
1,3-Diphenylisobenzofuran	1.2	Dichloroethylene	Room temp. (almost instantly)	—	288
1,3-Diphenylisobenzofuran	—	Xylene	Warm (0.5–1 hr.)	—	416
1,3-Diphenylisobenzofuran	—	—	Room temp.	—	416
1,3-Diphenylisobenzofuran	—	—	—	—	281
1,3-Di-p-tolylisobenzofuran	1.1	Benzene	Room temp. (5 min.)	92	39
1,3-Di-p-chlorophenylisobenzofuran	1.1	Benzene	Room temp. (5 min.)	94	39
1,3-Diphenyl-4,7-dimethylisobenzofuran	Excess	Ether or benzene	Room temp. (instantly)	>70	37
1,3-Diphenyl-5,6-dimethylisobenzofuran	1	Benzene	Room temp.	Quant.	38
1,3-Di-p-tolyl-5,6-dimethylisobenzofuran	1.1	Benzene	Room temp. (5 min.)	93	39
1,3-Di-p-chlorophenyl-5,6-dimethylisobenzofuran	1.1	Benzene	Room temp. (5 min.)	95	39
1,3-Di-(m,m'-dibromo-p-hydroxyphenyl)-isobenzofuran	1.26	Toluene	Reflux	—	280
1,3-Di-α-naphthylisobenzofuran	—	Xylene	—	—	417
1-Benzoyl-3-phenylisobenzofuran	—	—	—	—	287
1,3,5,6-Tetraphenylisobenzothiophene	9	None	Reflux (30 min.)	69	287
2,3,4,5-Di-(1',8'-naphthylene)-thiophene	11.3	None	225° (15 min.)	—‡	285
2,6-Dimethyl-3-propenyl-5,6-dihydro-1,2-pyran	1	—	—	37	418
α-Pyrone (coumalin)	1	Toluene	Reflux (10 hr.)	40	289
Coumalin	1	None	150°	—§	289
5-Methyl-α-pyrone	1.1	Toluene	Reflux	—	290
5-Ethyl-α-pyrone	1.1	Toluene	Reflux	—	290
4,6-Dimethyl-α-pyrone	1.3	None	150°	—§	289
α-Pyrone-5-carboxylic acid (coumalic acid)	1.1	None	200°	—§	289
Methyl coumalate	1.05	Toluene	Reflux (2–3 hr.)	30	289
Methyl coumalate	1.05	Xylene	Reflux (2–3 hr.)	30 §	289
4,6-Dimethyl-α-pyrone-5-carboxylic acid (isodehydracetic acid)	2	None	Fuse	—§	289
2,4,10-Trimethylbenzo[g]quinoline	5.65	Benzene	Reflux (6 hr.)	76	297
2,3-Dimethylquinoxaline	1	Dry toluene	Reflux (2.5 hr.)	50	282
Anthranil	1	Dry toluene	Water bath (30 min.)	—	282

* References 324–434 are listed on pp. 57–59.
† See p. 36 for the structure of this adduct.
‡ Adduct lost hydrogen sulfide under these conditions.
§ Adduct is a dianhydride.

TABLE VII

Adducts from Dienophiles Related to Maleic Anhydride

Dienophile (Moles per Mole Diene)	Diene	Solvent	Reaction Temperature and Time	Yield %	Ref.*
Maleic acid (0.61)	Butadiene	Water (emulsion)	50–60° (10 hr.)	Good	320
Maleic acid (1.12)	2,3-Dimethyl-1,3-butadiene	Water (emulsion)	40° (12 hr.)	Quant.	320
Maleic acid (1)	Anthracene	Dry toluene	Reflux (24 hr.)	87	128[a]
Maleic acid (1.8)	Furan	Water	Room temp. (3 days)	—	271
Fumaric acid	Acecyclone	—	Heat (5–6 hr.)	—	201
Fumaric acid (0.2)	1,1'-Bicyclohexenyl	None	190–200°	80	29
Fumaric acid (8.4)	Anthracene	Acetic acid	Reflux (72 hr.)	88	128[a]
Fumaric acid (3.8)	1-Vinylnaphthalene	Propionic acid	Reflux (110 hr.)	89 †	128[a]
Fumaric acid (1.2)	1-Vinyl-6-methoxynaphthalene	Acetic acid	Reflux (18 hr.)	71 †	128[a]
Ethyl hydrogen maleate (1)	1-Vinylnaphthalene	None	100° (15 hr.)		264
Dimethyl maleate (1)	Cyclopentadiene	None	Room temp. (24 hr.)	56	61
Dimethyl maleate (slight excess)	2,5-Dimethyl-3,4-diphenyl-1,3-cyclopentadienone	Benzene	Reflux	83	202
Dimethyl maleate (5.3)	Tetracyclone	None	160°	61	1
Dimethyl maleate (5)	Anthracene	Dry xylene	Reflux (72 hr.)	87	128[a]
Dimethyl maleate	Indene	None	250° (5 hr.)	—	261
Dimethyl fumarate (slight excess)	2,5-Dimethyl-3,4-diphenyl-1,3-cyclopentadienone	Benzene	Reflux (15 hr.)	73	202
Dimethyl fumarate (2.65)	Tetracyclone	None	170°	63	1
Dimethyl fumarate (2.65)	Tetracyclone	None	225°	70	1
Dimethyl fumarate (3)	Isopropenyl-2-methyl-1-cyclopentenylacetylene	None	190–200° (24 hr. in N₂)	—	395
Dimethyl fumarate (2.3)	Di-1-cyclohexenylacetylene	None	175° (24 hr. in N₂)	34	175
Dimethyl fumarate (2.3)	4-Methoxy-1-cyclohexenyl-1'-cyclopentenylacetylene	None	175° (24 hr. in N₂)	45	175
Dimethyl fumarate (10)	Anthracene	Dry xylene	Reflux (71 hr.)	87	128[a]
Diethyl maleate (1.06)	2,3-Dimethyl-1,3-butadiene	Water (emulsion)	60° (24 hr.)	—	320
Diethyl maleate (excess)	2,5-Dimethyl-3,4-diphenyl-1,3-cyclopentadienone	None	—	64	202
Diethyl maleate (1)	Isoeugenol	None	Reflux (4 hr.)	25	101
Diethyl maleate (1)	Isoeugenol methyl ether	None	Reflux (6 hr.)	50	101
Diethyl maleate (1)	cis-Isoeugenol ethyl ether	None	Reflux (4 hr.)	20	101
Diethyl maleate (1)	Isosafrole	None	Reflux (2 hr.)	69	101
Diethyl maleate (2.16)	1,3-Di-(m,m'-dibromo-p-hydroxyphenyl)-isobenzofuran	Toluene	Reflux	—	280
Diethyl fumarate (1.4)	Di-1-cyclohexenylacetylene	None	175° (7 hr. in CO₂)	31	175
Diisobutyl maleate (1)	Butadiene	Water (emulsion)	70° (24 hr.)	—	320
Fumaryl chloride	1,4-Diphenyl-1,3-butadiene	None	Heat	—	108
Fumaryl chloride	1,8-Diphenyl-1,3,5,7-octatetraene	Xylene	Reflux	—	108
Fumaryl chloride (0.43)	Cyclopentadiene	Dry ether	−10° (1 hr.); room temp. (12 hr.)	75	8

* References 324–434 are listed on pp. 57–59.
† Adduct aromatized under these conditions.

TABLE VII—*Continued*

ADDUCTS FROM DIENOPHILES RELATED TO MALEIC ANHYDRIDE

Dienophile (Moles per Mole Diene)	Diene	Solvent	Reaction Temperature and Time	Yield %	Ref.*
Fumaronitrile	Butadiene	Toluene	131° (432 hr.) †	76	419
N-Isobutylmaleimide (0.59)	Butadiene	Water (emulsion)	Room temp. (12 hr.)	Quant.	320
N-Isobutylmaleimide (1)	Isoprene	Water (emulsion)	40° (24 hr.)	—	320
N-Isobutylmaleimide (1)	2,3-Dimethyl-1,3-butadiene	Water (emulsion)	40° (12 hr.)	Quant.	320
N-Isobutylmaleimide (1)	Cyclopentadiene	Water (emulsion)	25° (6 hr.)	Quant.	320
N-Isobutylmaleimide (1.05)	Pyrrole	Water (emulsion)	50° (6 hr.)	—	320
Methylmaleic anhydride (citraconic anhydride)	2-Chloro-1,3-butadiene	—	—	0	420
Citraconic anhydride (1)	Cyclopentadiene	Benzene	Room temp.	—	5
Citraconic anhydride	22-Dihydrotachysterol	Ether	Room temp. (4 days)	—	223
Citraconic anhydride	Biosterol	—	140° (20 hr.)	90	354
Citraconic anhydride	Tachysterol acetate	—	—	—	221
Citraconic anhydride	1-Vinyl-6-methoxy-3,4-dihydronaphthalene	—	—	—	421
Citraconic anhydride (1.15)	Anthracene	Benzene None	Reflux (48 hr.) Fuse	70 § —	128[b] 236
Citraconic anhydride (0.3)	Anthracene	Dry toluene	Reflux (48 hr.)	96	128[a]
Citraconic anhydride (2)	1-Vinylnaphthalene	Propionic acid	Reflux (22 hr.)	49 ‡	128[a]
Citraconic anhydride (2.1)	1-Vinyl-6-methoxynaphthalene	Propionic acid	Reflux (21 hr.)	59 ‡	128[a]
Itaconic anhydride (0.65–0.8)	Cyclopentadiene	Benzene	Room temp.	—	5
Methylfumaric acid (mesaconic acid) (5)	Anthracene	Propionic acid	Reflux (96 hr.); 92° (72 hr.)	80	128[a]
Mesaconic acid (2.5)	1-Vinylnaphthalene	Propionic acid	Reflux (106 hr.)	57 ‡	128[a]
Mesaconic acid (2.1)	1-Vinyl-6-methoxynaphthalene	Propionic acid	Reflux (4 days)	64 ‡	128[a]
Dimethylmaleic anhydride (pyrocinchonic anhydride) (0.5)	Butadiene	Benzene	190–205° (72 hr.)	21	158
Pyrocinchonic anhydride (1)	Butadiene	None	160° (26 hr.)	50	419
Pyrocinchonic anhydride (0.53)	Cyclopentadiene	Benzene	100° (5 hr.)	—	275
Pyrocinchonic anhydride (0.2)	Cyclopentadiene	Benzene	100° (4 hr.)	—	121
Pyrocinchonic anhydride (0.5)	1,3-Cyclohexadiene	None	170–180° (3 days)	87.5	419
Pyrocinchonic anhydride	1-Propenylnaphthalene	—	Elevated temps.	0	415
Dichloromaleic anhydride (1.2)	Anthracene	None	160–170°	Quant.	422
Dibromomaleic anhydride (0.39)	Cyclopentadiene	Ether	Reflux (0.5 hr.)	—	7
Dibromomaleic anhydride (2)	1,3-Cyclohexadiene	Benzene	Reflux (5 hr.)	—	7
Dibromomaleic anhydride (1.2)	Anthracene	None	150–180°	—	236
Acetoxymaleic anhydride	Cyclopentadiene	—	—	—	185
3,6-Dihydrophthalic anhydride (0.28)	Butadiene	Dioxane	170–180° (12 hr.)	—	157
3,4,5,6-Tetrahydrophthalic anhydride (0.2)	Butadiene	Benzene	170–180° (12 hr.)	—	157

* References 324–434 are listed on pp. 57–59.
† Gaseous butadiene was passed into the heated toluene solution of the nitrile for 432 hours.
‡ Adduct aromatized under these conditions.
§ Product is a mixture of 1-methyl- and 2-methyl-6-methoxyhexahydrophenanthrene-1, 2-dicarboxylic anhydride.

TABLE VII—*Continued*

ADDUCTS FROM DIENOPHILES RELATED TO MALEIC ANHYDRIDE

Dienophile (Moles per Mole Diene)	Diene	Solvent	Reaction Temperature and Time	Yield %	Ref.*
3,6-*endo*-Methylene-3,4,5,6-tetrahydrophthalic anhydride (0.18)	Butadiene	Ligroin	170–180° (42 hr.)	72	157
3,6-Endoxo-3,4,5,6-tetrahydrophthalic acid (<1)	Butadiene	Dioxane	170–180° (18 hr.)	—†	273
3,6-Endoxo-3-methyl-3,4,5,6-tetrahydrophthalic acid (<1)	Butadiene	Dioxane	170–180° (16 hr.)	—†	273
3,4-Dihydronaphthalene-1,2-dicarboxylic anhydride (0.2)	Butadiene	None	100° (85 hr.)	63	423, 424
3,4-Dihydronaphthalene-1,2-dicarboxylic anhydride (0.5)	2,3-Dimethyl-1,3-butadiene	None	100° (20–25 hr.)	94–97	423, 424
3,4-Dihydronaphthalene-1,2-dicarboxylic anhydride (0.17)	Cyclopentadiene	None	100° (24 hr.)	48	425
3,4-Dihydronaphthalene-1,2-dicarboxylic anhydride	1,3-Cyclohexadiene	None	100° (8 days)	70	425
7-*tert*-Butyl-3,4-dihydronaphthalene-1,2-dicarboxylic anhydride (0.081)	Butadiene	None	150° (36 hr.)	87	426
7-Methoxy-3,4-dihydronaphthalene-1,2-dicarboxylic anhydride (0.093)	Butadiene	Dioxane	160–180° (13–15 hr.)	75–85	159
6-Methoxy-7-methyl-3,4-dihydronaphthalene-1,2-dicarboxylic anhydride (0.089)	Butadiene	Dioxane	160–180° (13–15 hr.)	75–85	159
6,7-Dimethoxy-3,4-dihydronaphthalene-1,2-dicarboxylic anhydride (0.083)	Butadiene	Dioxane	160–180° (13–15 hr.)	75–85	159
3,4-Dihydrophenanthrene-1,2-dicarboxylic anhydride	Butadiene	Dioxane	160–180° (24 hr.)	67	425
3,4-Dihydrophenanthrene-1,2-dicarboxylic anhydride	2,3-Dimethyl-1,3-butadiene	Dioxane	160–180° (24 hr.)	94	423–425
1,2-Dihydrophenanthrene-3,4-dicarboxylic anhydride (0.15)	Butadiene	Dioxane	160–180° (24 hr.)	87	424, 425
1,2-Dihydrophenanthrene-3,4-dicarboxylic anhydride (0.15)	2,3-Dimethyl-1,3-butadiene	Dioxane	160–180° (24 hr.)	81	424, 425
3,4-Dihydro-8,9-acephenanthrene-1,2-dicarboxylic anhydride	Butadiene	Dioxane	160–180° (24 hr.)	81	425
3,4-Dihydro-8,9-acephenanthrene-1,2-dicarboxylic anhydride	2,3-Dimethyl-1,3-butadiene	Dioxane	160–180° (24 hr.)	67–73	425

* References 324–434 are listed on pp. 57–59.
† Adduct is the anhydride.

REFERENCES TO TABLES

[324] Böeseken and van der Gracht, *Rec. trav. chim.*, **56**, 1203 (1937).

[325] Levina and Kiryushov, *J. Gen. Chem. U.S.S.R.*, **9**, 1834 (1939) [*C. A.*, **34**, 4051 (1940)].

[326] Jacquemain, *Compt. rend.*, **214**, 880 (1942) [*C. A.*, **38**, 3605 (1944)].

[327] Golovchanskaya, *J. Gen. Chem. U.S.S.R.*, **11**, 608 (1941) [*C. A.*, **35**, 6931 (1941)].

[328] Ruzicka, *Helv. Chim. Acta*, **19**, 419 (1936).

[329] Goldblatt and Palkin, *J. Am. Chem. Soc.*, **63**, 3517 (1941).

[330] Arbuzov and Abramov, *Ber.*, **67**, 1942 (1934).

[331] Kharasch, Nudenberg, and Fields, *J. Am. Chem. Soc.*, **66**, 1276 (1944).

[332] Koelsch, *J. Am. Chem. Soc.*, **65**, 1640 (1943).

[333] Arnold and Coyner, *J. Am. Chem. Soc.*, **66**, 1542 (1944).

[334] Allen, Eliot, and Bell, *Can. J. Research*, **17B**, 75 (1939).

[335] Bergmann and Weinberg, *J. Org. Chem.*, **6**, 134 (1941).

[336] Bergmann, Weizman, and Schapiro, *J. Org. Chem.*, **9**, 408 (1944).

[337] Huggins and Yokley, *J. Am. Chem. Soc.*, **64**, 1160 (1942).

[338] Asano and Kanematsu, *Ber.*, **65**, 1602 (1932).

[339] Kögl and Erxleben, *Ann.*, **479**, 11 (1930).

[340] Carothers, Williams, Collins, and Kirby, *J. Am. Chem. Soc.*, **53**, 4203 (1931).

[341] Favorskaya and Zakharova, *J. Gen. Chem. U.S.S.R.*, **10**, 446 (1940) [*C. A.*, **34**, 7844 (1940)].

[342] Carothers, Collins, and Kirby, *J. Am. Chem. Soc.*, **55**, 786 (1933).

[343] Favorskaya, *J. Gen. Chem. U.S.S.R.*, **10**, 461 (1940) [*C. A.*, **34**, 7845 (1940)].

[344] Johnson, Jobling, and Bodamer, *J. Am. Chem. Soc.*, **63**, 131 (1941).

[345] Backer and Blaas, *Rec. trav. chim.*, **61**, 785 (1942) [*C. A.*, **38**, 3646 (1944)].

[346] Klebanskii, Tzyurikh, and Dolgopolskii, *Bull. acad. sci. U.R.S.S.*, 189 (1935) [*C. A.*, **30**, 1259 (1936)].

[347] Kipping and Wild, *J. Chem. Soc.*, **1940**, 1239.

[348] Dimroth, Dietzel, and Stockstrom, *Ann.*, **549**, 256 (1941).

[349] Arbuzov, *Ber.*, **67**, 569 (1934).

[350] Lehmann, *Ber.*, **73**, 304 (1940).

[351] Dimroth and Stockstrom, *Ber.*, **76**, 68 (1943).

[352] Windaus and Thiele, *Ann.*, **521**, 160 (1935).

[353] Dalmer, Werder, and Moll, *Z. physiol. Chem.*, **224**, 86 (1934).

[354] Nakamiya, *Bull. Inst. Phys. Chem. Research Tokyo*, **13**, 63 (1934) [*C. A.*, **28**, 3453 (1934)].

[355] Nakamiya, *Bull. Inst. Phys. Chem. Research Tokyo*, **14**, 584 (1935) [*C. A.*, **30**, 1803 (1936)].

[356] Nakamiya, *Bull. Inst. Phys. Chem. Research Tokyo*, **17**, 186 (1938) [*C. A.*, **32**, 8432 (1938)].

[357] Hamano, *Sci. Papers Inst. Phys. Chem. Research Tokyo*, **32**, 44 (1937) [*C. A.*, **31**, 7440 (1937)].

[358] Wagner-Jauregg and Helmert, *Ber.*, **71**, 2535 (1938).

[359] Böeseken and Hoevers, *Rec. trav. chim.*, **49**, 1165 (1930).

[360] Morrell and Samuels, *J. Chem. Soc.*, **1932**, 2251.

[361] Morrell and Davis, *Trans. Faraday Soc.*, **32**, 209 (1936).

[362] Morrell and Davis, *J. Soc. Chem. Ind.*, **55**, 237T (1936).

[363] Morrell and Davis, *J. Soc. Chem. Ind.*, **55**, 261T (1936).

[364] Morrell and Davis, *J. Soc. Chem. Ind.*, **55**, 265T (1936).

[365] Farmer and Paice, *J. Chem. Soc.*, **1935**, 1630.

[366] Morrell and Davis, *J. Chem. Soc.*, **1936**, 1481.

[367] Carter, U. S. pat. 2,173,272 [*C. A.*, **34**, 453 (1940)].

[368] Alder and Windemuth, *Ann.*, **543**, 56 (1940).

[369] Alder and Holzrichter, *Ann.*, **524**, 145 (1936).

[370] Drake and Adams, *J. Am. Chem. Soc.*, **61**, 1326 (1939).
[371] Allen and Spanagel, *J. Am. Chem. Soc.*, **55**, 3773 (1933).
[372] Kharasch and Tawney, *J. Am. Chem. Soc.*, **63**, 2308 (1941).
[373] Dupont and Dulou, *Atti X° congr. intern. chim.*, **3**, 129 (1939) [*C. A.*, **33**, 9312 (1939)].
[374] Gillespie, Macbeth, and Swanson, *J. Chem. Soc.*, **1938**, 1820.
[375] Goodway and West, *J. Soc. Chem. Ind.*, **56**, 472T (1937).
[376] Goodway and West, *J. Chem. Soc.*, **1940**, 702.
[377] Sfiras, *Recherches Roure-Bertrand fils*, **1938**, 111.
[378] West, *J. Chem. Soc.*, **1941**, 140.
[379] Sandermann, *Ber.*, **71**, 648 (1938).
[380] Schöpf, von Gottberg, and Petri, *Ann.*, **536**, 216 (1938).
[381] Tishchenko and Bogomolov, *Byull. Vsesoyuz. Khim. Obshchestva im. D. I. Mendeleeva*, No. 3-4, 35 (1939) [*C. A.*, **34**, 4386 (1940)].
[382] Krestinskii, Persiantseva, and Novak, *J. Applied Chem. U.S.S.R.*, **12**, 1407 (1939) [*C. A.*, **34**, 3277 (1940)].
[383] Hovey and Hodgins, *Ind. Eng. Chem.*, **32**, 272 (1940).
[384] Eck and Hollingsworth, *J. Am. Chem. Soc.*, **64**, 140 (1942).
[385] Windaus and Zühlsdorff, *Ann.*, **536**, 204 (1938).
[386] Petrow, *J. Chem. Soc.*, **1939**, 998.
[387] Windaus and Langer, *Ann.*, **508**, 105 (1934).
[388] Windaus and Inhoffen, *Ann.*, **510**, 260 (1934).
[389] Honigmann, *Ann.*, **508**, 89 (1934).
[390] Heilbron, Moffet, and Spring, *J. Chem. Soc.*, **1937**, 411.
[391] Chakravorty, Levin, Wesner, and Reed, *J. Am. Chem. Soc.*, **65**, 1325 (1943).
[392] Wettstein, Fritzsche, Hunziker, and Miescher, *Helv. Chim. Acta*, **24**, 332E (1941).
[393] Cook and Lawrence, *J. Chem. Soc.*, **1938**, 58.
[394] Butz, *J. Am. Chem. Soc.*, **60**, 216 (1938).
[395] Nudenberg and Butz, *J. Am. Chem. Soc.*, **65**, 2059 (1943).
[396] Butz, Gaddis, Butz, and Davis, *J. Am. Chem. Soc.*, **62**, 995 (1940).
[397] Dufraisse, Velluz, and Velluz, *Bull. soc. chim. France*, [5] **5**, 1073 (1938).
[398] Polyakova, *Coke and Chem. U.S.S.R.*, No. 2-3, 75 (1938) [*C. A.*, **33**, 3368 (1939)].
[399] Bartlett and Cohen, *J. Am. Chem. Soc.*, **62**, 1183 (1940).
[400] Dufraisse, Velluz, and Velluz, *Bull. soc. chim. France*, [5] **5**, 600 (1938).
[401] Postovskii and Bednyagina, *J. Gen. Chem. U.S.S.R.*, **7**, 2919 (1937) [*C. A.*, **32**, 5396 (1938)].
[402] Beyer, *Ber.*, **70**, 1101 (1937).
[403] Diels and Friedrichsen, *Ann.*, **513**, 145 (1934).
[404] Beyer and Fritsch, *Ber.*, **74**, 494 (1941).
[405] Clar and Lombardi, *Ber.*, **65**, 1411 (1932).
[406] Cook, *J. Chem. Soc.*, **1931**, 3273.
[407] Clar, *Ber.*, **73**, 409 (1940).
[408] Cook, *J. Chem. Soc.*, **1932**, 1472.
[409] Clar, *Ber.*, **75**, 1283 (1942) [*C. A.*, **37**, 4727 (1943)].
[410] Clar, *Ber.*, **76**, 149 (1943).
[411] Clar, *Ber.*, **69**, 1671 (1936).
[412] Marschalk, *Bull. soc. chim. France*, [5] **8**, 354 (1941).
[413] Clar, *Ber.*, **76**, 257 (1943).
[414] Tamayo and Ayestaran, *Anales soc. españ. fís. quím.*, **36**, 44 (1940) [*C. A.*, **34**, 7288 (1940)].
[415] Fieser and Daudt, *J. Am. Chem. Soc.*, **63**, 782 (1941).
[416] Dufraisse and Priou, *Bull. soc. chim. France*, [5] **5**, 502 (1938).
[417] Weiss and Koltes, *Monatsh.*, **65**, 351 (1935).
[418] Delépine and Compagnon, *Compt. rend.*, **212**, 1017 (1941) [*C. A.*, **38**, 2339 (1944)].
[419] Ziegler, Schenck, Krockow, Siebert, Wenz, and Weber, *Ann.*, **551**, 1 (1942).
[420] King and Robinson, *J. Chem. Soc.*, **1941**, 465.
[421] Breitner, *Med. u. Chem.*, **4**, 317 (1942) [*C. A.*, **38**, 4953 (1944)].

[422] Diels and Thiele, *Ber.*, **71**, 1173 (1938).
[423] Fieser and Hershberg, *J. Am. Chem. Soc.*, **57**, 1508 (1935).
[424] Fieser and Hershberg, *J. Am. Chem. Soc.*, **57**, 2192 (1935).
[425] Fieser, Fieser and Hershberg, *J. Am. Chem. Soc.*, **58**, 1463 (1936).
[426] Fieser and Price, *J. Am. Chem. Soc.*, **58**, 1838 (1936).

GENERAL REFERENCES ON THE DIELS-ALDER REACTION

[427] Diels, *Z. angew. Chem.*, **42**, 911 (1929).
[428] Alder, *Handbuch der biologischen Arbeitsmethoden*, Ed. by Emil Abderhalden, Abt. 1, Chemische Methoden, Tl. 2, Halfte 2, Heft 9, 1933.
[429] Allen, *J. Chem. Education*, **10**, 494 (1933).
[430] Linstead, *J. Oil & Colour Chemists' Assoc.*, **18**, 107 (1935).
[431] Delaby, *Bull. soc. chim. France*, [5] **4**, 765 (1937).
[432] Diels, *Fortschr. Chem. org. Naturstoffe*, **3**, 1 (1939).
[433] Alder, *Die Chemie*, **55**, 53 (1942).
[434] Norton, *Chem. Revs.*, **31**, 319 (1942).

CHAPTER 2

THE DIELS-ALDER REACTION
ETHYLENIC AND ACETYLENIC DIENOPHILES

H. L. HOLMES

University of Saskatchewan

CONTENTS

NATURE OF THE REACTION

In addition to the reactions with maleic anhydride and related compounds described in Chapter 1, conjugated dienes react by 1,4-addition with olefinic and acetylenic compounds in which the unsaturated group is conjugated with one or more carbonyl or other unsaturated groups (CN, NO_2, SO_2R). Even certain vinyl and allyl compounds have been found to function as dienophiles. Typical examples are the reactions of butadiene with acrolein, β-nitrostyrene, allyl chloride, and acetylene-

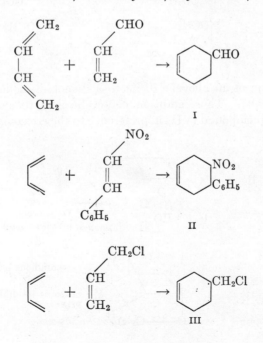

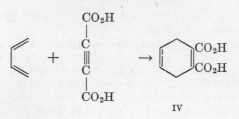

IV

dicarboxylic acid. The olefinic dienophiles yield cyclohexene derivatives (I–III), and the acetylenic dienophiles lead to derivatives of 1,4-dihydrobenzene (IV).

Formation of Stereoisomeric Adducts. The addition reactions of ethylenic and acetylenic dienophiles show stereochemical selectivity similar to that discussed in the preceding chapter. A *cis* dienophile yields a *cis* adduct, while a *trans* adduct results from the *trans* form. For example, the adduct (m.p. 191°) from *cis-o*-methoxycinnamic acid and 2,3-dimethylbutadiene is the *cis* compound (V), and the adduct (m.p. 159–159.5°) from *trans-o*-methoxycinnamic acid is the *trans* compound (VI).

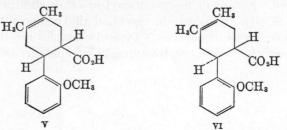

The addition of an alicyclic diene to a dienophile follows the Alder rule (Chapter 1). Thus, addition of acrylic acid to cyclopentadiene gives the *endo* compound (VII) in preference to the *exo* compound (VIII).

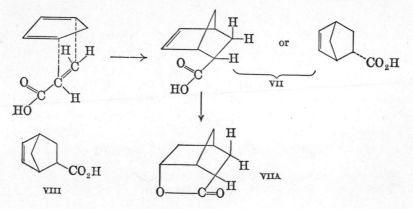

The configuration of VII was established by its conversion to the lactone (VIIA) by aqueous sulfuric acid.[1]

Formation of Structurally Isomeric Adducts. Two structural isomers are possible when an unsymmetrical diene and an unsymmetrical dieno-

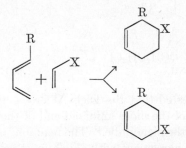

phile interact. Unfortunately the structures of the adducts have been rigidly established in only seven instances: acrolein + 1-phenylbutadiene, acrolein and methyl 3,4-dihydro-1-naphthoate + 2-ethoxy- and 2-methoxy-butadiene, 2,6-dimethoxy-4-n-amylcinnamic acid + isoprene, and derivatives of sorbic acid + acrylyl chloride and vinyl phenyl ketone. Acrolein and 1-phenylbutadiene give IX, as shown by conversion of the adduct through a number of steps to o-phenylbenzoic acid.[2]

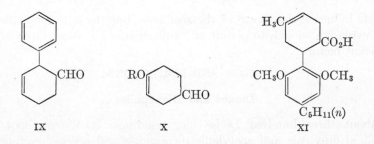

2-Methoxybutadiene (and 2-ethoxybutadiene) with acrolein give rise to a single product, X. On the other hand, 2,6-dimethoxy-4-n-amylcinnamic acid and isoprene, when heated, usually yield XI, although in a single experiment that could not be duplicated the isomeric adduct was formed. The principal product formed from acrylyl chloride and derivatives of sorbic acid is XII (79%), as established by conversion to 4-methylisophthalic acid. The orientation of ethyl sorbate and vinyl phenyl ketone, before reaction, must be just the reverse of the previous

[1] Alder, Stein, Liebmann, and Rolland, *Ann.*, **514**, 197 (1934).
[2] Lehmann and Paasche, *Ber.*, **68**, 1146 (1935).

case, for the main product (70%) is XIII; it was smoothly converted to β-methylanthraquinone by a three-step reaction.[3]

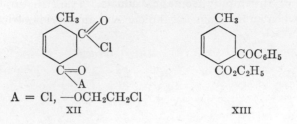

$A = Cl, —OCH_2CH_2Cl$

XII   XIII

It has been suggested that the Diels-Alder reaction is probably initiated by a coupling of the more anionoid end of the diene system with a cationoid carbon of the dienophile.[4] The reactions of 2-alkoxybutadienes with acrolein are in agreement with this hypothesis and may be formulated as shown. The Alder rule (Chapter 1) correctly predicts the formation of isomer IX from the interaction of 1-phenylbutadiene and acrolein. It seems likely that steric and Alder effects as well as electronic

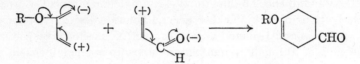

effects influence the course of the reactions, but the data available are not extensive enough to permit an evaluation of the importance of the different factors.

SCOPE AND LIMITATIONS

Dienes and Dienophiles

About three hundred Diels-Alder reactions, involving about one hundred ethylenic and acetylenic dienophiles and seventy conjugated dienes, have been carried out. The types of dienes which have been employed and examples of each type are shown in the following list.

Acyclic dienes—butadiene, alkylbutadienes, arylbutadienes.
Alicyclic compounds.
   Wholly alicyclic dienes—cyclopentadiene, cyclohexadiene, α-phellandrene, cycloheptadiene.
   Alicyclic-acyclic compounds—1-vinylcyclohexene, 1-vinyl-3,4-dihydronaphthalenes, 1-ethynyl-6-methoxy-3,4-dihydronaphthalene.
   Bicyclic compounds—bicyclohexenyl.

---

[3] Allen, Bell, Bell, and Van Allan, *J. Am. Chem. Soc.*, **62**, 656 (1940).
[4] Hudson and Robinson, *J. Chem. Soc.*, **1941**, 715.

Aromatic compounds.

Wholly aromatic compounds—anthracene, 9-bromoanthracene.

Aromatic-acyclic compounds—1-vinylnaphthalene, methyleneanthrone.

Heterocyclic compounds—furan, 2-methylfuran, 1,3-diphenyl-5,6-dimethylisobenzofuran.

The dienophiles discussed in this chapter may be divided into two main groups: ethylenic and acetylenic. In the ethylenic compounds the double bond is usually conjugated with one or more unsaturated groups, but certain substances with isolated double bonds, including ethylene itself, have been found to undergo addition in the typical Diels-Alder manner. The acetylenic compounds which have been employed contain the triple bond in conjugation with one or more carbonyl or cyanide groups. For convenient reference the dienophiles are shown in the following list.

Ethylenic compounds.

$R—CH{=}CH—Y$ and $Y—CH{=}CH—Y$

$R = H, CH_3, C_6H_5$.

$Y = CHO, CO_2H, CO_2R, COCl, COR, CN, NO_2, SO_2R, CH_2Cl, CH_2OH, CH_2NH_2, CH_2NCS, OCOR, Cl, Br, OR, SR, H$.

Acetylenic compounds.

$R—C{\equiv}C—Y$ and $Y—C{\equiv}C—Y$

$R = H, CH_3, C_6H_5$.

$Y = CHO, CO_2H, CO_2R, COR, CN, H$.

Ethylenic Dienophiles

α,β-**Unsaturated Carbonyl Compounds (Table V).** *Aldehydes.* The α,β-unsaturated aldehydes which have been employed in the Diels-Alder reaction are acrolein, crotonaldehyde and other alkylacroleins, cinnamaldehyde, and cyclopentene-1-aldehyde. Nearly all these substances react readily with acyclic and alicyclic dienes. The terminal methyl groups in β,β-dimethylacrolein appear to interfere somewhat, for the yield of the adduct with isoprene is low.[5] Cinnamaldehyde does not react with 1-vinylnaphthalene, nor does acrolein react with isosafrole (1-propenyl-3,4-methylenedioxybenzene). The unifunctional dienophiles such as acrolein [6] and crotonaldehyde [7] do not react normally with the furans but in the presence of certain catalysts (p. 87) lead to abnormal products.

[5] M. Naef et Cie., Fr. pat. 672,025 [*C. A.*, **24**, 2243 (1930)].

[6] Sherlin, Berlin, Serebrennikova, and Rabinovich, *J. Gen. Chem. U.S.S.R.*, **8**, 7 (1938) [*C. A.*, **32**, 5397 (1938)].

[7] Alder and Schmidt, *Ber.*, **76**, 183 (1943).

1,1,3-Trimethylbutadiene and acrolein give a mixture of the two possible isomers (XIV and XV) in about equal amounts.[5] From the

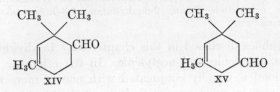

products (X) of the reaction of 2-alkoxybutadienes and acrolein, 4-ketocyclohexane-1-carboxylic acid can be prepared by oxidation and acid hydrolysis.[8]

The addition of acrolein to cyclopentadiene has been shown to give the *endo*-2,5-methano-Δ^3-tetrahydrobenzaldehyde (XVI).[1] Alder, Stein, et al.[9, 10, 11] have described the preparation of the hexahydro

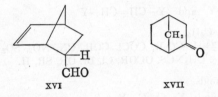

derivative, its conversion to the corresponding *exo* aldehyde (by saponification of the enol acetate formed from the *endo* aldehyde and acetic anhydride), and the preparation of the acids, alcohols, and amines (by Curtius degradation) of the two series. Norcamphor (XVII) has been prepared from the 2,5-methanohexahydrobenzaldehyde.

Cyclohexadiene and acrolein give 2,5-ethano-Δ^3-tetrahydrobenzaldehyde (XVIII) in good yield.[12] Cinnamaldehyde and 2,3-dimethylbutadiene yield 4,5-dimethyltetrahydrobiphenyl-2-aldehyde (XIX,

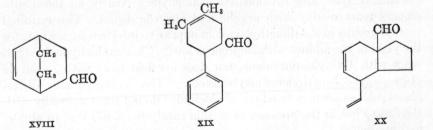

[8] Fiesselmann, *Ber.*, **75**, 881 (1942) [*C. A.*, **37**, 3417 (1943)].
[9] Alder, Stein, Schneider, Liebmann, Rolland, and Schulze, *Ann.*, **525**, 183 (1936).
[10] Alder, Stein, and Rolland, *Ann.*, **525**, 247 (1936).
[11] Alder, Stein, Rolland, and Schulze, *Ann.*, **514**, 211 (1934).
[12] Diels and Alder, *Ann.*, **478**, 137 (1930).

55%).[13] Cyclopentene-1-aldehyde is an example of a dienophile in which the double bond is situated in a ring. Hexatriene combines with this dienophile to give a hydrohydrindene with an angular aldehyde group, which has been formulated as XX.[14]

Acids and Acid Derivatives. α,β-Unsaturated acids, such as acrylic acid, crotonic acid, sorbic acid, and cinnamic and substituted cinnamic acids, react fairly readily with acyclic and alicyclic dienes. The esters of the acids have been used usually when the corresponding acids (e.g., ethylidenemalonic acid and ethoxymethyleneacetoacetic acid) [15] might be unstable at the reaction temperatures. Several unsaturated lactones (Δ^{α,β}-butenolide, β-angelica lactone, coumarin), though somewhat unreactive, have been successfully added to dienes. Only a few acid chlorides have been used.

Derivatives of hydrobiphenyl have been prepared by the addition of 1-arylbutadienes to acrylic acid and of butadienes to cinnamic acids.

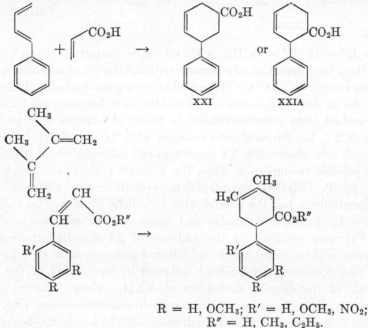

R = H, OCH₃; R′ = H, OCH₃, NO₂; R″ = H, CH₃, C₂H₅.

$$R = H, OCH_3; \quad R' = H, OCH_3, NO_2;$$
$$R'' = H, CH_3, C_2H_5.$$

XXII

By the first method a 72% yield of a phenyltetrahydrobenzoic acid was obtained (XXI or XXIA, structure not definitely established, for

[13] Fujise, Horiuti, and Takahashi, *Ber.*, **69**, 2102 (1936).
[14] Butz, *J. Am. Chem. Soc.*, **60**, 216 (1938).
[15] Alder and Rickert, *Ber.*, **72**, 1983 (1939).

it is not the acid of IX).[2] Various 1-aryl-1-methylbutadienes were employed also with acrylic acid and with crotonic acid.

The derivatives of hydrobiphenyl obtained by the second method have been used quite extensively in the synthesis of dibenzopyrones and their hydro derivatives,[16,17] hydrofluorenones,[13,18] and hydrophenanthridines.[18] o-Methoxycinnamic acid (cis and trans) and the corresponding hydroxy acid react readily with 2,3-dimethylbutadiene, unsatisfactorily with isoprene, and not at all with butadiene. The hydropyrone (XXIII) obtained by the demethylation and lactonization of XXII

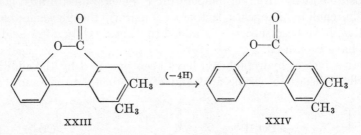

(R = R″ = H, R′ = OCH₃) with ethanolic potash is isomeric with that from the interaction of coumarin with 2,3-dimethylbutadiene under forcing conditions (260°). These hydropyrones are probably diastereomers, for on dehydrogenation they yield the same benzopyrone (XXIV). The adduct from o-methoxycinnamic acid and isoprene is considered to be XXV, for the analogous reaction with 2,6-dimethoxy-4-n-amylcinnamic acid gives solely XI (except in one instance, which it has not been possible to duplicate, when the isomeric adduct was isolated in 43% yield). Methyl o-veratrylidenepyruvate reacts normally with cyclopentadiene, but the adduct with butadiene could not be isolated.

Dimethylhexahydrofluorenone and many of its substitution products (XXVI) were obtained by the addition of 2,3-dimethylbutadiene to cinnamic acid (or ester) and to substituted cinnamic acids (3,4-dimethoxy- and 3,4-dimethoxy-6-nitro-) followed by cyclization of the acid chloride of the dihydro derivative of XXII. These hexahydrofluorenones have been converted to octahydrophenanthridines (XXVII) by ring enlargement of XXVI (hydrazoic acid) to hexahydro-9-phenanthridones, followed by conversion to the thio analog (phosphorus pentasulfide) and electrolytic reduction at a lead cathode.

[16] Adams, McPhee, Carlin, and Wicks, J. Am. Chem. Soc., 65, 356 (1943).

[17] Adams and Carlin, J. Am. Chem. Soc., 65, 360 (1943).

[18] Sugasawa, Kodama, and Hara, J. Pharm. Soc. Japan, 60, 356 (1940) [C. A., 34, 7291 (1940)].

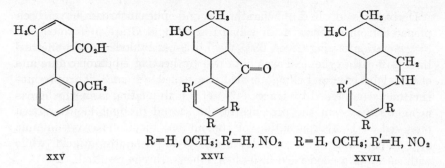

R=H, OCH₃; R'=H, NO₂ R=H, OCH₃; R'=H, NO₂

XXV   XXVI   XXVII

A considerable number of anthraquinones have been prepared from the adducts obtained from β-aroylacrylic acids and acyclic dienes as shown.[19] The adducts (XXVIII) result in almost quantitative yield.

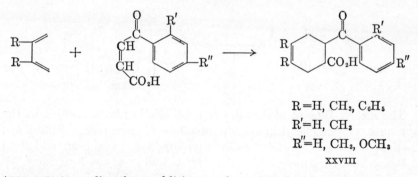

R=H, CH₃, C₆H₅
R'=H, CH₃
R''=H, CH₃, OCH₃
XXVIII

Attempts to cyclize these addition products failed, but when aromatization of the system with sulfur preceded ring closure, yields of 40% (based on XXVIII) of the respective anthraquinones resulted in most cases. Difficulty was experienced in the cyclization of the substituted anisoylbenzoic acid, but 2-methoxy-6,7-dimethylanthraquinone was obtained by cyclization of the corresponding benzylbenzoic acid and oxidation of the anthrone to the desired quinone.

Small amounts (1%) of high-melting isomers have been recovered from the saponification of the ester adducts formed from the interaction of β-benzoylacrylic acid and its 2,4-dimethyl derivative with 2,3-dimethylbutadiene in ethanol solution. The isomerism cannot be attributed to a rearrangement during the saponification, for the same product is obtained directly when toluene is the solvent.[20] It has been suggested that this isomerism is due to a migration of the double bond in the cyclohexene ring.[20, 21]

[19] Fieser and Fieser, *J. Am. Chem. Soc.*, **57**, 1679 (1935).
[20] Holmes, Husband, Lee, and Kawulka, *J. Am. Chem. Soc.*, **70**, 147 (1948).
[21] Bergmann and Eschinazi, *J. Am. Chem. Soc.*, **65**, 1405 (1943).

Derivatives of hydrophenanthrene and phenanthrene have been prepared from compounds in which rings A and C are preformed and by generation of ring C. A 68% yield of 9-phenyldodecahydrophenanthrene-10-carboxylic acid was obtained by heating equimolar amounts of bicyclohexenyl and cinnamic acid in a sealed system.[22] This product is often accompanied by traces (4%) of a high-melting isomer, whereas in an open system the presence of the second product has not been observed.[21] Dehydrogenation of the normal bicyclohexenyl-cinnamic acid adduct with sulfur afforded 9-phenyl-10-phenanthroic acid, while with selenium a good yield of 9-phenylphenanthrene resulted.

Generation of ring B of phenanthrene by lengthening the side chain of IX, followed by cyclization, failed at the first stage, for with hydrogen cyanide the benzoin, XXIX, was obtained instead of the expected cyanohydrin.[2]

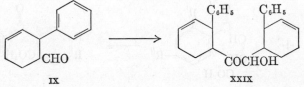

The second type of phenanthrene synthesis has been applied to the synthesis of possible degradation products of morphine. Butadiene, 2-ethoxybutadiene,[22a] and 2,3-dimethylbutadiene have been added to 3,4-dihydro-1-naphthoic acid (ester)[23,24] as well as to the 7-methoxy[23,24] and 5-bromo-7,8-dimethoxy derivatives.[23] The yields of adducts were quite satisfactory with 2,3-dimethylbutadiene, but from butadiene and 5-bromo-7,8-dimethoxy-3,4-dihydro-1-naphthoic acid the yield of the acid adduct (XXX) was 18%, and of the methyl ester, 8%. Similar

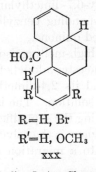

R=H, Br
R'=H, OCH₃

XXX

[22] Weizmann, Bergmann, and Berlin, *J. Am. Chem. Soc.*, **60**, 1331 (1938).
[22a] Holmes and Mann, *J. Am. Chem. Soc.*, **69**, 2000 (1947).
[23] Fieser and Holmes, *J. Am. Chem. Soc.*, **60**, 2548 (1938).
[24] Fieser and Holmes, *J. Am. Chem. Soc.*, **58**, 2319 (1936).

additions with substituted 3,4-dihydro-2-naphthoic acids led to analogous hexahydrophenanthrene-14-carboxylic acids.[22a,25]

In general the yield of addition products from acids is superior to that from their esters (Table III), and, except where the acids cause polymerization of the diene [26] or the acids are unstable to heat, the esters have found but limited use in the Diels-Alder reaction. However, the addition of ethyl cinnamate to isobenzofurans has been used in the synthesis of substituted β-naphthoic acids. A mixture of 1,3-diphenylisobenzo-

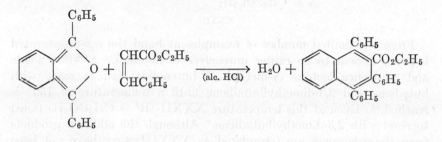

furan and ethyl cinnamate in ethanol led to the normal adduct, but in the presence of dry hydrogen chloride gas the bridge oxygen of the primary adduct was eliminated as a molecule of water and an 80% yield of ethyl 1,2,4-triphenyl-3-naphthoate was obtained. This ester is very resistant to hydrolysis. With hydriodic acid and phenol,[27] cyclization to, and reduction of, the ketone occurred simultaneously to give 1,4-diphenyl-2,3-benzofluorene, identical with that from indene and 1,3-diphenylisobenzofuran.

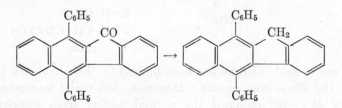

It has been found that traces of acrylic acid polymerize 2-ethoxy- and 2-methoxy-butadiene [26] at 120°. Ethyl esters have been substituted in this reaction for such thermally sensitive acids as ethoxymethylene-acetoacetic, ethylideneacetoacetic, and ethylidenemalonic acids. The

[25] Holmes and Trevoy, *Can. J. Research*, **B22**, 56 (1944), and unpublished work.
[26] Petrov, *J. Gen. Chem. U.S.S.R.*, **11**, 66 (1941) [*C. A.*, **36**, 1593 (1942)].
[27] Weiss and Beller, *Monatsh.*, **61**, 143 (1932).

adducts from these esters with butadiene and 2,3-dimethylbutadiene are represented by the generalized formula XXXI.

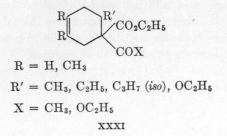

R = H, CH₃

R' = CH₃, C₂H₅, C₃H₇ (iso), OC₂H₅

X = CH₃, OC₂H₅

XXXI

From the limited number of examples at hand the α,β-unsaturated lactones appear to be rather unreactive dienophiles. $\Delta^{\alpha,\beta}$-Butenolide and β-angelica lactone (γ-methyl-$\Delta^{\alpha,\beta}$-butenolide) fail to react with butadiene and 2,3-dimethylbutadiene until a temperature of 150° is reached.[28] Even at this temperature XXXII (R' = CH₂CO₂H) failed to react with 2,3-dimethylbutadiene. Although the addition products from these lactones are formulated as XXXIII, they have not been successfully dehydrogenated to the completely aromatic phthalides. Coumarin fails to react with butadiene and isoprene, and it reacts with 2,3-dimethylbutadiene only under forcing conditions (260°) and in the presence of a large excess of this reagent.

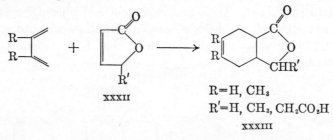

XXXII

R=H, CH₃
R'=H, CH₃, CH₂CO₂H

XXXIII

The use of acid chlorides has been limited by their tendency to polymerize the diene components. However, Alder and co-workers[1] by working at −10° obtained the normal adduct from *trans*-crotonyl chloride and cyclopentadiene. From acrylyl chloride and sorbyl chloride, a 79% yield of the normal adduct (XII) was obtained.[29]

Ketones. The α,β-unsaturated ketones that have been successfully employed are methyl vinyl ketone, benzalacetone, benzalacetophenone, diacetylethylene, dibenzalacetone, dibenzoylethylene and substituted dibenzoylethylenes, and vinyl phenyl ketone. However, failures have

[28] Linstead and Leavitt, private communication.
[29] Wagner-Jauregg and Helmert, *Ber.*, **71**, 2535 (1938).

been reported with the combinations: furans with methyl vinyl ketone and vinyl phenyl ketone; cyclone (tetraphenylcyclopentadienone) with benzalacetophenone and dibenzoylethylene; and cyclohexadiene with vinyl phenyl ketone. The failure of the last pair of reactants to undergo addition is rather surprising since under comparable conditions a 54% yield of 4-benzoyl-3,6-methano-Δ^1-cyclohexene was obtained from cyclopentadiene and this ketone.

The most direct route to the synthesis of 1,3-diarylisobenzofurans and o-diaroylbenzenes and their hydro derivatives is through the addition of dienes (butadiene, 1,4- and 2,3-dimethylbutadiene, 2,3-diphenylbutadiene, and cyclopentadiene) to various cis and trans dibenzoylethylenes (4,4'-dichloro-, 4,4'-dimethyl-, 2,4,6,2',4',6'-hexamethyl-). In general, yields of 80–90% are obtained. 1,2-Dimethyl-4,5-dibenzoyl-Δ^1-cyclohexene (XXXIV, R = CH$_3$) is readily cyclized (acetic anhydride and phosphoric acid) to 1,3-diphenyl-5,6-dimethyl-4,7-dihydroisobenzofuran (XXXV, R = CH$_3$).[30] Dehydrogenation (bromine and sodium acetate, but not sulfur) [31] opens the furan ring, and the resulting 4,5-dimethyl-1,2-dibenzoylbenzene is reductively recyclized by zinc in

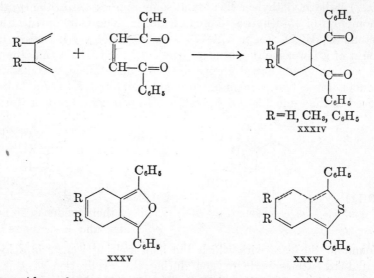

acetic acid or, better, in ethanolic sodium hydroxide. Exceptions to these generalizations have been encountered but may be attributed either to strain in the molecule (cyclopentadiene and dibenzoylethylene) [32] or to steric factors (2,3-dimethylbutadiene and dimesitoylethylene).

[30] Adams and Gold, J. Am. Chem. Soc., **62**, 56 (1940).
[31] Allen and Gates, J. Am. Chem. Soc., **65**, 1283 (1943).
[32] Adams and Wearn, J. Am. Chem. Soc., **62**, 1233 (1940).

1,3,5,6-Tetraphenylisobenzothiophene (XXXVI, R = C_6H_5) is obtained in 70% yield by the dehydrogenation of XXXV (R = C_6H_5) with sulfur.[31]

A pair of geometric isomers in the proportion of 10 to 1 results from the interaction of *trans*-dibenzoylethylene with hexadiene-2,4. Three formulas are possible, XXXVII–XXXIX. The high-melting and more abundant isomer is formulated as XXXIX, for on oxidation with monoperphthalic acid the substance yields a pair of epoxides.[33] The low-melting isomer, which occurs in the lesser amount, is either XXXVII or XXXVIII.

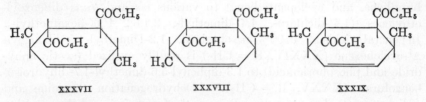

XXXVII   XXXVIII   XXXIX

The addition of 1-vinyl-6-methoxy-3,4-dihydronaphthalene to (*trans?*)[34] diacetylethylene has found some application in the synthesis of homologs of 15-dehydro-*x*-norequilenin.[35] The reaction furnished a diketone $C_{19}H_{22}O_3$ (m.p. 174–175°) in 25–30% yield, and a lesser amount of a lower-melting isomer (107–108°). Provided that the relative position of the acetyl groups has been maintained in the addition products, these two isomers are probably XL and XLI, for both are reduced to the same dihydro derivative. Experimental support for XLI

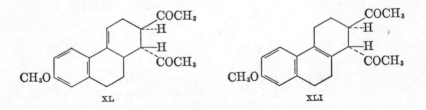

XL   XLI

is found in the ease with which the high-melting isomer is dehydrogenated by atmospheric oxygen during the cyclization of this 1,4-diketone with 0.1 N methanolic sodium methoxide. It is understandable that the dihydronaphthalene system of XLI should readily lose two atoms of hydrogen and pass into a stable naphthalene system. As would be expected, the dihydro adduct showed no such susceptibility to dehy-

[33] Adams and Geissman, *J. Am. Chem. Soc.*, **61**, 2083 (1939).

[34] Armstrong and Robinson, *J. Chem. Soc.*, **1934**, 1650.

[35] Goldberg and Müller, *Helv. Chim. Acta*, **23**, 831 (1940).

drogenation under similar conditions. The phenolic ketone from XLI*A* or XLI*B*, although it was never isolated analytically pure, shows an oestrogenic activity much greater than that of *dl*-isoequilenin (rings C/D

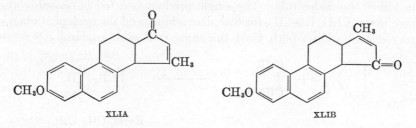

XLIA   XLIB

cis) and of about the same order of activity as *dl*-equilenin (rings C/D *trans*). This indirect evidence supports the earlier conclusion that the yellow diacetylcthylene is *trans*.

The relationship of the isomeric pairs of dodecahydrophenanthrenes from the interaction of dibenzoylethylene and benzalacetophenone with bicyclohexenyl is not yet clear.

α,β-Unsaturated Nitriles, Nitro Compounds, and Sulfones (Tables VI and VII). Relatively few examples of the use of the α,β-unsaturated nitriles and sulfones as dienophiles have been reported. Structures for the adducts from the nitriles (crotononitrile + cyclopentadiene and 1,3-dimethylbutadiene, sorbonitrile + 1,3- and 2,3-dimethylbutadiene) and from the sulfones (dihydrothiophene dioxide + butadiene, cyclopentadiene, and 2,3-dimethylbutadiene, *p*-tolyl vinyl sulfone + 2,3-dimethylbutadiene) are based solely on analogy. The reaction of dihydrothiophene dioxide with cyclopentadiene is formulated as shown.

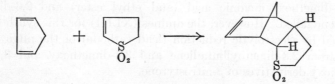

Nitroethylene and a few alkyl derivatives have found limited use as dienophiles, but β-nitrostyrene and its 3,4-dimethoxy and 3,4-methylenedioxy derivatives have been used frequently. The latter substances react satisfactorily with the acyclic dienes (butadiene, 2,3-dimethylbutadiene, 1,4- and 2,3-diphenylbutadiene, and isoprene) and the alicyclic dienes (cyclohexadiene, cyclopentadiene, α-phellandrene, and cyclone) and with methyleneanthrone. They fail to react with the simple furans (furan, 2-methylfuran, and 2,5-dimethylfuran) under normal conditions; however, the addition of β-nitrostyrene to 1,3-

diphenylisobenzofuran and its 5,6-dimethyl derivative has been reported.

The reaction of nitroethylene with cyclopentadiene at 110° appears to follow the Alder rule. The single product isolated is probably the *endo* form (XLII, R = H), for this nitro adduct and the cyclopentadiene-acrylic acid adduct both yield the same *endo*-norbornylamine.[11, 36, 37, 38]

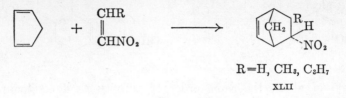

$$R = H, CH_3, C_3H_7$$

XLII

Substituted 2,3-dimethyl-1,4,11,12-tetrahydrophenanthridines (XLIV) have been prepared in 70–80% yield from the N-acyl derivatives of XLIII. The Hofmann degradation of the amide from the acid adduct

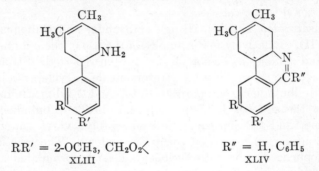

RR′ = 2-OCH₃, CH₂O₂<   R″ = H, C₆H₅
XLIII   XLIV

of 3,4-dimethoxycinnamic acid (and ethyl ester) and 2,3-dimethylbutadiene failed. However, the amines (XLIII) for this synthesis were obtained by electrolytic reduction (lead cathode) of the nitro adducts XLV from 2,3-dimethylbutadiene and 3,4-dimethoxy and 3,4-methylenedioxy derivatives of β-nitrostyrene.

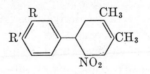

RR′ = 2-OCH₃, CH₂O₂<
XLV

[36] Alder, Rickert, and Windemuth, *Ber.*, **71**, 2451 (1938).
[37] Kenyon and Young, *J. Chem. Soc.*, **1941**, 263.
[38] Jones and Wallis, *J. Am. Chem. Soc.*, **48**, 169 (1926).

Allyl, Vinyl, and Related Compounds (Table VIII). Compounds with other than unsaturated groups next to the ethylenic linkage also function as dienophiles. Allyl compounds, vinyl compounds, styrene derivatives, and even ethylene will combine with the more reactive dienes at 170–180°, and with the less reactive ones under forcing conditions (200–300°).

Allyl alcohol and its derivatives (amine, cyanide, isothiocyanate, esters, and halides) have been found to react with 2,3-dimethylbutadiene, the alicyclic dienes (cyclopentadiene, cyclone, and piperylcyclone), and with anthracene. Temperatures of 170–180° are required to initiate the reaction of cyclopentadiene with allyl alcohol, and its chloride and bromide. (The more reactive allyl iodide decomposed under the same conditions, but addition proceeded satisfactorily at 100–105°). Temperatures in excess of 180° are required before anthracene reacts with either allyl alcohol or chloride to an appreciable extent.

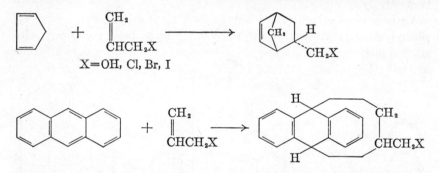

The steric course of the reaction between allyl alcohol and its esters (salicylate and phthalate) with cyclopentadiene conforms with the Alder rule, for the adducts on reduction and hydrolysis furnished *endo*-2,5-methanohexahydrobenzyl alcohol.

The addition of vinyl acetate to cyclopentadiene and 1,5,5-trimethylcyclopentadiene is the most direct synthetic route to norcamphor and dehydro-norcamphor, epicamphor, and camphor, respectively. Vinyl formate, vinyl chloride, and the dichloro- and trichloro-ethylenes have been used with acyclic dienes (butadiene and 2,3-dimethylbutadiene) and with alicyclic dienes (cyclopentadiene, 1,5,5-trimethylcyclopentadiene, methyl β-camphylate, and cyclohexadiene) as components in the Diels-Alder reaction. The reaction of anthracene with vinyl acetate required forcing conditions.

Almost a quantitative yield of dehydro-norbornyl acetate (XLVI, R = H) was obtained when slightly more than the required amount of cyclopentadiene was heated with vinyl acetate at 180°. A second product (XLVII), in which the components are in the ratio of two molecules of cyclopentadiene to one of vinyl acetate, accounted for the remainder of the reactants. Alder and Rickert [39] have described the

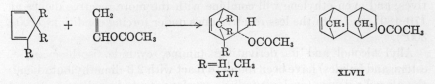

$$R=H, CH_3$$

hydrolysis of the acetate (XLVI, R = H) and the oxidation of dehydro-norborneol to dehydro-norcamphor, as well as the reduction of XLVI (R = H) and its subsequent hydrolysis and oxidation to norcamphor. 1,5,5-Trimethylcyclopentadiene, in a similar series of reactions, gave an overall yield of 26.6% of *dl*-borneol and 35.8% of *dl*-epiborneol. Chromic acid oxidation of these alcohols gave *dl*-camphor and *dl*-epicamphor [40] respectively.

Various vinyl ethers (vinyl butyl ether, vinyl ethyl ether, and vinyl phenyl ether) and vinyl *p*-tolyl thioether have been combined with several alicyclic dienes. The thioether combines with cyclopentadiene at 180° (52%).

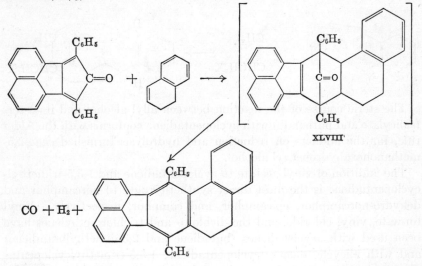

At suitable temperatures (200–220°) ethylene reacts with butadiene (18%), 2,3-dimethylbutadiene (50%), and cyclopentadiene (74%).[41] Similarly, a trace of the acetate of 1,4,5,8-*bis*-methano-Δ^6-β-octalol

[39] Alder and Rickert, *Ann.*, **543**, 1 (1939).
[40] Alder and Windemuth, *Ann.*, **543**, 41 (1939).
[41] Joshel and Butz, *J. Am. Chem. Soc.*, **63**, 3350 (1941).

(XLVII) that occurs in the reaction of vinyl acetate with cyclopentadiene is accounted for by the addition of a second molecule of cyclopentadiene to the primary adduct (XLVI, R = H).[41] This secondary adduct can be made the principal product by increasing the temperature and changing the proportion of the two reactants. The 1,2- and 1,4-dihydronaphthalenes react with cyclone, phencyclone, and piperylcyclone at 200–300°.[42] When the diene component is acecyclone [1,4-diphenyl-2,3(1,8-naphthylene)-cyclopentadienone], the *endo*-carbonyl group and two atoms of hydrogen are lost from the primary adduct (XLVIII) in the aromatization of the central ring.

Acetylenic Dienophiles (Tables IX and X)

Aldehydes. Acetylenic aldehydes (propargyl, tetrolic, and phenylpropiolic) have been used to only a very limited extent as dienophiles. Addition products of these aldehydes with 1,1- and 2,3-dimethylbutadiene, isoprene, 1,1,3-trimethylbutadiene, and cyclone have been described and some of their physical properties recorded.[5, 43] No attempt has been made to assign structures to reaction products for which alternative structures are possible. Pentaphenylbenzaldehyde was formed directly by heating phenylpropiolic aldehyde with cyclone.

Acids and Acid Derivatives. Although propiolic acid, substituted propiolic acids (tetrolic acid, phenylpropiolic acid), and their esters have been added successfully to a number of dienes,[43, 44] acetylenedicarboxylic acid and its methyl and ethyl esters have been most extensively studied. These acetylenes combine readily with all types of dienes, although the yields from the reaction of acetylenic esters with 2,3-diphenylbutadiene and isosafrole are reported to be low. Only one failure of this reaction has been reported (methyl acetylenedicarboxylate and 9,10-dibromoanthracene).[45]

Vinylacetylenes, when combined with acetylenic dienophiles, lead to benzene derivatives. Methyl propiolate and 1-ethynyl-6-methoxy-3,4-dihydronaphthalene afford a good yield of a separable mixture of two isomers (probably XLIX and L). From a consideration of electronic effects,[46] the main product (crystalline ester, 45%) would be formulated as XLIX. The oily ester (10%) would then be the isomeric adduct, L. This structure for the crystalline ester appears to be correct, although

[42] Arbuzov and Akhmed-Zade, *J. Gen. Chem. U.S.S.R.*, **12**, 206 (1942) [*C. A.*, **37**, 2732 (1943)].

[43] Dilthey, Schommer, and Trösken, *Ber.*, **66**, 1627 (1933).

[44] Dilthey, Thewalt, and Trösken, *Ber.*, **67**, 1959 (1934).

[45] Diels and Friedrichsen, *Ann.*, **513**, 145 (1934).

[46] Alder, *Angew. Chem.*, **55**, 53 (1942).

the proof is based only on the evidence that dehydrogenation (quinone) led to a phenanthroic acid, presumably the 6-methoxy-2-phenanthroic acid.[47]

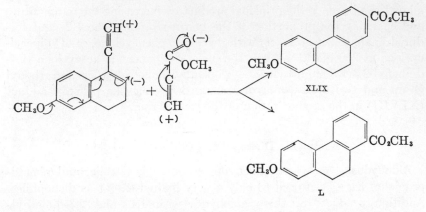

The addition products from the interaction of acetylenedicarboxylic acid and its esters with acyclic and alicyclic dienes are $\Delta^{1,4}$-dihydrophthalic acids and 3,6-alkano-$\Delta^{1,4}$-dihydrophthalic acids, respectively;[29, 44, 48-59] with anthracene, 9,10-dihydroanthracene-9,10-endo-α,β-maleic acid and its esters are formed.[60] 3,6-Epoxy-$\Delta^{1,4}$-dihydrophthalic acids or 1,4,5,8-bis-epoxy-$\Delta^{2,6}$-hexahydronaphthalene-9,10-dicarboxylic acids are the products from one and from two moles of furan.[54, 61, 62]

$\Delta^{1,4}$-Dihydrophthalic acid is readily separated from the traces of $\Delta^{1,4}$-dihydrobenzoic acid, $\Delta^{2,4}$- and $\Delta^{2,6}$-dihydrophthalic acids which are formed when a dioxane solution of butadiene and acetylenedicarboxylic acid is heated to 170–180°. Selective hydrogenation (colloidal palladium or palladized calcium carbonate) of the Δ^4-ethene, followed by dehydrogenation (bromine) of the Δ^1-tetrahydrophthalic acid to phthalic

[47] Dane, Höss, Eder, Schmitt, and Schön, *Ann.*, **536**, 183 (1938).
[48] Allen and Sheps, *Can. J. Research*, **11**, 171 (1934).
[49] Alder and Holzrichter, *Ann.*, **524**, 145 (1936).
[50] Diels and Alder, *Ann.*, **490**, 236 (1931).
[51] Alder and Windemuth, *Ann.*, **543**, 56 (1939).
[52] Alder and Rickert, *Ann.*, **524**, 180 (1936).
[53] Lohaus, *Ann.*, **516**, 295 (1935).
[54] Alder and Rickert, *Ber.*, **70**, 1354 (1937).
[55] Alder and Rickert, *Ber.*, **70**, 1364 (1937).
[56] Alder, *Ber.*, **71**, 2210 (1938).
[57] Allen, Eliot, and Bell, *Can. J. Research*, **17**, 75 (1939).
[58] Dupont and Dulou, *Angew. Chem.*, **51**, 755 (1938).
[59] Dupont and Dulou, *Atti. X°. congr. intern. chim.*, **3**, 123 (1939).
[60] Diels and Alder, *Ann.*, **486**, 191 (1931).
[61] Diels and Alder, *Ann.*, **490**, 243 (1931).
[62] Alder and Backendorf, *Ann.*, **535**, 101 (1938).

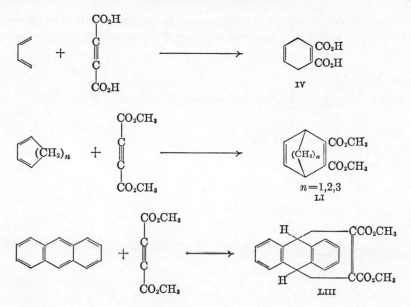

acid, established that acetylenedicarboxylic acid combines with buta-diene by a 1,4-mechanism. Isomerization accompanies the saponifica-tion of the methyl ester of IV.

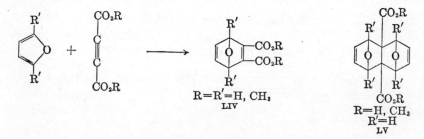

Alicyclic dienes have been more extensively used than their acyclic counterparts in Diels-Alder reactions with acetylenic dienophiles. The adducts obtained from cyclopentadienes and from 1,3-cycloheptadiene (LI, $n = 1$ and 3 respectively) are stable at their boiling points under reduced pressure but dissociate into their components at higher tem-peratures. The adducts from 1,3-cyclohexadienes (LI, $n = 2$), by con-trast, lose the bridge carbon atoms on heating.

Cyclopentadiene and its 1,5,5-trimethyl derivative react vigorously with methyl acetylenedicarboxylate at room temperature or lower, and the products of the reactions can be purified by distillation under reduced pressure. The reduction of 3,6-methano-$\Delta^{1,4}$-dihydrophthalic acid (or the methyl ester) over colloidal palladium or platinum oxide catalyst proceeds in a stepwise manner, and the hydrogenation may be inter-

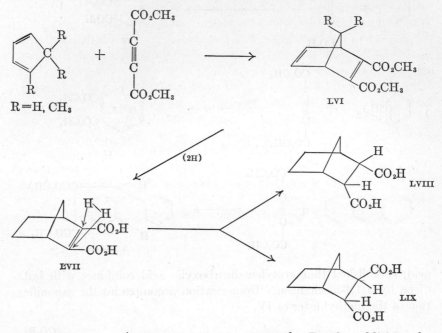

rupted after the Δ^4-linkage has been saturated. By the addition of a second mole of hydrogen (*exo* addition) to 3,6-methano-Δ^1-tetrahydrophthalic acid the *endo-cis*-3,6-methanohexahydrophthalic acid is re-

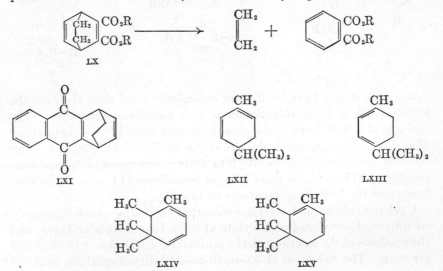

covered as the main product [9] (a small amount of *trans*-3,6-methano-hexahydrophthalic acid is also formed). The anhydride of 3,6-meth-ano-Δ^1-tetrahydrophthalic acid proved to be identical with that derived (three steps) from dibromomaleic anhydride and cyclopentadiene.[12]

The ethano group of the 3,6-ethano-$\Delta^{1,4}$-dihydrophthalic esters (LI, $n = 2$), like that of the ethanodihydrobenzene system of 1,4-ethano-1,4-dihydroanthraquinone (LXI), is sensitive to heat. The esters of acetylenedicarboxylic acid react smoothly with cyclohexadiene at 0°, and a yield of about 84% of the dimethyl ester of 3,6-ethano-$\Delta^{1,4}$-dihydrophthalic acid is obtained.[50] Heating the reaction mixture to 200° pyrolyzes the primary adduct to ethylene and the ester of phthalic acid. Thus, by identifying the ethylenic products of pyrolysis it has been possible to locate the conjugated systems of α-phellandrene (LXII), α-terpinene (LXIII), α-pyronene (LXIV), and β-pyronene (LXV).

The propano bridge of the cycloheptadiene adduct (LI, $n = 3$), like the methano bridge (LI, $n = 1$), is thermally stable. A conjugated

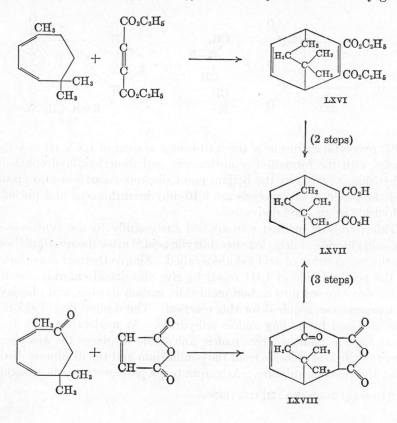

cyclopentadiene or cycloheptadiene derivative, isomeric with α-terpinene, is also formed by dehydrating α-terpineol, for with ethyl acetylenedicarboxylate a thermally stable adduct is formed. The perhydro acid (LXVII) of the adduct (LXVI) of this 1,5,5-trimethyl-1,3-cycloheptadiene with ethyl acetylenedicarboxylate was identical with an acid obtained from maleic anhydride and eucarvone by another route. The reduction of the ketone and the ethene of LXVIII completes the proof for the identity of this alicyclic diene.

Other dihydrobenzene systems with an ethano bridge result when derivatives of the anthracene-methyl acetylenedicarboxylate adduct (LIII) interact with conjugated dienes (butadiene, dimethylbutadienes, 1,1,3-trimethylbutadiene, and cyclopentadiene). Dimethyl 9,10-dihydroanthracene-9,10-*endo*-α,β-maleate (LIII) has been transformed into the corresponding acid, anhydride (anthracene-C_4O_3), acid chloride, amide, and nitrile. The anthracene-C_4O_3 adduct (LXIX) reacts vigorously with a number of simple acyclic dienes (Table XI) at temperatures below 100° to give the secondary adducts LXX. At temperatures above

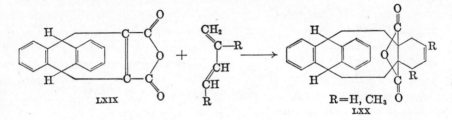

100°, pyrolytic extrusion of the 9,10-bridge system of LXX (R = CH_3) occurs with the formation of anthracene and dimethyldihydrophthalic anhydride, whereas at the boiling point disproportionation also occurs and the products of pyrolysis are 9,10-dihydroanthracene and phthalic anhydride or an alkyl derivative.

This pyrolytic method was applied successfully to the synthesis of the acid chloride of acetylenedicarboxylic acid,[63] after the usual methods for the preparation of acid chlorides failed. Simple thermal dissociation of the acid chloride of LIII failed to give the diacid chloride, for the latter decomposed into carbon monoxide, carbon dioxide, and phosgene at temperatures required for this reaction. The desired diacid chloride was obtained by adding maleic anhydride. At moderately high temperatures the more reactive maleic anhydride displaces the acetylenedicarboxylic acid chloride from the equilibrium and the dichloride distils from the reaction mixture. Attempts to prepare acetylenedicarboxylic

[63] Diels and Thiele, *Ber.*, **71**, 1173 (1938).

anhydride from LXIX by the same method failed; in boiling nitrobenzene solution, carbon monoxide and carbon dioxide were evolved
and LXXI was formed.

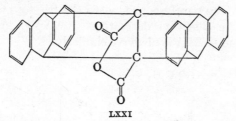

LXXI

The furans and the pyrones are the only heterocyclic dienes reported
to undergo normal diene reactions with acetylenic dienophiles. With
furans the nature of the reaction product depends upon the molar
proportion of the reactants. With methyl acetylenedicarboxylate and
one mole of furan a quantitative yield of methyl 3,6-epoxy-$\Delta^{1,4}$-dihydro-
phthalate (LIV, R′ = H) is obtained, while with two moles methyl
1,4,5,8-*bis*-epoxy-$\Delta^{2,6}$-hexahydronaphthalene-9,10-dicarboxyl-
ate is formed. The structural similarity of methyl 3,6-epoxy-$\Delta^{1,4}$-dihydro-
phthalate to LVI (R = H) is reflected in a number of its reactions, e.g.,
the reverse Diels-Alder at elevated temperatures and the selective hydrogenation of the Δ^4-ethene. This correspondence in properties does not
hold for the respective tetrahydro derivatives. Mineral acid eliminates
the oxygen bridge of LXXII while by pyrolysis (100–150°) the ethano
bridge is lost.[64] The addition of two atoms of hydrogen to the Δ^1-ethene

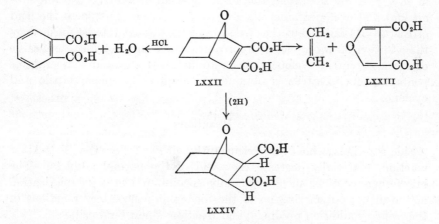

of LXXII is *endo*, and the carboxyls of the resulting *cis*-3,6-epoxy-
hexahydrophthalic acid are *exo* with respect to the oxygen bridge.

[64] Norton, *Chem. Revs.*, **31**, 469 (1942).

The addition products from pyrones and ethyl acetylenedicarboxylate show a similar sensitivity to heat. When the α-pyrone, LXXV, is heated with this ester a lively reaction ensues, accompanied by the evolution of carbon dioxide. The pyrolysis product is the triester of trimellitic acid (LXXVIII). The dimethyl derivatives (LXXVI) and the enol of γ-methylpyronone (LXXVII) behave similarly.

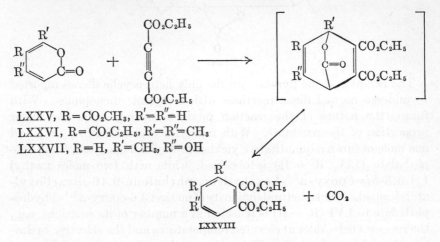

LXXV, R=CO_2CH_3, R'=R''=H
LXXVI, R=$CO_2C_2H_5$, R'=R''=CH_3
LXXVII, R=H, R'=CH_3, R''=OH

Other Acetylenic Compounds. The reactions of acetylene, phenylacetylene, diphenylacetylene, and phenylbenzoylacetylene with cyclone have been described.[43,65] The dinitrile of LI ($n = 1$) has been prepared in 83% yield by the interaction of acetylenedicarbonitrile (carbon subnitride) and cyclopentadiene.[10] Hydrolysis of the dinitrile to the acid of LI ($n = 1$) failed, but the structure of the adduct was established by the addition of two moles of hydrogen to furnish the hydro derivative of the maleonitrile-cyclopentadiene adduct. At elevated temperatures pentaphenylbenzonitrile is obtained from phenylpropiolic nitrile and cyclone.

Side Reactions

Side reactions, which run concurrently with or follow the Diels-Alder reaction, materially decrease the yield of the normal adducts. The interfering reactions most commonly encountered are: polymerization of the diene; polymerization of the dienophile; secondary reactions of the primary addition products; and reactions due to impurities.

Temperatures required to promote the Diels-Alder reaction are often such that polymerization of the diene may successfully compete with,

[65] Dilthey and Hurtig, *Ber.*, **67**, 495 (1934).

or even prevent, the primary reaction. This competing reaction has been noted in the reaction of allyl amine with cyclopentadiene, of 1-nitropentene-1 with cyclopentadiene, and of o-methoxycinnamic acid with butadiene. Some dienophiles (acids [26] and acid chlorides [1]) have been found to promote the polymerization of dienes. This troublesome reaction cannot be eliminated entirely, but its effect upon the yield may be minimized by the use of somewhat more than an equimolar amount of the diene (1.5 moles) and by diluting the reaction mixture with an inert solvent (benzene, toluene, or xylene [13]).

Polymerization of the dienophile may account for a further decrease in the yield. The dienophile in the reaction, acrolein + 2-methoxy- and 2-ethoxy-butadiene,[8,26] has been stabilized with hydroquinone.[6]

A number of secondary reactions of the addition products have been discussed previously. These changes involve: addition of a second mole of the diene to the primary adduct (cyclopentadiene + vinyl acetate and vinyl chloride, furan + acetylenedicarboxylic acid and its methyl ester); rearrangement and the addition of a second mole of the dienophile to the adduct;[14] elimination of the bridge system which may or may not be accompanied by dehydrogenation (ethyl cinnamate + 1,3-diphenyl-isobenzofuran, ethyl acetylenedicarboxylate + cyclohexadiene, styrene + piperylcyclone, 1,2-dihydronaphthalene + acecyclone); dehydrogenation by the solvent [66] (cinnamic acid + methyleneanthrone); and the reverse Diels-Alder reaction (see Chapter 1).

Traces of mineral acid may alter the course of the reaction. It has been reported [6,7] that, after several months at room temperature, such unifunctional dienophiles as acrolein, crotonaldehyde, methyl vinyl ketone, and vinyl phenyl ketone failed to react with furan and 2-methyl-furan. Traces of sulfuric acid or sulfur dioxide, sulfonic acids or their chlorides, but not formic acid or esters of sulfonic acids, promote the so-called "substitution-addition reaction"—exemplified by the formation of β-(2-furyl-)propionaldehyde from furan and acrolein. This exothermic reaction may proceed one stage further by a similar mechanism.

$$\text{[furan]}-H \rightarrow H-\text{[furan]}-CH_2CH_2CHO \rightarrow$$
$$CH_2\text{=}CHCHO$$

$$OHCCH_2CH_2-\text{[furan]}-CH_2CH_2CHO$$

[66] Bergmann, Haskelberg, and Bergmann, J. Org. Chem., 7, 303 (1942).

In the absence of a catalyst, N-methylpyrrole + acetylenedicarboxylic acid, 2-methylpyrrole and 4-methylimidazole + methyl acetylenedicarboxylate react similarly (Table X). These substituted maleic acids

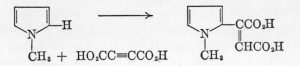

can react with a second mole of the heterocyclic diene, e.g., 2,4-dimethylpyrrole, N-methylindole, and 1-methylimidazole + methyl acetylenedicarboxylate. Dependence of the course of the reaction upon the

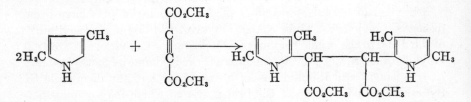

reagent is clearly illustrated by the formation of methyl 1-methyl-8,9-dihydroindole-4,5,6,7-tetracarboxylate (LXXIX) from N-methylpyrrole and methyl acetylenedicarboxylate. 1,2-Dimethylimidazole, pyridine, α-picoline, 2-stilbazole, quinoline, isoquinoline, and phenanthridine [see Norton, *Chem. Revs.*, **31**, 319 (1942)] react in an analogous manner with

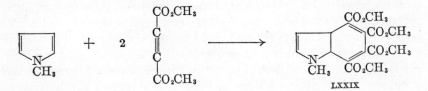

methyl acetylenedicarboxylate. The reaction mixture from the pyridines and their benzologs contains, as well as the stable adduct (LXXXI), a labile isomer (LXXX) which is isomerized to the stable form by heat or solution in ethanol, acetic acid, or sulfuric acid.

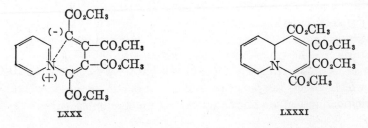

SELECTION OF EXPERIMENTAL CONDITIONS

Comparison of Dienes. The yield of addition products from acyclic dienes appears to be dependent to a greater extent upon the position of the substituents in the acyclic chain than upon the size of the groups. Alkyl, alkoxyl, and aryl groups on C_2, or C_2 and C_3, generally enhance the reactivity of the diene, whereas substitution of these groups on the terminal positions depresses the reactivity. Thus the following order holds for butadiene and some of the alkylbutadienes:

2,3-dimethylbutadiene > isoprene > butadiene > 2,4-hexadiene

The same is true for 2,3-diphenylbutadiene, 1,4-diphenylbutadiene, and 1- and 2-alkoxybutadienes.

Diene systems in five- and six-carbon rings are very reactive, and the reactivity does not decrease appreciably with increased substitution; usually 75–95% yields of the adducts are obtained.

Mixed aromatic-acyclic dienes exhibit reduced reactivity and often react only under forcing conditions.

Furans do not react with such dienophiles as methyl vinyl ketone, vinyl phenyl ketone, or crotonaldehyde even after several months at room temperature.

Comparison of Dienophiles. Despite the number of dienophiles that have been combined with the various types of dienes, no systematic study has been undertaken to determine the conditions (temperature, solvent, etc.) for optimum yields, and no quantitative comparison can be made of the reactivity of different classes of dienophiles. Examination of Tables I–IV will show that (1) ethylenic dienophiles usually give better yields than analogous acetylenes, (2) bifunctional dienophiles react more favorably than unifunctional ones, (3) α,β-unsaturated acids as a rule react better than their esters, and (4) the yields from β-nitrostyrene are as good as, if not superior to, those from vinyl phenyl ketone.

Reaction Conditions. Reactions have been carried out at temperatures ranging from $-10°$ to $300°$. Addition of some simpler dienophiles to the more reactive dienes proceeds with such vigor that the exothermic reaction must be controlled by cooling in an ice bath. These reactions are often complete in one hour, whereas the less reactive compounds may react to the extent of only a few per cent after many hours at high temperatures. Reactant pairs might conveniently be classified as reactive, normal, or unreactive. Cyclopentadiene + acrolein is a reactive system for which room temperature suffices; isoprene + 2,6-dimethoxy-4-n-amylcinnamic acid is a normally reactive system for which heating (185°)

is necessary; and butadiene + methyl 5-bromo-7,8-dimethoxy-3,4-dihydro-1-naphthoate is an unreactive system which requires a high temperature (225°) and a long reaction time (168 hours), and even under these conditions the yield of adduct is only 8%. The reaction of cinnamic acid with 2,3-dimethylbutadiene is influenced by temperature. The yield of adduct improved with increase in temperature; the highest yield (74%) was obtained at 170°, and then the yield fell progressively to 24% at 240°. Whether this is the result of the reversibility of the reaction (Chapter 1) has not been determined. Numerous combinations of conditions have been employed. The standard conditions that will generally give satisfactory results for many pairs of reactants are: *temperature*, 100–170°; *time*, ten to thirty hours; *solvent*, benzene, toluene, or xylene.

A few acyclic dienes have failed to give adducts. This may be attributed in part to polymerization of the diene in preference to addition to an unreactive dienophile (see Side Reactions, above). Inert solvents such as benzene, toluene, and xylene are employed [13] to minimize the tendency of dienes to polymerize. In a few reactions the yield of adduct was improved by the addition of small amounts of trichloroacetic acid [67] (see Chapter 1).

EXPERIMENTAL PROCEDURES

endo-2,5-Methano-Δ^3-tetrahydrobenzaldehyde (XVI)—Addition of Acrolein to Cyclopentadiene.[68] When a solution of 10 g. of acrolein in 15 ml. of ether is mixed with 14 g. of cyclopentadiene there is immediate reaction accompanied by the evolution of heat. When the initial vigorous reaction is over the tightly corked flask is allowed to stand for several hours at room temperature. After removal of the solvent, the product is distilled (b.p. 70–72°/20 mm.) in an atmosphere of carbon dioxide; yield 90–95%.

Sodium bisulfite reacts rapidly with the aldehyde in ethereal solution, and further purification of the product can be accomplished through the addition product.

4-Methyl-6-(2,6-dimethoxy-4-*n*-amylphenyl)-Δ^3-tetrahydrobenzoic Acid, (XI)—Addition of 2,6-Dimethoxy-4-*n*-amylcinnamic Acid to Isoprene.[17] A mixture of 10 g. of 2,6-dimethoxy-4-*n*-amylcinnamic acid, 40 ml. of 80% isoprene, and 40 ml. of dry xylene is heated in a steel bomb at 185° for forty hours. The mixture is cooled and diluted with twice its own volume of petroleum ether (b.p. 60–110°) and thoroughly shaken with 100 ml. of saturated aqueous sodium carbonate. On settling, the

[67] Wassermann, Fr. pat. 838,454 [*C. A.*, **33**, 7818 (1939)].
[68] Diels and Alder, *Ann.*, **460**, 98 (1928).

liquid separates into three phases, the middle of which is the sodium salt of the product, insoluble in both the aqueous and petroleum ether layers. This material is separated and washed with a mixture of petroleum ether and dilute aqueous sodium carbonate, again separated from the ternary mixture, and treated with 75 ml. of 10% hydrochloric acid and 75 ml. of ether. The mixture is shaken vigorously, and the aqueous layer withdrawn. The ether layer is washed three times with water and the solvent replaced by 30 ml. of petroleum ether (b.p. 60–110°). On standing for ten minutes the solution deposits 1 g. of solid which is unchanged starting material.

The mother liquor is placed in an icebox overnight, during which time a crystalline solid deposits; yield 6.2 g. Another 0.8 g. is obtained by concentrating the filtrate. The total yield, corrected for recovered starting material, is 62%. When crystallized from petroleum ether and from dilute ethanol (Darco), vacuum-sublimed three times, and again recrystallized from petroleum ether, the product forms very fine white needles, m.p. 115–115.5° (cor.).

Addition of Methyl 5-Bromo-7,8-dimethoxy-3,4-dihydro-1-naphthoate to Butadiene.[23] Twenty grams of methyl 5-bromo-7,8-dimethoxy-3,4-dihydro-1-naphthoate is heated in a sealed thick-walled Pyrex tube with 15 ml. of butadiene at 220–230° for seven days. After several fractional distillations, 9.2 g. of starting material is recovered and the bulk of the addition product collected in an 8.6-g. fraction boiling at 185–196° (3 mm.). Crystallization from petroleum ether gives 3.2 g. more starting material in the first crop, and the next crystallizate consists of crude addition product (2.4 g.), m.p. 89–100°. Two further crystallizations raise the melting point to 101–103°, and the average yield, not allowing for recovery of considerable starting material, is 8–9%. The mother liquors contain about 3.4 g. of an oil which fails to crystallize. The fully purified ester of XXX forms elongated prisms, m.p. 105–106°.

1-Propyl-2,5-methano-6-nitro-Δ^3-tetrahydrobenzene (XLII, R = C_3H_7) —Addition of 1-Nitro-1-pentene to Cyclopentadiene.[36] A solution of 15 g. of 1-nitro-1-pentene and 15 g. of cyclopentadiene in 10 ml. of benzene is heated for eight hours at 105–110° in a sealed tube. The reaction mixture is distilled in vacuum. After removal of the fore-run of dicyclopentadiene, the main fraction is collected as a pale yellow oil boiling over a range 122–125°/14 mm.; yield 17 g.

Addition of Δ^2-Dihydrothiophene-1-dioxide to Cyclopentadiene.[36] A solution of 5 g. of Δ^2-dihydrothiophenedioxide and 3 g. of cyclopentadiene in 15 ml. of toluene is heated in a sealed tube at 140–150° for ten hours. The solvent is removed under vacuum, and the residue is distilled at 0.1 mm. After a small amount of an oily fore-run boiling at 120–130°, the main fraction is collected at 135–145°, both at 0.1 mm. The distillate solidifies in the receiver to a waxy, camphorlike solid; weight 4 g. The product, after thorough pressing on a clay plate, melts at 141–142°.

The residue remaining in the distillation flask is crystallized from ethyl acetate. The crystalline product, m.p. 218°, is the result of the addition of two moles of cyclopentadiene to one of Δ^2-dihydrothiophenedioxide.

Dehydro-norbornyl Acetate (XLVI, R = H)—Addition of Vinyl Acetate to Cyclopentadiene.[39] One hundred grams of freshly distilled cyclopentadiene is heated in an autoclave with 150 g. (50% excess) of vinyl acetate at 185–190° for ten hours. From the oily reaction mixture 72 g. of vinyl acetate is recovered by distillation and the remaining oil is fractionated in vacuum. The fraction boiling at 73–77°/14 mm. is dehydro-norbornyl acetate; yield 100 g. (79%). A fraction boiling at 140–145°/14 mm. is the result of the addition of a second mole of cyclopentadiene to the primary adduct.

Diethyl 3,6-Diphenyl-$\Delta^{1,4}$-dihydrophthalate—Addition of Ethyl Acetylenedicarboxylate to *trans-trans*-1,4-Diphenylbutadiene.[53] A mixture of 4.4 g. of *trans-trans*-1,4-diphenylbutadiene and 3.7 g. of ethyl acetylenedicarboxylate is heated at 140–150° for five hours. The reaction mixture solidifies to a mass of glistening prisms; m.p. 88°, yield 90%.

Dimethyl 9,10-Dihydroanthracene-9,10-*endo*-α,β-maleate (LIII)—Addition of Methyl Acetylenedicarboxylate to Anthracene.[60] A mixture of 5 g. of anthracene and 5 ml. of methyl acetylenedicarboxylate is heated cautiously until a lively reaction sets in. In a short time, the reaction is complete. When the mixture is cooled it sets to a solid mass. To remove small traces of oily material the solid is pressed on a clay plate and then crystallized from acetonitrile and finally from methanol, m.p. 160–161°; yield, quantitative. From ethyl malonate the adduct crystallizes in stout crystals.

ABBREVIATIONS USED IN TABLES I–XI

A = acid chloride.
B = methyl ester.
C = ethyl ester.
D = the salicylate.
Quant. = quantitative yield.
Reflux = reflux temperature.
t. as subscript indicates that the reaction is carried out in a sealed tube or autoclave.

TABLE I

YIELDS OF ADDUCTS FROM ACETYLENIC AND ETHYLENIC DIENOPHILES

Acetylenic Dienophile	Diene	Temperature, °C	Yield, %	Reference*	Temperature, °C	Yield, %	Diene	Ethylenic Dienophile	Reference*
Ethyl acetylenedicarboxylate	Isosafrole	100	5	4	140	20	Isosafrole	Ethyl maleate	4
	Tetraphenylcyclopentadienone	300	22	48	170	63	Tetraphenylcyclopentadienone	Methyl fumarate	48
Methyl acetylenedicarboxylate	1,4-Diphenylbutadiene	140	90	53	Reflux	77	1,4-Diphenylbutadiene	Maleic anhydride	71
	Anthracene	20	100	60	Reflux	100	Anthracene	Maleic anhydride	72
	Cyclohexadiene	0	84	50	Room temp.	100	Cyclohexadiene	Maleic anhydride	68
	9,10-Dibromoanthracene	—	0	45	200	some	9,10-Dibromoanthracene	Maleic anhydride	60
	2,5-Dimethylfuran	100	100	62	Room temp.	100	2,5-Dimethylfuran	Maleic anhydride	73
	Tetraphenylcyclopentadienone	200	31	48	165	61	Tetraphenylcyclopentadienone	Methyl maleate	48
Acetylenedicarbonitrile	Cyclopentadiene	<20	83	70	<0	94	Cyclopentadiene	Maleonitrile	70
Propiolic acid	Cyclopentadiene	Room temp.	44	9	50	90	Cyclopentadiene	Acrylic acid	68

* References 69–116 are listed on pp. 172–173.

TABLE II

YIELDS OF ADDUCTS FROM UNIFUNCTIONAL AND BIFUNCTIONAL DIENOPHILES

Unifunctional Dienophile	Diene	Temperature, °C	Yield, %	Reference*	Diene	Temperature, °C	Yield, %	Bifunctional Dienophile	Reference*
Acrylic acid	Cyclopentadiene	50	90	68	Cyclopentadiene	0	100	Maleic anhydride	68
	1-Phenylbutadiene	100	77	2	1-Phenylbutadiene	80	Good	3,4-Dihydronaphthalic anhydride-1,2	75
Ethyl 3,4-dihydro-1-naphthoate	Butadiene	170	23	23	Butadiene	100	63		76
Ethyl 7-methoxy-3,4-dihydro-1-naphthoate	2,3-Dimethylbutadiene	180	74	23	2,3-Dimethylbutadiene	100	97	7-Methoxy-3,4-dihydronaphthalic anhydride-1,2	76
	Butadiene	160	31	23	Butadiene	160	85		77
1-Methyl-Δ^1-cyclohexen-3-one	Butadiene	—	0	74	Butadiene	100	75	p-Xyloquinone	78
Vinyl phenyl ketone	Cyclopentadiene	100	54	3	Cyclopentadiene	80	89	Dibenzoylethylene	30
	2,3-Dimethylbutadiene	>140	37	3	2,3-Dimethylbutadiene	100	100		30

* References 69–116 are listed on pp. 172–173.

TABLE III

YIELDS OF ADDUCTS FROM α,β-UNSATURATED ACIDS AND ESTERS

Dienophile	Diene	Temperature, °C	Yield, %	Reference*	Diene	Temperature, °C	Yield, %	Dienophile	Reference*
Benzoylacrylic acid	2,3-Dimethylbutadiene	100	98	19	2,3-Dimethylbutadiene	165	52	Methyl benzoylacrylate	19
5-Bromo-7,8-dimethoxy-3,4-dihydronaphthalene-1-carboxylic acid	Butadiene	195	18	23	Butadiene	225	8	Methyl 5-bromo-7,8-dimethoxy-3,4-dihydronaphthalene-1-carboxylate	23
Cinnamic acid	2,3-Dimethylbutadiene	170	74	13	2,3-Dimethylbutadiene	180	55	Ethyl cinnamate	13

* References 69–116 are listed on pp. 172–173.

TABLE IV

Yields of Adducts from β-Nitrostyrene and Vinyl Phenyl Ketone

β-Nitrostyrene	Temperature, °C	Yield, %	Reference*	Yield, %	Temperature, °C	Vinyl Phenyl Ketone	Reference*
Cyclohexadiene	100	20	79, 80	0	—	Cyclohexadiene	3
Cyclopentadiene	100	95	79, 80	54	—	Cyclopentadiene	3
2,3-Dimethylbutadiene	70	82	80	37	—	2,3-Dimethylbutadiene	3
2,5-Dimethylfuran	20	0	79, 80	0	—	2,5-Dimethylfuran	3
1,4-Diphenylbutadiene	140	40	79	30	—	1,4-Diphenylbutadiene	3
2,3-Diphenylbutadiene	140	9	79, 80	46	—	2,3-Diphenylbutadiene	3
Furan	20	0	79	0	—	Furan	3
α-Phellandrene	—	45	79, 80	37	—	α-Phellandrene	3

* References 69–116 are listed on pp. 172–173.

In Tables V through XI which follow are listed those examples of diene syntheses with ethylenic and acetylenic dienophiles that have been found in the literature prior to June 1, 1945.

TABLE V

The Diels-Alder Addition of α,β-Unsaturated Carbonyl Compounds

Addends	Products	Ratio of Diene to Dienophile	Solvent	Temperature, °C	Time, hours	B.P. or M.P.	Yield, %	References *
Acetylethylene (Methyl Vinyl Ketone)								
Butadiene	4-Acetylcyclohexene-1	—	None	140t.	8-10	184-185/747 mm.[7] †	75-80	81
Cyclohexadiene	3,6-Ethano-4-acetylcyclo-hexene-1	—	None	140t.	8-10	106-106.5/20 mm.[7]	50	81
2,3-Dimethylbutadiene	1,2-Dimethyl-4-acetylcyclo-hexene-1	—	None	140t.	8-10	218-220/747 mm.[7]	75-80	81
Isoprene		—	None	140t.	8-10	204.5-206/747 mm.[7]	75-80	81
Sylvan	(See footnote 2)	—	None	Room temp.	>320	—	0	82
Acrolein								
Butadiene	Δ^3-Tetrahydrobenzaldehyde	1.0	None	100t.	1	51-52/13 mm.[7, 13]	100	68
Cyclohexadiene	2,5-Ethano-Δ^3-tetrahydrobenzaldehyde	0.5	None	100t.	3.5	84-85/12 mm.[7]	Good	12
Cyclopentadiene	2,5-Methano-Δ^3-tetrahydrobenzaldehyde	1.2	Ether	Room temp.	24	70-72/20 mm.[7, 13]	90-95	10, 68

Diene	Product / Structure	Mole ratio	Solvent	Temp.[6]	Time	B.p.	Yield	Ref.
1-Diethylamino-butadiene	N(C₂H₅)₂ ... CHO	1.1	Ether	Room temp.	—	90–93/3 mm.[8]	—	83
1,1-Dimethylbutadiene	(See footnote 2)	1.0	None	180_t	48	74–75/12 mm.	—	5
1,3-Dimethylbutadiene	CH₃ / CH₃ ... CHO	1.0	None	100_t	3	71–73/10 mm.	Good	84
1,4-Dimethylbutadiene	(See footnote 2)	—	—	—	—	—	—	69
	2,5-Dimethyl-Δ³-tetrahydro-benzaldehyde	1.0	None	100_t	3	79/10 mm.[7]	Good	84
2,3-Dimethylbutadiene	3,4-Dimethyl-Δ³-tetrahydro-benzaldehyde	—	None	150_t	2–3	75/12 mm.	—	5
Di-α-naphthyliso-benzofuran	C₁₀H₇-α ... CHO ... C₁₀H₇-α	1.0	Absolute ethanol	80	1	—	—	85
α,α-Diphenyl-β,β-isobenzofuran	1,4-Diphenylnaphthaldehyde	—	Alcohol	100	0.5	—[8]	61	86
1-Ethoxybutadiene	OC₂H₅ ... CHO (See footnote 2)	0.86	None	100_t	3	90/11 mm.	52	87

* References 69–116 are listed on pp. 172–173.
† For table footnotes see pp. 134–135.

TABLE V—Continued

THE DIELS-ALDER ADDITION OF α,β-UNSATURATED CARBONYL COMPOUNDS

Addends	Products	Ratio of Diene to Dienophile	Solvent	Temperature, °C	Time, hours	B.P. or M.P.	Yield, %	References *
Acrolein (Cont'd) 2-Ethoxybutadiene	4-Ethoxy-Δ³-tetrahydrobenzaldehyde (See footnotes 2, 12)	1	—[4]†	100–110	3–4	104–105/ 13 mm.[7]	51	8
		—	None[4]	120–140.t	6	101.5–102/ 10 mm.	50[41]	26
	[structure: bicyclic ring system with CHO, CH₃, CH₂O groups]	0.6	Benzene[4]	Reflux[3]	24	—	68	8
		—	Benzene[4]	100.t	10	—	74	8
		—	Benzene[4]	165.t	0.75	—	74	8
Isosafrole	[structure: cyclohexene ring with CH₃, CHO] (See footnote 2)	—	—	—	—	—	0	4
Isoprene		—	None	100	—	63–64/ 10 mm.[7]	Good	84
		—	None	150.t	2–3	64–65/ 12 mm.[7]	—	5
2-Methoxybutadiene	4-Methoxy-Δ²-tetrahydrobenzaldehyde	0.8	Benzene[5]	160.t[5]	0.5	94–95/ 13 mm.[7, 9]	75	8
		—	None[4]	120–140.t	6	92–92.5/ 10 mm.	65[41]	26

Diene		Ref.	Ratio	Solvent	Temp.		b.p.	Yield	Ref.
1-Methylbutadiene (piperylene)	(CH₃, CHO structure)	—	—	—	—	—	—	—	69
1-Methyl-1(2',4'-dimethylphenyl)-butadiene	(See footnote 2)	0.9	None	100–110t.	2	179–181/12 mm.	35 [14]	2
Myrcene	(See footnote 2)	—	—	100t.	—	134–136/17 mm.	Good	84
α-Phellandrene	(See footnote 2)	0.9	—	100	2–3	128–130/12 mm.	Good	84
1-Phenyl-1-methyl-butadiene	(See footnote 2)	—	Benzene	100–105t.	2	48 / 172–174/12 mm.	— [14]	88
1-Phenylbutadiene / 2-Phenyl-Δ³-tetrahydrobenzaldehyde	(See footnote 2)	1.0	None	100t.	1	144/12 mm.	40 [14]	2

* References 69–116 are listed on pp. 172–173.
† For table footnotes see pp. 134–135.

TABLE V—Continued

THE DIELS-ALDER ADDITION OF α,β-UNSATURATED CARBONYL COMPOUNDS

Addends	Products	Ratio of Diene to Dienophile	Solvent	Temperature, °C	Time, hours	B.P. or M.P.	Yield, %	References*
Acrolein (Cont'd) 1-Propoxybutadiene	(See footnote 2) †	1.0	None	100t.	3	103–104/ 11 mm.	50	87
α-Terpinene	(See footnote 2)	—	None	120–150t.	—	116–119/ 10 mm.[15]	—	89
1,1,4-Tetramethyl-butadiene	2,2,5,5-Tetramethyl-Δ³-tetra-hydrobenzaldehyde	1.0	None	180–200t.	48	83–85/ 12 mm.	—	5
1,2,6,6-Tetra-methylcyclo-hexadiene (β-pyronene)	(See footnote 2)	—	None	110t.	3	123/15 mm.[7]	50	90

Diene / Dienophile	Structure	Ratio	Solvent	Temp.	Time (hr.)	B.p.		Yield (%)
1,5,5,6-Tetramethyl-cyclohexadiene (α-pyronene)	—	—	None	110t.	3	—	10	90
1-p-Tolyl-1-methyl-butadiene	(structure: CHO, CH₃, H₃C–C₆H₄)	0.95	Benzene	100–105t.	2	176–178/ 12 mm. 51	—[14]	88
1,1,3-Trimethyl-butadiene	(See footnote 2) (structure: CH₃, CH₃, CHO, H₃C)	1.0	None	150–200s.	48	78–79/ 12 mm.[7]	—	5
1,1,4-Trimethyl-butadiene	(See footnote 2) (structure: CH₃, CHO, CH₃)	1.0	None	150–200	2–3	78–80/ 12 mm.	—	5
Acrolein, β,β-dimethyl- Isoprene	(See footnote 2) (structure: CHO, CH₃, CH₃, CH₃)	1.0	None	180–200t.	48	80–85/ 12 mm.	Poor	5
Acrolein, β-ethyl- Isoprene	(See footnote 2) (structure: CHO, C₂H₅, CH₃)	1.0	None	180–200t.	2–3	86–88/ 12 mm.	—	5

* References 69–116 are listed on pp. 172–173.
† For table footnotes see pp. 134–135.

TABLE V—Continued

The Diels-Alder Addition of α,β-Unsaturated Carbonyl Compounds

Addends	Products	Ratio of Diene to Dienophile	Solvent	Temperature, °C	Time, hours	B.P. or M.P.	Yield, %	References*
Acrolein, α-methyl-β-ethyl- Isoprene	(structure) CH₃, CHO, C₂H₅, CH₃ (See footnote 2) †	1.0	None	180–200t.	48	88-90/ 12 mm.	—	5
Acrylic acid β-Chloroethyl sorbate A	(structure) CH₃, COCl, CO₂CH₂CH₂Cl (See footnote 16)	1.25	Xylene	140	5	150–154/ 0.2 mm.	77	29
Cyclopentadiene	2,5-Methano-Δ³-tetrahydro-benzoic acid	1.7	Ether	50	3–4	132–134/ 22 mm. [17]	83–90	68
Isoprene	(structure) CO₂H, CH₃ (See footnote 2)	1.0	None	150t.	2–3	97–98	—	5

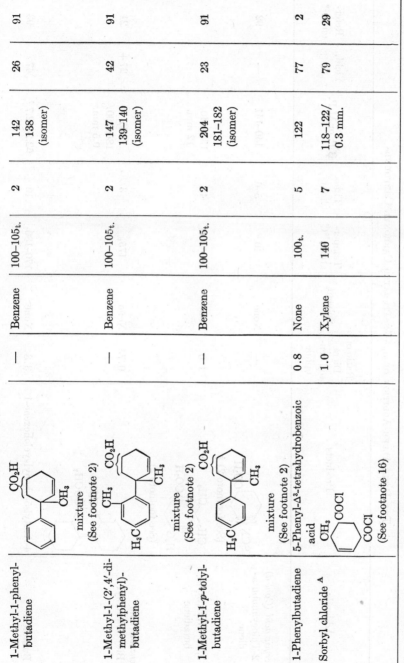

1-Methyl-1-phenyl-butadiene	mixture (See footnote 2)	—	Benzene	100–105t.	2	142 138 (isomer)	26	91
1-Methyl-1-(2',4'-dimethylphenyl)-butadiene	mixture (See footnote 2)	—	Benzene	100–105t.	2	147 139–140 (isomer)	42	91
1-Methyl-1-p-tolyl-butadiene	mixture (See footnote 2)	—	Benzene	100–105t.	2	204 181–182 (isomer)	23	91
1-Phenylbutadiene	5-Phenyl-Δ^3-tetrahydrobenzoic acid	0.8	None	100t.	5	122	77	2
Sorbyl chloride A	(See footnote 16)	1.0	Xylene	140	7	118–122/ 0.3 mm.	79	29

* References 69–116 are listed on pp. 172–173.
† For table footnotes see pp. 134–135.

TABLE V—*Continued*

THE DIELS-ALDER ADDITION OF α,β-UNSATURATED CARBONYL COMPOUNDS

Addends	Products	Ratio of Diene to Dienophile	Solvent	Temperature, °C	Time, hours	B.P. or M.P.	Yield, %	References [*]
Acrylic acid (Cont'd) 2-Thiocyanobutadiene	SCN⟨⟩CO₂H (See footnote 2) †	—	None	40 [38]	5-6	140-141	—	92
1,1,3-Trimethylbutadiene	CH₃,CH₃ ⟨⟩CO₂H H₃C (See footnote 2)	1.0	None	180-200t.	48	135-140/ 12 mm.	—	5
Benzalacetone Bicyclohexenyl	C₆H₅ COCH₃	0.75	None	175t.	3	135 180-190/ 0.5 mm.	27+	21
Butadiene	4-Acetyl-5-phenylcyclohexene-1	3.8	None	170-180t.	10	62.2-62.7 [7]	47	93

Diene / Product (structure)	Ratio	Solvent	Temp. (°C)	Time (hrs)	M.p. (°C)	Yield (%)	Ref.
Benzalacetophenone — Bicyclohexenyl (C₆H₅, COC₆H₅) isomer	1.0	None	180–185	6	216[18]	31	21
Butadiene — 4-Benzoyl-5-phenylcyclohexene-1 (O=C–C₆H₅, C₆H₅, CH₃)	3.0	None	180–185	6	153–154	5	21
	—	None	160–180t	10	100.4–101.5[7]	82	93
Isoprene	—	None	150t	10	105–106	56.6	93
Tetraphenylcyclopentadienone (C₆H₅, C₆H₅, COC₆H₅, C₆H₅)	0.9	Trichlorobenzene	140	18	341	—	3
(See footnote 43)	—	—	Room temp.	—	—	0	48
Benzalmalononitrile — 2,3-Dimethylbutadiene (H₃C, H₃C, CN, CN)	1.2	Benzene	185–195t	10	81–82	91	15
β-Benzoylacrylic acid — Bicyclohexenyl (CO₂H, COC₆H₅)	0.87	None	170–180	4	258–259	24	21
	0.87	Xylene	Reflux	7	258–259	22	21
(See footnote 19)	0.96	Ethanol	Reflux	8	258–259	27	21

* References 69–116 are listed on pp. 172–173.
† For table footnotes see pp. 134–135.

TABLE V—Continued

THE DIELS-ALDER ADDITION OF α,β-UNSATURATED CARBONYL COMPOUNDS

Addends	Products	Ratio of Diene to Dienophile	Solvent	Temperature, °C	Time, hours	B.P. or M.P.	Yield, %	References*
β-Benzoylacrylic acid (Cont'd) 2,3-Dimethylbutadiene	isomer	1.45	Absolute ethanol	100–105t.	96–120	143	95–98	19
			Absolute ethanol	100–105t.	96–120	189	—	19
2,3-Diphenylbutadiene B		2.3	—	165	15	147	52	3
β-Benzoylacrylic acid,2,4-dimethyl- 2,3-Dimethylbutadiene	isomer	1.8	Absolute ethanol	100–105t.	96–120	150.5	95–98	19
			Absolute ethanol	100–105t.	96–120	165.5	—	19

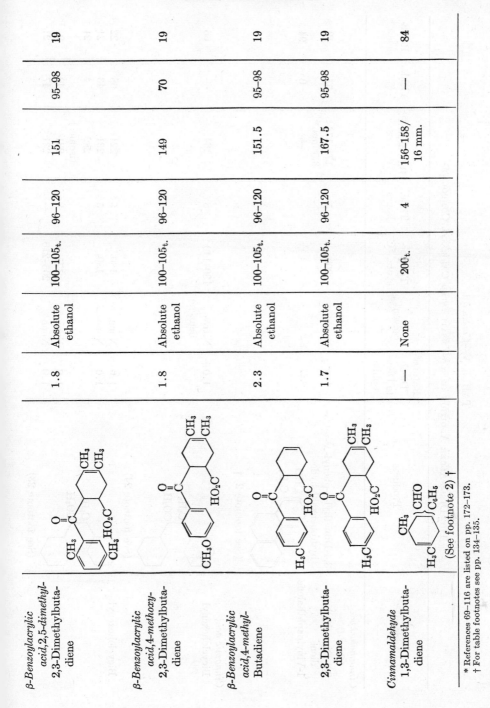

β-Benzoylacrylic acid,2,5-dimethyl- / 2,3-Dimethylbutadiene	1.8	Absolute ethanol	100–105t.	96–120	151	95–98	19
β-Benzoylacrylic acid,4-methoxy- / 2,3-Dimethylbutadiene	1.8	Absolute ethanol	100–105t.	96–120	149	70	19
β-Benzoylacrylic acid,4-methyl- / Butadiene	2.3	Absolute ethanol	100–105t.	96–120	151.5	95–98	19
2,3-Dimethylbutadiene	1.7	Absolute ethanol	100–105t.	96–120	167.5	95–98	19
Cinnamaldehyde / 1,3-Dimethylbutadiene	—	None	200t.	4	156–158/ 16 mm.	—	84

(See footnote 2) †

* References 69–116 are listed on pp. 172–173.
† For table footnotes see pp. 134–135.

TABLE V—*Continued*

THE DIELS-ALDER ADDITION OF α,β-UNSATURATED CARBONYL COMPOUNDS

Addends	Products	Ratio of Diene to Dienophile	Solvent	Temperature, °C	Time, hours	B.P. or M.P.	Yield, %	References *
Cinnamaldehyde (Cont'd)								
2,3-Dimethylbutadiene	3,4-Dimethyl-6-phenyl-Δ³-tetrahydrobenzaldehyde (CHO, C₆H₅)	1.6	None	200 t.	5	171–173/3.5 mm.²⁵	55	13
1-Vinylnaphthalene	(See footnote 2) †	—	—	—	—	—	0	94
Cinnamic acid								
Bicyclohexenyl	(C₆H₅, CO₂H) (See footnote 24)	1.0+	Nitrobenzene	130–140	8	164	—	66
Bicyclohexenyl	(C₆H₅, CO₂H) (See footnote 23)	1.0	None	180 t.	5	221	68	22
		1.0	None	180 t.	5	231	43	21
						282 (isomer)	4	21
		1.0	None	175	8	231	40	21
		1.0	None	205–210	—	231	47	21

Compound							
Bicyclohexenyl [c] (isomer)	1.0	None	200	4	85–86	—	22
2,3-Dimethylbutadiene	1.0	None	200	4	—	—	22
	1.5	Xylene	140t.	10	159–160	48	13
	1.5	Xylene	170t.	14	159–160	74	13
	1.5	Xylene	180t.	10	159–160	56	13
	1.5	Xylene	240t.	5	159–160	24	13
	—	Xylene	—t.	—	159–160	87	18
	1.4	None	180t.	10	133–143/1.5 mm.[26]	55	13
2,3-Dimethylbutadiene [c]	1.4	None	220t.	8	133–143/1.5 mm.	0	13
	1.4	None	200t.	5	133–143/1.5 mm.	20–30	13
α,α'-Diphenyl-β,β'-isobenzofuran [c]	0.9	Absolute ethanol	100	1	—	80	27
Methyleneanthrone	0.95	Nitrobenzene	Reflux	1	183–184	—	95

* References 69–116 are listed on pp. 172–173.
† For table footnotes see pp. 134–135.

TABLE V—*Continued*

THE DIELS-ALDER ADDITION OF α,β-UNSATURATED CARBONYL COMPOUNDS

Addends	Products	Ratio of Diene to Dienophile	Solvent	Temperature, °C	Time, hours	B.P. or M.P.	Yield, %	References [*]
Cinnamic acid, 3,4-dimethoxy- 2,3-Dimethylbutadiene	(See footnote 22) †	—	—	—	—	—	—	96
2,3-Dimethylbutadiene [c]		—	—	—	—	—	—	96
Cinnamic acid, 2,6-dimethoxy-4-n-amyl Isoprene		4.0	Xylene	185t.	4	133–134 [1]	43	17

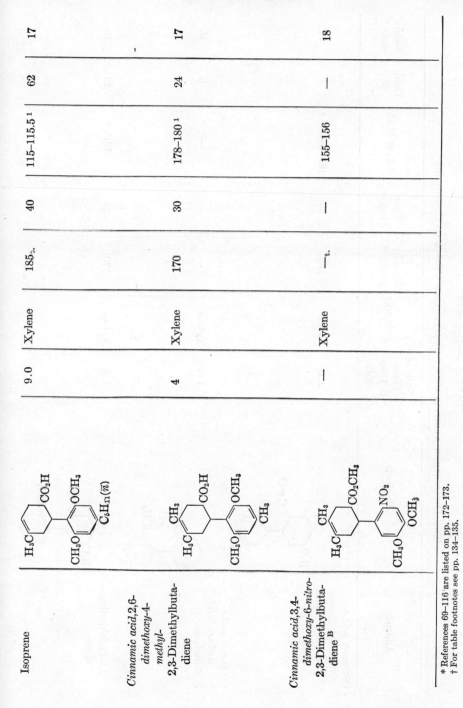

Isoprene	9.0	Xylene	185₃	40	115–115.5[1]	62	17
Cinnamic acid,2,6-dimethoxy-4-methyl- **2,3-Dimethylbutadiene**	4	Xylene	170	30	178–180[1]	24	17
Cinnamic acid,3,4-dimethoxy-6-nitro- **2,3-Dimethylbutadiene** [B]	—	Xylene	—†	—	155–156	—	18

* References 69–116 are listed on pp. 172–173.
† For table footnotes see pp. 134–135.

TABLE V—*Continued*

THE DIELS-ALDER ADDITION OF α,β-UNSATURATED CARBONYL COMPOUNDS

Addends	Products	Ratio of Diene to Dienophile	Solvent	Temperature, °C	Time, hours	B.P. or M.P.	Yield, %	References*
Cinnamic acid,o-hydroxy-(trans) 2,3-Dimethylbutadiene		3.0	Xylene	185t.	40	181–181.5¹†	4	16
Cinnamic acid,o-methoxy-(cis) Butadiene		1+	Xylene	—	—	—	0	16
2,3-Dimethylbutadiene		1.8	Xylene	170t.	28	191¹,²¹	48	16

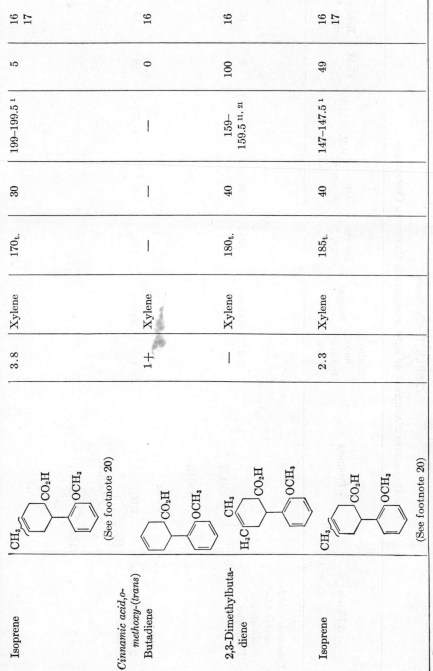

Diene	Product		Solvent	Temp.		m.p.		Ref.
Isoprene	(CH₃ / CO₂H / OCH₃ structure) (See footnote 20)	3.8	Xylene	170t.	30	199–199.5[1]	5	16 17
Cinnamic acid,o-methoxy-(trans) Butadiene	(CO₂H / OCH₃ structure)	1+	Xylene	—	—	—	0	16
2,3-Dimethylbuta-diene	(H₃C / CH₃ / CO₂H / OCH₃ structure)	—	Xylene	180t.	40	159–159.5[11,21]	100	16
Isoprene	(CH₃ / CO₂H / OCH₃ structure) (See footnote 20)	2.3	Xylene	185t.	40	147–147.5[1]	49	16 17

* References 69–116 are listed on pp. 172–173.
† For table footnotes see pp. 134–135.

TABLE V—*Continued*

THE DIELS-ALDER ADDITION OF α,β-UNSATURATED CARBONYL COMPOUNDS

Addends	Products	Ratio of Diene to Dienophile	Solvent	Temperature, °C	Time, hours	B.P. or M.P.	Yield, %	References *
*Cinnamic acid,2-methyl-4,6-dimethoxy-*Butadiene		8.0	Xylene	170t.	48	140–141 [1] †	8	16
2,3-Dimethylbuta-diene		4	Xylene	170t.	48	174–175 [1]	58	16

Dienophile / Diene	Structure	Molar ratio	Solvent	Temp. (°)	Time (hrs.)	B.p./M.p.	Yield %	Yield %
Coumarin Butadiene	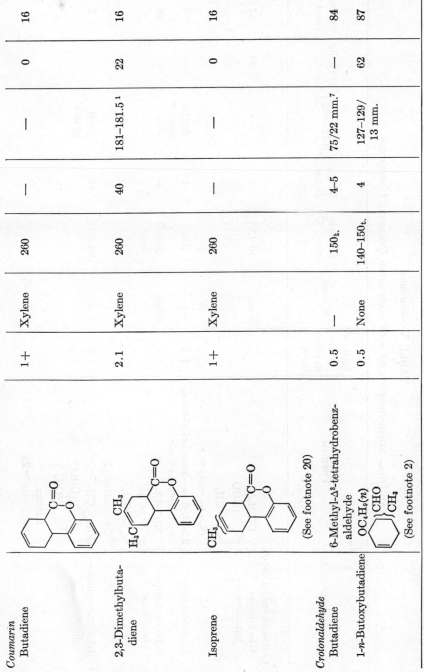	1+	Xylene	260	—	—	0	16
2,3-Dimethylbutadiene		2.1	Xylene	260	40	181–181.5[1]	22	16
Isoprene		1+	Xylene	260	—	—	0	16
(See footnote 20)								
Crotomaldehyde 6-Methyl-Δ^2-tetrahydrobenzaldehyde Butadiene		0.5	—	150t.	4–5	75/22 mm.[7]	—	84
1-*n*-Butoxybutadiene		0.5	None	140–150t.	4	127–129/ 13 mm.	62	87
$OC_4H_9(n)$ CHO CH_3 (See footnote 2)								

* References 69–116 are listed on pp. 172–173.
† For table footnotes see pp. 134–135.

TABLE V—*Continued*

THE DIELS-ALDER ADDITION OF α,β-UNSATURATED CARBONYL COMPOUNDS

Addends	Products	Ratio of Diene to Dienophile	Solvent	Temperature, °C	Time, hours	B.P. or M.P.	Yield, %	References*
Crotonaldehyde (Cont'd)								
1-Isobutoxy-butadiene	OC₄H₉(*iso*) CHO CH₃ (See footnote 2) †	—	None	140–150t.	5	—	49	87
Cyclopentadiene	2,5-Methano-6-methyl-Δ³-tetra-hydrobenzaldehyde	1.3	—	100t.	4	80/15 mm.[7, 42]	—	84
1-Diethylamino-butadiene	N(C₂H₅)₂ CHO CH₃ (See footnote 2)	1.0	Ether	Room temp.	—	—	—	83
1,1-Dimethylbuta-diene	CH₃ CH₃ CHO CH₃ mixture (See footnote 2)	1.0	None	180–200t.	48	79–81/12 mm.	—	5

Diene							
1,3-Dimethylbutadiene $\begin{array}{c}CH_3 \\ CHO \\ H_3C \quad CH_3\end{array}$ (See footnote 2)	0.4	—	150t.	4–5	81–82/12 mm.[7]	—	84
1,4-Dimethylbutadiene	—	—	—	—	—	—	69
2,5,6-Trimethyl-Δ^3-tetrahydrobenzaldehyde (2,3-Dimethylbutadiene)	0.5	None	150t.	5	89/12 mm.[7]	—	84
3,4,6-Trimethyl-Δ^3-tetrahydrobenzaldehyde	1.0	None	150–160t.	2–3	80–81/12 mm.[7]	—	5
1-Ethoxybutadiene $\begin{array}{c}OC_2H_5 \\ CHO \\ CH_3\end{array}$ (See footnote 2)	0.5	None	145–150t.	6	93–96/11 mm.	51	87
Isoprene $\begin{array}{c}CH_3 \\ CHO \\ CH_3\end{array}$ (See footnote 2)	0.7	None	150t.	4–5	92–93/25 mm.[7]	—	84
	—	None	150t.	2–3	73–74/12 mm.	—	5
2-Methoxybutadiene $\begin{array}{c}CHO \\ CH_3O \quad CH_3\end{array}$ (See footnote 2)	0.5	Benzene	160	2	102/12 mm.[9]	67	8
1-Methyl-2-vinylcyclohexene-1 (See footnote 2)	—	—	—	—	—	—	97

* References 69–116 are listed on pp. 172-173.
† For table footnotes see pp. 134-135.

TABLE V—*Continued*

THE DIELS-ALDER ADDITION OF α,β-UNSATURATED CARBONYL COMPOUNDS

Addends	Products	Ratio of Diene to Dienophile	Solvent	Temperature, °C	Time, hours	B.P. or M.P.	Yield, %	References [*]
Crotonaldehyde (Cont'd) Myrcene	(See footnote 2) †	0.5	—	150t.	2–4	143–144/ 12 mm.	—	84
α-Phellandrene	(See footnote 2)	0.5	—	100t.	—	143–144/ 18 mm.	—	84
1-*n*-Propoxybutadiene	(See footnote 2)	0.5	None	145–155t.	3	112–115/ 12 mm.	18	87
1,1,4,4-Tetramethyl-butadiene	2,2,5,5,6-Pentamethyl-Δ³-tetrahydrobenzaldehyde	1.0	None	180–200t.	48–72	86–88/ 12 mm.	—	5

Diene	Structure	Ratio	Solvent	Temperature	Time (hrs.)	B.p./M.p.		Yield %
1,1,3-Trimethyl-butadiene	CH₃ CH₃ / H₃C ⬡ CHO CH₃ (See footnotes 2, 11) mixture	—	—	180t.	5–7	93–95/18 mm.	—	84
		1.0	None	180–200t.	48	82–84/12 mm.	—	5
1,1,4-Trimethyl-butadiene	CH₃ CH₃ / CHO CH₃ / CH₃ (See footnote 2)		None	180–200t.	24–48	80–82/10 mm.	—	5
Crotonic acid Anthracene	H / CHCH₃ / CHCO₂H / H	0.64	None	150–200t.	6	191–193	—	60
Butadiene	6-Methyl-Δ³-tetrahydrobenzoic acid	1+	None	150–170t.	3	68	—	84
Cyclopentadiene ᴬ	CH₃—H / CH₂—H COCl	—	None	−10	—	—[40]	—	1
Bicyclohexenyl	CH₃ CO₂H (See footnote 24)	1.1	Nitro-benzene	130–140	8	164	—	66

* References 69–116 are listed on pp. 172–173.
† For table footnotes see pp. 134–135.

TABLE V—*Continued*

THE DIELS-ALDER ADDITION OF α,β-UNSATURATED CARBONYL COMPOUNDS

Addends	Products	Ratio of Diene to Dienophile	Solvent	Temperature, °C	Time, hours	B.P. or M.P.	Yield, %	References *
Crotonic acid (Cont'd) 1,3-Dimethylbutadiene	(See footnote 2) †	1.8	None	180t.	3	98	—	84
Isoprene	(See footnote 2)	1.0	None	150t.	2–3	81–83	—	5
1,1,3-Trimethylbutadiene	(i) (ii) (See footnotes 2, 10)	1.0 0.5	None None	180t. 150t.	— —	82–83 88.5–89	— —	5 84
Crotonolactone or Δ^{α,β}-butenolide Butadiene	Δ4-Tetrahydrophthalide (See footnotes 2, 27)	— —	— —	110t. 150–190t.	36 48	— 88–92/ 1.5 mm.	0 —	28 28

	Ratio	Solvent	Temp.	Time	b.p./m.p.	Yield	Ref.
2,3-Dimethylbutadiene *Crotonolactone,γ-methyl-* 4,5-Dimethyl-Δ⁴-tetrahydrophthalide	—	—	150t.	48	115–117/3.5 mm.	—	28
2,3-Dimethylbutadiene 2,4,5-Trimethyl-Δ⁴-tetrahydrophthalide	—	—	150–160t.	48	112–115/3.5 mm.	—	28
Cyclopentene-1-al 1,3,5-Hexatriene [structure: CHO, CH₂, CH]	—	Ethanol	90–95	—	173–175 [7, 9]	—	14
Diacetylethylene 2,3-Dimethylbutadiene 4,5-Diacetyl-1,2-dimethylcyclohexene-1	1.27	Benzene	100t.	6	36–37 [7]	—	98
1-Vinyl-6-methoxy-3,4-dihydronaphthalene [structure: COCH₃ COCH₃ CH₃O]	1.8	Benzene	110–115t.	48	174–175	25–30	99
[structure: COCH₃ COCH₃ CH₃O]	1.8	Benzene	110–115t.	48	107–108	—	99
1,2-Diacetylpropene-1 2,3-Dimethylbutadiene 4,5-Diacetyl-1,2,4-trimethylcyclohexene-1	1.7	Benzene	150t.	12	141/10 mm.	23	98

* References 69–116 are listed on pp. 172–173.
† For table footnotes see pp. 134–135.

TABLE V—Continued

THE DIELS-ALDER ADDITION OF α,β-UNSATURATED CARBONYL COMPOUNDS

Addends	Products	Ratio of Diene to Dienophile	Solvent	Temperature, °C	Time, hours	B.P. or M.P.	Yield, %	References[*]
Dibenzalacetone Butadiene		2.4	None	170–180t.	10	163.5–164.7	—	93
Dibenzoylethylene (cis) 2,3-Dimethylbutadiene	1,2-Dimethyl-4,5-dibenzoylcyclohexene-1	2.5+	Absolute ethanol	100	3	111–111.5 [1]†	100	30
Cyclopentadiene	3,6-Methano-4,5-dibenzoylcyclohexene-1	7.2	Absolute ethanol	80	4	160–161 [1]	—	30
Dibenzoylethylene (trans) Butadiene	4,5-Dibenzoylcyclohexene-1	1.7	Benzene	100t.	2	111.5–112 [1]	100	30
Cyclopentadiene	3,6-Methano-4,5-dibenzoylcyclohexene-1	3.5	Dry benzene	80	2	78–79 [1]	89	30
Bicyclohexenyl		1.4	Xylene	Reflux [28]	3	182	49	21
		1.4	Ethanol	Reflux	6	182	85	21
		1.0	Nitrobenzene	175	1	182	6	21
	isomer		Xylene	Reflux	3	162	—	21

Diene	Product	Ratio	Solvent	Temperature	Time (hrs)	M.p.	Yield %	Ref.
2,3-Dimethylbutadiene	1,2-Dimethyl-4,5-dibenzoylcyclohexene-1	2.5+	Absolute ethanol	100	3	111–111.5[1]	100	30
2,3-Diphenylbutadiene	1,2-Diphenyl-4,5-dibenzoylcyclohexene-1	1.0	Ethanol	Reflux	4	154–155	90	31
2,7-Diphenyl-4,5-dimethylisobenzofuran	[structure: H_3C, H_3C, C_6H_5, COC_6H_5, COC_6H_5, C_6H_5]	1.0	Xylene	Reflux	24	154–155	60	31
		1.1	Ethanol	Reflux	4	169	92	31
2,4-Hexadiene (1,4-dimethylbutadiene)	3,6-Dimethyl-4,5-dibenzoylcyclohexene-1	2.0	Toluene	100	18	136–137	64	33
		2.0	Toluene	100	18	86–88	8.6	33
Methyleneanthrone	[structure: COC_6H_5, COC_6H_5]	0.8	Trichlorobenzene	210	5	208	—	3
			Nitrobenzene	Reflux	5	286	—	3
Tetraphenylcyclopentadienone	—	—	—	Room temp.	—	—	0	48
Dibenzoylethylene,4,4'-dichloro-Butadiene	$COC_6H_4Cl(p)$ $COC_6H_4Cl(p)$	2.0	Benzene	80	12	125	92	32

* References 69–116 are listed on pp. 172–173.
† For table footnotes see pp. 134–135.

TABLE V—*Continued*

THE DIELS-ALDER ADDITION OF α,β-UNSATURATED CARBONYL COMPOUNDS

Addends	Products	Ratio of Diene to Dienophile	Solvent	Temperature, °C	Time, hours	B.P. or M.P.	Yield, %	References*
Dibenzoylethylene,4,4′-dichloro- (*Cont'd*) Cyclopentadiene	COC₆H₄Cl(p) COC₆H₄Cl(p) (See footnote 29) †	2.0	Benzene	80	12	139	92	32
2,3-Dimethylbutadiene	H₃C—COC₆H₄Cl(p) H₃C—COC₆H₄Cl(p)	2.0	Benzene	80	12	151	92	32
Dibenzoylethylene,4,4′-dimethyl- Butadiene	COC₆H₄CH₃(p) COC₆H₄CH₃(p)	2.0	Benzene	80	12	127	89	32

Cyclopentadiene $\overset{\text{CH}_2}{\bigcirc}$ $\begin{array}{l}COC_6H_4CH_3(p)\\ COC_6H_4CH_3(p)\end{array}$ (See footnote 29)	2.0	Benzene	80	12	106	67	32
2,3-Dimethylbuta-diene $H_3C\underset{H_3C}{\bigcirc}\begin{array}{l}COC_6H_4CH_3(p)\\ COC_6H_4CH_3(p)\end{array}$	2.0	Benzene	80	12	129	90	32
*Dibenzoylethylene, 2,4,6,2′,4′,6′-hexamethyl-*Butadiene $\bigcirc\begin{array}{l}COC_6H_2(CH_3)_3\\ COC_6H_2(CH_3)_3\end{array}$	2.0	Benzene	80	12	204	80	32
Cyclopentadiene $\overset{\text{CH}_2}{\bigcirc}\begin{array}{l}COC_6H_2(CH_3)_3\\ COC_6H_2(CH_3)_3\end{array}$ (See footnote 29)	2.0	Benzene	80	12	117	80	32
2,3-Dimethylbuta-diene —	—	Benzene	—	—	—	0	32

* References 69–116 are listed on pp. 172–173.
† For table footnotes see pp. 134–135.

TABLE V—*Continued*

THE DIELS-ALDER ADDITION OF α,β-UNSATURATED CARBONYL COMPOUNDS

Addends	Products	Ratio of Diene to Dienophile	Solvent	Temperature, °C	Time, hours	B.P. or M.P.	Yield, %	References *
3,4-*Dihydro-1-naphthoic acid* Butadiene [c]		3.4	None	140t.	41	164–166/5 mm.	21	24
		1.25	None	170t.	36	164–166/5 mm.	23	23
2,3-*Dimethylbutadiene* [c]		2.1	None	100t.	100	49–50[1] †	27	24
		1.4	None	170–180t.	36	49–50[1]	74	23

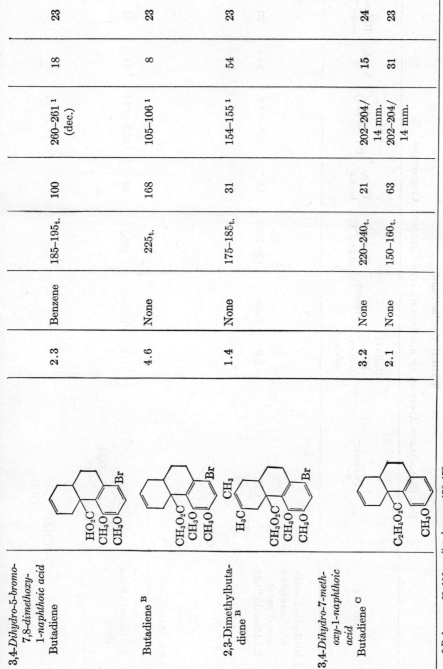

Diene							
3,4-Dihydro-5-bromo-7,8-dimethoxy-1-naphthoic acid Butadiene		2.3	Benzene	185–195t.	100	260–261[1] (dec.)	18	23
Butadiene [B]		4.6	None	225t.	168	105–106[1]	8	23
2,3-Dimethylbutadiene [B]		1.4	None	175–185t.	31	154–155[1]	54	23
3,4-Dihydro-7-methoxy-1-naphthoic acid Butadiene [C]		3.2	None	220–240t.	21	202–204/14 mm.	15	24
		2.1	None	150–160t.	63	202–204/14 mm.	31	23

* References 69–116 are listed on pp. 172–173.
† For table footnotes see pp. 134–135.

TABLE V—*Continued*

THE DIELS-ALDER ADDITION OF α,β-UNSATURATED CARBONYL COMPOUNDS

Addends	Products	Ratio of Diene to Dienophile	Solvent	Temperature, °C	Time, hours	B.P. or M.P.	Yield, %	References [*]
3,4-Dihydro-7-methoxy-1-naphthoic acid (Cont'd) 2,3-Dimethylbutadiene [c]		2.0	None	120–160[t].	48	67–68[1] [†]	85	23
3,4-Dihydro-6,7-dimethoxy-2-naphthoic acid 2,3-Dimethylbutadiene		1.5	Toluene	180[t].	48	175.5–178[1]	11.5	25

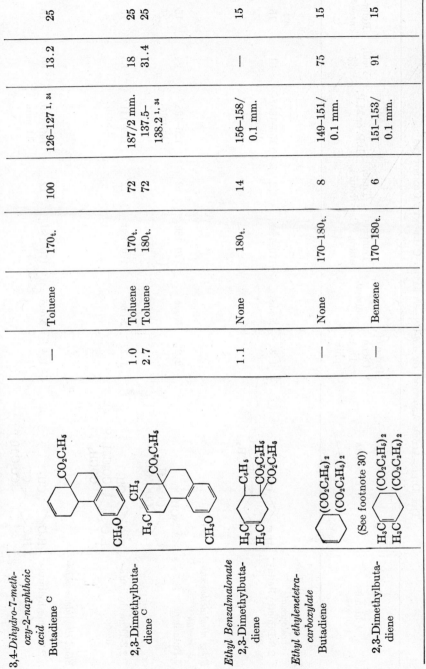

Diene	Product		Solvent	Temp.	Time (hrs.)	B.p. (M.p.)	Yield %	
3,4-Dihydro-7-methoxy-2-naphthoic acid Butadiene [c]	(structure)	—	Toluene	170 [t]	100	126–127 [1,34]	13.2	25
2,3-Dimethylbutadiene [c]	(structure)	1.0 / 2.7	Toluene / Toluene	170 [t] / 180 [t]	72 / 72	187/2 mm. / 137.5–138.2 [1,34]	18 / 31.4	25 / 25
Ethyl Benzalmalonate 2,3-Dimethylbutadiene	(structure)	1.1	None	180 [t]	14	156–158/0.1 mm.	—	15
Ethyl ethylenetetracarboxylate Butadiene	(See footnote 30)	—	None	170–180 [t]	8	149–151/0.1 mm.	75	15
2,3-Dimethylbutadiene	(structure)	—	Benzene	170–180 [t]	6	151–153/0.1 mm.	91	15

* References 69–116 are listed on pp. 172–173.
† For table footnotes see pp. 134–135.

TABLE V—*Continued*

THE DIELS-ALDER ADDITION OF α,β-UNSATURATED CARBONYL COMPOUNDS

Addends	Products	Ratio of Diene to Dienophile	Solvent	Temperature, °C	Time, hours	B.P. or M.P.	Yield, %	References *
Ethyl ethoxymethylene-acetoacetate 2,3-Dimethylbuta-diene		1.3	None	170–180t.	12	153–155/12 mm.	61	15
Ethyl ethylideneaceto-acetate Butadiene		2.2	None	170–180t.	12	126–128/11 mm.	24	15
2,3-Dimethylbuta-diene		1.27	None	170–180t.	12	139–141/2 mm.	83	15
Ethyl ethylidenecyano-acetate 2,3-Dimethylbuta-diene		1.4	None	170–180t.	12	146–149/11 mm.	69	15

Ethyl ethylidene-malonate Butadiene	CH_3 $(CO_2C_2H_5)_2$	3.1	None	170–180t.	14	125–135/11 mm.	54	15
Cyclohexadiene	CH_3 CH_2 CH_2 $(CO_2C_2H_5)_2$	—	None	190–200	12	155–156/11 mm.	—	15
Cyclopentadiene	CH_3 CH_2 $(CO_2C_2H_5)_2$ (See footnote 31) †	1.0	None	170–180	12	138–139/11 mm.	70	15
2,3-Dimethylbuta-diene	H_3C CH_3 H_3C $(CO_2C_2H_5)_2$	1.1	None	170–180t.	12	147–149/11 mm.	80	15
Ethyl isobutyral-malonate 2,3-Dimethylbuta-diene	H_3C $CH(CH_3)_2$ H_3C $(CO_2C_2H_5)_2$	1.7	None	170–180t.	12	155–157/11 mm.	—	15
Ethyl propional-malonate 2,3-Dimethylbuta-diene	H_3C C_2H_5 H_3C $(CO_2C_2H_5)_2$	—	None	180t.	12	149–150/11 mm.	—	15
Methyl 2,3-dimethoxy-benzalpyruvate Butadiene		—	—	—	—	—	0	4

* References 69–116 are listed on pp. 172–173.
† For table footnotes see pp. 134–135.

TABLE V—*Continued*

THE DIELS-ALDER ADDITION OF α,β-UNSATURATED CARBONYL COMPOUNDS

Addends	Products	Ratio of Diene to Dienophile	Solvent	Temperature °C	Time, hours	B.P. or M.P.	Yield, %	References*
Methyl 2,3-dimethoxy-benzalpyruvate (*Cont'd*)								
Cyclopentadiene		18.9	Ethanol	20	48	74–75	50	4
Vinyl phenyl ketone [32]								
Biphenylene-diphenylcyclopenta-dienone		—	Toluene	Reflux	2	273	—	3
Cyclohexadiene	— (See footnote 37) † 3,6-Methano-4-benzoylcyclo-hexene-1	—	Ethanol	100	—	—	0	3
Cyclopentadiene		1.3	Toluene	95–100t.	30	122–124/ 3 mm.	54	3
2,5-Dimethylfuran	— (See footnote 37)	—	—	20	—	—	0	3
2,3-Dimethylbuta-diene	1,2-Dimethyl-4-benzoylcyclo-hexene-1	5.3	—	70	24	163–165/ 6 mm.	37	3

Diene	Dienophile		Solvent	Temp.	Time	M.p./B.p.	Yield %	Ref.
1,4-Diphenylbutadiene	3,6-Diphenyl-4-benzoylcyclohexene-1	1.0	Xylene	140	48	250–255/5 mm.	30 [33]	3
2,3-Diphenylbutadiene	1,2-Diphenyl-4-benzoylcyclohexene-1	1.0	Xylene	140	60	83	46	3
Ethyl sorbate	Ethyl 4-methyl-6-benzoyl-Δ^2-tetrahydrobenzoate (See footnote 35)	0.9	Xylene	140	18	162–163 [34]	70	3
Furan	— (See footnote 37)	—	—	20	—	—	0	3
Isoprene	[structure] CH₃— —COC₆H₅ (See footnote 2)	1.5	Toluene	100 t.	24	120–122/2 mm.[39]	—	3
Methyleneanthrone	[structure] COC₆H₅ / O	0.7	Nitrobenzene	180–190	2.5	192	84	3
2-Methylfuran (sylvan)	— (See footnote 37)	—	—	20	—	—	0	3
(1,8-Naphthylene)-diphenylcyclopentadienone	[structure] C₆H₅ COC₆H₅ C₆H₅	0.4	Toluene	Reflux	2	273	—	3

* References 69–116 are listed on pp. 172–173.
† For table footnotes see pp. 134–135.

TABLE V—*Continued*

THE DIELS-ALDER ADDITION OF α,β-UNSATURATED CARBONYL COMPOUNDS

Addends	Products	Ratio of Diene to Dienophile	Solvent	Temperature, °C	Time, hours	B.P. or M.P.	Yield, %	References *
Vinyl phenyl ketone (Cont'd) α-Phellandrene	(See footnote 2)	—	Ethanol	—	—	183–185/ 2 mm.	37	3
1-Phenyl-4-methyl-butadiene	(See footnotes 2, 36)	0.9	Trichloro-benzene	Reflux	8	61	36	3
Tetraphenylcyclo-pentadienone		0.25	Toluene	Reflux	36	210	95–100	3

* References 69–116 are listed on pp. 172–173.
[1] The melting point recorded is corrected.
[2] The structure is not definitely established.
[3] The reaction was carried out in an atmosphere of nitrogen.
[4] The reaction mixture contains some hydroquinone.
[5] A pressure of 7 to 8 atmospheres was developed in the sealed system.

[6] The product gradually decomposes on standing at room temperature in the sealed tube.

[7] Characterized as the semicarbazone.

[8] Characterized as the oxime.

[9] Characterized as the 2,4-dinitrophenylhydrazone.

[10] The ester of this acid resists hydrolysis so that figure *i* probably is the structure for this adduct and not *ii*.

[11] This aldehyde can be oxidized with silver oxide to the acid obtained from crotonic acid and 1,1,3-trimethylbutadiene (10b).

[12] The enol ether is readily hydrolyzed by dilute mineral acid.

[13] The product was distilled in a stream of carbon dioxide.

[14] Purified by formation of the sodium bisulfite addition product.

[15] The addition product dissociates completely into its components when distilled at atmospheric pressure.

[16] The acid was dehydrogenated to 4-methylisophthalic acid.

[17] The adduct melts at body temperature.

[18] The addition product of benzalacetophenone and bicyclohexenyl failed to give any ketone derivatives.

[19] The bicyclohexenyl-β-benzoylacrylic acid adduct will not add bromine.

[20] These authors in their second paper[1e] show that the methyl group is probably located at C_1.

[21] A mixture of the 2,3-dimethylbutadiene adducts from *cis*- and *trans*-o-methoxycinnamic acid melts at 144–156°.

[22] This acid could not be degraded to the corresponding amine by the Hofmann degradation of the amide.

[23] Selenium dehydrogenation of this product is accompanied by decarboxylation, and 1-phenylphenanthrene results.

[24] Unless the dienophilic ethene is flanked by two carbonyl groups no dehydrogenation is effected by nitrobenzene.

[25] Characterized as the phenylhydrazone.

[26] Saponification of the ester gives the acid, m.p. 159–160°.

[27] Dehydrogenation of this lactone to phthalide was not achieved.

[28] After refluxing in xylene the reaction mixture stood for twelve hours at 0°.

[29] These 1,4-diketones could not be converted to furan derivatives.

[30] Hydrogenation followed by saponification of this tetraethyl ester by ethanolic alkali gives *cis*-hexahydrophthalic acid, m.p. 190–191° (dec.), while acid hydrolysis leads to the *trans* isomer, m.p. 222°.

[31] This bicyclo-(1,2,2)-heptene adds phenyl azide.

[32] Vinyl phenyl ketone was not used directly but was formed in the reaction mixture from the action of potassium acetate upon β-chloropropiophenone. β-Dialkylaminopropiophenone hydrochlorides can also be used.

[33] The analytical figures differed from those calculated by 1%.

[34] The melting point recorded is that of the acid.

[35] Eight isomers are possible from this addition reaction, but no attempt was made to separate all the stereoisomers. 2-Benzoyl-4-methylbenzoic acid was obtained by dehydrogenation.

[36] Sixteen isomers are possible here, but again no attempt was made to isolate the isomers.

[37] No addition occurred between cyclohexadiene, furan, 2-methylfuran, and 2,5-dimethylfuran and vinyl phenyl ketone, prepared from an ethanolic solution of β-chloropropiophenone and potassium acetate. In every case β-ethoxypropiophenone was isolated and characterized as its 2,4-dinitrophenylhydrazone.

[38] The reaction is exothermic.

[39] This adduct decomposes (reverse Diels-Alder) on distillation.

[40] The acid melts at 95–96°.

[41] A trace of acrylic acid in the acrolein causes immediate polymerization of the diene.

[42] An isomeric adduct is formed on prolonged heating.

[43] The *endo*-carbonyl group is lost under these experimental conditions.

TABLE VI

The Diels-Alder Addition of α,β-Unsaturated Nitro Compounds

Addends	Products	Ratio of Diene to Dienophile	Solvent	Temperature, °C	Time, hours	B.P. or M.P.	Yield, %	References*
Nitroamylene (1-nitro-1-pentene)								
Butadiene	4-Nitro-5-propylcyclohexene-1	1.5	None	100-110t.	6	118/11 mm.[1]†	—	36
Cyclopentadiene	3,6-Methano-4-nitro-5-propylcyclohexene-1	1.8	Benzene	105-110t.	8	122-125/14 mm.[1]	72	36
2,3-Dimethylbutadiene	1,2-Dimethyl-4-nitro-5-propylcyclohexene-1	1.1	None	100-110t.	6	146-147/12 mm.[1]	—	36
Nitroethylene								
Cyclopentadiene	3,6-Methano-4-nitrocyclo-hexene-1 (See footnote 7)	5.5	Absolute ether	105-110t.	8	70-90/15 mm.	—	36
Nitropropylene (1-nitro-1-propene)								
Cyclopentadiene	3,6-Methano-4-nitro-5-methylcyclohexene-1	1.1	Glacial acetic acid	118	8	94-95/14 mm.[1]	55	36
β-Nitrostyrene								
Butadiene	4-Nitro-5-phenylcyclohexene-1	1.6	Toluene	150t.	5	103	70	80

Diene	Product	Ratio	Solvent	Temp.	Time (hrs.)	B.p./M.p.	Yield (%)	Ref.
Cyclohexadiene	3,6-Ethano-4-nitro-5-phenylcyclohexene-1	—	—	—	—	138–142/1 mm.	20	79
Cyclopentadiene	3,6-Methano-4-nitro-5-phenylcyclohexene-1	—	—	—	—	145/1 mm.	95	80
2,3-Dimethylbutadiene	1,2-Dimethyl-4-nitro-5-phenylcyclohexene-1 (See footnote 8)	1.8	—	Reflux	2–3	96	82	79
		—	—	—	—	96	82	80
2,5-Dimethylfuran	—	—	—	100	—	—	0	79
		—	—	—	—	—	0	80
1,4-Diphenylbutadiene	3,5,6-Triphenyl-4-nitrocyclohexene-1	—	o-Dichlorobenzene	—	—	130	40	79
		—	o-Dichlorobenzene	—	—	130	80	80
2,3-Diphenylbutadiene	1,2,5-Triphenyl-4-nitrocyclohexene-1	—	—	2, 3	—	175	9	79
		—	o-Dichlorobenzene	—	—	175	9	80
1,3-Diphenylisobenzofuran	1,3-Diphenylisobenzofuran (C_6H_5, C_6H_5, NO_2, C_6H_5)	1.0	Ethanol	Reflux	3	163	100	80
1,3-Diphenyl-5,6-dimethylisobenzofuran	1,3-Diphenyl-5,6-dimethylisobenzofuran (H_3C, H_3C, C_6H_5, C_6H_5, NO_2, C_6H_5)	1.0	Ethanol	Reflux	3	182	100	80

* References 69–116 are listed on pp. 172–173.

† For table footnotes see p. 139.

TABLE VI—*Continued*

THE DIELS-ALDER ADDITION OF α,β-UNSATURATED NITRO COMPOUNDS

Addends	Products	Ratio of Diene to Dienophile	Solvent	Temperature, °C	Time, hours	B.P. or M.P.	Yield, %	References*
β-Nitrostyrene (Cont'd)								
Furan	—	—	—	—	—	—	0	79
							0	80
Isoprene		—	—	—	—	—	7	79
		2.2	—	70–80	2720	52	58	80
	(See footnote 5)					52		
Methyleneanthrone		—	Acetic acid	Reflux	—	255	3 [4]	79
			—	[2]	16	255	3	80
2-Methylfuran	—	—	—	100	—	—	0	79
				—			0	80
α-Phellandrene		—	—	—	—	190/1 mm.	45	79
	(See footnote 5)							80
Tetraphenylcyclopentadienone	Pentaphenylbenzene (See footnotes 2 and 9)	—	Trichlorobenzene	Reflux	—	—	—	80

β-*Nitrostyrene, 3,4-di-methoxy-* **2,3**-Dimethylbutadiene (See footnote 6)	1.5	Xylene	175–180t.	10	129–130	80	96
β-*Nitrostyrene, 3,4-meth-ylenedioxy-* **2,3**-Dimethylbutadiene	1.5	Xylene	175–180t.	10	91	70	96

* References 69–116 are listed on pp. 172–173.
[1] The redistilled adduct is pale yellow.
[2] Oxides of nitrogen evolved.
[3] Five per cent yield of a hydrocarbon ($C_{21}H_{26}$, m.p. 77°) obtained.
[4] Twenty-five per cent yield of bz-1-phenyl-bz-2-nitrobenzanthrone obtained.
[5] The structure of the adduct not established.
[6] The nitro group was reduced electrolytically in an acid medium at a lead cathode. The ethene remained unattacked.
[7] This nitro adduct can be reduced to an amine which is identical with that obtained from the Curtius degradation of the cyclopentadiene–acrylic acid addition product.
[8] This adduct is soluble in aqueous alkali.
[9] The *endo*-carbonyl group is lost under these experimental conditions.

TABLE VII

The Diels-Alder Addition of α,β-Unsaturated Nitriles and Sulfones

Addends	Products	Ratio of Diene to Dienophile	Solvent	Temperature, °C	Time, hours	B.P. or M.P.	Yield, %	References[*]
Crotononitrile								
Cyclopentadiene	2,5-Methano-6-methyl-Δ³-tetrahydrobenzonitrile	1.3	None	150–160t.	6	87–88.5/ 12 mm.	48	100
1,3-Dimethylbutadiene	(See footnote 1)	1.5	None	160t.	5	93–95/ 13.5 mm.	95–100	100
		—	—	140	8	93–95/ 13.5 mm.	95–100	100
Sorbonitrile								
2,3-Dimethylbutadiene	3,4-Dimethyl-6-propenyl-Δ³-tetrahydrobenzonitrile	1.7	None	170t.	4	126.5–127.5/ 10 mm.	42	100
1,3-Dimethylbutadiene	(See footnote 1)	1.7	None	170t.	4	120–121/ 10 mm.	—	101 100

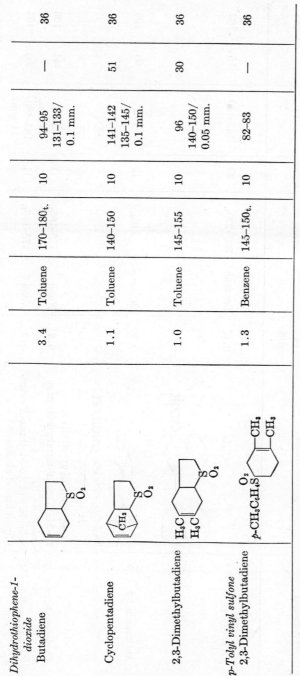

Dihydrothiophene-1-dioxide Butadiene		3.4	Toluene	170–180t.	10	94–95 131–133/ 0.1 mm.	—	36
Cyclopentadiene		1.1	Toluene	140–150	10	141–142 135–145/ 0.1 mm.	51	36
2,3-Dimethylbutadiene		1.0	Toluene	145–155	10	96 140–150/ 0.05 mm.	30	36
p-Tolyl vinyl sulfone 2,3-Dimethylbutadiene		1.3	Benzene	145–150t.	10	82–83	—	36

* References 69–116 are listed on pp. 172–173.
† Structure not definitely established.

TABLE VIII

Diels-Alder Additions with Allyl, Vinyl, and Related Compounds

Addends	Products	Ratio of Diene to Dienophile	Solvent	Temperature, °C	Time, hours	B.P. or M.P.	Yield, %	References *
Allyl alcohol Acecyclone		0.17	Benzene	200–220t.	30	149–150	15	102
Anthracene [1] †		0.5	Benzene	210t.	12	112	90	103
Cyclopentadiene	(See footnote 2) 2,5-Methano-Δ^3-tetrahydrobenzyl alcohol	0.8	None	175–185t.	11	92–95/ 13 mm.	44	103
Cyclopentadiene D	Salicylate of 2,5-Methano-Δ^3-tetra-hydrobenzyl alcohol	0.9	None [3]	175–185t.	11	185–186/ 11 mm.	60	103

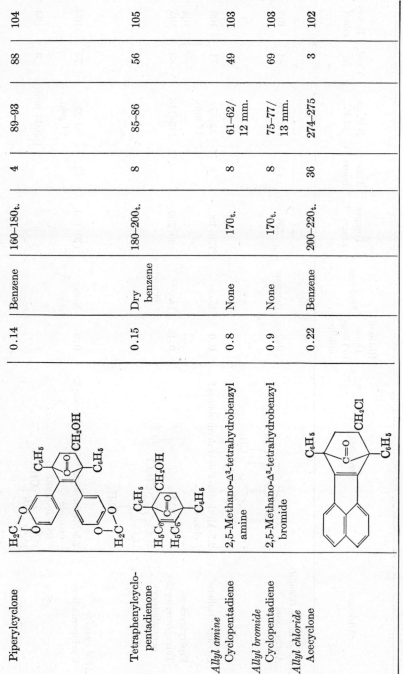

Diene / Dienophile	Moles	Solvent	Temp.	Hrs.	M.p./B.p.	Yield %	Ref.
Piperylcyclone	0.14	Benzene	160–180t.	4	89–93	88	104
Tetraphenylcyclopentadienone	0.15	Dry benzene	180–200t.	8	85–86	56	105
Allyl amine / Cyclopentadiene	0.8	None	170t.	8	61–62/12 mm.	49	103
Allyl bromide / Cyclopentadiene	0.9	None	170t.	8	75–77/13 mm.	69	103
Allyl chloride / Acecyclone	0.22	Benzene	200–220t.	36	274–275	3	102

* References 69–116 are listed on pp. 172–173.
† For table footnotes see p. 152.

TABLE VIII—*Continued*

DIELS-ALDER ADDITIONS WITH ALLYL, VINYL, AND RELATED COMPOUNDS

Addends	Products	Ratio of Diene to Dienophile	Solvent	Temperature, °C	Time, hours	B.P. or M.P.	Yield, %	References *
Allyl chloride (Cont'd)								
Anthracene		0.2	Benzene	220t.	13	115–116	84	103
Cyclopentadiene	2,5-Methano-Δ³-tetrahydrobenzyl chloride	0.6	None	170–180t.	8	54–57/ 11 mm.	74	103
Piperylcyclone	—	—	—	180–200t.	—	—	—8 †	104
Tetraphenylcyclopentadienone		0.15	Dry benzene			115–118	83	105
Allyl cyanide								
Cyclopentadiene	2,5-Methano-Δ³-tetrahydrobenzyl cyanide (See footnote 4)	0.8	None	170–180t.	12	89–93/ 11 mm.	75	103
						165/11 mm.	3	103

		Ratio	Solvent	Temp.	Time	B.p./M.p.	Yield	Ref.
Allyl iodide Cyclopentadiene	2,5-Methano-Δ²-tetrahydrobenzyl iodide	0.97	None	100–105t.[5]	5	105–115/15 mm.	—	103
Allyl isothiocyanate Cyclopentadiene	2,5-Methano-Δ²-tetrahydrobenzyl isothiocyanate	1.0	None	145–155t.	12	120–123/12 mm.	—	103
2,3-Dimethylbutadiene	3,4-Dimethyl-Δ³-tetrahydrobenzyl isothiocyanate	1.1	None	145–155t.	12	137–138/12 mm.	7	103
Anethole Piperylcyclone	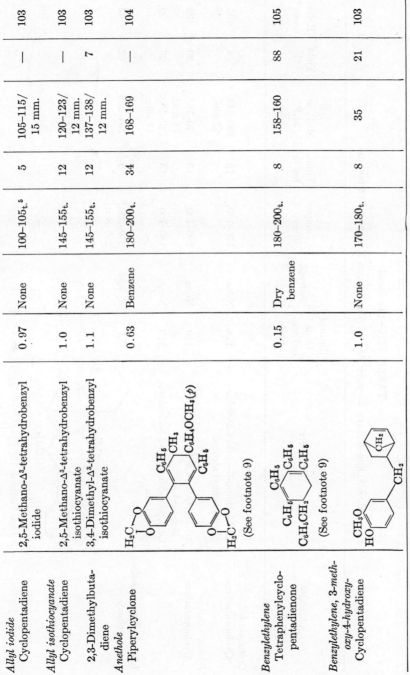 (See footnote 9)	0.63	Benzene	180–200t.	34	168–169	—	104
Benzylethylene Tetraphenylcyclo- pentadienone	(See footnote 9)	0.15	Dry benzene	180–200t.	8	158–160	88	105
Benzylethylene, 3-meth- oxy-4-hydroxy- Cyclopentadiene		1.0	None	170–180t.	8	35	21	103

* References 69–116 are listed on pp. 172–173.
† For table footnotes see p. 152.

TABLE VIII—*Continued*

DIELS-ALDER ADDITIONS WITH ALLYL, VINYL, AND RELATED COMPOUNDS

Addends	Products	Ratio of Diene to Dienophile	Solvent	Temperature, °C	Time, hours	B.P. or M.P.	Yield, %	References *
Crotyl alcohol Cyclopentadiene	2,5-Methano-6-methyl-Δ^3-tetra-hydrobenzyl alcohol	1.8	None	170–180 t.	12	100–115/ 12 mm.	14	103
Dichloroethylene Cyclopentadiene	3,6-Methano-4,5-dichlorocyclo-hexene-1	1.0	None	180–190	15	70–76/ 11 mm.	20	39
	1,4,5,8-*bis*-Methano-2,3-dichloro-Δ^6-octalin	1.0	None	180–190	15	140–150/ 11 mm.	26	39
1,2-Dihydronaphthalene Acecyclone		0.7	Xylene	240–280 } t. 280–300	5	254–256	62	42

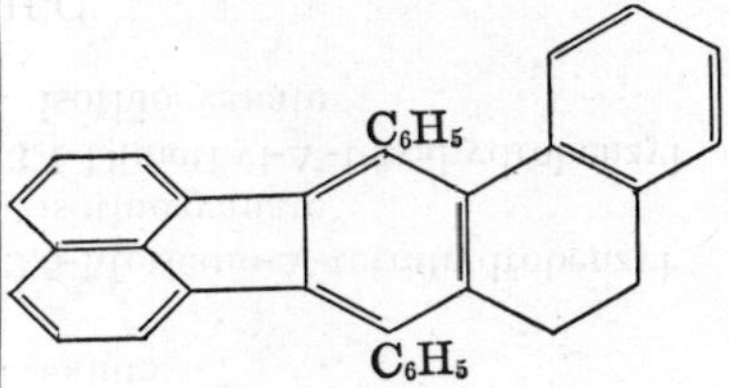

(See footnote 10) †

Diene	Structure		Solvent	Temp.	Time	M.p.	Yield (%)	Ref.
Tetraphenylcyclopentadienone		0.7	Benzene or xylene	230–240t.	12	159–160	60	42
Phencyclone		0.7	Xylene	180–200t.	5	306–308 (dec.)	100	42
Piperylcyclone 1,4-*Dihydronaphthalene*		0.56	Xylene	230–240	7	—	—[8]†	42
Phencyclone		0.9	Xylene	140–150t.	5–6	316–318	—	42
Piperylcyclone		0.7	Xylene	230–240t.	8–9	174–175	63	42

* References 69–116 are listed on pp. 172–173.
† For table footnotes see p. 152.

TABLE VIII—*Continued*

DIELS-ALDER ADDITIONS WITH ALLYL, VINYL, AND RELATED COMPOUNDS

Addends	Products	Ratio of Diene to Dienophile	Solvent	Temperature, °C	Time, hours	B.P. or M.P.	Yield, %	References*
1,4-Dihydronaphthalene (*Cont'd*) Tetraphenylcyclopentadienone		0.67	Xylene	230–240t.	8	155–156	70	42
2,5-Endomethylene-Δ³-tetrahydrobenzaldehyde Cyclopentadiene		2.8	None	170–175t.	8	142–143/18 mm.	—	106
Ethylene Butadiene	Cyclohexene	—	None	200t.	17	82.6–83.6/758 mm.	18	41
Cyclopentadiene	3,6-Methanocyclohexene-1	—	None	190–200t.	23	44–46	74	41
2,3-Dimethylbutadiene	1,2-Dimethylcyclohexene-1	—	None	200t.	21	137.6–138.2/760 mm.	50	41

Diene / Dienophile	Product							
Indene α,α'-Diphenyl-β,β'-isobenzofuran	(structure; C₆H₅, C₆H₅)	—	Absolute ethanol + HCl	100	1	199	70	27
Stilbene Tetraphenylcyclopentadienone	Hexaphenylbenzene	—	None	—	—	421–422	—	43
Styrene Piperylcyclone	(structure; C₆H₅, C₆H₅, C₆H₅, CH₂O)	0.73	Benzene	180–190t.	25	191.5–192.5	—	104
	(See footnote 9)	—	Dry benzene	—	—	157–158	—	105
Tetraphenylcyclopentadienone	(structure; H₅C₆, H₅C₆, C₆H₅, C₆H₅)							
Styrene,3,4-dimethoxy-ω-benzamino- 2,3-Dimethylbutadiene	(See footnote 9)	—	—	—	—	—	0	96
Trichloroethylene Cyclopentadiene (2 moles)	1,4,5,8 *bis*-Methano-2,2,3-trichloro-Δ⁶-octalin (structure)	—	None	175–180t.	—	158–160/11 mm.	—	39

* References 69–116 are listed on pp. 172–173.

TABLE VIII—*Continued*

DIELS-ALDER ADDITIONS WITH ALLYL, VINYL, AND RELATED COMPOUNDS

Addends	Products	Ratio of Diene to Dienophile	Solvent	Temperature, °C	Time, hours	B.P. or M.P.	Yield, %	References*
Vinyl acetate								
Anthracene	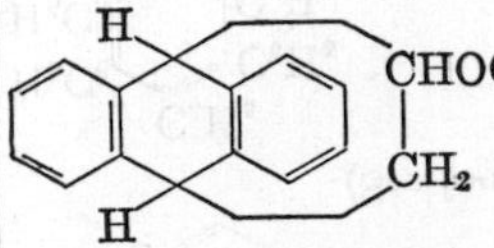	0.24	Xylene	220–230	17	100–101	40	39
Butadiene	4-Acetoxycyclohexene-1	1.1	None	180t.	12	168–175 [6]	6	39
Cyclohexadiene	3,6-Ethano-4-acetoxycyclohexene-1	0.98	None	180t.	12	125 [7]	—	39
Cyclopentadiene	3,6-Methano-4-acetoxycyclohexene-1	0.87	None	185–190t.	10	73–77/14 mm.	43	39
	Acetate of 1,4,5,8-*bis*-methano-Δ^6-β-octalol	0.87	None	185–190t.	10	140–145/14 mm.	6	39
2,3-Dimethylbutadiene	1,2-Dimethyl-4-acetoxy-1-cyclohexene	0.82	None	180t.	12	112 [7]	—	39
Methyl β-camphylate	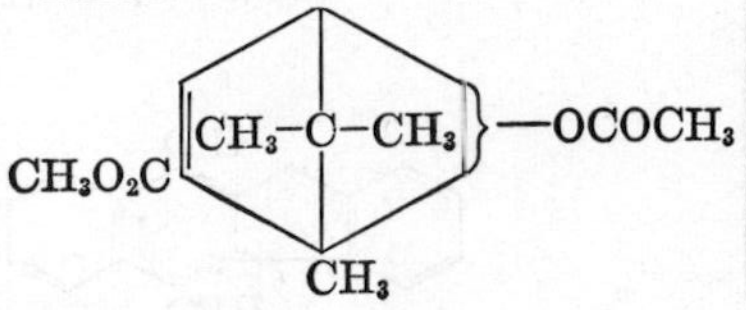	—	None	230	14	142–146/12 mm.	84	40

(See footnote 2) †

Diene / Dienophile	Product	Mole ratio	Solvent	Temp.	Time, hrs	B.p./M.p.	Yield %	Ref.
1,5,5-Trimethyl-cyclopentadiene $CH_3-C-CH_2-OCOCH_3$ / CH_3	mixture	—	None	235–240	20	92–94/12 mm.	88	40
Trimethylcyclo-pentadiene? (Damsky)		—	None	170–180	12	203–212/760 mm.	—	40
Vinylacetic acid — Cyclopentadiene	2,5-Methano-Δ^3-tetrahydrophenyl-acetic acid (See footnote 4)	0.9	None	175–180t.	8	142–143/13 mm.	45	103
Vinyl bromide — Acecyclone	1,4-Diphenyl-2,3-(1,8-naphthylene)-benzene	0.18	Benzene	180–200t.	24	160–161	75	102
Vinyl chloride — Cyclopentadiene	3,6-Methano-4-chloro-1-cyclohexene	0.94	None	170–180t.	15	46–47/12 mm.	44	39
	1,4,5,8-bis-Methano-2-chloro-Δ^6-octalin	0.94	None	170–180t.	15	128–133/12 mm.	24	39
Vinyl butyl ether — Acecyclone	1,4-Diphenyl-2,3-(1,8-naphthylene)-benzene (See footnote 9)	0.22	Benzene	180–200t.	12	160–161	33	102
Vinyl ethyl ether — Acecyclone	1,4-Diphenyl-2,3-(1,8-naphthylene)-benzene (See footnote 9)	0.27	Benzene	180	14	160–161	77	102

* References 69–116 are listed on pp. 172–173.
† For table footnotes see p. 152.

TABLE VIII—*Continued*

DIELS-ALDER ADDITIONS WITH ALLYL, VINYL, AND RELATED COMPOUNDS

Addends	Products	Ratio of Diene to Dienophile	Solvent	Temperature, °C	Time, hours	B.P. or M.P.	Yield, %	References*
Vinyl formate								
Acecyclone	1,4-Diphenyl-2,3-(1,8-naphthylene)-benzene	—	Benzene	180–200t.	16	160–161	77	102
Cyclopentadiene	—	—	None	—	—	—	40–45	39
Vinyl phenyl ether								
Acecyclone	1,4-Diphenyl-2,3-(1,8-naphthylene)-benzene	0.26	Benzene	180–200t.	12	160–161	66.5	102
Vinyl p-tolyl thioether								
Cyclopentadiene	p-CH₃C₆H₄S	1.0	None	180–190t.	15	175–178/ 11 mm.	52	36

* References 69–116 are listed on pp. 172–173.
1 The dienophile used was a 30% aqueous solution of allyl alcohol.
2 The structure of the adduct is not definitely established.
3 A trace of hydroquinone was added to the reaction mixture.
4 No rearrangement of allyl cyanide to crotononitrile occurs during the addition. The same holds true for the acid.
5 Allyl iodide is sensitive to higher temperatures.
6 The reaction product when hydrogenated and hydrolyzed was characterized as cyclohexanol.
7 The melting point of the phenylurethane.
8 The adduct could not be isolated in a pure state.
9 The *endo*-carbonyl group is lost under these experimental conditions.
10 Two hydrogen atoms and the *endo*-carbonyl group were lost under these experimental conditions.

TABLE IX

THE DIELS-ALDER ADDITION OF ACETYLENIC DIENOPHILES WITH ACYCLIC AND CARBOCYCLIC DIENES

Addends	Products	Ratio of Diene to Dienophile	Solvent	Temperature, °C	Time, hours	B.P. or M.P.	Yield, %	References *
Acetylene								
Tetraphenylcyclopenta-dienone	1,2,3,4-Tetraphenylbenzene (See footnotes 3 and 25)	—	—	—	—	190–191	—	43
Acetylenedicarbonitrile								
Cyclopentadiene	3,6-Dihydro-3,6-methanophthal-onitrile	2.5	None	<20	—	44–45	83	70
Diphenylfulvene	3,6-Dihydro-3,6-benzohydryli-denemethanophthalonitrile	1.0	Benzene	100	1	168–169	61	70
Acetylenedicarboxylic acid								
1-Benzylcyclopentadiene	3,6-Methano-3-benzyl-3,6-dihydrophthalic acid	1.0	Ether	Room temp.	24	—	—	49
2-Benzylcyclopentadiene	3,6-Methano-4-benzyl-3,6-dihydrophthalic acid	1.0	Ether	Room temp.	24	—	—	49
Butadiene	3,6-Dihydrophthalic acid	2.3	Dioxane	170–180t.	—	153	34	107
	4,5-Dihydrophthalic acid	—	—	—	—	—	—	107
	2,3-Dihydrophthalic acid	—	—	—	—	123	—	107
	A dihydrobenzoic acid	2.3	Dioxane	170–180t.	—	—	—	107
	(See footnote 2) †							

* References 69–116 are listed on pp. 172–173.
† For table footnotes see p. 160.

TABLE IX—*Continued*

THE DIELS-ALDER ADDITION OF ACETYLENIC DIENOPHILES WITH ACYCLIC AND CARBOCYCLIC DIENES

Addends	Products	Ratio of Diene to Dienophile	Solvent	Temperature, °C	Time, hours	B.P. or M.P.	Yield, %	References*
Acetylenedicarboxylic acid (Cont'd)								
Cyclopentadiene	3,6-Methano-3,6-dihydrophthalic acid	1.03	Ether	0^5 †	—	170	—	50
Methyl α-camphylate	CO_2CH_3 / CO_2H / CO_2H / CH_3-C-CH_3 / CH_3 (See footnote 8)	0.86	Ether	100	12	—	—	51
1,5,5-Trimethylcyclopentadiene	CO_2H / CO_2H / CH_3-C-CH_3 / CH_3 (See footnote 8)	0.55	Ether	120–130t.	12	—	—	51

Diene / Dienophile	Product	d	Solvent	Temp.		B.p./M.p.		%
Trimethylcyclopentadiene? (Damsky)[9]	(See footnote 8)	1.05	Ether	0	12	175–176	—	51
Diphenylacetylene Tetraphenylcyclopentadienone	Hexaphenylbenzene (See footnote 25)	—	None	—	—	421–422	—	43, 65
Ethyl acetylenedicarboxylate 2-Benzylcyclopentadiene	Diethyl 3,6-methano-4-benzyl-3,6-dihydrophthalate	1.09	None	Room temp.[5]	1	222–224/11 mm.[11]	—	52
Cyclohexadiene	Diethyl phthalate (See footnote 10)	1.06	None	200	1	153–160/760 mm.	—	52
trans-trans-1,4-Diphenylbutadiene	Diethyl 3,6-diphenyl-3,6-dihydrophthalate (See footnote 12)	0.98	None	140–150	5	88	90	53
trans-1,2-Dihydrophthalic acid	Diethyl phthalate	1.02	None	220	2	—	—	52
Isosafrole	6,7-Methylenedioxy-3-methyl-3,4-dihydronaphthalene-1,2-dicarboxylic acid anhydride	0.94	None	100[13]	1	178	5	4
α-Phellandrene	Diethyl 4-methylphthalate (See footnote 14)	1.02	None	200	1–2	164/11 mm.[15]	—	52
α-Terpinene[16,17]	Diethyl 3-methyl-6-isopropyl phthalate (See footnote 18)	1.0	None	200	1	180–195/15 mm.	—	55, 56
Tetraphenylcyclopentadienone	Diethyl tetraphenylphthalate (See footnotes 19, 25)	1.0, 0.22	None, None, None	160, 300–310, Reflux	1, 2	205–206, 187–188[1]	96, 22, 0	44, 48, 48
Trimethylcyclopentadiene? (Damsky)[9]	—	0.85	None	260–280	1	174–175/20 mm.	Good	51
1-Vinylnaphthalene	(See footnote 20)	—	—	—	—	—	—[26]	94

* References 69–116 are listed on pp. 172–173.
† For table footnotes see p. 160.

TABLE IX—*Continued*

THE DIELS-ALDER ADDITION OF ACETYLENIC DIENOPHILES WITH ACYCLIC AND CARBOCYCLIC DIENES

Addends	Products	Ratio of Diene to Dienophile	Solvent	Temperature, °C	Time, hours	B.P. or M.P.	Yield, %	References*
Methyl acetylenedicarboxylate								
Anthracene	Dimethyl 9,10-dihydroanthracene-9,10-endo-α,β-maleate (See footnote 21) †	—	None	Room temp.⁵	—	160–161	100	60
9-Bromoanthracene	Dimethyl 9-bromo-9,10-dihydroanthracene-9,10-endo-α,β-maleate	0.5	None	—	—	178	—	45
Butadiene	Dimethyl 3,6-dihydrophthalate (See footnotes 8, 22)	1.0	None	100t.	20	—	—	50
β-Chloroethyl sorbate	[structure: benzene ring with CH₃, CO₂CH₃, CO₂CH₃, CO₂CH₂CH₂Cl]	1.0	Xylene	140	8	190–194/0.25 mm.	—	29
Cycloheptadiene	Dimethyl 3,6-propano-3,6-dihydrophthalate (See footnotes 8, 23)	1.0	None	198	1	—	84	54
Cyclohexadiene⁶	Dimethyl 3,6-ethano-3,6-dihydrophthalate (See footnote 7)	0.9	None	0	1	—	84	50

Diene	Dienophile	Ratio	Solvent	Temp.	Time (hr.)	B.p./M.p.	Yield %	Ref.
Cyclopentadiene	Dimethyl 13,6-methano-3,6-dihydrophthalate	1.0	None	0 [5]	—	134-135/11 mm.	—	50
9,10-Dibromoanthracene	Dimethyl 9,10-dibromo-9,10-dihydroanthracene-9,10-endo-α,β-maleate	—	None	—	—	—	0	45
2,3-Diphenylbutadiene	Dimethyl 4,5-diphenylphthalate	—	None	190	—[24]	—	Poor	57
Methyl α-camphylate	[structure: CO_2CH_3, CH_3–C–CH_3, CO_2CH_3, CH_3]	0.77	Ether	110-115t.	10	162-165/3 mm., 72	94	51
1,2,6-Tetramethylcyclohexadiene (β-pyronene)	Dimethyl 3,4-dimethylphthalate	1.05	—	Pyrolysis 100	2	—	—	58, 59
1,5,5-Tetramethylcyclohexadiene (α-pyronene)	Dimethyl 3-methylphthalate	1.05	—	Pyrolysis 100	2	—	—	58, 59
Tetraphenylcyclopentadienone (See footnote 25)	Dimethyl tetraphenylphthalate	0.3	None	200 / 160	1	258	31 / 100	48, 44
1,5,5-Trimethyl-1,3-cyclopentadiene	[structure: CO_2CH_3, CH_3–C–CH_3, CO_2CH_3, CH_3]	0.7	Ether	Room temp.	—	142-143/12 mm.	74	51

* References 69–116 are listed on pp. 172–173.
† For table footnotes see p. 160.

TABLE IX—*Continued*

The Diels-Alder Addition of Acetylenic Dienophiles with Acyclic and Carbocyclic Dienes

Addends	Products	Ratio of Diene to Dienophile	Solvent	Temperature, °C	Time, hours	B.P. or M.P.	Yield, %	References*
Phenylacetylene Tetraphenylcyclopentadienone	Pentaphenylbenzene (See footnote 25) †	—	None	—	—	246–247	—	43
Phenylbenzoylacetylene Tetraphenylcyclopentadienone	C_6H_5 C_6H_5 COC_6H_5 H_5C_6 H_5C_6 C_6H_5 (See footnote 25)	0.54	None	195	0.16	340–341 [1]	92	48
Phenylpropiolic acid Tetraphenylcyclopentadienone	Pentaphenylbenzoic acid (See footnote 25)	1.0	None	190	1	345	—	43 44
Tetraphenylcyclopentadienone B	Methyl pentaphenylbenzoate (See footnote 25)	1.0	None	190	0.5	342	100	44
Phenylpropiolic aldehyde Tetraphenylcyclopentadienone	Pentaphenylbenzaldehyde (See footnote 25)	—	—	—	—	—	—	43
Phenylpropiolic nitrile Tetraphenylcyclopentadienone	Pentaphenylbenzonitrile (See footnote 25)	—	None	—	—	271–272	—	43

Propargyl aldehyde

Diene	Product	Ratio	Solvent	Temp.	Time	B.p./M.p.	Yield %	Ref.
2,3-Dimethylbutadiene		1.0	None	150-200t.	48	77-78/12 mm.	—	5
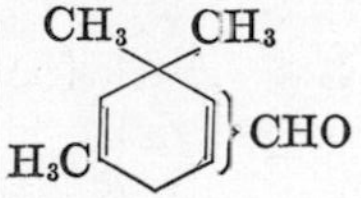 1,1,3-Trimethylbutadiene (structure: H_3C with CH_3, CH_3, CHO) (See footnote 4)		1.0	None	150-200t.	48	82-84/12 mm.	—	5

Propiolic acid

Diene	Product	Ratio	Solvent	Temp.	Time	B.p./M.p.	Yield %	Ref.
Cyclopentadiene	2,5-Methano-2,5-dihydrobenzoic acid	1.0	None	Room temp.	—	93-94	44	9
1-Ethynyl-6-methoxy-3,4-dihydronaphthalene [B]	Methyl 7-methoxy-9,10-dihydrophenanthrene-2-carboxylate	0.5	None or dioxane	Reflux	8	86	45 [26]	47
	Methyl 7-methoxy-9,10-dihydrophenanthrene-1-carboxylate	0.5	None or dioxane	Reflux	8	Oil	10 [27]	47

Tetrolic acid

Diene	Product	Ratio	Solvent	Temp.	Time	B.p./M.p.	Yield %	Ref.
Tetraphenylcyclopentadienone (See footnote 25)	Tetraphenyl-o-toluic acid	—	None	200t.	1	302	—	44
Tetraphenylcyclopentadienone [C]	Ethyl tetraphenyl-o-toluate	0.4	None	200t.	1	205	90	44

Tetrolic aldehyde

Diene	Product	Ratio	Solvent	Temp.	Time	B.p./M.p.	Yield %	Ref.
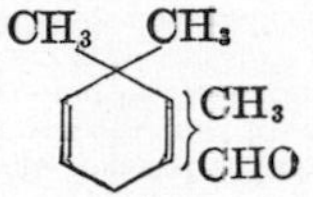 1,1-Dimethylbutadiene (structure: CH_3, CH_3, CHO) (See footnote 4)		1.0	None	150-180t.	48	100-105/12 mm.	—	5
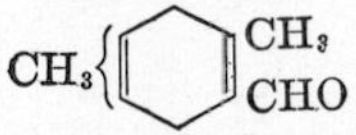 Isoprene (structure: CH_3, CH_3, CHO) (See footnote 4)		1.0	None	130t.	48	90-95/12 mm.	—	5

* References 69–116 are listed on pp. 172–173.
† For table footnotes see p. 160.

FOOTNOTES TO TABLE IX

1 The melting point is corrected.

2 The position of the double bonds is not definitely established.

3 The same tetraphenylbenzene was obtained from the tetraphenylcyclopentadienone-maleic anhydride adduct.

4 The structure of the adduct has not been established.

5 The reaction is exothermic.

6 The product used was about 30% cyclohexadiene.

7 This dihydro ester can be catalytically reduced over colloidal palladium to give, after saponification, the Δ^1-tetrahydro acid. This is identical with that obtained by Diels and Alder [12] from cyclohexadiene and dibromomaleic anhydride.

8 This addition product was not isolated but was immediately reduced to the Δ^1-tetrahydro adduct.

9 The structure of this diene is not definitely known.

10 At the temperature of this reaction the primary addition product is unstable and loses a molecule of ethylene.

11 The acid melts at 232°.

12 The reaction product was dehydrogenated to 3,6-diphenylphthalic acid and this in turn converted to terphenyl.

13 The reaction mixture was heated for an additional five minutes at 200°.

14 A molecule of isopropylethylene is lost during the reaction.

15 For identification the diester was saponified to 4-methylphthalic acid.

16 The reagent used in this reaction was that obtained directly from the dehydration of α-terpineol.

17 During the dehydration of α-terpineol to α-terpinene an isomeric product containing a conjugated diene system is formed, for it also reacts with ethyl acetylenedicarboxylate. Unlike the α-terpinene adduct, this adduct does not lose ethylene during the distillation.

18 Ethylene is evolved during the reaction.

19 This diester cannot be saponified.

20 The reaction gave an ill-defined oily condensation product.

21 The anhydride from this diester is identical with that obtained from anthracene and dibromomaleic anhydride followed by the elimination of the bromine. Bromine removed four hydrogen atoms from the Δ^1-tetrahydro ester.

22 Methyl $\Delta^{1, 4}$-dihydrophthalate was reduced to the Δ^1-tetrahydro acid to give phthalic acid.

23 There is no thermal cleavage of the propano bridge.

24 The reaction mixture was heated until it was a deep brown.

25 The endo-carbonyl group is lost as a molecule of carbon monoxide.

26 The acid melts at 206–207°.

27 The acid melts at 152–153°.

TABLE X

THE DIELS-ALDER ADDITION OF ACETYLENIC DIENOPHILES TO HETEROCYCLIC DIENES

Addends	Products	Ratio of Diene to Dienophile	Solvent	Temperature, °C	Time, hours	B.P. or M.P.	Yield, %	References*
Acetylenedicarboxylic acid								
Furan (2 moles)		2+	None	100	1.5	158 (dec.)	—	61
N-Methylpyrrole		0.98	Ether	35	—	222–223 (dec.)	Quant.	108
		0.98	Ether	35	—	164	—	108
Ethyl acetylenedicar-boxylate								
Ethyl isodehydro-acetate	Triethyl 3,5-dimethyltrimellitate (See footnote 3) †	1.0	None	190–200	1	200–218/12 mm.[4]	50	54

* References 69–116 are listed on pp. 172–173.
† For table footnotes see p. 169.

161

TABLE X—*Continued*

THE DIELS-ALDER ADDITION OF ACETYLENIC DIENOPHILES TO HETEROCYCLIC DIENES

Addends	Products	Ratio of Diene to Dienophile	Solvent	Temperature, °C	Time, hours	B.P. or M.P.	Yield, %	References *
Ethyl acetylenedicarboxylate (Cont'd)								
Furan	Diethyl 3,6-epoxy-3,6-dihydrophthalate (See footnote 1) †	1.25	None	100	18	—	—	54
Methyl coumalinate	1,2-Diethyl 4-methyl trimellitate (See footnote 2)	—	None	155–200	1	180–205/12 mm.[7]	—	54
2-Methylfuran (sylvan)	Diethyl 3,6-epoxy-3-methyl-3,6-dihydrophthalate (See footnote 1)	0.86	Benzene	80	3	—	—	54
γ-Methylpyronone		1.20	None	100	10	—	—	62
	Diethyl 3-methyl-5-hydroxyphthalate (See footnote 6)	0.87	None	170–210	0.5	—[5]	—	54
Methyl acetylenedicarboxylate								
2,5-Dimethylfuran	Dimethyl 3,6-epoxy-3,6-dimethyl-3,6-dihydrophthalate (See footnote 1)	1.0	None	100	10	—	Quant.	62
1,2-Dimethylimidazole	CO_2CH_3 CO_2CH_3 CO_2CH_3 CO_2CH_3 CH_3 N N H_3C CH_3 (See footnote 10)	0.5	Absolute ether	Room temp.	—	163 (dec.)[8]	—	109

		Moles	Solvent	Temp.	Time (hr.)	M.p.	Yield (%)	Reference
N-α-Dimethyl-indole	(structure: C=CH, CO$_2$CH$_3$, CO$_2$CH$_3$; CH$_3$, CH$_3$)	0.5	None	Room temp.	72	129 [9]	—	110
3,5-Dimethylpyra-zole	C$_{16}$H$_{22}$O$_4$N$_4$	1.0	Ether	Room temp.	24	188 [11]	4	109
	C$_{11}$H$_{14}$O$_4$N$_2$	1.0	Ether	Room temp.	24	58	—	109
2,3-Dimethylpyr-role	(structure: H$_3$C, H$_3$C, CCO$_2$CH$_3$, H H—CCO$_2$CH$_3$) (See footnote 12)	1.0	Petroleum ether and benzene	Room temp.	—	98	—	109
	(structure: H$_3$C, H$_3$C, N, H, CCO$_2$CH$_3$, CH$_2$O$_2$CCH)	1.0	Petroleum ether and benzene	Room temp.	—	132	—	109
2,4-Dimethylpyr-role	(structure: H$_3$C, N, H, CH$_3$; CH, CO$_2$CH$_3$; CH, CO$_2$CH$_3$; H$_3$C, N, H, CH$_3$)	2.0	Benzene	Room temp.	24	165	Quant.	108
Furan	Dimethyl 3,6-epoxy-3,6-dihydrophthalate (See footnote 1)	1.04	None	100t.	18	—	100	61
Furan (2 moles)	(structure: CO$_2$CH$_3$, CO$_2$CH$_3$)	2.0+	None	100t.	18	148 (dec.)	—	62 / 61

163

* References 69–116 are listed on pp. 172–173.
† For table footnotes see p. 169.

TABLE X—*Continued*

THE DIELS-ALDER ADDITION OF ACETYLENIC DIENOPHILES TO HETEROCYCLIC DIENES

Addends	Products	Ratio of Diene to Dienophile	Solvent	Temperature, °C	Time, hours	B.P. or M.P.	Yield, %	References*
Methyl acetylenedicarboxylate (Cont'd) Isoquinoline		0.5	Absolute ether	0	72	165–167[13] †	31	111
		0.5	Absolute ether	0	48	167–169	54	112
	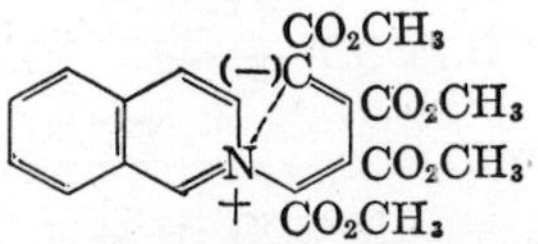	0.5	Ether	0	48	124–125[14]	2	112
2-Methylfuran	Dimethyl 3,6-epoxy-3-methyl-3,6-dihydrophthalate (See footnote 1)	1.20	—	100	10	—	—	62
4,(5)-Methylimidazole	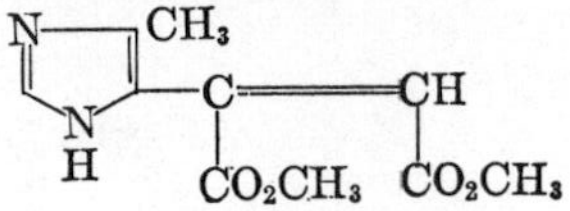 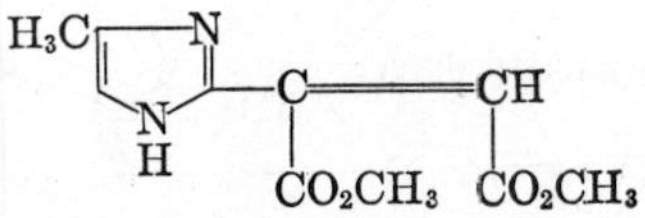 (See footnote 15)	1.0	Absolute ether	Room temp.	—	103–104	—	109

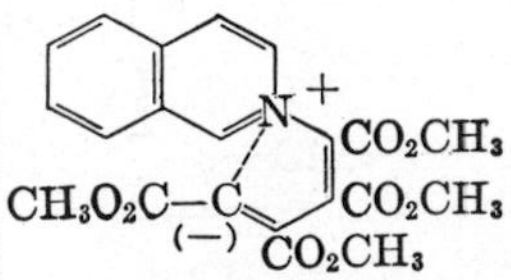

164

Compound		Solvent	Temperature	Hours		Yield	References
N-Methylindole	0.47	—	Room temp.	2400^{16}	157–158	—	109
α-Methylpyrrole	0.97	Petroleum ether	Room temp.	12	52	—	109
(See footnote 12)	1.12	Benzene	Room temp.	12	111	Quant.	113 109
N-Methylpyrrole (See footnote 17)	0.5	Benzene	Room temp.	24	145–148	Quant.	108
α-Picoline	0.55	Ether	0	72	126	—	114
	0.55	Ether	0	72	138	—	114

165

* References 69–116 are listed on pp. 172–173.
† For table footnotes see p. 169.

TABLE X—Continued

THE DIELS-ALDER ADDITION OF ACETYLENIC DIENOPHILES TO HETEROCYCLIC DIENES

Addends	Products	Ratio of Diene to Dienophile	Solvent	Temperature, °C	Time, hours	B.P. or M.P.	Yield, %	References*
Methyl acetylenedicarboxylate (Cont'd)								
Pyrazole		1.0	Ether	Room temp.	48	158	—	109
	isomer	1.0	Ether	Room temp.	48	139	—	109
		—	Absolute ether	Room temp.	5	124	—	115
		—	Absolute ether	Room temp.	24	124–125	—	111
Pyridine		—	Absolute ether	Room temp.	24	187	—	111

			Solvent	Temp.	Time	M.p.		Ref.
Quinaldine		—	Ether	0	6	204	—	111
	(See footnote 18) †	—	Ether	Room temp.	48	174–175	—	111
Quinoline		—	Absolute ether	0	72	181–182	—	111
		—	Benzene	Reflux	0.5	177	—	115

* References 69–116 are listed on pp. 172–173.
† For table footnotes see p. 169.

167

TABLE X—*Continued*

THE DIELS-ALDER ADDITION OF ACETYLENIC DIENOPHILES TO HETEROCYCLIC DIENES

Addends	Products	Ratio of Diene to Dienophile	Solvent	Temperature, °C	Time, hours	B.P. or M.P.	Yield, %	References *
Methyl acetylenedicarboxylate (*Cont'd*) Stilbazole		—	Ether	Room temp.	72	187–188	—	116
		—	Ether	—	—	205–206	—	116
		—	Xylene	Reflux	—	192	—	116

| 2,3,4-Trimethyl-pyrrole | H_3C CH_3 CO_2CH_3 H_3C N $CHCO_2CH_3$ H (See footnote 10) | 1.0 | 0 | — | 137–138 | — | 109 |

* References 69–116 are listed on pp. 172–173.

1 The primary addition product was not isolated, but was reduced without purification to the Δ^1-tetrahydro adduct.

2 During the reaction 230 ml. of carbon dioxide was collected. The theoretical amount is 350 ml.

3 During the reaction 1800 ml. of carbon dioxide was collected. The theoretical amount is 2700 ml.

4 The acid melts at 168°.

5 Saponification of the ester with hydrochloric acid at 100° effects a simultaneous decarboxylation, for the resulting acid agrees with the 3-hydroxy-5-methylbenzoic acid (m.p. 208°) of Bishop and Tingle (Dissertation, Münich, 1889).

6 During the reaction 580 ml. of carbon dioxide was evolved. The theoretical amount is 800 ml.

7 Trimellitic acid melts at 231°.

8 The tetramethyl 1,8-dimethyl-1,8-dihydropyrimidazole-4,5,6,7-tetracarboxylate crystallizes in red needles.

9 The addition product crystallizes in reddish-yellow needles.

10 No isomeric product was obtained analogous to the addition of the same ester to 2,3-dimethylpyrrole.

11 This reaction product (base : ester = 2 : 1) settles out of the reaction mixture; the second product is recovered from the mother liquors.

12 It is the author's conclusion, although there is no evidence, that the higher-melting isomer is the *trans* form. Both isomers can be hydrogenated to the same dihydro adduct, identical with that from maleic anhydride and 2,3-dimethylpyrrole.

13 The crystals are brick-red.

14 These crystals are greenish yellow and have a greenish-yellow fluorescence.

15 The point of attachment of the dimethyl maleate residue to the methylimidazole nucleus has not been established.

16 The same product is obtained if the reaction mixture is allowed to stand 700 hours.

17 Yellowish-green crystals from methanol.

18 It is not possible to convert the labile adduct into the stable adduct by thermal means. This is the exception to the rule.

169

TABLE XI

Adducts from Anthracene-C₄O₃ (LXIX, p. 84)

Addends	Products	Ratio of Diene to Dienophile	Solvent	Temperature, °C	Time, hours	B.P. or M.P.	Yield, %	References *
Anthracene-C₄O₃ Anthracene-C₄O₃	(See footnote 1)	1.0	Nitrobenzene or phenol	Reflux	8	360	30 [2]	45
Butadiene		3.3	Benzene	100ₜ.	72	212	100	45
Cyclopentadiene		124	—	Reflux	0.75	279–280	—	45

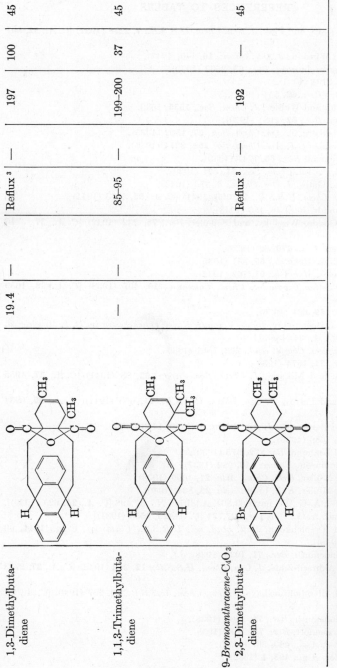

Diene							
1,3-Dimethylbutadiene	45	100	197	—	Reflux[3]	—	19.4
1,1,3-Trimethylbutadiene	45	37	199–200	—	85–95	—	—
9-*Bromoanthracene*-C_4O_3 2,3-Dimethylbutadiene	45	—	192	—	Reflux[3]	—	—

* References 69–116 are listed on pp. 172–173.
[1] Carbon monoxide and carbon dioxide are the other products of the reaction.
[2] The yield is poorer if phenol is used as the solvent.
[3] The reaction is exothermic.

REFERENCES TO TABLES

[69] Arbuzov, Zinov'eva, and Fink, *J. Gen. Chem. U.S.S.R.*, **7**, 2278 (1937) [*C. A.*, **32**, 507 (1938)].

[70] Blomquist and Winslow, *J. Org. Chem.*, **10**, 149 (1945).

[71] Kuhn and Wagner-Jauregg, *Ber.*, **63**, 2662 (1930).

[72] Clar, *Ber.*, **64**, 2194 (1931).

[73] Diels and Alder, *Ber.*, **62**, 554 (1929).

[74] Robinson, Todd, and Walker, *J. Chem. Soc.*, **1935**, 1530.

[75] Diels and Alder, *Ber.*, **62**, 2081 (1929).

[76] Fieser and Hershberg, *J. Am. Chem. Soc.*, **57**, 1508 (1935).

[77] Fieser and Hershberg, *J. Am. Chem. Soc.*, **58**, 2314 (1936).

[78] Fieser and Seligman, *Ber.*, **68**, 1747 (1935).

[79] Allen and Bell, *J. Am. Chem. Soc.*, **61**, 521 (1939).

[80] Allen, Bell, and Gates, *J. Org. Chem.*, **8**, 373 (1943).

[81] Petrov, *J. Gen. Chem. U.S.S.R.*, **11**, 309 (1941) [*C. A.*, **35**, 5873 (1941)].

[82] Alder and Schmidt, *Ber.*, **76**, 183 (1943).

[83] Langenbeck, Gödde, Weschky, and Schaller, *Ber.*, **75**, 232 (1942) [*C. A.*, **37**, 3746 (1943)].

[84] Diels and Alder, *Ann.*, **470**, 62 (1929).

[85] Weiss and Koltes, *Monatsh.*, **65**, 351 (1935).

[86] Weiss and Abeles, *Monatsh.*, **61**, 162 (1932).

[87] Wichterle, *Collection Czechoslov. Chem. Commun.*, **10**, 497 (1938) [*C. A.*, **33**, 1659 (1939)].

[88] Lehmann, *Ber.*, **69**, 631 (1936).

[89] Tishchenko and Bogomolov, *Byull. Vesoyuz. Khim. Obschchestva im D. I. Mendeleeva*, **1939**, No. 3–4, 35 [*C. A.*, **34**, 4386 (1940)].

[90] Dupont and Dulou, *Compt. rend.*, **202**, 1861 (1936).

[91] Lehmann, *Ber.*, **71**, 1874 (1938).

[92] Kotake, Mita, and Mikami, *J. Chem. Soc. Japan*, **62**, 88 (1941) [*C. A.*, **37**, 4055 (1943)].

[93] Natsinskaya and Petrov, *J. Gen. Chem. U.S.S.R.*, **11**, 665 (1941) [*C. A.*, **35**, 6934 (1941)].

[94] Bergmann and Bergmann, *J. Am. Chem. Soc.*, **59**, 1443 (1937).

[95] Clar, *Ber.*, **69**, 1686 (1936).

[96] Sugasawa and Kodama, *Ber.*, **72**, 675 (1939).

[97] Meggy and Robinson, *Nature*, **140**, 282 (1937).

[98] Goldberg and Müller, *Helv. Chim. Acta*, **21**, 1699 (1938).

[99] Goldberg and Müller, *Helv. Chim. Acta*, **23**, 831 (1940).

[100] I. G. Farbenind. A.-G., Fr. pat. 663,564. Addition No. 37,498 [*C. A.*, **24**, 625 (1930)].

[101] I. G. Farbenind. A.-G., Ger. pat. 527,771 [*C. A.*, **25**, 4556 (1931)].

[102] Abramov and Tsyplenkova, *Bull. acad. sci. U.R.S.S., Classe sci. chim.*, **1944**, 60 [*C. A.*, **39**, 1639 (1945)].

[103] Alder and Windemuth, *Ber.*, **71**, 1939 (1938).

[104] Arbuzov and Akhmed-Zade, *J. Gen. Chem. U.S.S.R.*, **12**, 212 (1942) [*C. A.*, **37**, 2733 (1943)].

[105] Abramov and Mitropolitanskaya, *J. Gen. Chem. U.S.S.R.*, **10**, 207 (1940) [*C. A.*, **34** 7284 (1940)].

[106] Alder and Windemuth, *Ber.*, **71**, 2409 (1938).

[107] Alder and Backendorf, *Ber.*, **71**, 2199 (1938).

[108] Diels and Alder, *Ann.*, **490**, 267 (1931).

[109] Diels and Alder, *Ann.*, **498**, 1 (1932).

[110] Diels and Alder, *Ann.*, **490,** 277 (1931).
[111] Diels and Alder, *Ann.*, **498,** 16 (1932).
[112] Diels and Harms, *Ann.*, **525,** 73 (1936).
[113] Diels and Alder, *Ann.*, **486,** 211 (1931).
[114] Diels and Pistor, *Ann.*, **530,** 87 (1937).
[115] Diels and Alder, *Ann.*, **510,** 87 (1934).
[116] Diels and Möller, *Ann.*, **516,** 45 (1935).

CHAPTER 3

THE PREPARATION OF AMINES BY REDUCTIVE ALKYLATION

WILLIAM S. EMERSON

Monsanto Chemical Company
Dayton, Ohio

CONTENTS

174

INTRODUCTION

Reductive alkylation is the term applied to the process of introducing alkyl groups into ammonia or a primary or secondary amine by means of an aldehyde or ketone in the presence of a reducing agent. The present discussion is limited to those reductive alkylations in which the reducing agent is hydrogen and a catalyst or "nascent" hydrogen, usually from a metal-acid combination; most of these reductive alkylations have been carried out with hydrogen and a catalyst. The principal variation excluded is that in which the reducing agent is formic acid or one of its derivatives; this modification is known as the Leuckart reaction.

The process of reductive alkylation of ammonia consists in the addition of ammonia to a carbonyl compound and reduction of the addition compound or its dehydration product. The reaction usually is carried out in ethanol solution when the reduction is to be effected catalytically.

$$RCHO + NH_3 \rightleftarrows RCHOHNH_2 \searrow^{2(H)}$$
$$\updownarrow \qquad \rightarrow RCH_2NH_2$$
$$RCH{=}NH \nearrow^{2(H)}$$

Since the primary amine is formed in the presence of the aldehyde it may react in the same way as ammonia, yielding an addition compound, a Schiff's base ($RCH=NCH_2R$), and, finally, a secondary amine. Similarly, the primary amine may react with the imine, forming an addition product which also is reduced to a secondary amine.[1] Finally, the

$$RCH{=}NH + RCH_2NH_2 \rightleftarrows \underset{\underset{NH_2}{|}}{RCHNHCH_2R} \xrightarrow{2(H)} (RCH_2)_2NH + NH_3$$

secondary amine may react with either the aldehyde or the imine to give products which are reduced to tertiary amines.

$$(RCH_2)_2NH + RCHO \rightleftarrows \underset{\underset{OH}{|}}{(RCH_2)_2NCHR} \xrightarrow{2(H)} (RCH_2)_3N + H_2O$$

$$(RCH_2)_2NH + RCH{=}NH \rightleftarrows \underset{\underset{NH_2}{|}}{(RCH_2)_2NCHR} \xrightarrow{2(H)} (RCH_2)_3N + NH_3$$

Similar reactions may occur when the carbonyl compound employed is a ketone.

As indicated by the equation above, in an alkylation by an aldehyde a primary alkyl group becomes attached to the nitrogen atom. When the alkylation is effected by a ketone a secondary alkyl group is introduced. The method cannot be used for the attachment of a tertiary alkyl group to the nitrogen atom.

Various types of secondary and tertiary amines can be prepared by reductive alkylation. Some symmetrical secondary amines are prepared by the reduction of a mixture of two moles of an aldehyde or a ketone and one mole of ammonia. Symmetrical and unsymmetrical secondary

$$2R'COR + NH_3 + 4(H) \rightarrow \left(\underset{R}{\overset{R'}{>}}CH\right)_2 NH + 2H_2O$$

(R = hydrogen or alkyl)

amines are available from the reduction of a mixture of a primary amine and an aldehyde or ketone. An experimental variation in the prepara-

$$R'COR + R''NH_2 + 2(H) \rightarrow \underset{R}{\overset{R'}{>}}CHNHR'' + H_2O$$

(R = hydrogen or alkyl)

[1] Schwoegler and Adkins, *J. Am. Chem. Soc.*, **61**, 3499 (1939).

tion of secondary amines consists in the isolation and subsequent reduction of the Schiff's base (see p. 189).

$$RCHO + R'NH_2 \rightarrow RCH{=}NR' \xrightarrow{2(H)} RCH_2NHR'$$

Certain tertiary amines containing three identical groups attached to the nitrogen atom can be prepared from ammonia and a carbonyl compound. Those containing two identical groups can be prepared either from a secondary amine and one mole of an aldehyde or a ketone, or from a primary amine and two moles of an aldehyde or a ketone. Te. tiary amines containing three dissimilar alkyl groups can be prepar d only from a secondary amine and a carbonyl compound.

$$3R'COR + NH_3 + 6(H) \rightarrow \left(\begin{matrix} R' \\ R \end{matrix}\!\!>\!\!CH\right)_{\!3} N$$

$$2R'COR + R''NH_2 + 4(H) \searrow$$
$$R'COR + \begin{matrix} R' \\ R \end{matrix}\!\!>\!\!CHNHR'' + 2(H) \nearrow \left(\begin{matrix} R' \\ R \end{matrix}\!\!>\!\!CH\right)_{\!2} NR''$$

$$R'COR + R''R'''NH + 2(H) \rightarrow \begin{matrix} R' \\ R \end{matrix}\!\!>\!\!CHNR''R'''$$

(R = hydrogen or alkyl)

If an amine to be used in a reductive alkylation is one which itself is prepared by a process of reduction it may be possible to employ the precursor instead of the amine (see p. 183). For example, di-n-butyl-aniline is prepared conveniently by hydrogenation of a mixture of nitrobenzene and n-butyraldehyde.[2]

$$C_6H_5NO_2 + 2n\text{-}C_3H_7CHO + 5H_2 \rightarrow C_6H_5N(C_4H_9)_2 + 4H_2O$$

The usefulness of each of the various reactions formulated above is modified by the structural features of the carbonyl compound and of the amine employed or formed. A carbonyl compound which has little tendency to undergo addition of ammonia or an amine may be reduced largely to the carbinol, with the result that the reductive alkylation fails. Similarly, structural features of the particular reactants may favor the formation of an amine or amines of a degree of alkylation different from that desired. Such effects of structure are considered in detail in the next section. It may be said at the outset that in a great many preparations it has been found possible to obtain high yields of amines of the desired degree of alkylation by proper choice of the conditions.

[2] Emerson and Uraneck, *J. Am. Chem. Soc.*, **63**, 749 (1941).

SCOPE AND UTILITY OF THE REACTIONS

Preparation of Primary Amines (Table IX)

From Aliphatic Aldehydes. The lower aliphatic aldehydes (those containing four carbon atoms or less) are too reactive to be of much value in the usual reductive alkylation processes for the preparation of primary amines. Thus, formaldehyde and ammonia react rapidly to form hexamethylenetetramine, which is reduced to a mixture of methylamine and trimethylamine.[3] With acetaldehyde, propionaldehyde, and the butyraldehydes the primary amines may be contaminated not only by the corresponding secondary amines but also by heterocyclic amines. For example, from a reductive alkylation of ammonia with n-butyraldehyde over Raney nickel catalyst, the products isolated were n-butylamine (32%), di-n-butylamine (12%), and 2-n-propyl-3,5-diethylpyridine (23%).[4] Thus, even though good yields of ethylamine (68%)

$$3CH_3CH_2CH_2CHO + NH_3 \rightarrow$$

and n-butylamine (69%) have been obtained by use of the aldehydes and nickel catalyst [5] the method does not appear to have found commercial application in the synthesis of the simple amines. However, it is possible that the industrial synthesis of methylamine from methanol and ammonia in the presence of copper chromite catalyst is really of the reductive alkylation type. The alcohol may be in equilibrium with the aldehyde and hydrogen, and these may react with the ammonia to yield methylamine, the formation of which would be favored by the very large ratio of ammonia to formaldehyde actually present. The facts that primary and secondary alcohols are converted to the corresponding primary amines on heating with ammonia and a catalyst, whereas tertiary alcohols do not react, afford strong support for the view that amination of alcohols proceeds through dehydrogenation to aldehydes or ketones.

Aliphatic aldehydes containing five or more carbon atoms can be converted to the primary amines in yields of 60% or better by reduction in the presence of an excess of ammonia and with a nickel catalyst.[5] The secondary amines, formed to a lesser extent, are easily removed in the distillation of the product. The usefulness of the method in the

[3] Meister, Lucius, and Bruning, Ger. pat. 148,054 [Frdl. **1**, 26 (1905)].
[4] Winans and Adkins, J. Am. Chem. Soc., **55**, 2051 (1933).
[5] Mignonac, Compt. rend., **172**, 223 (1921).

preparation of saturated primary amines containing primary alkyl groups of more than four carbon atoms apparently is limited only by the availability of the corresponding aldehydes. Because of the fact that only one operation is required, reductive alkylation is likely to be preferred to other methods of conversion of aldehydes to primary amines, such as the reduction of oximes and phenylhydrazones. A comparison of the yields of n-heptylamine which have been obtained by these and other methods (Table I, p. 202) illustrates the value of the reductive alkylation.

There are few data concerning the effects of structure in the preparation of primary aliphatic amines. A few unsaturated aldehydes, such as acrolein, crotonaldehyde, and cinnamaldehyde, have given the saturated primary amines in unspecified yields.[6,7] Glucose has been converted to the corresponding primary amine in 26% yield.[8] Isobutyraldehyde has been converted to isobutylamine, but in unspecified yield.[9] Phenylacetaldehyde has given a 64% yield of β-phenylethylamine.[1]

From Aromatic Aldehydes. Benzaldehyde is converted to benzylamine in a yield of about 90% by the hydrogenation of benzaldehyde in the presence of an equimolar quantity of ammonia.[10] The reaction is carried out with ethanol as the solvent and with Raney nickel catalyst. A small amount (about 7%) of dibenzylamine is formed also, but the boiling points of the two products are widely separated. The secondary amine probably is formed not only from the primary amine and the aldehyde (see p. 176) but also from a condensation product of the hydro-

$$3C_6H_5CHO + 2NH_3 \rightarrow C_6H_5CH \underset{N=CHC_6H_5}{\overset{N=CHC_6H_5}{\diagup}} \xrightarrow[Ni]{3H_2} (C_6H_5CH_2)_2NH + C_6H_5CH_2NH_2$$

benzamide type. A comparison of the various methods of synthesis of benzylamine is given in Table II, p. 203.

Only a few other aromatic aldehydes have been converted to primary amines by reductive alkylation. o-Tolualdehyde is converted to the primary amine in 83% yield, and even o-chlorobenzaldehyde gives an excellent (88%) yield of o-chlorobenzylamine by reaction with ammonia in the presence of hydrogen and a nickel catalyst.[10] p-Ethylbenz-

[6] Baur, U. S. pat. 1,966,478 [*C. A.*, **28**, 5470 (1934)].

[7] I.G. Farbenind. A.-G., Suppl. Fr. pat. 37,923 (to Fr. pat. 628,641) [*C. A.*, **26**, 151 (1932)].

[8] Wayne and Adkins, *J. Am. Chem. Soc.*, **62**, 3314 (1940).

[9] I.G. Farbenind. A.-G., U. S. pat. 1,762,742 [*C. A.*, **24**, 3800 (1930)].

[10] Winans, *J. Am. Chem. Soc.*, **61**, 3566 (1939).

aldehyde has been converted to the amine in 71% yield.[5] Furfural has given furfurylamine in yields as high as 79%.[10] Aldehydes containing other aromatic nuclei apparently have not been used in the reaction.

From Ketones. Most of the yields reported in preparations of primary amines from simple aliphatic ketones are better than 50%. The yields from acetone and methyl ethyl ketone, in preparations carried out with hydrogen and a nickel catalyst, are only about 30%.[11] However, methyl n-propyl ketone [12] and methyl isopropyl ketone [1] are converted to the primary amines in yields of 90% and 65%, respectively. As might be predicted on the basis of steric factors, pinacolone and diisopropyl ketone give somewhat lower yields of the primary amines (51% and 48%, respectively).[1] From di-n-butyl ketone, the yield is 72%,[1] while from methyl n-hexyl ketone it is 93%.[5] The yield of cyclohexylamine from cyclohexanone is about 80%.[5,13] One γ,δ-unsaturated methyl ketone $[(CH_3)_2C=CHCH_2CH_2COCH_3]$ has been converted to the unsaturated primary amine in 60% yield.[5] One α,β-unsaturated ketone, mesityl oxide, has been converted to the saturated amine in 60% yield.[7]

Aryl alkyl ketones are converted to the primary amine in somewhat lower yields. With a fivefold excess of ammonia and high-pressure hydrogenation over Raney nickel catalyst, acetophenone is converted to α-phenylethylamine in yields of 45–50%.[14] Benzohydrylamine has been obtained from benzophenone in only 19% yield.[1] The only recorded application of the process to a quinone is the conversion of anthraquinone to the 9,10-diamine by treatment with ammonia and sodium hydrosulfite.[15]

Preparation of Secondary Amines (Table X)

From Ammonia and Aliphatic Aldehydes and Ketones. The reduction of a mixture of two moles of a ketone or aliphatic aldehyde and one of ammonia usually leads to a mixture of amines of all three types. For example, the products from n-butyraldehyde, ammonia, hydrogen, and a nickel catalyst are n-butylamine (up to 31%), di-n-butylamine (up to 40%), and tri-n-butylamine (up to 22%).[16] Diethylamine has been

[11] Skita and Keil, *Ber.*, **61**, 1682 (1928).

[12] Olin and Schwoegler, U. S. pat. 2,278,372 [*C. A.*, **36**, 4829 (1942)].

[13] Cantarel, *Compt. rend.*, **210**, 403 (1940).

[14] Robinson and Snyder, *Org. Syntheses*, **23**, 68 (1943).

[15] Vorozhtsov and Shkitin, *J. Gen. Chem. U.S.S.R.*, **10**, 883 (1940) [*C. A.*, **35**, 4375 (1941)].

[16] Vanderbilt, U. S. pat. 2,219,879 [*C. A.*, **35**, 1065 (1941)].

obtained from acetaldehyde in 50% yield,[17] but the few other aliphatic aldehydes which have been studied have given yields of 20–30% of the secondary amines.[18] In a few preparations of secondary amines the primary amine obtained as a by-product from one run is added to the next reaction mixture. By this method it is possible to obtain diethylamine from acetaldehyde and ammonia in yields as high as 84%.[16, 19]

Acetone and methyl ethyl ketone are converted to the secondary amines in yields of 30–40%,[18, 20] whereas diethyl ketone gives only 20% of the secondary amine.[20] Cyclohexanone has been converted to dicyclohexylamine in 54% yield.[11] A platinum catalyst was used with all these ketones. In the presence of hydrogen and a nickel catalyst, acetonylacetone and ammonia reacted to form the dimethylpyrrole (59% yield) and the related pyrrolidine (28% yield).[1]

$$CH_3COCH_2CH_2COCH_3 + NH_3 \xrightarrow{H_2(Ni)}$$

Acetylacetone, by contrast, furnished acetamide in quantitative yield.

From Ammonia and Aromatic Aldehydes. The reduction of a mixture of two moles of an aromatic aldehyde and one of ammonia provides an excellent route to diaralkylamines. Thus, over a nickel catalyst benzaldehyde yields 81% of the secondary amine with only 12–17% of the primary amine.[10, 21] Similar results are obtained with o-tolualdehyde and even with o-chlorobenzaldehyde (85% of secondary amine and 4% of primary amine). From furfural a 66% yield of difurfurylamine has been obtained. A comparison of various preparations of dibenzylamine, shown in Table III, p. 204, indicates the value of the method.

The aromatic aldehydes which have been converted to secondary amines by this process are listed in Table X.

From Primary Amines and Carbonyl Compounds. As mentioned previously, the reactions which occur in reductive alkylations of primary amines are of the type shown on p. 182. Whether or not the reduction will involve the addition product or the Schiff's base will depend upon the relative rates of the reactions. Probably in most instances it is the Schiff's base which is reduced; even though the equilibria may be so unfavorable that the Schiff's base cannot be isolated, removal of this

[17] Grigorovskii, Berkov, Gorlad, Margolina, and Levitskaya, *Org. Chem. Ind.*, **7,** 671 (1940) [*C. A.*, **35,** 5094 (1941)].

[18] Skita, Keil, and Havemann, *Ber.*, **66,** 1400 (1933).

[19] Christ, Ger. pat. 671,839 [*C. A.*, **33,** 6340 (1939)].

[20] Skita and Keil, *Ber.*, **61,** 1452 (1928).

[21] Winans, U. S. pat. 2,217,630 [*C. A.*, **35,** 1065 (1941)].

component by reduction may disturb the equilibria to such an extent that all the secondary amine is formed by this reduction.

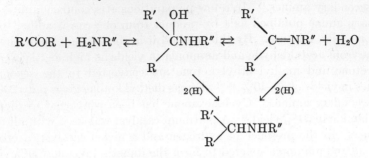

When the Schiff's base can be isolated easily it may be advantageous to separate it before the reduction is carried out. If the Schiff's base forms readily, but is too unstable to permit convenient isolation, then it may be desirable to heat a solution of the reactants for a certain time and reduce the base without isolating it. Thus there are three modifications of procedure, all of which may be equivalent when applied to pairs which react very readily to form Schiff's bases. For purposes of classification, the term "reductive alkylation" will be used to designate those preparations in which no attempt to promote the formation of the Schiff's base was made. Preparations in which the reactants were brought together under conditions favorable for the formation of the condensation product will be referred to as reductions of Schiff's bases even though the base was not isolated.

Aliphatic Amines and Aldehydes. Methylamine has been converted to dimethylamine in unspecified yield by treatment with formaldehyde, zinc, and hydrochloric acid.[22] The reduction of a mixture of ethylamine and acetaldehyde over a platinum catalyst has given diethylamine and triethylamine in yields of 22% and 16%, respectively;[11] with nickel the yields were 55% and 19%, respectively.[16] Di-n-butylamine and tri-n-butylamine have been obtained in yields of 48% and 47%, respectively, from butylamine and butyraldehyde with a nickel catalyst;[16] cyclohexylamine and butyraldehyde gave 91% of the secondary amine.[23, 24] The secondary amines from cyclohexylamine and mannose and arabinose have been obtained in unspecified yields by reduction of the mixtures over nickel.[11, 25] Ethanolamine has been alkylated by several aldehydes in reductions over a platinum catalyst.[26] The yields of secondary amines

[22] Meister, Lucius, and Bruning, Ger. pat. 73,812 [*Frdl.*, **3**, 15 (1896)].

[23] Adkins, *Reactions of Hydrogen*, University of Wisconsin Press, 1937, p. 56.

[24] Adkins and Winans, U. S. pat. 2,045,574 [*C. A.*, **30**, 5589 (1936)].

[25] Skita and Keil, Brit. pat. 313,617 (*Chem. Zentr.*, **1930**, I, 1052).

[26] Cope and Hancock, *J. Am. Chem. Soc.*, **64**, 1503 (1942).

from n-butyraldehyde, n-valeraldehyde, and n-caproaldehyde were 68%, 70%, and 71%, respectively. The yield in an alkylation with isobutyraldehyde was somewhat lower (62%), but that with 2-ethylhexanal was higher (91%).

Some interesting variations in yields have been observed in the alkylation of derivatives of β-phenylethylamine.[27] β-(3,4-Dimethoxyphenyl)-β-methylethylamine gave 64% of the N-n-propyl derivative in an alkylation with propionaldehyde, hydrogen, and nickel catalyst. When

$$CH_3O\text{—}C_6H_3\text{—}CH(CH_3)CH_2NH_2 + CH_3CH_2CHO + H_2 \xrightarrow{Ni}$$
$$CH_3O$$

$$CH_3O\text{—}C_6H_3\text{—}CH(CH_3)CH_2NHC_3H_7 + H_2O$$
$$CH_3O$$

acetaldehyde was used, the yield of the N-ethyl derivative was only 36%. In the ethylation of the β-methoxyphenyl-α-methylethylamines, the p-methoxyphenyl isomer gave a 48% yield of the secondary amine and the m-methoxyphenyl derivative a 70% yield.

$$CH_3O\text{—}C_6H_4\text{—}CH_2CHNH_2 + CH_3CHO + H_2 \xrightarrow{Pt} CH_3O\text{—}C_6H_4\text{—}CH_2CHNHC_2H_5$$
$$\qquad\qquad\underset{CH_3}{|} \qquad\qquad\qquad\qquad\qquad\qquad\qquad\underset{CH_3}{|}$$

There are but few examples of the preparation of secondary amines by the reductive alkylation of primary aliphatic amines with aromatic aldehydes (see Table X). The corresponding Schiff's bases have been used more frequently in such preparations (see p. 190).

Aliphatic Amines or Nitro Compounds and Ketones. Purely aliphatic secondary amines have been prepared in great variety by the reductive alkylation of primary amines with ketones. Most of the reductions have been effected with the aid of a platinum catalyst, although nickel and palladium have been employed.

The yields obtained from simple primary amines and simple ketones usually are good (50–100%). It is to be expected that yields will be affected by steric factors in both the ketone and the amine, but few relevant data have been collected. In alkylations of cyclohexylamine with acetone, methyl ethyl ketone, diethyl ketone, and cyclohexanone carried out under comparable conditions with hydrogen and a platinum catalyst, the yields were 79%, 60%, 31%, and 63%, respectively.[11] In alkylations of ethanolamine with these same ketones the yields were all above 95%;[26] even with diisobutyl ketone the yield was 94%.

[27] Woodruff, Lambooy, and Burt, *J. Am. Chem. Soc.*, **62**, 922 (1940).

Several diketones have been used in these alkylations. With most of the α-diketones the reductions were carried out over palladium catalyst, and only one of the carbonyl groups took part in the reaction. Thus, the product isolated from cyclohexylamine and 2,3-hexanedione was that in which the carbonyl group next to the methyl group had reacted.[28] Undoubtedly, other reactions occurred also; the yield of the

$$CH_3CH_2CH_2COCOCH_3 + C_6H_{11}NH_2 + H_2 \xrightarrow{Pd} CH_3CH_2CH_2COCHCH_3 + H_2O$$
$$\underset{NHC_6H_{11}}{|}$$

product indicated in the equation was only 10%. Similarly, a keto amine was obtained (29% yield) from methylamine and this diketone when the reduction was carried out over palladium catalyst.[28] However, with platinum catalyst an amino alcohol was formed (30% yield).[29, 30]

$$CH_3CH_2CH_2COCOCH_3 + CH_3NH_2 + 2H_2 \xrightarrow{Pt} CH_3CH_2CH_2CHOHCHCH_3$$
$$\underset{NHCH_3}{|}$$

Acetylacetone and ethanolamine, in a reduction over platinum, gave the dihydroxy amine.[25] Similar products have been obtained in about

$$CH_3COCH_2COCH_3 + H_2NCH_2CH_2OH + 2H_2 \xrightarrow{Pt} CH_3CHOHCH_2CHCH_3 + H_2O$$
$$\underset{NHCH_2CH_2OH}{|}$$

25% yield from cyclohexylamine with acetylacetone [11, 30] and its α-methyl derivative.[29]

$$CH_3COCHCOCH_3 + C_6H_{11}NH_2 + 2H_2 \xrightarrow{Pt} CH_3CHOHCHCHCH_3$$
$$\underset{CH_3}{|} \qquad\qquad\qquad \underset{H_3C\ \ NHC_6H_{11}}{|\ \ |}$$

It was mentioned earlier (p. 177) that in the preparation of secondary and tertiary amines a substance which is easily reduced to a primary amine can be employed in place of the primary amine. Only three aliphatic nitro compounds have been so used with aliphatic ketones. The reduction of a mixture of nitromethane and acetone with hydrogen and platinum gives methylisopropylamine in 59% yield;[2] the reductive alkylation of 4-nitro-1-phenyl-2,3-dimethyl-5-pyrazolone with acetone or methyl ethyl ketone is reported to give a nearly quantitative yield of the corresponding secondary amine.[31]

[28] Skita, Keil, and Baesler, Ber., **66**, 858 (1933).
[29] Skita and Keil, Ber., **62**, 1142 (1929).
[30] Skita and Keil, Z. angew. Chem., **42**, 501 (1929).
[31] Skita, Keil, and Stuhmer, Ber., **75**, 1696 (1942).

An example of the relatively few recorded reductive alkylations of primary aliphatic amines by simple aromatic ketones is that of ethanolamine by acetophenone.[26] The yield is 95%. No simple diaryl ketone

$$C_6H_5COCH_3 + H_2NCH_2CH_2OH + H_2 \xrightarrow{Pt} C_6H_5CHNHCH_2CH_2OH + H_2O$$
$$\underset{CH_3}{|}$$

has been used in a reductive alkylation with a primary aliphatic amine.

Diketones containing one or more aryl groups react in the same way as the aliphatic diketones. Keto amines are obtained with palladium catalyst,[28] and amino alcohols with platinum catalyst.[29]

$$C_6H_5COCOCH_3 + C_6H_{11}NH_2 + H_2 \xrightarrow{Pd} C_6H_5COCHNHC_6H_{11} \quad (19\%)$$
$$\underset{CH_3}{|}$$

$$C_6H_5COCOC_6H_5 + C_6H_{11}NH_2 + H_2 \xrightarrow{Pd} C_6H_5COCHNHC_6H_{11} \quad (24\%)$$
$$\underset{C_6H_5}{|}$$

$$C_6H_5COCOC_6H_5 + C_6H_{11}NH_2 + 2H_2 \xrightarrow{Pt} C_6H_5CHOHCHNHC_6H_{11}$$
$$\underset{C_6H_5}{|}$$

Aromatic Amines and Aldehydes; Aromatic Nitro Compounds, Azo Compounds, etc., and Aldehydes.

Aniline is converted to ethylaniline by treatment with acetaldehyde and hydrogen in the presence of nickel or platinum,[32, 33] or by reduction with zinc and sulfuric[34] or sulfurous acid.[35] Most of the higher n-alkylanilines have been prepared by reduction with hydrogen and nickel catalyst (yields, 45–65%);[32] the presence of a small quantity of sodium acetate (1 g. for a 0.1 M run) is desirable. In reductive alkylations with aldehydes, hydrogen, and nickel catalyst, α-naphthylamine gives 88% of the N-ethyl derivative and 80% of the N-n-butyl derivative,[36] whereas from β-naphthylamine the yields of the corresponding secondary amines are 64% and 63%, respectively. The number of substituted anilines which have been alkylated by this method is relatively small. The yields from p-toluidine, p-anisidine, and p-aminophenol are about the same as those from aniline. Aluminum and aqueous sodium hydroxide have been used to effect the reduction in some alkylations of p-aminophenol, but the yields of the

[32] Emerson and Walters, J. Am. Chem. Soc., **60**, 2023 (1938).
[33] Emerson, U. S. pat. 2,298,284 [C. A., **37**, 1450 (1943)].
[34] Lockemann, Ger. pat. 491,856 [Frdl., **16**, 356 (1931)].
[35] Chemische Fabriken Vorm. Weiler-ter Meer, Ger. pat. 376,013 [Frdl., **14**, 398 (1926)].
[36] Emerson and Robb, J. Am. Chem. Soc., **61**, 3145 (1939).

secondary amines were not reported.[37,38] Similarly, N-methyl-*o*-anisidine has been obtained in unspecified yield from *o*-anisidine, formaldehyde, zinc, and aqueous sodium hydroxide.[39] In the presence of acids, aromatic amines react with aldehydes of low molecular weight to form resins and quinoline derivatives,[40] so acidic reducing media usually are not employed. However, in the preparation of N-benzoyl-N'-ethyl-*p*-phenylenediamine, acetaldehyde-ammonia was used as the source of acetaldehyde and zinc and sulfuric acid as the reducing agent.[34]

$$C_6H_5CONH\!\!-\!\!\langle\quad\rangle\!\!-\!\!NH_2 + CH_3CHOHNH_2 + 2(H) \xrightarrow{\ Zn\ +\ H_2SO_4\ }$$

$$C_6H_5CONH\!\!-\!\!\langle\quad\rangle\!\!-\!\!NHCH_2CH_3 + NH_3 + H_2O$$
$$(94\%)$$

A preparation of N-ethylarsanilic acid (p-$C_2H_5NHC_6H_4AsO_3H_2$) in 5% yield from arsanilic acid and acetaldehyde, hydrogen, and nickel catalyst has been reported;[41] the low yield may be due to poisoning of the catalyst by the arsenic compound.

That hindrance around the amino group is of little consequence in alkylations of this type is shown by the high yields obtained in the preparations of secondary amines from mesidine (2,4,6-trimethyl-aniline) and isobutyraldehyde (91%) and isovaleraldehyde (94%).[42]

$$H_3C\!\!-\!\!\overset{CH_3}{\underset{CH_3}{\langle\quad\rangle}}\!\!-\!\!NH_2 + (CH_3)_2CHCHO + 2(H) \xrightarrow{\ Zn\ +\ HCl\ }$$

$$H_3C\!\!-\!\!\overset{CH_3}{\underset{CH_3}{\langle\quad\rangle}}\!\!-\!\!NHCH_2CH(CH_3)_2 + H_2O$$

These reductions were effected with zinc and hydrochloric acid, and the high yields may be due in part to the acidic medium. This reducing agent cannot be used in similar alkylations of aniline derivatives in which *ortho* or *para* positions are unsubstituted, since these amines react with aliphatic aldehydes in the presence of acid to give quinoline derivatives and resins.[40]

[37] Bean, Brit. pat. 503,400 [*C. A.*, **33**, 7317 (1939)].

[38] Bean, U. S. pat. 2,338,482 [*C. A.*, **38**, 3666 (1944)].

[39] Morgan and British Dyestuffs Corp., Swiss pat. 91,563 (*Chem. Zentr.*, **1922, III,** 837).

[40] Sprung, *Chem. Revs.*, **26**, 297 (1940).

[41] Doak, Eagle, and Steinman, *J. Am. Chem. Soc.*, **62**, 3010 (1940).

[42] Emerson, Neumann, and Moundres, *J. Am. Chem. Soc.*, **63**, 972 (1941).

rimary amines are prepared by reduction, it
ne the preparation and alkylation of such an
tion. Secondary amines are obtained in 60–
tion of a mixture of an aromatic nitro com-
ver Raney nickel catalyst in the presence of
nitro compound contains an amino, hydroxyl,
n the *para* position, the amount of tertiary
duct is increased (see Table X).[43, 44, 45] Acidic
sed in the reductive alkylation of nitro com-
r than formaldehyde;[46] evidently the concen-
ine remains so low that the condensations to
s and resins (p. 186) occur only very slowly.
ondary amines by the reductive alkylation of
tic aldehydes, hydrogen, and Raney nickel
ue solvent, the yields pass through a maximum
thylaniline is obtained in yields of about 50%;
; *n*-butylaniline, about 95%; *n*-amylaniline,
aniline, about 40%.[43] *n*-Propylaniline has not
parable experimental conditions.
ions of aromatic nitroso compounds to second-
ported, but the yields are low.[47] Azobenzene
ry amines in reactions with aliphatic aldehydes
r nickel catalyst, but the readily available azo
oupling give mixtures of secondary and tertiary
the reaction of *p*-phenylazodimethylaniline,
rogen yields almost equal quantities of *n*-
-*n*-butyl-N',N'-dimethyl-*p*-phenylenediamine.

$$(CH_3)_2NC_6H_4N\!\!=\!\!NC_6H_5 \xrightarrow[(H_2)]{C_3H_7CHO}$$

$$(CH_3)_2NC_6H_4N(C_4H_9)_2 + C_6H_5NHC_4H_9$$
$$(73\%) \qquad\qquad (76\%)$$

various reductive alkylation procedures with
thesis of *n*-butylaniline is shown in Table IV,

hydes that have been used in direct reductive
omatic amines are benzaldehyde, anisaldehyde,

Am. Chem. Soc., **62,** 69 (1940).
53, 4373 (1931).
[C. A., **35,** 6602 (1941)].
ublished work.
of Illinois, 1940.
r, J. Am. Chem. Soc., **63,** 751 (1941).

veratric aldehyde, and furfural, and only a few yields have been reported. Most secondary amines which might be made from such combinations are prepared by reduction of the Schiff's base (see p. 191) rather than by the direct procedure. It is of interest that the yield of N-benzyl-β-naphthylamine obtained by the reductive alkylation of β-naphthylamine with benzaldehyde, hydrogen, and nickel catalyst is much better (58%) than that reported (24%) for the similar preparation of the α-amine.[36]

$$\text{(naphthalene)}NH_2 + C_6H_5CHO + H_2 \xrightarrow{Ni} \text{(naphthalene)}NHCH_2C_6H_5 + H_2O$$

Apparently no advantage is to be gained by the reductive alkylation of a nitro, nitroso, or azo compound with an aromatic aldehyde; the yields of benzylaniline so obtained from nitrobenzene,[43] nitrosobenzene,[47] and azobenzene[48] are only 33%, 47%, and 49%, respectively.

Aromatic Amines, Aromatic Nitro, Nitroso, or Azo Compounds and Ketones. N-Isopropylaniline is obtained in 31% yield from aniline, acetone, zinc, and hydrochloric acid;[42] under the same conditions, N-isopropylmesidine is obtained in only 18% yield. p-Aminophenol is

$$H_3C\text{-(ring with CH}_3\text{, CH}_3\text{)}NH_2 + CH_3COCH_3 + 2(H) \xrightarrow{Zn + HCl} H_3C\text{-(ring with CH}_3\text{, CH}_3\text{)}NHCH(CH_3)_2 + H_2O$$

converted to the N-isopropyl derivative when an acetone solution of the base is heated to the boiling point and then reduced over platinum catalyst;[49] none of the secondary amine is obtained when hydrogenation at room temperature is attempted.[50]

The highest reported yield in a preparation of this type is that (91%) of the secondary amine from α-naphthylamine and N,N-diethylacetopropylamine.[51] This is also the only reported use of palladium catalyst

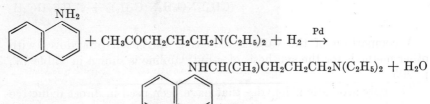

$$\text{(naphthalene)}NH_2 + CH_3COCH_2CH_2CH_2N(C_2H_5)_2 + H_2 \xrightarrow{Pd}$$

$$NHCH(CH_3)CH_2CH_2CH_2N(C_2H_5)_2 + H_2O$$

in the preparation of a secondary amine by a reductive alkylation involving a primary aromatic amine and a monoketone. It is possible that

[49] Major, *J. Am. Chem. Soc.*, **53**, 2803 (1931).
[50] Major, *J. Am. Chem. Soc.*, **53**, 1901 (1931).
[51] Bergman, Brit. pat. 547,301 [*C. A.*, **37**, 5985 (1943)].

the yields in such syntheses (see Table X) could be improved by the use of this catalyst.

Hydrogenation of a solution of aniline and methylphenylglyoxal over palladium catalyst leads to the formation of either the keto amine or

$$C_6H_5COCHCH_3 \quad (49\%)$$
$$|$$
$$NHC_6H_5$$

$$C_6H_5NH_2 + C_6H_5COCOCH_3 \xrightarrow{H_2, Pd}$$

$$C_6H_5CHOHCHCH_3 \quad (46\%)$$
$$|$$
$$NHC_6H_5$$

the hydroxy amine, depending on the amount of catalyst used.[28] Only the keto amine is obtained from p-toluidine and p-anisylmethylglyoxal.[28]

$$p\text{-}CH_3C_6H_4NH_2 + p\text{-}CH_3OC_6H_4COCOCH_3 + H_2 \xrightarrow{Pd}$$

$$p\text{-}CH_3C_6H_4COCHCH_3 + H_2O$$
$$|$$
$$NHC_6H_4CH_3\text{-}p$$
$$(49\%)$$

A number of preparations of secondary amines from ketones and aromatic nitro and nitroso compounds have been reported. In general, the use of a nitro compound appears less attractive than the use of the primary aromatic amine. However, in a few preparations higher yields have been obtained with nitro compounds than with amines. Thus, isopropylaniline has been obtained from nitrobenzene, acetone, hydrogen, and platinum catalyst in 53% yield;[2] N-isopropyl-p-aminophenol has been obtained in 45% yield from the nitrophenol, acetone, hydrogen, and platinum catalyst,[52, 53, 54] and in 50% yield from the aminophenol and the same reagents.[49]

No successful preparations involving diaryl ketones in the alkylation of primary aromatic amines or their precursors have been recorded.

Preparation of Secondary Amines by Reduction of Schiff's Bases

As indicated earlier, secondary amines can be prepared from primary amines and carbonyl compounds by way of the Schiff's bases, with or without isolation and purification of these intermediates. This method has been used most extensively with primary aromatic amines.

[52] Major, *J. Am. Chem. Soc.*, **53**, 190 (1931).
[53] Major, U. S. pat. 1,978,433 [*C. A.*, **29**, 178 (1935)].
[54] Major, U. S. pat. 1,989,707 [*C. A.*, **29**, 1833 (1935)].

From Schiff's Bases Derived from Aliphatic Amines. The isolation and reduction of purely aliphatic Schiff's bases containing from five to ten carbon atoms has been accomplished, but such bases are unstable and their isolation is difficult. They have been prepared in yields of 50–80%, and they have given the secondary amines in yields of 40–65% by catalytic reduction.[55] Schiff's bases derived from aldehydes having α-methylene groups undergo condensations of the aldol type on being heated.[56, 57, 58] Because of the occurrence of such condensations higher-

$$2RCH_2CH{=}NR' \rightarrow R'NH_2 + RCH_2CH{=}\underset{\underset{R}{|}}{C}CH{=}NR' \xrightarrow{H_2}$$

$$RCH_2CH_2\underset{\underset{R}{|}}{C}HCH_2NHR'$$

boiling amines may be expected as by-products from the reduction of the Schiff's bases, particularly if vigorous conditions are used in the preparation or isolation of the intermediates.[58]

Unsaturated Schiff's bases of the type produced by the condensation just described can be prepared also from α,β-unsaturated aldehydes and amines. Many of them have been reduced to the corresponding saturated amines. Platinum catalyst has been used most frequently, and the yields generally have been above 50%.

The Schiff's bases from simple aliphatic amines and benzaldehyde are more readily prepared, and they are reduced to alkylbenzylamines in 70–100% yields by hydrogenation over nickel or platinum catalyst. A number of amines of the general type $ArCH_2CH_2NHAr'$ have been obtained in excellent yields by hydrogenation over nickel or platinum catalysts of the Schiff's bases prepared from substituted phenylethyl-amines, including some with substituents in the side chain, and substituted benzaldehydes (see Table X). Similar secondary amines have been prepared from substituted benzylamines.

Schiff's bases derived from aliphatic ketones are not common intermediates. Those derived from diisobutyl ketone and 1-amino-2-propanol, 2-amino-1-propanol, 3-amino-1-propanol, and 2-amino-1-butanol have given high yields (83–93%) of the corresponding secondary amines by reduction over platinum catalysts.[59, 60, 61] A few derived from

[55] Campbell, Sommers, and Campbell, *J. Am. Chem. Soc.*, **66**, 82 (1944).
[56] Kharasch, Richlin, and Mayo, *J. Am. Chem. Soc.*, **62**, 494 (1940).
[57] Emerson, Hess, and Uhle, *J. Am. Chem. Soc.*, **63**, 872 (1941).
[58] Skita and Pfeil, *Ann.*, **485**, 152 (1931).
[59] Cope and Hancock, *J Am. Chem. Soc.*, **66**, 1453 (1944).
[60] Hancock and Cope, *J. Am. Chem. Soc.*, **66**, 1738 (1944).
[61] Hancock, Hardy, Heyl, Wright, and Cope, *J. Am. Chem. Soc.*, **66**, 1747 (1944).

simple alkylamines and activated carbonyl compounds, including glyoxylic acid, pyruvic acid, and acetoacetic ester, have given lower yields of the amines.[62]

From Schiff's Bases Derived from Aromatic Amines. Only isoamyl-aniline and isoamyl-o-toluidine have been prepared by the reduction of a Schiff's base derived from an aromatic amine and a simple aliphatic aldehyde.[63] In these preparations a nickel catalyst was used; the yields of the secondary amines obtained were not reported. A number of Schiff's bases prepared from the hydroxyanilines and branched-chain aldehydes have been reduced over platinum or nickel in good yields. For example, the base from o-aminophenol and 2-ethylbutyraldehyde was converted to the amine in 91% yield.[64]

$$o\text{-HOC}_6\text{H}_4\text{N}\!\!=\!\!\text{CHCH}(\text{C}_2\text{H}_5)_2 + \text{H}_2 \xrightarrow{\text{Pt}} o\text{-HOC}_6\text{H}_4\text{NHCH}_2\text{CH}(\text{C}_2\text{H}_5)_2$$

Cinnamalaniline[65] and p-crotonalaminophenol[64] appear to be the only unsaturated anils that have been reduced. The reduction was effected with magnesium and methanol in the first instance, but the yield of phenylpropylaniline was not reported. The reduction in the second preparation was carried out with hydrogen and nickel catalyst, and the yield of p-butylaminophenol was 33%. The Schiff's bases derived from aniline (and several substituted anilines) and glucose or sorbose have been converted to the amines by hydrogenation over nickel catalyst, but the yields of the products are not available.[66]

The condensation product of aniline and acetoacetic ester has been reduced to the amine in 30% yield.[62] No other anil derived from a ketone appears to have been reduced.

$$\underset{\overset{|}{\text{CH}_3}}{\text{C}_6\text{H}_5\text{N}\!\!=\!\!\text{CCH}_2\text{CO}_2\text{C}_2\text{H}_5} + \text{H}_2 \xrightarrow{\text{Pt}} \underset{\overset{|}{\text{CH}_3}}{\text{C}_6\text{H}_5\text{NHCHCH}_2\text{CO}_2\text{C}_2\text{H}_5}$$

The Schiff's bases from aromatic aldehydes and aromatic amines are readily available, and many of them have been reduced to secondary amines. Catalytic reduction has been carried out most often over nickel catalyst at moderate temperatures in either high-pressure or low-pressure equipment. The reduction of benzalaniline over copper chromite at 175° is quantitative,[23, 67] but other anils apparently have not been reduced over this catalyst.

[62] Skita and Wulff, *Ann.*, **453**, 190 (1927).
[63] Mailhe, *Bull. soc. chim. France*, [4] **25**, 324 (1919).
[64] Fitch, U. S. pat. 2,270,215 [*C. A.*, **36**, 3189 (1942)].
[65] Zechmeister and Truka, *Ber.*, **63**, 2883 (1930).
[66] Salzberg, U. S. pat. 2,193,433 [*C. A.*, **34**, 4742 (1940)].
[67] Adkins and Connor, *J. Am. Chem. Soc.*, **53**, 1091 (1931).

Chemical reducing agents have been employed in great variety for the reduction of benzalaniline and its derivatives. Electrolytic reduction is quite satisfactory for the conversion of aniline and substituted aniline derivatives of the chlorobenzaldehydes to the secondary amines,[68] and this method may be useful with other anils containing substituents which might be removed in catalytic reduction or which might exert a poisoning effect on the catalyst. A comparison of the various methods of reduction of benzalaniline, together with other methods of synthesis of benzylaniline, is shown in Table V, p. 206.

No systematic studies have been made of the effects of structure on yields in the reduction of anils of the type $ArCH=NAr'$, and although a great many such compounds have been converted to the secondary amines the variety of reducing agents and conditions is so great that no generalizations can be made from the data at hand. The anils that have been reduced are listed in Table X.

Preparation of Tertiary Amines (Table XI)

From Ammonia and Aldehydes and Ketones. This modification has found application only in the preparation of triethyl- and tripropyl-amines, the reductions having been carried out over platinum catalyst in unreported yields.[20] A related preparation is that of trimethylamine in 89% yield from ammonium chloride and formaldehyde, in which part of the formaldehyde serves as the reducing agent.[69]

From Primary Aliphatic Amines or Primary Aliphatic Nitro Compounds and Aldehydes and Ketones. Dialkylmethylamines have been obtained in 30–90% yields by the reductive alkylation of nitromethane with aliphatic aldehydes over a platinum catalyst.[2,70] The best yield (92%) was obtained with acetaldehyde, and the poorest (30%) with n-hexaldehyde.

Several amines of the type $ArCH(CH_3)CH_2NH_2$ and $ArCH_2CH-(CH_3)NH_2$ have been methylated by treatment with formaldehyde and hydrogen over nickel catalyst.[27] The yields of tertiary amines were in the range of 51–84%. Dimethylaminoethanol has been obtained similarly from the primary amine in yield as high as 88%,[71] and 2-dimethyl-amino-1-phenylpropanol in 84% yield.[27] The only example of the use of platinum catalyst in a methylation of this type is the conversion of

[68] Law, *J. Chem. Soc.*, **101**, 154 (1912).
[69] Adams and Marvel, *Org. Syntheses*, *Coll. Vol.* I, 531 (1941).
[70] Private communication from E. H. Huntress.
[71] Cass and K'burg, U. S. pat. 2,194,294 [*C. A.*, **34**, 4742 (1940)].

4-amino-1-phenyl-2,3-dimethyl-5-pyrazolone to the tertiary amine in unspecified yield.[18, 72]

In an experiment in which ethylamine was treated with a mixture of acetaldehyde and benzaldehyde, hydrogen, and platinum catalyst, diethylbenzylamine (28% yield) was obtained.[11] This appears to be the only attempt at the simultaneous introduction of two different alkyl groups by the use of two aldehydes.

Only one instance has been recorded of the conversion of a primary aliphatic amine to a tertiary amine by reductive alkylation with a simple ketone: 4-amino-1-phenyl-2,3-dimethyl-5-pyrazolone gave the diisopropylamino compound in unspecified yield on treatment with acetone, hydrogen, and platinum catalyst.[18] Methylamine and ethylamine have been reductively alkylated by treatment with a mixture of formaldehyde or acetaldehyde and a 1,2- or 1,3-diketone, hydrogen, and platinum catalyst.[73, 74] The products were dialkylaminoalcohols, generally obtained in unreported yields. The cyclic tertiary amine was the major

$$CH_3NH_2 + C_6H_5COCOCH_3 + CH_2O + 3H_2 \xrightarrow{Pt}$$

$$C_6H_5CHOHCH(CH_3)N(CH_3)_2 + 2H_2O$$

product from cyclohexylamine, acetonylacetone, hydrogen, and platinum catalyst.[29, 30]

$$C_6H_{11}NH_2 + CH_3COCH_2CH_2COCH_3 + 2H_2 \xrightarrow{Pt}$$
$$+ 2H_2O$$

From Primary Aromatic Amines, Nitro Compounds, or Azo Compounds and Aldehydes and Ketones. Primary aromatic amines with substituents in the 2,4 or 2,4,6 positions have been converted to the dimethyl derivatives by reductive alkylation with formaldehyde, zinc, and hydrochloric acid;[42, 75, 76] other aldehydes have not been tested. The yields in these methylations ranged from 50% to 90%. The primary amines employed carried alkyl groups and halogen atoms as substituents in the ring. No variations in yield ascribable to steric hindrance were noted, but the removal of iodine atoms from the ortho and para positions[75] and of bromine atoms from ortho positions was noted.[76] Tribromoaniline,

[72] I.G. Farbenind. A.-G., Ger. pat. 479,348 (*Chem. Zentr.*, **1929, II,** 1592).

[73] Skita and Keil, *Ber.*, **63,** 34 (1930).

[74] Skita and Keil, *Monatsh.*, **53–54,** 753 (1929).

[75] Emerson and Ringwald, *J. Am. Chem. Soc.*, **63,** 2843 (1941).

[76] Emerson, Dorf, and Deutschman, *J. Am. Chem. Soc.*, **62,** 2159 (1940).

for example, gave *p*-bromodimethylaniline in 88% yield. Aromatic primary amines without substituents in the reactive *ortho* and *para* positions are converted to resins by treatment with formaldehyde in acid solution.

$$Br\langle\bigcirc\rangle NH_2 + 2CH_2O + 8(H) \rightarrow Br\langle\bigcirc\rangle N(CH_3)_2 + 2HBr + 2H_2O$$

(with Br substituents on the ring)

p-Aminobenzoic acid has been converted to the tertiary amine by methylation with formaldehyde, hydrogen, and a catalyst (platinum, nickel, or cobalt), but the yields are not reported.[77]

Aromatic nitro compounds can be converted to dialkylarylamines in yields of 34–70% by reductive alkylation in the presence of acetic acid with hydrogen, platinum catalyst, and aliphatic aldehydes other than formaldehyde.[2] If the nitro compound carries a methyl, methoxyl, hydroxyl, or amino group in the *para* position, the use of acetic acid is unnecessary (see p. 187).[43, 44, 45] The convenience of this method of preparing tertiary amines directly from nitro compounds is illustrated by the comparison of various preparations of di-*n*-butylaniline shown in Table VI, p. 206.

The formation of tertiary amines by reductive alkylation of azo compounds formed by coupling has been mentioned (p. 187).[48]

Benzaldehyde has been used as the alkylating agent in the preparation of tertiary amines from *p*-nitrophenol and *p*-nitroaniline. Both reactions were carried out over platinum catalyst. The tertiary amine was isolated in unspecified yield from the nitrophenol;[52, 53, 54] both nitrogen atoms of the nitro amine were alkylated, tetrabenzyl-*p*-phenylenediamine being obtained in 50% yield.[44] These appear to be the only examples of the use of an aromatic aldehyde as the alkylating agent in the preparation of tertiary amines from aromatic nitro compounds, and no similar preparations from primary aromatic amines or azo compounds are recorded.

From Secondary Aliphatic Amines and Aldehydes and Ketones. Many secondary aliphatic amines have been alkylated with aliphatic aldehydes. The yields of tertiary amines obtained have varied from almost zero to as high as 100%. The highest yields are obtained when formaldehyde is the alkylating agent (with hydrogen and platinum catalyst) and when the alkyl groups attached to the nitrogen atom of the secondary amine are primary or when they form a pyrrolidine or piperidine ring system. Nevertheless, good yields are obtained in

[77] Skita and Stuhmer, Ger. pat. 716,668 [*C. A.*, **38**, 2345 (1944)].

methylations even when both the alkyl groups of the secondary amine are secondary, as in the following example.[18] In contrast, the alkylation

$$CH_3CH_2CHNHCHCH_2CH_3 + CH_2O + H_2 \xrightarrow{Pt} CH_3CH_2CHNCHCH_2CH_3 + H_2O$$
$$\underset{CH_3 \quad C_2H_5}{\qquad\qquad\qquad} \underset{CH_3 \quad C_2H_5}{\qquad\qquad\qquad\qquad\qquad}$$
(64%)

of diisopropylamine with propionaldehyde gives only a 26% yield, and that of di-*sec*-butylamine with heptaldehyde only a 6% yield. However,

$$[(CH_3)_2CH]_2NH + CH_3CH_2CHO + H_2 \xrightarrow{Pt} [(CH_3)_2CH]_2NCH_2CH_2CH_3 + H_2O$$
(26%)

$$[CH_3CH_2CH(CH_3)]_2NH + CH_3(CH_2)_5CHO + H_2 \xrightarrow{Pt}$$

$$[CH_3CH_2CH(CH_3)]_2N(CH_2)_6CH_3 + H_2O$$
(6%)

good yields are obtained with the higher aliphatic aldehydes when the secondary amine contains only primary alkyl groups.

Most of the preparations of this type have been carried out with hydrogen and platinum catalyst; there are a few examples of the use of nickel catalyst and of chemical reductions (see Table XI).

The only recorded alkylation of a secondary aliphatic amine with an aromatic aldehyde is the preparation, in unspecified yield, of benzyldimethylamine from dimethylamine, benzaldehyde, hydrogen, and platinum.[73]

Only poor yields (up to 47%) are obtained in the preparation of tertiary amines from aliphatic secondary amines and ketones. The yields decrease with increasing size and complexity of the groups attached to the nitrogen atom of the amine or the carbonyl group of the ketone. These effects are shown in Tables VII and VIII, p. 207.

From Secondary Aromatic Amines and Aldehydes and Ketones. Simple alkylanilines can be alkylated in good yields (55–93%) by treatment with formaldehyde or acetaldehyde and zinc and acid. Higher aliphatic aldehydes and aromatic aldehydes have not been tested in similar preparations. The only recorded synthesis of a tertiary amine from an arylalkylamine and a ketone is that employing methylaniline and methyl ethyl glyoxal.[28]

$$C_6H_5NHCH_3 + CH_3COCOCH_2CH_3 + H_2 \xrightarrow{Pd} CH_3CHCOCH_2CH_3$$
$$\underset{C_6H_5NCH_3}{\qquad\qquad\qquad\qquad\qquad\qquad\qquad}$$
(7%)

Of the diarylamines, only diphenylamine has been alkylated by the aid of aldehydes.[18] The reactions were carried out over platinum catalyst, and good yields of the methyl (65%) and ethyl (80%) derivatives were obtained. The yield of the propyl derivative was 53%, and that of the butyl and isobutyl derivatives 33% and 7%, respectively.

SELECTION OF EXPERIMENTAL CONDITIONS

Primary Amines. Of the various procedures for obtaining primary amines, the hydrogenation of an ethanolic solution of ammonia and an aldehyde or an aliphatic ketone in the presence of a Raney nickel catalyst has proved most effective.[1,5,10] The ammonia, usually as a standard ethanolic solution, is used in excess to minimize secondary amine formation.[1,10] When less than one equivalent of ammonia is used, the amount of secondary amine produced increases markedly.[10] The best results have been achieved with hydrogen at pressures of 20–150 atm. At pressures below 20 atm. the hydrogenation is too slow for convenience.[10] A temperature of at least 40° is necessary for the reaction to start,[10] and good results have been obtained from 40° to 150°.[78] For reductions run at 40–75°, 3% of Raney nickel based on the aldehyde is recommended,[10] whereas at 125–150° only 0.5–1.0% is needed.[1]

In the preparation of α-phenylethylamine from acetophenone, ammonia, and hydrogen over Raney nickel catalyst the reduction is run without a solvent.[14] As the temperature required for reasonably rapid reduction (150°) is above the critical temperature of ammonia, an initial pressure of about 330 atm. is required and hydrogen must be added when the pressure falls to 230 atm.

Secondary Amines. The experimental conditions for preparing a secondary amine by hydrogenating an ethanolic solution of an aldehyde or ketone and ammonia are very much the same as for the preparation of a primary amine except that two moles of the carbonyl compound are used for each mole of ammonia.[10,18] With 3% of Raney nickel catalyst, pressures of 20 to 100 atm. and temperatures of 40–75° have proved satisfactory.[10] In these reactions where water is a product, the reaction is facilitated by the solvent, ethanol, which keeps the mixture in a single phase.[10] With 1 g. of platinum catalyst for every 0.17 mole of aldehyde or ketone the reaction proceeds smoothly in aqueous suspension at 3 atm. and 25°, although at 90° the reaction time is reduced appreciably.[11] Even at 90° and 15 atm. the use of a third the amount of catalyst mentioned above not only markedly lengthens the reaction time but also leads to primary amines as the principal products of the reaction.[11] It

---

[78] Adkins, *Reactions of Hydrogen*, University of Wisconsin Press, 1937.

is therefore advisable to use an alcohol solvent, a rather large quantity of catalyst (3% of Raney nickel catalyst), fairly high pressures (perhaps 20 atm.), and a temperature such that hydrogenation proceeds rapidly.

The preparation of secondary amines by the hydrogenation of an ethanolic solution of a primary amine and an aldehyde or ketone may be conducted conveniently in either high- or low-pressure equipment. At 100 to 150 atm. and 125°, 4 g. of nickel on kieselguhr or 10 g. of Raney nickel catalyst is used for a 0.4 to 0.5 M run.[23] The reaction is complete in one to two hours. Usually equimolar amounts of the amine and carbonyl compound are employed,[18, 23, 79] although a 30% excess of the carbonyl compound may be used to ensure complete reaction of the amine.[26, 59, 60, 61] Somewhat milder conditions than those described above are effective. Thus at 75° in a ligroin solvent, a 0.5 M run requires three to twelve hours with 10 g. of Raney nickel catalyst. On the other hand at 150° only 3 g. of Raney nickel catalyst and at 160° 1 g. of copper chromite is necessary for the smooth hydrogenation of a 0.3 M run.[26] Under these conditions the reaction between an amine and a ketone proceeds equally smoothly with or without ethanol as solvent. The use of ethanol is recommended in alkylations with aldehydes to avoid polymerization.[26] It is also advisable to cool the solution of the amine during the addition of the aldehyde. With acetic acid as the solvent extensive polymerization of the aldehyde results.[26, 32]

At pressures of 1 to 2 atm. excellent results have been obtained in 1 M runs using 0.5 g. of platinum oxide catalyst which was reduced before the start of the alkylation.[26] Ethanol or acetic acid was used as the solvent. Alkylation with aldehydes and aliphatic methyl ketones proceeded smoothly without external heat. Such ketones as aceto-phenone, dipropyl ketone, dibutyl ketone, and l-menthone required temperatures of 50–60° in the alkylation of ethanolamine and a longer time (twenty to thirty hours as against seven), while diisobutyl ketone did not react. In place of the 0.5 g. of platinum oxide, 3 g. of palladinized charcoal could serve as the catalyst, although the reaction was much slower, requiring thirty-one hours at 60°. Successful alkylations have also been obtained with colloidal platinum in aqueous suspension.[18] Raney nickel can also be used, but at low pressures a large amount of catalyst is necessary. Good results have been obtained in 0.1 M runs with 1 mole of nickel.[27, 32, 36] With aromatic amines and aliphatic alde-hydes, the use of sodium acetate as a condensing agent (1 g. for a 0.1 M run) increases the yield markedly.[32, 36]

The best way to prepare secondary amines from Schiff's bases is to hydrogenate them catalytically in either high- or low-pressure equip-

[79] Henze and Humphreys, *J. Am. Chem. Soc.*, **64**, 2878 (1942).

ment. With a nickel on kieselguhr catalyst (3 g. for a 0.07 M run) benzalaniline is reduced in five minutes at 65°.[23] With copper chromite (2 g. for a 0.47 M run) the same transformation may be effected in twenty-five minutes at 175°.[23] In low-pressure equipment (2–3 atm.) both pre-reduced platinum and palladium on charcoal are satisfactory catalysts, but Raney nickel leads to side reactions with aliphatic Schiff's bases.[55] Yields of 33–63% with aliphatic Schiff's bases containing 5–9 carbon atoms have been obtained, using 0.2 g. of platinum oxide for 0.3 mole of the Schiff's base, pressures of 2–3 atm., and room temperature.[55]

In preparing secondary amines by the reductive alkylation of nitro compounds, low pressures have been employed primarily.[43] Typical conditions are 0.1 mole of the nitro compound, 0.12 to 0.3 mole of the aldehyde, 3–6 g. of Raney nickel, 150 ml. of ethanol as a solvent, and 2 g. of sodium acetate as a condensing agent.[33, 43] Sodium acetate is by far the most effective condensing agent for this purpose; neither sodium carbonate nor sodium formate is of value.[33] At 3 atm. pressure these alkylations require twelve to twenty-four hours for completion,[43] although most of the reaction is complete in one to two hours (see example below). With ketones as the alkylating agents, an acid condensing agent is necessary.[2] This is usually acetic acid (10 ml. for a 0.1 M run) with platinum (0.1 g. on this scale) used in place of nickel as the hydrogenation catalyst.

Tertiary Amines. The hydrogenation procedures for the reductive alkylation of primary or secondary amines to give tertiary amines are similar to those described previously for the preparation of primary and secondary amines. The carbonyl compound is generally used in excess, although good yields have been obtained with equivalent amounts.[73]

In general, acids act as strong condensing agents in reductive alkylations. Acid systems are therefore seldom used for preparing primary or secondary amines, except where steric hindrance prevents tertiary amine formation as in the case of mesidine.[42] Zinc, hydrochloric acid, and formaldehyde have been used quite frequently to methylate primary and secondary amines to tertiary amines.[42, 80] With powdered zinc the technique has been to dissolve the amine in dilute hydrochloric acid, add the formaldehyde, and then gradually add the zinc (a threefold excess) along with additional hydrochloric acid.[80] With amalgamated zinc all the reagents except the hydrochloric acid were heated to boiling in glacial acetic acid and then the latter was added gradually over a five-hour period and the refluxing continued to a total of twenty-four hours.[42] This high-temperature technique is best suited for hindered

[80] Wagner, *J. Am. Chem. Soc.*, **55**, 724 (1933).

aromatic amines which are sluggish in their reactions.[42] The formaldehyde is used in excess (0.2–0.4 mole for 0.1 mole of amine). With
alkylanilines whose reactive *ortho* and *para* positions are unsubstituted,
the formation of diarylmethanes is avoided by using an equivalent
amount of formaldehyde and conducting the reaction at 25°.[80]

The reductive alkylation of nitro compounds, except where such
activating groups as methyl, hydroxyl, alkoxyl, and amino are *para* to
the nitro group, is effected with an acid condensing agent.[2] Typical
conditions are 0.1 mole of the nitro compound, 0.3 mole of the aldehyde,
10 ml. of glacial acetic acid as the condensing agent, 150 ml. of ethanol
solvent, and 0.1 g. of platinum oxide catalyst. Under these conditions
ketones give secondary amines. Raney nickel may be used as the
catalyst with trimethylamine hydrochloride as the condensing agent, but
this combination is not so effective as that previously described.

ILLUSTRATIVE PREPARATIONS

Benzylamine.[10] Three hundred and eighteen grams (3 moles) of
benzaldehyde is added to a solution of 51 g. (3 moles) of ammonia in
300 ml. of cooled ethanol in the hydrogenation autoclave with 10 g. of
Raney nickel catalyst.[78] Under an initial pressure of 90 atm. hydrogen
absorption starts at 40° and is complete in thirty minutes at a final
temperature of 70°. Distillation of the filtered reaction product gives
287 g. (89%) of benzylamine, b.p. 70–80°/8 mm. and 21.7 g. (7%) of
dibenzylamine, b.p. 140–150°/7 mm.

Dibenzylamine.[10] The preparation is the same as that described for
benzylamine except that half as much ammonia (25.5 g., 1.5 moles) is
used. The yield of benzylamine is 12%, and that of dibenzylamine 81%.

2-(2-Octylamino)-ethanol.[26] In a 1-l. bottle containing 50 ml. of
absolute ethanol, 0.5 g. of platinum oxide [81] is reduced to platinum by
shaking in an atmosphere of hydrogen. A solution of 61 g. of ethanolamine in 100 ml. of absolute ethanol and 166 g. of methyl hexyl ketone
is added. The mixture becomes warm from the heat of the reaction.
The solution is rinsed into the bottle containing the platinum catalyst
with 50 ml. of absolute ethanol and reduced by shaking with hydrogen
at 1–2 atm. pressure for seven hours. The reduction is rapid and
exothermic. The catalyst is removed by filtration, and the bottle and
catalyst are rinsed with 75 ml. of benzene. The benzene and ethanol are
removed from the filtrate by distillation at atmospheric pressure, and
the residue is distilled in vacuum through a Widmer column. The excess

---

[81] Adams, Voorhees, and Shriner, *Org. Syntheses*, *Coll. Vol.* I, 463 (1941).

ketone is recovered as a fore-run. There is practically no distillation residue. The pure amine boils at 130.0–130.5°/12 mm.; yield 166 g., 96%.

N-*n*-Heptylaniline.[32] In the pressure bottle of an apparatus for catalytic reduction [82] are placed 9.3 g. (0.1 mole) of aniline, 1 g. of sodium acetate, 150 ml. of ethanol, 34.2 g. (0.3 mole) of *n*-heptaldehyde, and 58 g. of Raney nickel.[78] The bottle is evacuated, and then an initial pressure of 3 atm. of hydrogen is applied. When, after about thirty-six hours, 0.20–0.25 mole of hydrogen has been absorbed, the reduction is stopped and the catalyst is removed by filtration. The ethanol is then distilled from the filtrate. The residue is subjected to steam distillation and allowed to cool before extracting with three 75-ml. portions of ether. After the combined extracts have been dried over potassium hydroxide, the ether is distilled on the steam bath. The residue is distilled at reduced pressure, the fraction taken being 125–130°/30 mm. The yield is 10 g. (65%).

Benzylaniline.[67] An autoclave for high-pressure hydrogenation is charged with 0.47 mole of benzalaniline and 2 g. of copper chromite.[78] When the reduction is conducted at 175° and 100 atm. hydrogen pressure for four-tenths hour, the yield of benzylaniline is 100%.

In a similar experiment [83] the autoclave is charged with 0.077 mole of benzalaniline in 50 ml. of ethanol and 1 g. of nickel on kieselguhr. At 100 atm. pressure the hydrogenation is conducted for fifteen minutes at 70°. The yield of benzylaniline is 13.5 g. (96.5%), b.p. 144–146°/1 mm.

Butylidenepropylamine.[55] A 250-ml. three-necked conical-bottomed flask, fitted with reflux condenser, mercury seal stirrer, and dropping funnel, is packed in an ice bath. It is charged with 23.6 g. (0.4 mole) of *n*-propylamine, and 28.8 g. (0.4 mole) of butyraldehyde is added gradually over a period of two hours. The reaction mixture is stirred for an additional fifteen minutes; potassium hydroxide flakes are then added, and the mixture is allowed to stand until separation into two layers appears complete; this requires about ten minutes. The organic layer is then removed and allowed to stand over crushed potassium hydroxide in the refrigerator overnight. The dried material is decanted into a 100-ml. conical-bottomed Claisen flask, a few pellets of potassium hydroxide are added, and the material is distilled. There is a small preliminary fraction; the temperature then rises rapidly to 120°, and the bulk of the material distils at 120–124°. The yield is 70%, n_D^{20} 1.4149, d_4^{20} 0.7611. When the treatment with potassium hydroxide is

[82] Adams and Voorhees, *Org. Syntheses, Coll. Vol.* **I**, 61 (1941).
[83] Winans and Adkins, *J. Am. Chem. Soc.*, **54**, 306 (1932).

omitted and another drying agent is substituted, the boiling point of the product rises gradually and continuously, and there is no plateau.

Propylbutylamine.[55] A suspension of 0.20 g. of platinum oxide [81] in 50 ml. of absolute ethanol is shaken with hydrogen at 25 lb. pressure for ten minutes, or until no more hydrogen is absorbed. The hydrogen pressure is then released, and 31.6 g. of freshly distilled butylidenepropylamine (0.28 mole), 50 ml. of absolute ethanol, and 3 ml. of propylamine are added to the catalyst mixture. The mixture is shaken with hydrogen at an initial pressure of 51 lb. until no more hydrogen is absorbed; this requires forty minutes, and 0.26 mole of hydrogen is taken up. The catalyst is removed, and the ethanolic solution is distilled through a small Whitmore-Fenske column at atmospheric pressure and a 4:1 reflux ratio until the ethanol is removed. The residue is distilled through the same column under reduced pressure. The yield of product boiling at 92–93°/200 mm. is 20.8 g. (65%).

N,N-Dimethylmesidine.[42] The apparatus consists of a 1-l. three-necked flask equipped with a reflux condenser, dropping funnel, and mechanical stirrer. In it are placed 10.1 g. (0.075 mole) of mesidine, 17 g. (0.23 mole) of 40% aqueous formaldehyde, 100 g. (1.53 mole) of amalgamated zinc, and 100 ml. of glacial acetic acid. This mixture is refluxed over an electric hot plate for about twenty-four hours, 200 ml. (2.5 moles) of concentrated hydrochloric acid being added during the first five hours. Afterwards the reaction mixture is diluted with water, and sodium hydroxide is added until zinc salts start to precipitate. The product is then extracted with benzene, and the benzene solution is distilled. The N,N-dimethylmesidine boils at 210–221°; yield 8.5 g. (70%).

N-n-Butylaniline.[33, 43] In the pressure bottle of an apparatus for catalytic reduction are placed 12.3 g. (0.10 mole) of freshly distilled nitrobenzene, 2 g. of fused sodium acetate, 150 ml. of 95% ethanol, 9.4 g. (0.13 mole) of freshly distilled n-butyraldehyde and 3 g. of Raney nickel.[78] The bottle is evacuated, and then an initial pressure of 3 atm. of hydrogen is applied. When, after one to two hours, 0.40 to 0.43 mole of hydrogen has been absorbed the reduction is stopped and the catalyst is removed by filtration. After 6 ml. of concentrated hydrochloric acid has been added to the filtrate, the ethanol is distilled on the steam bath. The residue is diluted with 100 ml. of water, made alkaline with 6.5 g. of sodium hydroxide, and then allowed to cool before extraction with three 50-ml. portions of ether. After the combined extracts have been dried over potassium hydroxide, the ether is distilled on the steam bath. The residue is then distilled at atmospheric pressure, the fraction boiling at 235–245° being collected. The yield is 11.5–12 g. (77–81%).

If 22 g. (0.30 mole) of butyraldehyde is used and the reduction is then allowed to run eighteen hours, the yield rises to 13.7–14.3 g. (92–96%). This method is time-consuming and more costly because of the larger amount of aldehyde used, even though the yield is higher.

N,N-Di-*n*-Butylaniline.[2] If, in the preparation just described, 22 g. (0.30 mole) of butyraldehyde is used and 10 ml. of glacial acetic acid is substituted for the sodium acetate and 0.1 g. of platinum oxide [81] for the Raney nickel, 0.66 mole of hydrogen is absorbed in ninety-six hours. The reaction mixture is worked up in the same manner to obtain 14.5 g. (69%) of N,N-di-*n*-butylaniline, b.p. 265–275°.

TABLE I

Preparation of *n*-Heptylamine

Method	Yield, %	Ref.*
Reductive alkylation of ammonia with *n*-heptaldehyde	60	5
Reductive alkylation of ammonia with *n*-heptaldehyde	59	1
Reductive alkylation of ammonia with *n*-heptaldehyde	53–63	14
Reduction of *n*-heptaldoxime with ammonium amalgam	93	84
Reduction of *n*-heptaldoxime with sodium and ethanol	60–73	85
Reduction of *n*-heptaldoxime with sodium and ethanol	69	86
Reduction of *n*-heptaldoxime with hydrogen and Raney nickel	64 †	87
Reduction of *n*-heptaldehyde phenylhydrazone with sodium amalgam and acetic acid	23	88
Hofmann reaction with caprylamide	30	89
Reduction of heptylamide with hydrogen and copper chromite	39 ‡	90
Reaction of *n*-heptyl bromide with ammonia	47 §	91

* References 84–91 are listed on p. 254.
† There is also formed 16% of di-*n*-heptylamine.
‡ There is also formed 58% of di-*n*-heptylamine.
§ There is also formed 37% of di-*n*-heptylamine.

TABLE II

PREPARATION OF BENZYLAMINE

Method	Yield		Ref.*
	Benzyl-amine %	Dibenzyl-amine %	
Reductive alkylation of ammonia with benzaldehyde	89	7	10
Reduction of benzaldoxime with aluminum amalgam	88	—	92
Reduction of benzaldoxime with hydrogen and palladium	Almost quant.	—	93
Reduction of benzaldoxime with zinc and acetic acid	94	—	94
Reduction of benzaldoxime with hydrogen and nickel	90	—	95
Reduction of benzaldoxime acetate with hydrogen and palladium	91	—	96
Reduction of benzaldoxime with hydrogen and nickel on kieselguhr	77	19	4
Reduction of benzaldoxime with hydrogen and Raney nickel	73	20	4
Reduction of benzaldazine with hydrogen and nickel on kieselguhr	68	26	4
Treatment of benzylmagnesium chloride with chloramine	92	—	97
Treatment of benzylmagnesium chloride with hydroxylamine O-benzyl ether	79	—	98
Treatment of benzyl chloride with sodium iodide and hexamethylenetetramine	82.5	—	99
Curtius degradation of phenylacetic acid	92	—	100
Gabriel synthesis	90	—	101
Treatment of benzyl chloride with liquid ammonia	53	39	102
Electrolytic reduction of the imino ether hydrochloride	76	—	103
Electrolytic reduction of benzamide	74	—	104
Electrolytic reduction of benzaldehyde phenylhydrazone	43	12 †	105
Reduction of benzonitrile with hydrogen and palladium in acetic acid	80	—	96
Reduction of benzonitrile with hydrogen and nickel	72	5	106
Reduction of benzonitrile with hydrogen and platinum in the presence of acetic anhydride	69	—	107

* References 92–107 are listed on p. 254.
† There is also formed 23% of benzyl alcohol.

TABLE III

Preparation of Dibenzylamine

Method	Yield		Ref.*
	Benzyl- amine %	Dibenzyl- amine %	
Reductive alkylation of ammonia with benzaldehyde	12	81	10
Disproportionation of benzylamine in the presence of hydrogen and palladium in boiling xylene	—	90	108
Treatment of benzylamine with trimethylbenzylammonium bromide	—	90	109
Reduction of benzonitrile with hydrogen and platinum in ethanol	21	79	107
Hydrolysis of dibenzylcyanamide	—	55	110
Reduction of benzaldoxime with hydrogen and Raney nickel	20	75	87

* References 108–110 are listed on p. 254.

TABLE IV

PREPARATION OF N-n-BUTYLANILINE

Method	Yield, %	Ref.*
Reductive alkylation of nitrobenzene with n-butyraldehyde, hydrogen, Raney nickel, and sodium acetate	94, 96	43
Reductive alkylation of azobenzene with n-butyraldehyde	71	48
Reductive alkylation of nitrosobenzene with n-butyraldehyde	56	47
Reductive alkylation of aniline with n-butyraldehyde	47	32
Alkylation of aniline with n-butyl bromide	75	111
Alkylation of aniline with n-butyl bromide	69	112
Alkylation of aniline with n-butyl chloride	60	112
Alkylation of aniline with n-butyl chloride	49 †	113
Alkylation of aniline with n-butyl methanesulfonate	68	114
Alkylation of aniline with n-butyl p-toluenesulfonate	64	114
Alkylation of aniline with n-butyl p-toluenesulfonate	66	112
Alkylation of aniline with aluminum n-butoxide	77	115
Alkylation of formanilide with n-butyl bromide	50	116
Alkylation of aniline with n-butyl alcohol over silica gel	24 ‡	117

* References 111–117 are listed on p. 254.
† There is also formed 16% of di-n-butylaniline.
‡ There is also formed 8% of di-n-butylaniline.

TABLE V

PREPARATION OF BENZYLANILINE

Method	Yield, %	Ref.*
Reduction of benzalaniline with hydrogen and copper chromite	100	67
Reduction of benzalaniline with hydrogen and nickel	97	83
Reduction of benzalaniline with hydrogen and nickel	Almost quant.	118
Reduction of benzalaniline with hydrogen and nickel	Excellent	119
Reduction of benzalaniline with magnesium and methanol	70–90	65
Reduction of benzalaniline electrolytically	83	68
Reduction of benzalaniline with sodium amalgam and ethanol	74	120
Reduction of benzalaniline with sodium amyloxide	73	121
Reductive alkylation of nitrobenzene with benzaldehyde	33	43
Reductive alkylation of azobenzene with benzaldehyde	49	48
Alkylation of aniline with benzyl chloride	85–87	122
Alkylation of aniline with benzyl alcohol and alumina	81	123
Alkylation of formanilide with benzaldehyde and formic acid	29	124

* References 118–124 are listed on p. 254.

TABLE VI

PREPARATION OF DI-n-BUTYLANILINE

Method	Yield, %	Ref.*
Reductive alkylation of nitrobenzene with n-butyraldehyde, hydrogen, and platinum	69	2
Alkylation of aniline with n-butyl p-toluenesulfonate	80	112
Alkylation of aniline with n-butyl phosphate	78.5	125
Alkylation of aniline hydrochloride with n-butyl alcohol	75.5	126

* References 125–126 are listed on p. 254.

TABLE VII

ALKYLATIONS WITH ACETONE [18]

Secondary Amine Alkylated	Yield of Tertiary Amine %
$CH_3CH_2CH(CH_3)NHCH_3$	47
$(CH_3)_2CH(CH_2)_2NHCH_2CH_3$	24
$(CH_3)_2CH(CH_2)_2NH(CH_2)_2CH(CH_3)_2$	14
$CH_3CH_2CH(CH_3)NHCH_2CH_3$	2

TABLE VIII

ALKYLATION OF METHYL sec-BUTYLAMINE [18]

Ketone	Yield of Tertiary Amine %
CH_3COCH_3	47
$CH_3COCH_2CH_3$	18
$CH_3CO(CH_2)_2CH_3$	17
$CH_3CO(CH_2)_3CH_3$	8
$CH_3CO(CH_2)_4CH_3$	3
$CH_3CO(CH_2)_5CH_3$	0.6
$CH_3CH_2COCH_2CH_3$	0.02
Cyclohexanone	15
2-Methylcyclohexanone	0
3-Methylcyclohexanone	5
4-Methylcyclohexanone	4

TABULAR SURVEY OF REDUCTIVE ALKYLATIONS REPORTED PRIOR TO JANUARY 1, 1945

TABLE IX

PREPARATION OF PRIMARY AMINES

A. From Ammonia and Aliphatic Aldehydes

Carbonyl Compound	Reducing Agent	Products Isolated	Yield, %	Ref.*
CH2O (Ammonium sulfate, rather than ammonia, was used in this reaction.)	Electrolytic (lead cathode)	CH3NH2	—	3
		(CH3)3N	—	5
CH3CHO	H2 + Ni	CH3CH2NH2	68	22
		(CH3CH2)2NH	—	
CH3CHO	Zn + HCl	CH3CH2NH2	—	5
CH3(CH2)2CHO	H2 + Ni	CH3(CH2)3NH2	69	4
		[CH3(CH2)3]2NH	—	
CH3(CH2)2CHO	H2 + Ni	CH3(CH2)3NH2	32	
		[CH3(CH2)3]2NH	12	
		substituted pyridine (ring bearing C2H5, H5C2(CH2)2–, CH3(CH2)2–, N)		
CH3(CH2)2CHO	H2 + Ni	CH3(CH2)3NH2	23	9
(CH3)2CHCHO	H2 + Ni	(CH3)2CHCH2NH2	—	9
CH3(CH2)5CHO	H2 + Ni	CH3(CH2)6NH2	53–63	14
CH3(CH2)5CHO	H2 + Ni	CH3(CH2)6NH2	60	5
CH3(CH2)5CHO	H2 + Ni	CH3(CH2)6NH2	59	1
CH3(CH2)5CHO	H2 + Ni	CH3(CH2)6NH2	32	4
		[CH3(CH2)6]2NH	12	
CH2=CHCHO	H2 + Ni	CH3(CH2)2NH2	Good	6, 7

Aldehyde	Reagent	Amine	Yield	References
$CH_3CH=CHCHO$	$H_2 + Ni + Co$	$CH_3(CH_2)_3NH_2$ $[CH_3(CH_2)_3]_2NH$	Good —	6, 7
$CH_3(CH_2)_2CH=C(CH_2CH_3)CHO$	$H_2 + Ni$	$CH_3(CH_2)_3CH(CH_2CH_3)CH_2NH_2$	60	7
$(CH_3)_2C=CH(CH_2)_2C(CH_3)=CHCHO$	$H_2 + Pt$	$(CH_3)_2CH(CH_2)_3CH(CH_3)(CH_2)_2NH_2$	—	20
Glucose	$H_2 + Ni$	$CH_2OH(CHOH)_4CH_2NH_2$	26	8
$C_6H_5CH_2CHO$	$H_2 + Ni$	$C_6H_5CH_2CH_2NH_2$	64	1
$C_6H_5CH_2CHO$	$Al-Hg + H_2O$	$C_6H_5CH_2CH_2NH_2$ $(C_6H_5CH_2CH_2)_2NH$	— —	127
$C_6H_5CH=CHCHO$	$H_2 + Ni$	$C_6H_5(CH_2)_3NH_2$	—	6, 7

B. From Ammonia and Aromatic Aldehydes

Aldehyde	Reagent	Amine	Yield	References
C_6H_5CHO	$H_2 + Ni$	$C_6H_5CH_2NH_2$ $(C_6H_5CH_2)_2NH$	89 7	10
C_6H_5CHO	$H_2 + Ni$	$C_6H_5CH_2NH_2$	70	13
C_6H_5CHO	$H_2 + Ni$	$C_6H_5CH_2NH_2$	48	1
C_6H_5CHO	$H_2 + Ni$	$C_6H_5CH=NCH_2C_6H_5$	equal parts	5
$o\text{-}CH_3C_6H_4CHO$	$H_2 + Ni$	$o\text{-}CH_3C_6H_4CH_2NH_2$ $(o\text{-}CH_3C_6H_4CH_2)_2NH$	83 16	10
$o\text{-}ClC_6H_4CHO$	$H_2 + Ni$	$o\text{-}ClC_6H_4CH_2NH_2$ $(o\text{-}ClC_6H_4CH_2)_2NH$	88 8	10
$p\text{-}C_2H_5C_6H_4CHO$	$H_2 + Ni$	$p\text{-}C_2H_5C_6H_4CH_2NH_2$	71	5
Furfural	$H_2 + Ni$	Furfurylamine Difurfurylamine	79 6	10
Furfural	$H_2 + Ni$	Furfurylamine	60	1
Furfural	$H_2 + Ni$	Furfurylamine	50	14

* References 127–133 are listed on p. 254.

TABLE IX—*Continued*

PREPARATION OF PRIMARY AMINES

C. From Ammonia and Ketones

Carbonyl Compound	Reducing Agent	Products Isolated	Yield, %	Ref.*
CH_3COCH_3	$H_2 + Ni$	$(CH_3)_2CHNH_2$	62	5
		$[(CH_3)_2CH]_2NH$	10	
CH_3COCH_3	$H_2 + Ni$	$(CH_3)_2CHNH_2$	32	11
CH_3COCH_3	$Na + CH_3CH_2OH$	$(CH_3)_2CHNH_2$	—	128
		$[(CH_3)_2CH]_2NH$	—	
$CH_3COCH_2CH_3$	$H_2 + Ni$	$CH_3CH_2CH(CH_3)NH_2$	29	11
$CH_3CH_2COCH_2CH_3$	$H_2 + Ni$	$(CH_3CH_2)_2CHNH_2$	—	11
$CH_3CO(CH_2)_2CH_3$	$H_2 + Ni$	$CH_3(CH_2)_2CH(CH_3)NH_2$	88–91	12
$CH_3CO(CH_2)_2CH_3$	$Na + CH_3CH_2OH$	$CH_3(CH_2)_2CH(CH_3)NH_2$	—	128
$(CH_3)_2CHCH_2COCH_3$	$H_2 + Ni$	$(CH_3)_2CHCH_2CH(CH_3)NH_2$	65	1
$(CH_3)_3CCOCH_3$	$H_2 + Ni$	$(CH_3)_3CCH(CH_3)NH_2$	51	1
$(CH_3)_2CHCOCH(CH_3)_2$	$H_2 + Ni$	$[(CH_3)_2CH]_2CHNH_2$	48	1
$CH_3CO(CH_2)_4CH_3$	$H_2 + Ni$	$CH_3(CH_2)_4CH(CH_3)NH_2$	75–80	129
$CH_3CO(CH_2)_4CH_3$	$H_2 + Ni$	$CH_3(CH_2)_4CH(CH_3)NH_2$	50–55	14
$CH_3CO(CH_2)_5CH_3$	$H_2 + Ni$	$CH_3(CH_2)_5CH(CH_3)NH_2$	93	5
$CH_3(CH_2)_3CO(CH_2)_3CH_3$	$H_2 + Ni$	$[CH_3(CH_2)_3]_2CHNH_2$	72	1
Cyclohexanone	$H_2 + Ni$	Cyclohexylamine	80	13
Cyclohexanone	$H_2 + Ni$	Cyclohexylamine	79	5
Cyclohexanone	$H_2 + Pt$	Cyclohexylamine	50	11
Cyclohexanone	$H_2 + Ni$	Cyclohexylamine	—	9

Carbonyl compound	Catalyst	Amine	Yield (%)	Reference
$(CH_3)_2C=CHCOCH_3$	$H_2 + Ni$	$(CH_3)_2CHCH_2CH(CH_3)NH_2$	60	7
$(CH_3)_2C=CH(CH_2)_2COCH_3$	$H_2 + Ni$	$(CH_3)_2C=CH(CH_2)_2CH(CH_3)NH_2$	60	5
$CH_3(CH_2)_{13}CO(CH_2)_2CO_2H$	$H_2 + Ni$	$CH_3(CH_2)_{13}CHNH_2(CH_2)_2CO_2H$	30	130
$CH_3COCH_2COCH_3$	$H_2 + Ni$	CH_3CONH_2	100	1
$C_6H_5COCH_3$	$H_2 + Ni$	$C_6H_5CH(CH_3)NH_2$	44–52	14
$C_6H_5COCH_3$	$H_2 + Ni$	$C_6H_5CH(CH_3)NH_2$	25–35	5
$C_6H_5COCH_3$	$H_2 +$	$C_6H_5CH(CH_3)NH_2$	15	131
		$C_6H_5CHOHCH_3$	40	
$C_6H_5COCH_2CH_3$	$H_2 + Ni$	$C_5H_5CH(CH_2CH_3)NH_2$	23–35	5
$o\text{-}HOC_6H_4COCH_2CH_3$	$H_2 + Ni$	$o\text{-}HOC_6H_4CH(CH_2CH_3)NH_2$	Quantitative	131
$m\text{-}HOC_6H_4COCH_2CH_3$	$H_2 + Ni$	$m\text{-}HOC_6H_4CHOHCH_2CH_3$	Sole product	131
$p\text{-}HOC_6H_4COCH_2CH_3$	$H_2 + Ni$	$p\text{-}HOC_6H_4CH(CH_2CH_3)NH_2$	Poor	131
$o\text{-}CH_3OC_6H_4COCH_2CH_3$	$H_2 + Ni$	$o\text{-}CH_3OC_6H_4CH(CH_2CH_3)NH_2$	Poor	131
		$o\text{-}CH_3OC_6H_4CHOHCH_2CH_3$	—	
$p\text{-}CH_3OC_6H_4COCH_2CH_3$	$H_2 + Ni$	$p\text{-}CH_3OC_6H_4CH(CH_2CH_3)NH_2$	Poor	131
		$p\text{-}CH_3OC_6H_4CHOHCH_2CH_3$	—	
$C_6H_5CH_2COCH_3$	$H_2 + Ni$	$C_6H_5CH_2CH(CH_3)NH_2$	Quantitative	131
$C_6H_5CH_2COCH_3$	$H_2 + Ni$	$C_6H_5CH_2CH(CH_3)NH_2$	40	132
$p\text{-}HOC_6H_4CH_2COCH_3$	$H_2 + Ni$	$p\text{-}HOC_6H_4CH_2CH(CH_3)NH_2$	97	133
$C_6H_5COC_6H_5$	$H_2 + Ni$	$(C_6H_5)_2CHNH_2$	19	1

(anthraquinone structure)	$Na_2S_2O_4$	(9,10-diaminoanthracene structure)	35	15

* References 127–133 are listed on p. 254.

TABLE X

Preparation of Secondary Amines

A. From Ammonia and Aliphatic Aldehydes

Carbonyl Compound	Reducing Agent	Products Isolated	Yield, %	Ref.*
CH_3CHO	$H_2 + Ni$	$CH_3CH_2NH_2$ $(CH_3CH_2)_2NH$ $(CH_3CH_2)_3N$	20, 4,† —† 50, 68,† 84† 20, 2,† 16†	16, 17, 19
$CH_3(CH_2)_2CHO$	$H_2 + Ni$	$CH_3(CH_2)_3NH_2$ $[CH_3(CH_2)_3]_2NH$ $[CH_3(CH_2)_3]_3N$	15–31, —† 17–40, 80† 8–22, 20†	16, 19
$(CH_3)_2CHCH_2CHO$	$H_2 + Ni$	$[(CH_3)_2CH(CH_2)_2]_2NH$ $(CH_3)_2CH(CH_2)_2NH_2$	27 15	18
$CH_3(CH_2)_5CHO$	$H_2 + Pt$	$[CH_3(CH_2)_6]_2NH$	—	20
$(CH_3)_2C=CH(CH_2)_2C(CH_3)=CHCHO$	$H_2 + Pt$	$[(CH_3)_2CH(CH_2)_3CH(CH_3)(CH_2)_2]_2NH$	23	18
$(CH_3)_2C=CH(CH_2)_2C(CH_3)=CHCHO$	$H_2 + Pt$	$[(CH_3)_2CH(CH_2)_3CH(CH_3)(CH_2)_2]_2NH$	—	20

B. From Ammonia and Aromatic Aldehydes

Carbonyl Compound	Reducing Agent	Products Isolated	Yield, %	Ref.*
C_6H_5CHO	$H_2 + Ni$	$(C_6H_5CH_2)_2NH$ $C_6H_5CH_2NH_2$	81, 81 12, 17	10, 21
C_6H_5CHO	$H_2 + Pt$	$(C_6H_5CH_2)_2NH$	—	11
C_6H_5CHO	$H_2 + Pd$	$(C_6H_5CH_2)_2NH$	—	134
$o\text{-}CH_3C_6H_4CHO$	$H_2 + Ni$	$(o\text{-}CH_3C_6H_4CH_2)_2NH$	82, 59 11, 14	10, 21
$o\text{-}ClC_6H_4CHO$	$H_2 + Ni$	$(o\text{-}ClC_6H_4CH_2)_2NH_2$ $o\text{-}ClC_6H_4CH_2NH_2$	85 4	10
Furfural	$H_2 + Ni$	Difurfurylamine Furfurylamine	66, 66 12, 12	10, 21
Furfural	$H_2 + Ni$	Difurfurylamine	—	21

C. From Ammonia and Ketones

Carbonyl Compound	Reducing Agent	Products Isolated	Yield, %	Ref.
CH_3COCH_3	$H_2 + Pt$	$[(CH_3)_2CH]_2NH$	28	20
CH_3COCH_3	$H_2 + Pt$	$[(CH_3)_2CH]_2NH$	27	18
$CH_3COCH_2CH_3$	$H_2 + Pt$	$[CH_3CH_2CH(CH_3)]_2NH$	37	18
$CH_3COCH_2CH_3$	$H_2 + Pt$	$[CH_3CH_2CH(CH_3)]_2NH$	—	20
$CH_3CH_2COCH_2CH_3$	$H_2 + Pt$	$[(CH_3CH_2)_2CH]_2NH$	20	20
Cyclohexanone	$H_2 + Pt$	Dicyclohexylamine	54	11
Cyclohexanone	$H_2 + Pt$	Dicyclohexylamine	—	20
$CH_3COCH_2CH_2COCH_3$	$H_2 + Ni$	(see structures)	59 / 28	1
$C_6H_5COCH_3$	$H_2 + Pt$	$[C_6H_5CH(CH_3)]_2NH$	—	11

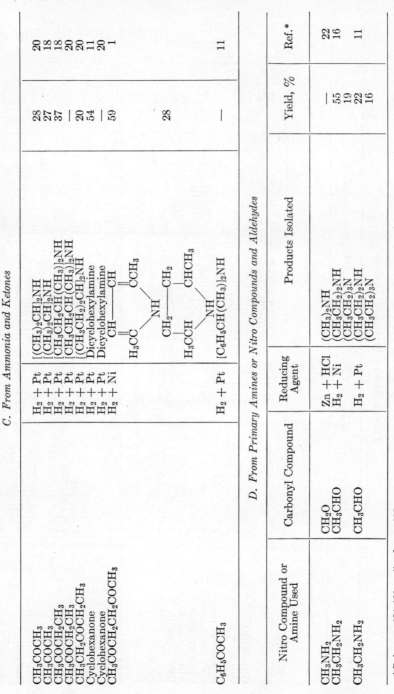

D. From Primary Amines or Nitro Compounds and Aldehydes

Nitro Compound or Amine Used	Carbonyl Compound	Reducing Agent	Products Isolated	Yield, %	Ref.*
CH_3NH_2	CH_2O	$Zn + HCl$	$(CH_3)_2NH$	—	22
$CH_3CH_2NH_2$	CH_3CHO	$H_2 + Ni$	$(CH_3CH_2)_2NH$	55	16
			$(CH_3CH_2)_3N$	19	
$CH_3CH_2NH_2$	CH_3CHO	$H_2 + Pt$	$(CH_3CH_2)_2NH$	22	11
			$(CH_3CH_2)_3N$	16	

* References 134–180 are listed on p. 255.

† In the presence of ammonia *plus the primary amine isolated from a previous run.*

TABLE X—Continued

PREPARATION OF SECONDARY AMINES

D. From Primary Amines or Nitro Compounds and Aldehydes—Continued

Nitro Compound or Amine Used	Carbonyl Compound	Reducing Agent	Products Isolated	Yield, %	Ref.*
$CH_3(CH_2)_3NH_2$	$CH_3(CH_2)_2CHO$	$H_2 + Ni$	$[CH_3(CH_2)_3]_2NH$ $[CH_3(CH_2)_3]_3N$	48 47	16
$(CH_3)_2CH(CH_2)_2NH_2$	CH_3CHO	$H_2 + Pt$	$(CH_3)_2CH(CH_2)_2NHCH_2CH_3$	67	18
$(CH_3)_2CH(CH_2)_2NH_2$	$(CH_3)_2C=CH(CH_2)_2C(CH_3)=CHCHO$	$H_2 + Pt$	$CH_3(CH_2)_2CH(CH_3)(CH_2)_2CH(CH_3)(CH_2)_2NH(CH_2)_2CH(CH_3)_2$	91	18
Cyclohexylamine	$CH_3(CH_2)_2CHO$	$H_2 + Ni$	$C_6H_{11}NH(CH_2)_3CH_3$	—	23, 24
Cyclohexylamine	Arabinose	$H_2 + Ni$	$C_6H_{11}NHCH_2(CHOH)_3CH_2OH$	68	11, 25
Cyclohexylamine	Mannose	$H_2 + Pt$	$C_6H_{11}NHCH_2(CHOH)_4CH_2OH$	62	11, 25
$HO(CH_2)_2NH_2$	$CH_3(CH_2)_2CHO$	$H_2 + Pt$	$HO(CH_2)_2NH(CH_2)_3CH_3$	70	26
$HO(CH_2)_2NH_2$	$(CH_3)_2CHCHO$	$H_2 + Pt$	$HO(CH_2)_2NHCH_2CH(CH_3)_2$	71	26
$HO(CH_2)_2NH_2$	$CH_3(CH_2)_3CHO$	$H_2 + Pt$	$HO(CH_2)_2NH(CH_2)_4CH_3$	91	26
$HO(CH_2)_2NH_2$	$CH_3(CH_2)_5CHO$	$H_2 + Pt$	$HO(CH_2)_2NH(CH_2)_6CH_3$	90	26
$HO(CH_2)_2NH_2$	$CH_3(CH_2)_3CH=C(CH_2CH_3)CHO$	$H_2 + Pt$	$HO(CH_2)_2NHCH_2CH(CH_2CH_3)(CH_2)_4CH_3$	89	26
$CH_3CHOHCH_2NH_2$	$(CH_3)_2CHCH_2CH_2CHO$	$H_2 + Pt$	$CH_3CHOHCH_2NH(CH_2)_2CH(CH_3)_2$	90	59
$(CH_3)_2COHCH_2NH_2$	$(CH_3)_2CHCH_2CH_2CHO$	$H_2 + Pt$	$(CH_3)_2COHCH_2NH(CH_2)_2CH(CH_3)_2$	89	60
$CH_3COCH_2C(CH_3)_2NH_2$	CH_2O	—	$CH_3COCH_2C(CH_3)_2NHCH_3$	72–80	135
$CH_3COCH_2C(CH_3)_2NH_2$	CH_3CHO	—	$CH_3COCH_2C(CH_3)_2NHCH_2CH_3$	Quantitative	136
$CH_3COCH_2C(CH_3)_2NH_2$	C_6H_5CHO	—	$CH_3COCH_2C(CH_3)_2NHCH_2C_6H_5$	—	136
$H_2N(CH_2)_2NH_2$	CH_3CH_2CHO	$H_2 + Ni$	$H_2N(CH_2)_2NH(CH_2)_2CH_3$	42	137
$H_2N(CH_2)_2NH_2$	$CH_3(CH_2)_2CHO$	$H_2 + Ni$	$CH_3(CH_2)_3NH(CH_2)_2NH(CH_2)_3CH_3$	59	137
$H_2N(CH_2)_2NH_2$	$CH_3(CH_2)_5CHO$	$H_2 + Ni$	$H_2N(CH_2)_2NH(CH_2)_6CH_3$	13	137
$H_2N(CH_2)_2NH_2$	$CH_3(CH_2)_3CH(CH_2CH_3)CHO$	$H_2 + Ni$	$H_2N(CH_2)_2NHCH_2CH(CH_2CH_3)(CH_2)_3CH_3$	60	137
$H_2N(CH_2)_2NH_2$	$CH_3(CH_2)_{10}CHO$	$H_2 + Ni$	$H_2N(CH_2)_2NH(CH_2)_{11}CH_3$	61	137

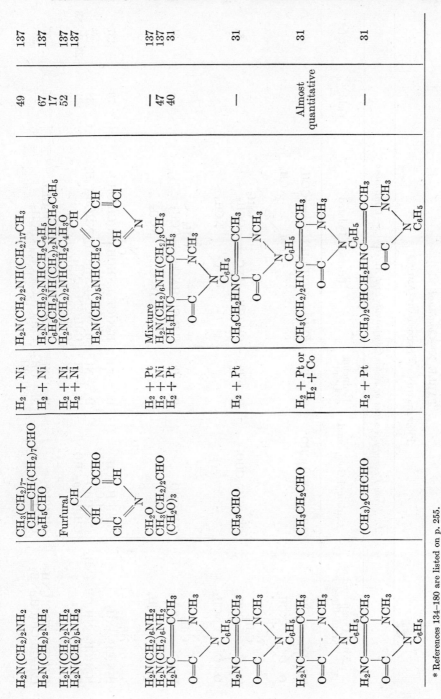

TABLE X—*Continued*

PREPARATION OF SECONDARY AMINES

D. From Primary Amines or Nitro Compounds and Aldehydes—Continued

Nitro Compound or Amine Used	Carbonyl Compound	Reducing Agent	Products Isolated	Yield, %	Ref.*
$H_2NC{=}CCH_3$, $O{=}C$ N NCH_3, C_6H_5	$(CH_3)_2CHCH_2CHO$	$H_2 + Pt$	$(CH_3)_2CH(CH_2)_2HNC{=}CCH_3$, NCH_3, $O{=}C$ N, C_6H_5	—	31
$H_2NC{=}CCH_3$, $O{=}C$ N NCH_3, C_6H_5	$CH_3(CH_2)_5CHO$	$H_2 + Pt$	$CH_3(CH_2)_6HNC{=}CCH_3$, NCH_3, $O{=}C$ N, C_6H_5	—	31
$H_2NC{=}CCH_3$, $O{=}C$ N NCH_3, C_6H_5	C_6H_5CHO	$H_2 + Pt$	$C_6H_5CH_2HNC{=}CCH_3$, NCH_3, $O{=}C$ N, C_6H_5	—	31
$H_2N(CH_2)_6NH_2$	$CH_3(CH_2)_3CH(CH_2CH_3)CHO$	$H_2 + Pd$	$H_2N(CH_2)_6NHCH_2CH(CH_2CH_3){-}(CH_2)_3CH_3$	70	137
$H_2N(CH_2)_2NH(CH_2)_2NH_2$, $C_6H_5(CH_2)_2NH_2$	C_6H_5CHO, $CH_3(CH_2)_2CHO$	$H_2 + Ni$, $H_2 + Ni$	$H_2N(CH_2)_2NH(CH_2)_2NHCH_2C_6H_5$, $C_6H_5(CH_2)_2NH(CH_2)_2NH_2$, $C_6H_5(CH_2)_2NH(CH_2)_3CH_3$, $C_6H_5(CH_2)_2N[(CH_2)_3CH_3]_2$	38, 21, 36, 11	137, 23, 24, 83
$C_6H_5CH(CH_3)CH_2NH_2$, $C_6H_5CH_2CH(CH_3)NH_2$	CH_3CHO, CH_2O	$H_2 + Ni$, $Al + CH_3{-}CH_2OH$	$C_6H_5CH(CH_3)CH_2NHCH_2CH_3$, $C_6H_5CH_2CH(CH_3)NHCH_3$	94, —	27, 138

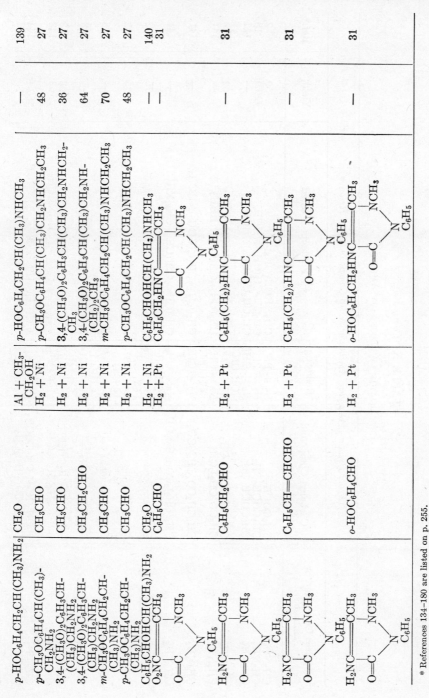

p-HOC$_6$H$_4$CH$_2$CH(CH$_3$)NH$_2$	CH$_2$O	Al + CH$_3$-CH$_2$OH	p-HOC$_6$H$_4$CH$_2$CH(CH$_3$)NHCH$_3$	—	139
p-CH$_3$OC$_6$H$_4$CH(CH$_3$)-CH$_2$NH$_2$	CH$_3$CHO	H$_2$ + Ni	p-CH$_3$OC$_6$H$_4$CH(CH$_3$)CH$_2$NHCH$_2$CH$_3$	48	27
3,4-(CH$_3$O)$_2$C$_6$H$_3$CH-(CH$_3$)CH$_2$NH$_2$	CH$_3$CHO	H$_2$ + Ni	3,4-(CH$_3$O)$_2$C$_6$H$_3$CH(CH$_3$)CH$_2$NHCH$_2$-CH$_3$	36	27
3,4-(CH$_3$O)$_2$C$_6$H$_3$CH-(CH$_3$)CH$_2$NH$_2$	CH$_3$CH$_2$CHO	H$_2$ + Ni	3,4-(CH$_3$O)$_2$C$_6$H$_3$CH(CH$_3$)CH$_2$NH-(CH$_2$)$_2$CH$_3$	64	27
m-CH$_3$OC$_6$H$_4$CH$_2$CH-(CH$_3$)NH$_2$	CH$_3$CHO	H$_2$ + Ni	m-CH$_3$OC$_6$H$_4$CH$_2$CH(CH$_3$)NHCH$_2$CH$_3$	70	27
p-CH$_3$OC$_6$H$_4$CH$_2$CH-(CH$_3$)NH$_2$	CH$_3$CHO	H$_2$ + Ni	p-CH$_3$OC$_6$H$_4$CH$_2$CH(CH$_3$)NHCH$_2$CH$_3$	48	27
C$_6$H$_5$CHOHCH(CH$_3$)NH$_2$	CH$_2$O	H$_2$ + Ni	C$_6$H$_5$CHOHCH(CH$_3$)NHCH$_3$	—	140
	C$_6$H$_5$CHO	H$_2$ + Pt	C$_6$H$_5$CH$_2$HNCH—CCH$_3$	—	31
(structure)	C$_6$H$_5$CH$_2$CH$_2$CHO	H$_2$ + Pt	C$_6$H$_5$(CH$_2$)$_2$HNCH—CCH$_3$	—	31
(structure)	C$_6$H$_5$CH=CHCHO	H$_2$ + Pt	C$_6$H$_5$(CH$_2$)$_3$HNCH—CCH$_3$	—	31
(structure)	o-HOC$_6$H$_4$CHO	H$_2$ + Pt	o-HOC$_6$H$_4$CH$_2$HNCH—CCH$_3$	—	31

TABLE X—*Continued*

PREPARATION OF SECONDARY AMINES

E. From Primary Aliphatic Amines or Nitro Compounds and Ketones

Nitro Compound or Amine Used	Carbonyl Compound	Reducing Agent	Products Isolated	Yield, %	Ref.*
CH_3NO_2	CH_3COCH_3	$H_2 + Pt$	$CH_3NHCH(CH_3)_2$	59	2
CH_3NH_2	$CH_3COCH_2CH_3$	$H_2 + Pt$	$CH_3CH_2CH(CH_3)NHCH_3$	69	18
CH_3NH_2	$CH_3COCH_2CH_3$	$Na + CH_3$-CH_2OH	$CH_3CH_2CH(CH_3)NHCH_3$	—	141
CH_3NH_2	$CH_3CH_2COCH_2CH_3$	$H_2 + Pt$	$(CH_3CH_2)_2CHNHCH_3$	62	18
CH_3NH_2	$CH_3CO(CH_2)_2CH_3$	$Na + CH_3$-CH_2OH	$CH_3(CH_2)_2CH(CH_3)NHCH_3$	—	141
CH_3NH_2	$CH_3CH_2CO(CH_2)_2CH_3$	$Na + CH_3$-CH_2OH	$CH_3(CH_2)_2CH(CH_2CH_3)NHCH_3$	—	141
CH_3NH_2	$CH_3(CH_2)_2CO(CH_2)_2CH_3$	$Na + CH_3$-CH_2OH	$CH_3(CH_2)_2CH[(CH_2)_2CH_3]NHCH_3$	—	141
CH_3NH_2	Cyclohexanone	$Na + CH_3$-CH_2OH	$C_6H_{11}NHCH_3$	75	142
CH_3NH_2	Cycloheptanone	$Na + CH_3$-CH_2OH	$C_7H_{13}NHCH_3$	75	142
CH_3NH_2	Cycloheptanone	$Na + CH_3$-CH_2OH	$C_7H_{13}NHCH_3$	—	128
CH_3NH_2	$C_6H_5CH_2COCH_3$	$Na + CH_3$-CH_2OH	$C_6H_5CH_2CH(CH_3)NHCH_3$	—	128
CH_3NH_2	p-$HOC_6H_4CH_2COCH_3$	$H_2 + Ni$	p-$HOC_6H_4CH_2CH(CH_3)NHCH_3$	93	143
CH_3NH_2	p-$HOC_6H_4CH_2COCH_3$	$Al + CH_3$-CH_2OH	p-$HOC_6H_4CH_2CH(CH_3)NHCH_3$	93	143
CH_3NH_2	m-$CH_3OC_6H_4CH_2CH_2COCH_3$	$Al + H_2O$	m-$CH_3OC_6H_4CH_2CH(CH_3)NHCH_3$	80–90	144
CH_3NH_2	$CH_3COCO(CH_2)_2CH_3$	$H_2 + Pd$	$CH_3CH(NHCH_3)CO(CH_2)_2CH_3$	29	28

Amine	Carbonyl compound	Catalyst	Product	Yield	References
CH_3NH_2	$CH_3COCO(CH_2)_2CH_3$	$H_2 + Pt$	$CH_3CH(NHCH_3)CHOH(CH_2)_2CH_3$; $H_3CCOH{-}CH_2$ / NCH_3 / $CH_3(CH_2)_2CH{-}CHCHOH(CH_2)_2CH_3$	30 ; 17	29, 30
CH_3NH_2	$C_6H_5COCOCH_3$	$H_2 + Pt$	$C_6H_5CHOHCH(CH_3)NHCH_3$	63	30, 145
CH_3NH_2	$C_6H_5COCOCH_3$	$H_2 + Pt$	$C_6H_5CHOHCH(CH_3)NHCH_3$	50	29
CH_3NH_2	$C_6H_5COCOCH_3$	$H_2 + Pt$	$C_6H_5CHOHCH(CH_3)NHCH_3$	30–49	146, 147
CH_3NH_2	$C_6H_5COCOCH_3$	$H_2 + Ni$	$C_6H_5CHOHCH(CH_3)NHCH_3$	Good	131
CH_3NH_2	$C_6H_5COCOCH_3$	$H_2 + Pd$	$C_6H_5CHOHCH(CH_3)NHCH_3$	16–36	28
CH_3NH_2	$p\text{-}CH_3OC_6H_4COCOCH_3$	$H_2 + Pd$	$C_6H_5COCH(CH_3)NHCH_3$	16–41	28
CH_3NH_2	$C_6H_5COCOC_6H_5$	$H_2 + Pd$	$p\text{-}CH_3OC_6H_4COCH(CH_3)NHCH_3$	44	29, 30
CH_3NH_2	$CH_3COCH_2COCH_3$	$H_2 + Pt$	$C_6H_5CH(NHCH_3)CHOHC_6H_5$	—	73
CH_3NH_2	$C_6H_5COCH_2COCH_3$	$H_2 + Pt$	$CH_3CH(NHCH_3)CH_2CHOHCH_3$	—	29, 30
CH_3NH_2	$C_6H_5O(CH_2)_2COCH_2CH(CH_3){-}CO(CH_2)_2CH_3$	$H_2 + Pt$	$C_6H_5O(CH_2)_2CH(CH_3)NHCH_3$; $CH_3(CH_2)_2CHNHCH_3$	35 ; —	148
$CH_3CH_2NH_2$	$CH_3COCH_2CH_3$	$H_2 + Pt$	$CH_3CH_2CH(CH_3)NHCH_2CH_3$	84	18
$CH_3CH_2NH_2$	$CH_3COCH_2CH_3$	$H_2 + Pt$	$CH_3CH_2CH(CH_3)NHCH_2CH_3$	Good	20
$CH_3CH_2NH_2$	Cyclohexanone	$H_2 + Ni$	$C_6H_{11}NHCH_2CH_3$	Good	20
$CH_3CH_2NH_2$	$o\text{-}HOC_6H_4COCH_2CH_3$	$H_2 + Pt$	$o\text{-}HOC_6H_4CH(CH_2CH_3)NHCH_2CH_3$	Excellent	131
$CH_3CH_2NH_2$	$C_6H_5CH_2COCH_3$	$H_2 + Pt$	$C_6H_5CH_2CH(CH_3)NHCH_2CH_3$	82	149
$CH_3CH_2NH_2$	$CH_3COCH_2COCH_3$	$H_2 + Pt$	$C_6H_5CHOHCH(CH_3)NHCH_2CH_3$	55	73
$CH_3CH_2NH_2$	$C_6H_5COCH_2COCH_3$	$H_2 + Pt$	$C_6H_5CHOHCH(CH_3)NHCH_2CH_3$	39	73
$CH_3(CH_2)_3NH_2$	$C_6H_5COCH_2COCH_3$	$H_2 + Ni$	$CH_3(CH_2)_3NHCH(CH_3)_2$	34	73
$(CH_3)_2CH(CH_2)_2NH_2$	CH_3COCH_3	$H_2 + Ni$	$CH_3(CH_2)_3NHCH(CH_3)CH_2CH_3$	52	79
$(CH_3)_2CH(CH_2)_2NH_2$	$C_6H_5COCOCH_3$	$H_2 + Pt$	$C_6H_5CHOHCH(CH_3)NH(CH_2)_2CH(CH_3)_2$	51	79
	$C_6H_5COCH_2COCH_3$	$H_2 + Pt$	$C_6H_5CHOHCH(CH_3)NH(CH_2)_2{-}CH(CH_3)_2$	—	73
				17	73
$(CH_3CH_2)_2CHNH_2$	$CH_3COCH_2CH_3$	$H_2 + Pt$	$(CH_3CH_2)_2CHNHCH(CH_3)CH_2CH_3$	61	18
$(CH_3CH_2)_2CHNH_2$	$C_6H_5COCOC_6H_5$	$H_2 + Pd$	$C_6H_5COCH(C_6H_5)NHCH(CH_2CH_3)_2$	9	28
$CH_3(CH_2)_6NH_2$	$C_6H_5COCOCH_3$	$H_2 + Pt$	$C_6H_5CHOHCH(CH_3)NH(CH_2)_6CH_3$	—	73
Cyclohexylamine	CH_3COCH_3	$H_2 + Pt$	$C_6H_{11}NHCH(CH_3)_2$	79	11

* References 134–180 are listed on p. 255.

TABLE X—*Continued*

PREPARATION OF SECONDARY AMINES

E. From Primary Aliphatic Amines or Nitro Compounds and Ketones—Continued

Nitro Compound or Amine Used	Carbonyl Compound	Reducing Agent	Products Isolated	Yield, %	Ref.*
Cyclohexylamine	$CH_3CH_2COCH_2CH_3$	H_2 + Pt	$C_6H_{11}NHCH(CH_2CH_3)_2$	31	11
Cyclohexylamine	$CH_3COCH_2CH_3$	H_2 + Pt	$C_6H_{11}NHCH(CH_3)CH_2CH_3$	60	11
Cyclohexylamine	Cyclohexanone	H_2 + Ni	Dicyclohexylamine	70	23, 24, 83
Cyclohexylamine	Cyclohexanone	H_2 + Pt	Dicyclohexylamine	63	11
Cyclohexylamine	CH_3COCH_2OH	H_2 + Pt	$C_6H_{11}NHCH(CH_3)CH_2OH$	—	11
Cyclohexylamine	$CH_3CH_2COCOCH_3$	H_2 + Pd	$CH_3CH_2COCH(CH_3)NHC_6H_{11}$	18	28
Cyclohexylamine	$CH_3(CH_2)_2COCOCH_3$	H_2 + Pd	$CH_3(CH_2)_2COCH(CH_3)NHC_6H_{11}$	10	28
Cyclohexylamine	$C_6H_5COCOCH_3$	H_2 + Pd	$C_6H_5COCH(CH_3)NHC_6H_{11}$	19	28
Cyclohexylamine	$C_6H_5COCOC_6H_5$	H_2 + Pd	$C_6H_5COCH(C_6H_5)NHC_6H_{11}$	24	28
Cyclohexylamine	$p\text{-}CH_3OC_6H_4COCOCH_3$	H_2 + Pt	$p\text{-}CH_3OC_6H_4COCH(CH_3)NHC_6H_{11}$	—	29
Cyclohexylamine	$CH_3COCH_2COCH_3$	H_2 + Pd	$CH_3CHOHCH_2CH(CH_3)NHC_6H_{11}$	24	28
Cyclohexylamine	$CH_3COCH(CH_3)COCH_3$	H_2 + Pt	$CH_3CHOHCH(CH_3)CH(CH_3)NHC_6H_{11}$	27	11, 30
$HO(CH_2)_2NH_2$	CH_3COCH_3	H_2 + Pt	$HO(CH_2)_2NHCH(CH_3)_2$	—	29
$HO(CH_2)_2NH_2$	$CH_3COCH_2CH_3$	H_2 + Pt	$HO(CH_2)_2NHCH(CH_3)CH_2CH_3$	95	26
$HO(CH_2)_2NH_2$	$CH_3CO(CH_2)_2CH_3$	H_2 + Pt	$HO(CH_2)_2NHCH(CH_3)(CH_2)_2CH_3$	98	26
$HO(CH_2)_2NH_2$	$CH_3COCH_2CH(CH_3)_2$	H_2 + Pt	$HO(CH_2)_2NHCH(CH_3)CH_2CH(CH_3)_2$	95	26
$HO(CH_2)_2NH_2$	$CH_3CO(CH_2)_3CH_3$	H_2 + Pt	$HO(CH_2)_2NHCH(CH_3)(CH_2)_3CH_3$	97	26
$HO(CH_2)_2NH_2$	$CH_3CO(CH_2)_4CH_3$	H_2 + Pt	$HO(CH_2)_2NHCH(CH_3)(CH_2)_4CH_3$	98	26
$HO(CH_2)_2NH_2$	$CH_3(CH_2)_2CO(CH_2)_2CH_3$	H_2 + Pt	$HO(CH_2)_2NHCH[(CH_2)_2CH_3]_2$	98	26
$HO(CH_2)_2NH_2$	$CH_3CO(CH_2)_5CH_3$	H_2 + Pt	$HO(CH_2)_2NHCH(CH_3)(CH_2)_5CH_3$	96	26
$HO(CH_2)_2NH_2$	$CH_3CO(CH_2)_6CH_3$	H_2 + Pt	$HO(CH_2)_2NHCH(CH_3)(CH_2)_6CH_3$	96	26
$HO(CH_2)_2NH_2$	$CH_3(CH_2)_3CO(CH_2)_3CH_3$	H_2 + Pt	$HO(CH_2)_2NHCH[(CH_2)_3CH_3]_2$	92	26
$HO(CH_2)_2NH_2$	$CH_3(CH_2)_3CO(CH_2)_3CH_3$	H_2 + Pt	$HO(CH_2)_2NHCH[(CH_2)_3CH_3]_2$	94	26
$HO(CH_2)_2NH_2$	$(CH_3)_2CHCH_2COCH_2CH(CH_3)_2$	H_2 + Pt	$HO(CH_2)_2NHCH[CH_2CH(CH_3)_2]_2$	94	26

Amine	Carbonyl Compound	Reducing Agent	Product	Yield (%)	Reference
$HO(CH_2)_2NH_2$	$CH_3CO(CH_2)_7CH_3$	$H_2 + Pt$	$HO(CH_2)_2NHCH(CH_3)(CH_2)_7CH_3$	97	26
$HO(CH_2)_2NH_2$	Cyclohexanone	$H_2 + Pt$	$HO(CH_2)_2NHC_6H_{11}$	96	26
$HO(CH_2)_2NH_2$	[cyclohexanone ring: CH_2, CH_2CHCH_3, CH_2CH_2, CO]	$H_2 + Pt$	[ring: CH_2, CH_2CHCH_3, CH_2CH_2] $HO(CH_2)_2HNCH$	88	26
$HO(CH_2)_2NH_2$	[ring: H_3CCH, CH_2CHCH_3, CH_2CH_2, CO]	$H_2 + Pt$	[ring: $CHCH_3$, CH_2CH_2, CH_2CH_2] $HO(CH_2)_2HNCH$	98	26
$HO(CH_2)_2NH_2$	[ring: CH_2, CH_2CHCH_3, CH_2CH_2, $CH_2C(CH_3)_2$, $C=O$]	$H_2 + Pt$	[ring: CH_2CHCH_3, $CH(CH_3)CH_2$, $CH_2C(CH_3)_2$] $CHNH(CH_2)_2OH$	98	26
$HO(CH_2)_2NH_2$	1-Menthone	$H_2 + Pt$	[ring: CH_2, $CH_2C(CH_3)_2$, $CH(CH_3)CH_2$, $CHCH(CH_3)_2$] $CHNH(CH_2)_2OH$	80	26
$HO(CH_2)_2NH_2$	$CH_3COC_6H_5$	$H_2 + Pt$	$C_6H_5CH(CH_3)NH(CH_2)_2OH$	95	26
$HO(CH_2)_2NH_2$	$CH_3(CH_2)_2COCOCH_3$	$H_2 + Pd$	$CH_3(CH_2)_2COCH(CH_3)NH(CH_2)_2OH$	17	28
$HO(CH_2)_2NH_2$	$C_6H_5COCOCH_3$	$H_2 + Pd$	$C_6H_5COCH(CH_3)NH(CH_2)_2OH$	23	28
$HO(CH_2)_2NH_2$	$C_6H_5COCOCH_3$	$H_2 + Pt$	$C_6H_5CHOHCH(CH_3)NH(CH_2)_2OH$	20	73
$HO(CH_2)_2NH_2$	$CH_3COCH_2COCH_3$	$H_2 + Pt$	$CH_3CHOHCH_2CH(CH_3)NH(CH_2)_2OH$	—	25
$CH_3CHOHCH_2NH_2$	CH_3COCH_3	$H_2 + Pt$	$CH_3CHOHCH_2NHCH(CH_3)_2$	97	59
$CH_3CHOHCH_2NH_2$	$CH_3CH_2COCH_2CH_3$	$H_2 + Pt$	$CH_3CHOHCH_2NHCH(CH_3)CH_2CH_3$	99	59
$CH_3CHOHCH_2NH_2$	$CH_3COCH_2COCH_3$	$H_2 + Pt$	$CH_3CHOHCH_2NHCH(CH_3)_2$	88	59
$CH_3CHOHCH_2NH_2$	$CH_3COCH_2CH(CH_3)_2$	$H_2 + Pt$	$CH_3CHOHCH_2NHCH(CH_3)CH_2-CH(CH_3)_2$	95	59
$CH_3CHOHCH_2NH_2$	$CH_3CO(CH_2)_4CH_3$	$H_2 + Pt$	$CH_3CHOHCH_2NHCH(CH_3)(CH_2)_4CH_3$	97	59
$CH_3CHOHCH_2NH_2$	$CH_3(CH_2)_2CO(CH_2)_2CH_3$	$H_2 + Pt$	$CH_3CHOHCH_2NHCH((CH_2)_2CH_3)_2$	97	59

* References 134–180 are listed on p. 255.

TABLE X—Continued

PREPARATION OF SECONDARY AMINES

E. From Primary Aliphatic Amines or Nitro Compounds and Ketones—Continued

Nitro Compound or Amine Used	Carbonyl Compound	Reducing Agent	Products Isolated	Yield, %	Ref.*
$CH_3CHOHCH_2NH_2$	$CH_3CO(CH_2)_5CH_3$	$H_2 + Pt$	$CH_3CHOHCH_2NHCH(CH_3)(CH_2)_5CH_3$	96	59
$CH_3CHOHCH_2NH_2$	$CH_3(CH_2)_3CO(CH_2)_3CH_3$	$H_2 ++ Pt$	$CH_3CHOHCH_2NHCH[(CH_2)_3CH_3]_2$	81	59
$CH_3CHOHCH_2NH_2$	$CH_3(CH_2)_4CO(CH_2)_4CH_3$	$H_2 ++ Pt$	$CH_3CHOHCH_2NHCH[(CH_2)_4CH_3]_2$	88	59
$CH_3CHOHCH_2NH_2$	$CH_3(CH_2)_5CO(CH_2)_5CH_3$	$H_2 +++ Pt$	$CH_3CHOHCH_2NHCH[(CH_2)_5CH_3]_2$	80.5	59
$CH_3CHOHCH_2NH_2$	$CH_3(CH_2)_6CO(CH_2)_6CH_3$	$H_2 +++ Pt$	$CH_3CHOHCH_2NHCH[(CH_2)_6CH_3]_2$	94	59
$CH_3CHOHCH_2NH_2$	$CH_3(CH_2)_8CO(CH_2)_8CH_3$	$H_2 + Pt$	$CH_3CHOHCH_2NHCH[(CH_2)_8CH_3]_2$	68	59
$CH_3CHOHCH_2NH_2$	Cyclohexanone	$H_2 + Pt$	$CH_3CHOHCH_2NHC_6H_{11}$	95	59
$CH_3CHOHCH_2NH_2$	$H_3CCH\langle\overset{CH_2CH_2}{CH_2CH_2}\rangle CO$	$H_2 + Pt$	$CH_3CHOHCH_2NHCH\langle\overset{CHCH_3}{CH_2CH_2}\rangle$	93	59
$HOCH_2CH(CH_3)NH_2$	$CH_3CH_2COCH_2CH_3$	$H_2 + Pt$	$HOCH_2CH(CH_3)NHCH(CH_2CH_3)_2$	64	60
$HOCH_2CH(CH_3)NH_2$	$CH_3(CH_2)_2CO(CH_2)_2CH_3$	$H_2 ++ Pt$	$HOCH_2CH(CH_3)NHCH[(CH_2)_2CH_3]_2$	84	60
$HOCH_2CH(CH_3)NH_2$	$CH_3(CH_2)_3CO(CH_2)_3CH_3$	$H_2 +++ Pt$	$HOCH_2CH(CH_3)NHCH[(CH_2)_3CH_3]_2$	72	60
$HOCH_2CH(CH_3)NH_2$	Cyclohexanone	$H_2 + Pt$	$HOCH_2CH(CH_3)NHC_6H_{11}$	82	60
$HO(CH_2)_3NH_2$	$CH_3CO(CH_2)_4CH_3$	$H_2 + Pt$	$HO(CH_2)_3NHCH(CH_3)(CH_2)_4CH_3$	90	61
$HO(CH_2)_3NH_2$	$CH_3(CH_2)_2CO(CH_2)_2CH_3$	$H_2 + Pt$	$HO(CH_2)_3NHCH[(CH_2)_2CH_3]_2$	98	61
$HO(CH_2)_3NH_2$	$CH_3CO(CH_2)_5CH_3$	$H_2 + Pt$	$HO(CH_2)_3NHCH(CH_3)(CH_2)_5CH_3$	90	61
$HO(CH_2)_3NH_2$	Cyclohexanone	$H_2 + Pt$	$HO(CH_2)_3NHC_6H_{11}$	78	61
$HOCH_2CH(CH_2CH_3)NH_2$	CH_3COCH_3	$H_2 + Pt$	$HOCH_2CH(CH_2CH_3)NHCH(CH_3)_2$	93	60
$HOCH_2CH(CH_2CH_3)NH_2$	$CH_3(CH_2)_3CO(CH_2)_3CH_3$	$H_2 + Pt$	$HOCH_2CH(CH_2CH_3)NHCH[(CH_2)_3CH_3]_2$	50	60
$HOCH_2CH(CH_2CH_3)NH_2$	Cyclohexanone	$H_2 + Pt$	$HOCH_2CH(CH_2CH_3)NHC_6H_{11}$	68	60
$(CH_3)_2COHCH_2NH_2$	CH_3COCH_3	$H_2 + Pt$	$(CH_3)_2COHCH_2NHCH(CH_3)_2$	96	60
$(CH_3)_2COHCH_2NH_2$	$CH_3CH_2COCH_2CH_3$	$H_2 ++ Pt$	$(CH_3)_2COHCH_2NHCH(CH_2CH_3)_2$	96	60
$(CH_3)_2COHCH_2NH_2$	$CH_3CO(CH_2)_4CH_3$	$H_2 + Pt$	$(CH_3)_2COHCH_2NHCH(CH_3)(CH_2)_4CH_3$	98	60

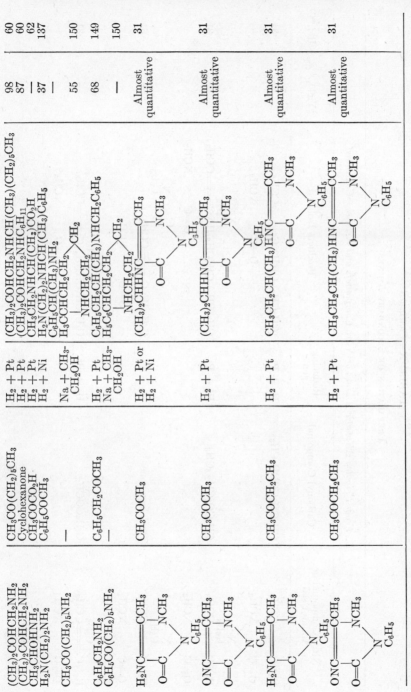

Amine	Carbonyl Compound	Reducing Agent	Product	Yield (%)	Reference
$(CH_3)_2COHCH_2NH_2$	$CH_3CO(CH_2)_5CH_3$	$H_2 + Pt$	$(CH_3)_2COHCH_2NHCH(CH_3)(CH_2)_5CH_3$	98	60
$(CH_3)_2COHCH_2NH_2$	Cyclohexanone	$H_2 + Pt$	$(CH_3)_2COHCH_2NHC_6H_{11}$	87	60
$CH_3CHOHNH_2$	CH_3COCO_2H	$H_2 + Pt$	$CH_3CH_2NHCH(CH_3)CO_2H$	—	62
$H_2N(CH_2)_2NH_2$	$C_6H_5COCH_3$	$H_2 + Ni$	$C_6H_5CH(CH_3)NHCH(CH_3)C_6H_5$	37	137
$CH_3CO(CH_2)_5NH_2$	—	$Na + CH_3CH_2OH$	$H_3CCHCH_2CH_2\ \backslash CH_2$ / $NHCH_2CH_2$	55	150
$C_6H_5CH_2NH_2$	$C_6H_5CH_2COCH_3$	$H_2 + Pt$	$C_6H_5CH_2CH(CH_3)NHCH_2C_6H_5$	68	149
$C_6H_5CO(CH_2)_5NH_2$	—	$Na + CH_3CH_2OH$	$H_5C_6CHCH_2CH_2\ \backslash CH_2$ / $NHCH_2CH_2$	—	150

* References 134–180 are listed on p. 255.

TABLE X—*Continued*

PREPARATION OF SECONDARY AMINES

E. *From Primary Aliphatic Amines or Nitro Compounds and Ketones—Continued*

Nitro Compound or Amine Used	Carbonyl Compound	Reducing Agent	Products Isolated	Yield, %	Ref.*
H_2NC=CCH_3, NCH_3, O=C–N, C_6H_5	$CH_3CH_2COCH_2CH_3$	$H_2 + Pt$	$(CH_3CH_2)_2CHHNC$=CCH_3, NCH_3, O=C–N, C_6H_5	—	31
H_2NC=CCH_3, NCH_3, O=C–N, C_6H_5	$CH_3CO(CH_2)_5CH_3$	$H_2 + Pt$	$CH_3(CH_2)_5CH(CH_3)HNC$=CCH_3, NCH_3, O=C–N, C_6H_5	—	31
H_2NC=CCH_3, NCH_3, O=C–N, C_6H_5	Cyclohexanone	$H_2 + Pt$	$C_6H_{11}HNC$=CCH_3, NCH_3, O=C–N, C_6H_5	—	31
H_2NC=CCH_3, NCH_3, O=C–N, C_6H_5	$C_6H_5COCH_3$	$H_2 + Pt$	$C_6H_5CH(CH_3)HNC$=CCH_3, NCH_3, O=C–N, C_6H_5	—	31

F. *From Primary Aromatic Amines, Nitro, Nitroso, or Azo Compounds and Aldehydes*

Amine, Nitro, Nitroso, or Azo Compound Used	Carbonyl Compound	Reducing Agent	Products Isolated	Yield, %	Ref.*
$C_6H_5NH_2$	CH_2O	$Zn + NaOH$	$C_6H_5NHCH_3$	55	151
$C_6H_5NO_2$	CH_2O	$H_2 + Ni$	$C_6H_5NHCH_3$	50	43
$C_6H_5NH_2$	CH_2O	$Zn + NaOH$	$C_6H_5NHCH_3$	—	39
$C_6H_5NH_2$	CH_3CHO	$Zn + H_2SO_4$	$C_6H_5NHCH_2CH_3$	82	34
$C_6H_5NO_2$	CH_3CHO	$Zn + H_2SO_4$	$C_6H_5NHCH_2CH_3$	80	34
C_6H_5NO	CH_3CHO	$H_2 + Ni$	$C_6H_5NH_2$	80	47
$C_6H_5NH_2$	CH_3CHO	$Zn + H_2SO_3$	$C_6H_5NHCH_2CH_3$	21	35
$C_6H_5NO_2$	CH_3CHO	$H_2 + Ni$	$C_6H_5NHCH_2CH_3$	60	43
$C_6H_5NH_2$	CH_3CHO	$H_2 + Ni$	$C_6H_5NHCH_2CH_3$	57, 63	32, 33
$C_6H_5NH_2$	CH_3CHO	$H_2 + Pt$	$C_6H_5NHCH_2CH_3$	58	32, 33
$C_6H_5NH_2$	CH_3CHO	$H_2 + Ni$ (NaOH)	$C_6H_5NHCH_2CH_3$	41	32
$C_6H_5NH_2$	CH_3CHO	$H_2 + Ni$	$C_6H_5N(CH_2CH_3)_2$	25	32
$C_6H_5NH_2$	CH_3CH_2CHO	$H_2 + Ni$	$C_6H_5NH(CH_2)_2CH_3$	10	32
$C_6H_5NO_2$	$CH_3(CH_2)_2CHO$	$H_2 + Ni$	$C_6H_5NH(CH_2)_2CH_3$	52	43
$C_6H_5NO_2$	$CH_3(CH_2)_2CHO$	$H_2 + Ni$	$C_6H_5NH(CH_2)_2CH_3$	94, 96	33
$C_6H_5N{=}NC_6H_5$	$CH_3(CH_2)_2CHO$	$H_2 + Ni$	$C_6H_5NH(CH_2)_2CH_3$	74–92	48
C_6H_5NO	$CH_3(CH_2)_2CHO$	$H_2 + Ni$	$C_6H_5NH_2$	71	47
$C_6H_5NH_2$	$CH_3(CH_2)_2CHO$	$H_2 + Ni$	$C_6H_5NH(CH_2)_3CH_3$	56	32
$C_6H_5NO_2$	$CH_3(CH_2)_2CHO$	$H_2 + Ni$	$C_6H_5N[(CH_2)_3CH_3]_2$	—	33
$C_6H_5NH_2$	$CH_3(CH_2)_3CHO$	$H_2 + Ni$	$C_6H_5NH(CH_2)_4CH_3$	47	32, 33
$C_6H_5NO_2$	$CH_3(CH_2)_3CHO$	$H_2 + Ni$	$C_6H_5NH(CH_2)_4CH_3$	27–74	
$C_6H_5NH_2$	$CH_3(CH_2)_5CHO$	$H_2 + Ni$	$C_6H_5NH(CH_2)_6CH_3$	12–20	
$C_6H_5NO_2$	$CH_3(CH_2)_5CHO$	$H_2 + Ni$	$C_6H_5NH(CH_2)_6CH_3$	84	43
$C_6H_5NH_2$	$CH_3(CH_2)_5CHO$	$H_2 + Ni$	$C_6H_5NH(CH_2)_6CH_3$	62	32
$C_6H_5NO_2$	$CH_3(CH_2)_2CHO$	$H_2 + Ni$	$C_6H_5NHCH_2C_6H_5$	74	48
$C_6H_5NOHCH_2C_6H_5$	$CH_3(CH_2)_2CHO$	$H_2 + Ni$	$C_6H_5NHCH_2C_6H_5$	65	32, 33
$C_6H_5N{=}NC_6H_5$	C_6H_5CHO	$H_2 + Ni$	$C_6H_5NHCH_2C_6H_5$	40	43
			$C_6H_5NHCH_2C_6H_5$	54	2
			$C_6H_5NHCH_2C_6H_5$	49	48

* References 134–180 are listed on p. 255.

TABLE X—Continued

PREPARATION OF SECONDARY AMINES

F. From Primary Aromatic Amines, Nitro, Nitroso, or Azo Compounds and Aldehydes—Continued

Amine, Nitro, Nitroso, or Azo Compound Used	Carbonyl Compound	Reducing Agent	Products Isolated	Yield, %	Ref.*
C_6H_5NO	C_6H_5CHO	H_2 + Ni	$C_6H_5NHCH_2C_6H_5$	47	47
$C_6H_5NO_2$	C_6H_5CHO	H_2 + Ni	$C_6H_5NH_2$	—	43
		Zn + H_2SO_3	$C_6H_5NHCH_2C_6H_5$	33	35
$o\text{-}CH_3C_6H_4NH_2$	CH_3CHO	H_2 + Ni	$o\text{-}CH_3C_6H_4NHCH_2CH_3$	80	36
$p\text{-}CH_3C_6H_4NH_2$	CH_3CHO	H_2 + Ni	$p\text{-}CH_3C_6H_4NHCH_2CH_3$	50	43
$p\text{-}CH_3C_6H_4NO_2$	$CH_3(CH_2)_2CHO$	H_2 + Ni	$p\text{-}CH_3C_6H_4NH(CH_2)_3CH_3$	85, 40	36
$p\text{-}CH_3C_6H_4NH_2$	$CH_3(CH_2)_2CHO$	H_2 + Ni	$p\text{-}CH_3C_6H_4NH(CH_2)_3CH_3$	53	33, 43
			$p\text{-}CH_3C_6H_4N[(CH_2)_3CH_3]_2$	58	
$p\text{-}CH_3C_6H_4NO_2$	$CH_3(CH_2)_5CHO$	H_2 + Ni	$p\text{-}CH_3C_6H_4NH(CH_2)_6CH_3$	19	
			$p\text{-}CH_3C_6H_4N[(CH_2)_6CH_3]_2$	35	
				34	
$2,4,6\text{-}(CH_3)_3C_6H_2NH_2$	$(CH_3)_2CHCHO$	Zn + HCl	$2,4,6\text{-}(CH_3)_3C_6H_2NHCH_2CH(CH_3)_2$	91	42
$2,4,6\text{-}(CH_3)_3C_6H_2NH_2$	$(CH_3)_2CHCH_2CHO$	Zn + HCl	$2,4,6\text{-}(CH_3)_3C_6H_2NH(CH_2)_2CH(CH_3)_2$	94	42
$2,4,6\text{-}(CH_3)_3C_6H_2NO_2$	$(CH_3)_2CHCH_2CHO$	Zn + HCl	$2,4,6\text{-}(CH_3)_3C_6H_2NH(CH_2)_2CH(CH_3)_2$	61	42
$p\text{-}ClC_6H_4NO_2$	$CH_3(CH_2)_2CHO$	H_2 + Ni	$p\text{-}ClC_6H_4NH_2$	—	33
			$p\text{-}ClC_6H_4NH(CH_2)_3CH_3$	—	
			$C_6H_5N[(CH_2)_3CH_3]_2$	—	
$p\text{-}HOC_6H_4NH_2$	CH_3CHO	Al + NaOH	$p\text{-}HOC_6H_4NHCH_2CH_3$	56	37, 38
$p\text{-}HOC_6H_4NO_2$	$CH_3(CH_2)_2CHO$	H_2 + Ni	$p\text{-}HOC_6H_4NH(CH_2)_3CH_3$	39	45
$p\text{-}HOC_6H_4NH_2$	$CH_3(CH_2)_2CHO$	Al + NaOH	$p\text{-}HOC_6H_4N[(CH_2)_3CH_3]_2$	28, 77, 90	37, 38
$p\text{-}HOC_6H_4NH_2$	$(CH_3)_2CHCHO$	H_2 + Ni	$p\text{-}HOC_6H_4NHCH_2CH(CH_3)_2$	82	64
$p\text{-}HOC_6H_4NO_2$	$(CH_3)_2CHCHO$	H_2 + Ni	$p\text{-}HOC_6H_4NHCH_2CH(CH_3)_2$	—	45
$p\text{-}HOC_6H_4NO_2$	$(CH_3)_2CHCHO$	Zn + NaOH	$p\text{-}HOC_6H_4NHCH_2CH(CH_3)_2$	—	45
$p\text{-}HOC_6H_4NO$	$CH_3(CH_2)_2CHO$	H_2 + Pt	$p\text{-}HOC_6H_4NH(CH_2)_3CH_3$	—	45
$p\text{-}HOC_6H_4NH_2$	$CH_3(CH_2)_3CHO$	Al + NaOH	$p\text{-}HOC_6H_4NH(CH_2)_4CH_3$	—	37, 38

Amine	Carbonyl compound	Reducing agent	Product	Yield (%)	References
$p\text{-}HOC_6H_4NH_2$	$(CH_3CH_2)_2CHCHO$	$Al + NaOH$	$p\text{-}HOC_6H_4NHCH_2CH(CH_2CH_3)_2$	10, 56	37, 38
$p\text{-}HOC_6H_4NH_2$	$CH_3CH{=}CHCHO$	$H_2 + Ni$	$p\text{-}HOC_6H_4NH(CH_2)_3CH_3$	95	64
$p\text{-}HOC_6H_4NH_2$	$CH_3CH_2CH{=}C(CH_3)CHO$	$H_2 + Pt$	$p\text{-}HOC_6H_4NHCH_2CH(CH_3)(CH_2)_2CH_3$	103	64
$p\text{-}HOC_6H_4NH_2$	$CH_3CH(CH_3)CH{=}C(CH_3)CHO$	$H_2 + Pt$	$p\text{-}HOC_6H_4NHCH_2CH(CH_3)CH_2CH(CH_3)_2$	—	64
$p\text{-}HOC_6H_4NH_2$	C_6H_5CHO	$H_2 + Ni$	$p\text{-}HOC_6H_4NHCH_2C_6H_5$	—	152
$o\text{-}CH_3OC_6H_4NH_2$	CH_2O	$Zn + NaOH$	$o\text{-}CH_3OC_6H_4NHCH_3$	51	39
$p\text{-}CH_3OC_6H_4NH_2$	CH_3CHO	$H_2 + Ni$	$p\text{-}CH_3OC_6H_4NHCH_2CH_3$	65	33, 36
$p\text{-}CH_3OC_6H_4NH_2$	$CH_3(CH_2)_2CHO$	$H_2 + Ni$	$p\text{-}CH_3OC_6H_4NH(CH_2)_3CH_3$	25	33, 36
$p\text{-}CH_3OC_6H_4NO_2$	$CH_3(CH_2)_2CHO$	$H_2 + Ni$	$p\text{-}CH_3OC_6H_4N[(CH_2)_3CH_3]_2$	31	43
$p\text{-}CH_3OC_6H_4NH_2$	$(CH_3CH_2)_2NCH_2CHO \cdot HCl$	$H_2 + Ni$	$p\text{-}CH_3OC_6H_4NH(CH_2)_2N(CH_2CH_3)_2$	50	51
$p\text{-}C_6H_5CONHC_6H_4NH_2$	CH_3CHO	$Zn + H_2SO_4$	$p\text{-}C_6H_5CONHC_6H_4NHCH_2CH_3$	94	34
$p\text{-}C_6H_5CONHC_6H_4NH_2$	CH_3CH_2CHO	$Zn + CH_3CO_2H$	$p\text{-}C_6H_5CONHC_6H_4NH(CH_2)_2CH_3$	70	34
$p\text{-}HO_2CC_6H_4NH_2$	$C_6H_5CH(CH_3)CHO$	$H_2 + Pt,\ Ni\ or\ Co$	$p\text{-}HO_2CC_6H_4NHCH_2CH(CH_3)C_6H_5$	—	77
$p\text{-}CH_3O_2CC_6H_4NH_2$	CH_3CH_2CHO	$Zn + CH_3CO_2H$	$p\text{-}CH_3O_2CC_6H_4NH(CH_2)_2CH_3$	30	153
$p\text{-}CH_3O_2CC_6H_4NH_2$	$CH_3(CH_2)_2CHO$	$Zn + CH_3CO_2H$	$p\text{-}CH_3O_2CC_6H_4NH(CH_2)_3CH_3$	47	153
$p\text{-}CH_3CH_2O_2CC_6H_4NH_2$	CH_3CH_2CHO	$Zn + CH_3CO_2H$	$p\text{-}CH_3CH_2O_2CC_6H_4NH(CH_2)_2CH_3$	45	153
$p\text{-}CH_3CH_2O_2CC_6H_4NH_2$	$CH_3(CH_2)_2CHO$	$H_2 + Pt,\ Ni\ or\ Co$	$p\text{-}CH_3CH_2O_2CC_6H_4NH(CH_2)_3CH_3$	—	77
$p\text{-}CH_3CH_2O_2CC_6H_4NH_2$	CH_3CH_2CHO	$Zn + CH_3CO_2H$	$p\text{-}CH_3CH_2O_2CC_6H_4NH(CH_2)_2CH_3$	80	153
$p\text{-}CH_3CH_2O_2CC_6H_4NH_2$	$(CH_3)_2CHCHO$	$H_2 + Pt,\ Ni\ or\ Co$	$p\text{-}CH_3CH_2O_2CC_6H_4NH(CH_2)_3CH_3$	—	77
$p\text{-}CH_3CH_2O_2CC_6H_4NH_2$	C_6H_5CHO	$H_2 + Pt,\ Ni\ or\ Co$	$p\text{-}CH_3CH_2O_2CC_6H_4NHCH_2C_6H_5$	—	77
$p\text{-}CH_3CH_2O_2CC_6H_4NH_2$	$p\text{-}CH_3OC_6H_4CHO$	$H_2 + Pt,\ Ni\ or\ Co$	$p,p'\text{-}CH_3CH_2O_2CC_6H_4NHCH_2C_6H_4OCH_3$	—	77
$p\text{-}CH_3CH_2O_2CC_6H_4NH_2$	$3,4\text{-}CH_2O_2C_6H_3CHO$	$H_2 + Pt,\ Ni\ or\ Co$	$4,3',4'\text{-}CH_3CH_2O_2CC_6H_4NHCH_2C_6H_3O_2CH_2$	—	77
$p\text{-}CH_3CH_2O_2CC_6H_4NH_2$	Furfural	$H_2 + Pt,\ Ni\ or\ Co$	$p\text{-}CH_3CH_2O_2CC_6H_4NHCH_2C_4H_3O$	—	77
$p\text{-}H_2NOCC_6H_4NH_2$	CH_3CH_2CHO	$Zn + CH_3CO_2H$	$p\text{-}H_2NOCC_6H_4NH(CH_2)_2CH_3$	54	153
$p\text{-}H_2NOCC_6H_4NH_2$	$CH_3(CH_2)_2CHO$	$Zn + CH_3CO_2H$	$p\text{-}H_2NOCC_6H_4NH(CH_2)_3CH_3$	60	153

* References 134–180 are listed on p. 255.

TABLE X—Continued

PREPARATION OF SECONDARY AMINES

F. From Primary Aromatic Amines, Nitro, Nitroso, or Azo Compounds and Aldehydes—Continued

Amine, Nitro, Nitroso, or Azo Compound Used	Carbonyl Compound	Reducing Agent	Products Isolated	Yield, %	Ref.*
p-$H_2O_3AsC_6H_4NH_2$	CH_3CHO	H_2 + Ni	p-$H_2O_3AsC_6H_4NHCH_2CH_3$	5	41
α-$C_{10}H_7NH_2$	CH_3CHO	H_2 + Ni	α-$C_{10}H_7NHCH_2CH_3$	88	36
α-$C_{10}H_7NH_2$	$CH_3(CH_2)_2CHO$	H_2 + Ni	α-$C_{10}H_7NH(CH_2)_3CH_3$	80	33, 36
α-$C_{10}H_7NO_2$	$CH_3(CH_2)_2CHO$	H_2 + Ni	α-$C_{10}H_7NH(CH_2)_3CH_3$	60	43
α-$C_{10}H_7NO_2$	$CH_3(CH_2)_3CHO$	H_2 + Ni	α-$C_{10}H_7NH(CH_2)_4CH_3$	43	43
α-$C_{10}H_7NO_2$	C_6H_5CHO	H_2 + Ni	α-$C_{10}H_7NHCH_2C_6H_5$	24	33, 36
β-$C_{10}H_7NH_2$	CH_2O	Zn + NaOH	β-$C_{10}H_7NHCH_3$	—	39
β-$C_{10}H_7NH_2$	CH_3CHO	H_2 + Ni	β-$C_{10}H_7NHCH_2CH_3$	64	36
β-$C_{10}H_7NH_2$	$CH_3(CH_2)_2CHO$	H_2 + Ni	β-$C_{10}H_7NH(CH_2)_3CH_3$	63	36
β-$C_{10}H_7NH_2$	C_6H_5CHO	H_2 + Ni	β-$C_{10}H_7NHCH_2C_6H_5$	58	36
CH_3O— (8-nitroquinoline structure, NO_2)	$CH_3CO(CH_2)_3$-$N(CH_2CH_3)_2$	H_2 + Pd	CH_3O— (quinoline structure) $NHCH(CH_3)(CH_2)_3N(CH_2CH_3)_2$	87	154

G. From Primary Aromatic Amines, Nitro, or Nitroso Compounds and Ketones

Amine, Nitro or Nitroso Compound Used	Carbonyl Compound	Reducing Agent	Products Isolated	Yield, %	Ref.*
$C_6H_5NO_2$	CH_3COCH_3	H_2 + Pt	$C_6H_5NHCH(CH_3)_2$	53	2
$C_6H_5NH_2$	CH_3COCH_3	Zn + HCl	$C_6H_5NHCH(CH_3)_2$	31	42
$C_6H_5NO_2$	CH_3COCH_3	H_2 + Pt	None	0	52

Compound Reduced	Carbonyl Compound	Catalyst	Product	Yield (%)	References*
$C_6H_5NH_2$	Cyclohexanone	$H_2 + Pt$	$C_6H_5NHC_6H_{11}$	—	11
$C_6H_5NH_2$	$CH_3CO(CH_2)_3N(CH_2CH_3)_2$	$H_2 + Ni$	$C_6H_5NHCH(CH_3)(CH_2)_3N(CH_2CH_3)_2$	86	51
$C_6H_5NH_2$	$C_6H_5COCH_3$	$H_2 + Pd$	$C_6H_5COCH(CH_3)NHC_6H_5$	49	28
$C_6H_5NH_2$	$C_6H_5COCOCH_3$	$H_2 + Pd$	$C_6H_5CHOHCH(CH_3)NHC_6H_5$	46	28
$p\text{-}CH_3C_6H_4NH_2$	$p\text{-}CH_3OC_6H_4COCOCH_3$	$H_2 + Pd$	$p,p'\text{-}CH_3OC_6H_4COCH(CH_3)NHC_6H_4CH_3$	49	28
$2,4,6\text{-}(CH_3)_3C_6H_2NH_2$	CH_3COCH_3	$Zn + HCl$	$2,4,6\text{-}(CH_3)_3C_6H_2NHCH(CH_3)_2$	18	42
$o\text{-}ClC_6H_4NH_2$	$CH_3CO(CH_2)_3N(CH_2CH_3)_2$	$Zn + HCl$	$o\text{-}ClC_6H_4NHCH(CH_3)(CH_2)_3N(CH_2CH_3)_2$	67	51
$o\text{-}HOC_6H_4NO_2$	CH_3COCH_3	$H_2 + Pt$	None	0	52
$m\text{-}HOC_6H_4NO_2$	CH_3COCH_3	$H_2 + Pt$	None	0	52
$p\text{-}HOC_6H_4NO$	CH_3COCH_3	$H_2 + Pt$	$p\text{-}HOC_6H_4NHCH(CH_3)_2$	60, 0	49, 53, 54
$p\text{-}HOC_6H_4NO$	CH_3COCH_3	$H_2 + Pt$	$p\text{-}HOC_6H_4NHCH(CH_3)_2$	54	52
$p\text{-}HOC_6H_4NH_2$	CH_3COCH_3	$H_2 + Pt$	$p\text{-}HOC_6H_4NHCH(CH_3)_2$	50	49
$p\text{-}HOC_6H_4NO_2$	CH_3COCH_3	$H_2 + Pt$	$p\text{-}HOC_6H_4NHCH(CH_3)_2$	45	52, 53, 54
$p\text{-}HOC_6H_4NH_2$	CH_3COCH_3	$H_2 + Pt$	None	—	50
$p\text{-}HOC_6H_4NO_2$	CH_3COCH_3	$H_2 + Pt$	$p\text{-}HOC_6H_4NHCH(CH_3)_2$	34	52, 53, 54
$p\text{-}HOC_6H_4NO_2$	$CH_3COCH_2CH_3$	$H_2 + Pt$	$p\text{-}HOC_6H_4NHCH(CH_3)CH_2CH_3$	60	52
$p\text{-}HOC_6H_4NO_2$	$CH_3CH_2COCH_2CH_3$	$H_2 + Pt$	$p\text{-}HOC_6H_4NHCH(CH_2CH_3)_2$	0	52
$p\text{-}HOC_6H_4NO_2$	Menthone	$H_2 + Pt$	None	0	52
$p\text{-}HOC_6H_4NO_2$	$C_6H_5COCH_3$	$H_2 + Pt$	None	0	52
$p\text{-}CH_3OC_6H_4NO_2$	$CH_3CO(CH_2)_2N(CH_2CH_3)_2$	$H_2 + Ni$	$p\text{-}CH_3OC_6H_4NHCH(CH_3)(CH_2)_2N(CH_2CH_3)_2$	80–100	154
$1\text{-}HO\text{-}2,4\text{-}C_6H_4(NO_2)_2$	CH_3COCH_3	$H_2 + Pt$	$1\text{-}HO\text{-}2,4\text{-}H_2NC_6H_3NHCH(CH_3)_2$	—	52
$1\text{-}CH_3CH_2O\text{-}2,4\text{-}C_6H_3(NO_2)_2$	$CH_3(CH_2)_2COCOCH_3$	$H_2 + Pd$	$p\text{-}CH_3(CH_2)_2COCH(CH_3)NHC_6H_4OCH_2CH_3$	41	28
$o\text{-}H_2NC_6H_4NO_2$	CH_3COCH_3	$H_2 + Pt$	None	0	52
$o\text{-}H_2NC_6H_4NO_2$	CH_3COCH_3	$H_2 + Pt$	$o\text{-}C_6H_4(NH_2)_2$, $o\text{-}H_2NC_6H_4NHCH(CH_3)_2$	35, 10	44
$m\text{-}H_2NC_6H_4NO_2$	CH_3COCH_3	$H_2 + Pt$	$m\text{-}C_6H_4(NH_2)_2$	50	44
$p\text{-}H_2NC_6H_4NO_2$	CH_3COCH_3	$H_2 + Pt$	$p\text{-}C_6H_4[NHCH(CH_3)_2]_2$	80	44
$p\text{-}C_6H_4(NH_2)_2$	CH_3COCH_3	$H_2 + Pt$	$p\text{-}C_6H_4[NHCH(CH_3)_2]_2$	40	44
$p\text{-}C_6H_4(NH_2)_2$	CH_3COCH_3	$H_2 + Pt + CuO$, $Cr_2O_3 + BaO$	$p\text{-}C_6H_4[NHCH(CH_3)_2]_2$	—	155
$p\text{-}H_2NC_6H_4NO_2$	$CH_3COCH_2CH_3$	$H_2 + Pt$	$p\text{-}C_6H_4[NHCH(CH_3)CH_2CH_3]_2$	70	44
$p\text{-}C_6H_4(NH_2)_2$	$CH_3COCH_2CH_3$	$H_2 + Pt + CuO$, $Cr_2O_3 + BaO$	$p\text{-}C_6H_4[NHCH(CH_3)CH_2CH_3]_2$	50	155

* References 134–180 are listed on p. 255.

TABLE X—*Continued*

PREPARATION OF SECONDARY AMINES

G. From Primary Aromatic Amines, Nitro, or Nitroso Compounds and Ketones—Continued

Amine, Nitro or Nitroso Compound Used	Carbonyl Compound	Reducing Agent	Products Isolated	Yield, %	Ref.*

p-C₆H₄(NH₂)₂	CH₃COCH₂CH₃	H₂ + Ni	p-C₆H₄[NHCH(CH₃)CH₂CH₃]₂
			CH₃CH₂CH(CH₃)—
			
			  HNCH ... CHNHCH(CH₃)CH₂CH₃
			   CH₂CH₂ CH₂CH₂
				43	155

p-H₂NC₆H₄NO₂	CH₃CH₂COCH₂CH₃	H₂ + Pt	p-C₆H₄(NH₂)₂ p-C₆H₄[NHCH(CH₂CH₃)₂]₂	70 20	44
α-C₁₀H₇NH₂	CH₃CO(CH₂)₃-N(CH₂CH₃)₂	H₂ + Pd	α-C₁₀H₇NHCH(CH₃)(CH₂)₃N(CH₂CH₃)₂	91	51
p-HO₂CC₆H₄NH₂	CH₃COCH₃	H₂ + Pt, Ni or Co	p-HO₂CC₆H₄NHCH(CH₃)₂	—	77
p-HO₂CC₆H₄NH₂	C₆H₅COCH₂CH₃	H₂ + Pt, Ni or Co	p-HO₂CC₆H₄NHCH(CH₂CH₃)C₆H₅	—	77
p-CH₃CH₂O₂CC₆H₄NH₂	CH₃COCH₃	H₂ + Pt, Ni or Co	p-CH₃CH₂O₂CC₆H₄NHCH(CH₃)₂	—	77
p-CH₃CH₂O₂CC₆H₄NH₂	C₆H₅COCH₂CH₃	H₂ + Pt, Ni or Co	p-CH₃CH₂O₂CC₆H₄NHCH(CH₂CH₃)C₆H₅	—	77

H. By Reduction of Schiff's Bases Derived from Aliphatic Amines

Schiff's Base	Reducing Agent	Product	Yield, %	Ref.*
HN=C(CH₃)CO₂H + NH₃ (with CH₂ / CH₂ / HN=CHCH / H₃CCH / O / CHCH₃ structure)	H₂ + Pt	H₂NCH(CH₃)CO₂H	30	62
	H₂ + Ni	(H₂NH₂CCH ... CHCH₃ structure)	70	156
HN=CHCH (with CH₂ / CH₂ / H₃CCH / O / CHCH₃)	H₂ + Ni	(H₂NH₂CCH ... CHCH₃ structure)	15	156
		[NH ...]₂ structure	62	156
HN=CHCH (with CH₂ / CH / H₃CCH / O / CCH₃)		(H₂NH₂CCH ... CHCH₃ structure)	—	156

* References 134–180 are listed on p. 255.

TABLE X—Continued

PREPARATION OF SECONDARY AMINES

H. By Reduction of Schiff's Bases Derived from Aliphatic Amines—Continued

Schiff's Base	Reducing Agent	Product	Yield, %	Ref.*
$CH_3CON{=}C(CH_3)CH_2CO_2CH_2CH_3$†	$H_2 + Pt$	$H_2NCH(CH_3)CH_2CO_2CH_2CH_3$	—	62
$CH_3N{=}CHCH(CH_3)_2$	$Na + CH_3CH_2OH$	$CH_3NHCH_2CH(CH_3)_2$	59	157
$CH_3N{=}CHCH_2CH(CH_3)_2$	$Na + CH_3CH_2OH$	$CH_3NH(CH_2)_2CH(CH_3)_2$	46	157
$CH_3N{=}CHCH{=}C(CH_3)(CH_2)_2\text{-}CH{=}C(CH_3)_2$†	$H_2 + Pt$	$CH_3NH(CH_2)_2CH(CH_3)(CH_2)_3\text{-}CH(CH_3)_2$	Low	20
$CH_3N{=}CHC_6H_5$	$H_2 + Ni$	$CH_3NHCH_2C_6H_5$	Excellent	119
$CH_3N{=}CHC_6H_5$	Electrolytic Pb cathode	$CH_3NHCH_2C_6H_5$		158
$CH_3N{=}CHC_6H_5$	$Na{-}Hg + CH_3CH_2OH$	$CH_3NHCH_2C_6H_5$		159
$o\text{-}CH_3N{=}CHC_6H_4CH_3$	$H_2 + Ni$	$o\text{-}CH_3NHCH_2C_6H_4CH_3$	Excellent	119
$p\text{-}CH_3N{=}CHC_6H_4CH_3$	$H_2 + Ni$	$p\text{-}CH_3NHCH_2C_6H_4CH_3$	Excellent	119
$CH_3N{=}CHCH_2C_6H_5$	$Na + CH_3CH_2OH$	$CH_3NH(CH_2)_2C_6H_5$		160
$CH_3CH_2N{=}CHCH_3$	Electrolytic Pb cathode	$(CH_3CH_2)_2NH$	43	158
$CH_3CH_2N{=}CHCH_2CH_3$†	$H_2 + Pt$	$CH_3CH_2NH(CH_2)_2CH_3$	33	55
$CH_3CH_2N{=}CH(CH_2)_2CH_3$†	$H_2 + Pt$	$CH_3CH_2NH(CH_2)_3CH_3$		55
$CH_3CH_2N{=}CHCH_2CH(CH_3)_2$†	$H_2 + Ni$	$CH_3CH_2NH(CH_2)_2CH(CH_3)_2$	20	63
$CH_3CH_2N{=}CHCH_2CH(CH_3)_2$†	$H_2 + Pt$	$CH_3CH_2NH(CH_2)_2CH(CH_3)_2$	16	58
$CH_3CH_2N{=}CHCH{=}C(CH_3)(CH_2)_2\text{-}CH{=}C(CH_3)_2$†	$H_2 + Pt$	$CH_3CH_2NHCH_2CH[CH(CH_3)_2](CH_2)_2\text{-}CH(CH_3)_2$	55	20
$CH_3CH_2N{=}CHCO_2H$	$H_2 + Pt$	$CH_3CH_2NHCH_2CO_2H$		62
$CH_3CH_2N{=}C(CH_3)CO_2H$	$H_2 + Pt$	$CH_3CH_2NHCH(CH_3)CO_2H$	30	62
$CH_3CH_2N{=}C(CH_3)CH_2CO_2CH_2CH_3$†	$H_2 + Pt$	$CH_3CH_2NHCH(CH_3)CH_2CO_2CH_2CH_3$		62
$CH_3CH_2N{=}CHC_6H_5$	$H_2 + Ni$	$CH_3CH_2NHCH_2C_6H_5$	Excellent	119
$CH_3CH_2N{=}CHC_6H_5$†	$Na{-}Hg + CH_3CH_2OH$	$CH_3CH_2NHCH_2C_6H_5$	70	159
$CH_3CH_2N{=}CHC_6H_5$†	$H_2 + Ni$	$CH_3CH_2NHCH_2C_6H_5$		63

Schiff's base	Reduction	Product	Yield	Ref.[*]
$CH_3CH_2N{=}CHC_6H_5$†	$H_2 + Ni$	$CH_3CH_2NHCH_2C_6H_5$ $C_6H_5CH_3$ $CH_3CH_2NH_2$ NH_3 $(CH_3)_2NH$ $(CH_3)_3N$	Mostly	161
$CH_3(CH_2)_2N{=}CHCH_3$†	$H_2 + Pt$	$CH_3(CH_2)_2NHCH_2CH_3$	40	55
$CH_3(CH_2)_2N{=}CH(CH_2)_2CH_3$†	$H_2 + Pt$	$CH_3(CH_2)_2NH(CH_2)_3CH_3$	45	55
$CH_3(CH_2)_2N{=}CHCH(CH_3)_2$†	$H_2 + Pt$	$CH_3(CH_2)_2NHCH_2CH(CH_3)_2$	63	55
$CH_3(CH_2)_2N{=}CHCH_2CH(CH_3)_2$†	$H_2 + Ni$	$CH_3(CH_2)_2NH(CH_2)_2CH(CH_3)_2$	47	55
$CH_3(CH_2)_2N{=}CHC_6H_5$	$H_2 + Pt$	$CH_3(CH_2)_2NHCH_2C_6H_5$	Excellent	119
$CH_3(CH_2)_2N{=}CHC_6H_5$†	$Na{-}Hg + CH_3CH_2OH$	$CH_3(CH_2)_2NHCH_2C_6H_5$	—	159
$(CH_3)_2CHN{=}CH(CH_2)_2CH_3$†	$H_2 + Pt$	$(CH_3)_2CHNH(CH_2)_3CH_3$	44	55
$CH_3(CH_2)_3N{=}CH_2$	$H_2 + Ni$	$CH_3(CH_2)_3NHCH_3$	26	79
$CH_3(CH_2)_3N{=}CHCH_3$†	$H_2 + Pt$	$CH_3(CH_2)_3NHCH_2CH_3$	52	55
$CH_3(CH_2)_3N{=}CHCH_3$	$H_2 + Ni$	$CH_3(CH_2)_3NHCH_2CH_3$	31	79
$CH_3(CH_2)_3N{=}CHCH_2CH_3$†	$H_2 + Pt$	$CH_3(CH_2)_3NH(CH_2)_2CH_3$	54	55
$CH_3(CH_2)_3N{=}CHCH_2CH_3$	$H_2 + Ni$	$CH_3(CH_2)_3NH(CH_2)_2CH_3$	31	79
$CH_3(CH_2)_3N{=}CHCH(CH_3)_2$	$H_2 + Ni$	$CH_3(CH_2)_3NHCH_2CH(CH_3)_2$	56	79
$CH_3(CH_2)_3N{=}CH(CH_2)_3CH_3$	$H_2 + Ni$	$CH_3(CH_2)_3NH(CH_2)_4CH_3$	51	79
$CH_3(CH_2)_3N{=}CHCH_2CH(CH_3)_2$†	$H_2 + Pt$	$CH_3(CH_2)_3NH(CH_2)_2CH(CH_3)_2$	58	55
$CH_3(CH_2)_3N{=}CHCH_2CH(CH_3)_2$	$H_2 + Ni$	$CH_3(CH_2)_3NH(CH_2)_2CH(CH_3)_2$	41	79
$CH_3(CH_2)_3N{=}CHC_6H_5$	$Na{-}Hg + CH_3CH_2OH$	$CH_3(CH_2)_3NHCH_2C_6H_5$	Excellent	119
$(CH_3)_2CHCH_2N{=}CHC_6H_5$†	$H_2 + Pt$	$(CH_3)_2CHCH_2NHCH_2C_6H_5$	—	159
$(CH_3)_2CH(CH_2)_2N{=}CHCH{=}C(CH_3){-}$ $(CH_2)_2CH{=}C(CH_3)_2$†	$H_2 + Pt$	$(CH_3)_2CH(CH_2)_2NH(CH_2)_2CH(CH_3){-}$ $CH(CH_3)_2$	—	20
$(CH_3)_2CH(CH_2)_2N{=}C(CH_3)CH_2CO_2{-}$ CH_2CH_3†	$H_2 + Pt$	$(CH_3)_2CH(CH_2)_2NHCH(CH_3)CH_2CO_2{-}$ CH_2CH_3	50	62
$C_5H_{11}N{=}CHC_6H_5$†	$Na{-}Hg + CH_3CH_2OH$	$C_5H_{11}NHCH_2C_6H_5$	Almost quantitative	159
$C_6H_{13}N{=}CHC_6H_5$†	$H_2 + Pt$	$C_6H_{13}NHCH_2C_6H_5$	Almost quantitative	118
$CH_3CH_2CH_2C(CH_3){=}CHN{=}CHCH(CH_3){-}$ CH_2CH_3	$H_2 + Ni$	$CH_3CH_2CH_2CH(CH_3)CH_2NHCH_2CH(CH_3){-}$ CH_2CH_3	83	162

[*] References 134–180 are listed on p. 255.

† These Schiff's bases probably were purified before reduction.

TABLE X—*Continued*

PREPARATION OF SECONDARY AMINES

H. By Reduction of Schiff's Bases Derived from Aliphatic Amines—Continued

Schiff's Base	Reducing Agent	Product	Yield, %	Ref.*
$CH_3(CH_2)_2C(CH_3)\!=\!CHN\!=\!CHCH(CH_3)(CH_2)_2CH_3\dagger$	$H_2 + Ni$	$CH_3(CH_2)_2CH(CH_3)CH_2NHCH_2CH(CH_3)(CH_2)_2CH_3$	88	162
$(CH_3CH_2)_2C\!=\!CHN\!=\!CHCH(CH_2CH_3)_2\dagger$	$H_2 + Ni$	$(CH_3CH_2)_2CHCH_2NHCH_2CH(CH_2CH_3)_2$	92	162
$CH_3(CH_2)_2C(CH_2CH_3)\!=\!CHN\!=\!CHCH(CH_2CH_3)(CH_2)_3CH_3\dagger$	$H_2 + Ni$	$CH_3(CH_2)_3CH(CH_2CH_3)CH_2NHCH_2CH(CH_2CH_3)(CH_2)_3CH_3$	94	162
$C_6H_{11}N\!=\!CHCH_3\dagger$	$H_2 + Pt$	$C_6H_{11}NHCH_2CH_3$	8	58
		$C_6H_{11}NH(CH_2)_3CH_3$	39	
$C_6H_{11}N\!=\!CHCH_2CH_3\dagger$	$H_2 + Pt$	$C_6H_{11}NHCH_2CH(CH_3)(CH_2)_2CH_3$	49	58
$C_6H_{11}N\!=\!CHCH_2CH_3\dagger$ + CH_3CHO	$H_2 + Pt$	Cyclohexylamine	—	
		$C_6H_{11}NH(CH_2)_3CH_3$	—	
		$C_6H_{11}NHCH_2CH(CH_3)CH_2CH_3$	30	58
$C_6H_{11}N\!=\!CHCH_2CH_3\dagger$ + CH_3CH_2CHO		$C_6H_{11}NHCH_2CH(CH_3)(CH_2)_2CH_3$	—	
$C_6H_{11}N\!=\!CHCH_2CH_3\dagger$	$H_2 + Pt$	$C_6H_{11}NH(CH_2)_2CH_3$	76	58
$C_6H_{11}N\!=\!CHCH_2CH_3\dagger$ + C_6H_5CHO	$H_2 + Pt$	$C_6H_{11}NHCH_2CH(CH_3)CH_2C_6H_5$	11	58
		$C_6H_{11}NHCH_2CH(CH_3)CH_2C_4H_3O$ (α-furyl)	9	
		$C_6H_{11}NHCH_2CH(CH_3)CH_2C_4H_7O$ (α-tetrahydrofuryl)	8	
$C_6H_{11}N\!=\!CHCH_2CH_3\dagger$ + furfural	$H_2 + Pt$	$C_6H_{11}NHCH_2CH(CH_3)CH_2C$〈ring: $CH\!=\!CH—CH_2—CH_2—O$〉	0.7	58

Schiff's base	Catalyst	Product	Yield	Reference
C₆H₁₁N=CH(CH₂)₂CH₃†	H₂ + Pt	C₆H₁₁NHCH₂CH(CH₂CH₃)(CH₂)₃CH₃	75	58
C₆H₁₁N=CH(CH₂)₂CH₃†	H₂ + Pt	C₆H₁₁NH(CH₂)₃CH₃	45	55
C₆H₁₁N=CHCH(CH₃)₂† + CH₂O	H₂ + Pt	C₆H₁₁NHCH₂C(CH₃)₂CH₂OH	65	58
C₆H₁₁N=CHCH=CHCH₃†	H₂ + Pt	C₆H₁₁NH(CH₂)₃CH₃	52	58
C₆H₁₁N=CHCH₂CH(CH₃)₂†	H₂ + Pt	C₆H₁₁NH(CH₂)₂CH[CH(CH₃)₂]CH₂CH₂—CH(CH₃)₂	50	58
			15	
C₆H₁₁N=CHC(CH₃)=CHCH₃	H₂ + Pt	C₆H₁₁NHCH₂CH(CH₃)CH₂CH₃	61	58
C₆H₁₁N=CHC(CH₃)=CHCH₂CH₃†	H₂ + Pt	C₆H₁₁NHCH₂CH(CH₃)(CH₂)₂CH₃	49	58
C₆H₁₁N=CH(CH₂)₅CH₃†	H₂ + Pt	C₆H₁₁NHCH₂CH[(CH₂)₄CH₃](CH₂)₆CH₃	42	58
C₆H₁₁N=CHC(CH₂CH₃)=CH(CH₂)₂—CH₃†	H₂ + Pt	C₆H₁₁NHCH₂CH(CH₂CH₃)(CH₂)₃CH₃	56	58
C₆H₁₁N=CHC[CH(CH₃)₂]=CHCH₂—CH(CH₃)₂†	H₂ + Pt	C₆H₁₁NHCH₂CH[CH(CH₃)₂](CH₂)₂—CH(CH₃)₂	62	58
C₆H₁₁N=CHCH[CH(CH₃)₂](CH₂)₂—CH=C(CH₃)₂†	H₂ + Pt	C₆H₁₁NHCH₂CH[CH(CH₃)₂](CH₂)₃—CH(CH₃)₂	—	20
C₆H₁₁N=CHC[(CH₂)₄CH₃]=CH(CH₂)₅—CH₃†	H₂ + Pt	C₆H₁₁NHCH₂CH[(CH₂)₄CH₃](CH₂)₆CH₃	26	58
C₆H₁₁N=CH(CH₃)₂CH₂OH†	H₂ + Pt	C₆H₁₁NHCH₂C(CH₃)₂CH₂OH	38	58
C₆H₁₁N=C(CH₃)CO₂H†	H₂ + Pt	C₆H₁₁NHCH(CH₃)CO₂H	50	62
C₆H₁₁N=C(CH₃)CH₂CO₂CH₂CH₃†	H₂ + Pt	C₆H₁₁NHCH(CH₃)CH₂CO₂CH₂CH₃	15	62
C₆H₁₁N=CH(CH₂)₃C₆H₅†	H₂ + Pt	C₆H₁₁NH(CH₂)₃C₆H₅	16	58
C₆H₁₁N=CHC(CH₃)=CHC₆H₅†	H₂ + Pt	C₆H₁₁NHCH₂CH(CH₂C₆H₅)(CH₂)₃C₆H₅	61	58
C₆H₁₁N=CHC(CH₂C₆H₅)=CH(CH₂)₂—C₆H₅†	H₂ + Pt	C₆H₁₁NHCH₂CH(CH₃)CH₂C₆H₅	69	58
		C₆H₁₁NHCH₂CH(CH₂C₆H₅)(CH₂)₃C₆H₅		
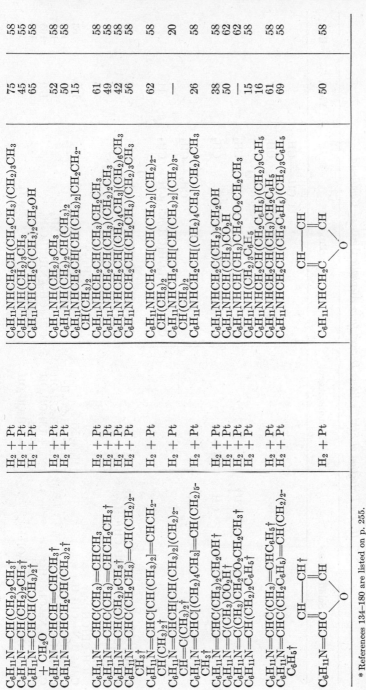	H₂ + Pt	C₆H₁₁NHCH₂ (see structure)	50	58

* References 134–180 are listed on p. 255.
† These Schiff's bases probably were purified before reduction.

TABLE X—Continued

PREPARATION OF SECONDARY AMINES—Continued

H. By Reduction of Schiff's Bases Derived from Aliphatic Amines—Continued

Schiff's Base	Reducing Agent	Product	Yield, %	Ref.*
$C_6H_{11}N=CHC(CH_3)=CHC$ (ring with O)	$H_2 + Pt$	$C_6H_{11}NHCH_2CH(CH_3)CH_2C$ (ring, $=CH$–$CH=$, CH, O)	7	58
		$C_6H_{11}NHCH_2CH(CH_3)CH_2C$ (ring, CH_2–CH_2, CH, O)	2	—
		$C_6H_{11}NHCH_2CH(CH_3)CH_2CH$ (ring, CH_2–CH_2, CH_2, O)	11	—
$CH_3CHOHCH_2N=C[CH_2CH(CH_3)_2]_2$†	$H_2 + Pt$	$CH_3CHOHCH_2NH[CH_2CH(CH_3)_2]_2$	93	59
$HOCH_2CH(CH_3)N=C[CH_2CH(CH_3)_2]_2$†	$H_2 + Pt$	$HOCH_2CH(CH_3)NH[CH_2CH(CH_3)_2]_2$	93	60
$HO(CH_2)_3N=C[CH_2CH(CH_3)_2]_2$†	$H_2 + Pt$	$HO(CH_2)_3NH[CH_2CH(CH_3)_2]_2$	93	61
$HOCH_2CH(CH_2CH_3)N=C$–$[CH_2CH(CH_3)_2]_2$†	$H_2 + Pt$	$HOCH_2CH(CH_2CH_3)NHCH$–$[CH_2CH(CH_3)_2]_2$	83	60
$C_6H_5CH_2N=CHCH_3$†	$H_2 + Ni$	$C_6H_5CH_2NHCH_2CH_3$	Low	63
$C_6H_5CH_2N=CHC_6H_5$†	$Zn + CH_3CO_2H$	$(C_6H_5CH_2CH_2)_2NH$	—	163
$C_6H_5CH_2N=CHCH_2C_6H_5$	$Na + CH_3CH_2OH$	$C_6H_5(CH_2)_2N(CH_2)_2C_6H_5$	25	164
$C_6H_5(CH_2)_2N=CHC_6H_5$†	$Na + CH_3CH_2OH$	$C_6H_5(CH_2)_2NHCH_2C_6H_5$	100	165
$C_6H_5(CH_2)_2N=CHC_6H_5$†	$H_2 + Pd$	$C_6H_5(CH_2)_2NHCH_2C_6H_5$	96	166
o-$C_6H_5(CH_2)_2N=CHC_6H_4OH$†	$Na + CH_3CH_2OH$	o-$C_6H_5(CH_2)_2NHCH_2C_6H_4OH$	15	165
		$C_6H_5(CH_2)_2NH_2$	31	

Schiff base	Reducing agent	Amine	Yield (%)	References*
$p\text{-}C_6H_5(CH_2)_2N{=}CHC_6H_4OH$†	$Na + CH_3CH_2OH$	$p\text{-}C_6H_5(CH_2)_2NHCH_2C_6H_4OH$	65	165
$p\text{-}C_6H_5(CH_2)_2N{=}CHC_6H_4OCH_3$†	$Na + CH_3CH_2OH$	$p\text{-}C_6H_5(CH_2)_2NHCH_2C_6H_4OCH_3$	Excellent	165
$3',4'\text{-}C_6H_5(CH_2)_2N{=}CHC_6H_3(OCH_3)OH$†	$Na + CH_3CH_2OH$	$3',4'\text{-}C_6H_5(CH_2)_2NHCH_2C_6H_3(OCH_3)OH$	47	165
$3',4'\text{-}C_6H_5(CH_2)_2N{=}CHC_6H_3(OCH_3)_2$†	$H_2 + Pt$	$3',4'\text{-}C_6H_5(CH_2)_2NHCH_2C_6H_3(OCH_3)_2$	Almost quantitative	167
$C_6H_5(CH_2)_2N{=}CHCH_2C_6H_5$	$H_2 + Ni$	Mixture		118
$p\text{-}HOC_6H_4(CH_2)_2N{=}CHC_6H_5$†	$Na{-}Hg + CH_3CH_2OH$	$p\text{-}HOC_6H_4(CH_2)_2NHCH_2C_6H_5$	—	168
$4,2'\text{-}HOC_6H_4(CH_2)_2N{=}CHC_6H_3\text{-}(OCH_3)_2$†	$Na{-}Hg + CH_3CH_2OH$	$4,3'\text{-}HOC_6H_4(CH_2)_2NHCH_2C_6H_3\text{-}(OCH_3)_2$	—	168
$4,3'\text{-}HOC_6H_4(CH_2)_2N{=}CHC_6H_3O_2\text{-}CH_2$†	$Na{-}Hg + CH_3CH_2OH$	$4,2'\text{-}HOC_6H_4(CH_2)_2NHCH_2C_6H_4OH$	—	168
	$Na{-}Hg + CH_3CH_2OH$	$4,3'\text{-}HOC_6H_4(CH_2)_2NHCH_2C_6H_3O_2\text{-}CH_2$	—	168
$4,4'\text{-}CH_3OC_6H_4(CH_2)_2N{=}CHC_6H_4OCH_3$†	$H_2 + Pt$	$4,4'\text{-}CH_3OC_6H_4(CH_2)_2NHCH_2C_6H_4OCH_3$	Quantitative	167
$4,3'\text{-}CH_3OC_6H_4(CH_2)_2N{=}CHC_6H_3\text{-}(OCH_3)_2$†	$H_2 + Pt$	$4,3'\text{-}CH_3OC_6H_4(CH_2)_2NHCH_2\text{-}C_6H_3(OCH_3)_2$	Quantitative	167
$3,4,4'\text{-}(CH_3O)_2C_6H_3(CH_2)_2N{=}CHC_6H_4\text{-}OCH_3$†	$H_2 + Pt$	$3,4,4'\text{-}(CH_3O)_2C_6H_3(CH_2)_2NHCH_2\text{-}C_6H_4OCH_3$	Quantitative	167
$3,4,3',4'\text{-}(CH_3O)_2C_6H_3(CH_2)_2N{=}CHC_6H_3\text{-}(OCH_3)_2$†	$H_2 + Pt$	$3,4,3',4'\text{-}(CH_3O)_2C_6H_3(CH_2)_2NHCH_2\text{-}C_6H_3(OCH_3)_2$	Quantitative	167
$3,4,3',4'\text{-}(CH_3O)_2C_6H_3(CH_2)_2N{=}CHC_6H_3\text{-}O_2CH_2$†	$H_2 + Pt$	$3,4,3',4'\text{-}(CH_3O)_2C_6H_3(CH_2)_2NHCH_2\text{-}C_6H_3O_2CH_2$	Quantitative	167
$3,4,3',4'\text{-}CH_2O_2C_6H_3(CH_2)_2N{=}CHC_6H_3\text{-}(OCH_3)_2$†	$H_2 + Pd$	$3,4,3',4'\text{-}CH_2O_2C_6H_3(CH_2)_2NHCH_2\text{-}C_6H_3(OCH_3)_2$	—	169
$3,4,3',4'\text{-}CH_2O_2C_6H_3(CH_2)_2N{=}CHC_6H_3\text{-}O_2CH_2$†	$H_2 + Pt$	$3,4,3',4'\text{-}CH_2O_2C_6H_3(CH_2)_2NHCH_2\text{-}C_6H_3O_2CH_2$	Quantitative	167
$o\text{-}CH_3OC_6H_4CH(CH_3)CH_2N{=}CHC_6H_5$†	$H_2 + Ni$	$o\text{-}CH_3OC_6H_4CH(CH_3)CH_2NHCH_2C_6H_5$	85	27
$m\text{-}CH_3OC_6H_4CH(CH_3)CH_2N{=}CHC_6H_5$†	$H_2 + Ni$	$m\text{-}CH_3OC_6H_4CH(CH_3)CH_2NHCH_2C_6H_5$	50	27
$p\text{-}CH_3OC_6H_4CH(CH_3)CH_2N{=}CHC_6H_5$†	$H_2 + Ni$	$p\text{-}CH_3OC_6H_4CH(CH_3)CH_2NHCH_2C_6H_5$	78	27
$C_6H_5CH_2CH(CH_3)N{=}CHC_6H_5$†	$H_2 + Ni$	$C_6H_5CH_2CH(CH_3)NHCH_2C_6H_5$	72	27
$o\text{-}CH_3OC_6H_4CH_2CH(CH_3)N{=}CHC_6H_5$†	$H_2 + Ni$	$o\text{-}CH_3OC_6H_4CH_2CH(CH_3)NHCH_2C_6H_5$	64	27
$m\text{-}CH_3OC_6H_4CH_2CH(CH_3)N{=}CHC_6H_5$†	$H_2 + Ni$	$m\text{-}CH_3OC_6H_4CH_2CH(CH_3)NHCH_2C_6H_5$	55	27
$H_5C_6CHNH{>}CHC_6H_5$†	$H_2 + Ni$	$H_{11}C_6CHNH{>}CHC_6H_{11}$	85	23

* References 134–180 are listed on p. 255.

† These Schiff's bases probably were purified before reduction.

TABLE X—Continued

PREPARATION OF SECONDARY AMINES

H. By Reduction of Schiff's Bases Derived from Aliphatic Amines—Continued

Schiff's Base	Reducing Agent	Product	Yield, %	Ref.*
(bicyclic furanyl–C=N–C(furanyl)H–CH structure)†	H_2 + Ni	(bicyclic furanyl–CH–NH–CH structure)	82	23
$CH_3CH_2C{=}N{\rangle}CO$†	H_2 + Ni	$CH_3CH_2CHNH{\rangle}CHOH$	76	23
$C_6H_{11}C{=}N{\rangle}CO$†	H_2 + Ni	$C_6H_{11}CHNH{\rangle}CHOH$	77	23
$C_6H_{11}CHNH{\rangle}CO$† $C_6H_5C{=}N{\rangle}CO$†	H_2 + Ni	$C_6H_{11}CHNH{\rangle}CHOH$ $C_6H_{11}CHNH{\rangle}CHOH$	82	23
$C_6H_5CHNH{\rangle}CO$† $C_6H_5CH{\langle}N{=}CHC_6H_5$†	Na—Hg + CH_3CH_2OH	$C_6H_5CH{\langle}\,^{NHCH_2C_6H_5}$	—	170
$CH_3CHOHNH_2$‡ $C_6H_{11}NHCOH(CH_3)CO_2H$†	H_2 + Pt H_2 + Pt	$CH_3CH_2NH_2$ $C_6H_{11}NHCH(CH_3)CO_2H$	75 29	62 62

I. By Reduction of Schiff's Bases Derived from Aromatic Amines

Schiff's Base	Reagent	Product	Yield (%)	References[*]
$C_6H_5N=CHCH_2CH(CH_3)_2$†	$H_2 + Ni$	$C_6H_5NH(CH_2)_2CH(CH_3)_2$	—	63
$C_6H_5N=CH(CHOH)_4CH_2OH$	$H_2 + Ni$	$C_6H_5NHCH_2(CHOH)_4CH_2OH$	—	66
$C_6H_5N=C(CH_2OH)(CHOH)_3CH_2OH$	$H_2 + Ni$	$C_6H_5NHCH(CH_2OH)(CHOH)_3CH_2OH$	30	66
$C_6H_5N=C(CH_3)CH_2CO_2CH_2CH_3$†	$H_2 + Pt$	$C_6H_5NHCH(CH_3)CH_2CO_2CH_2CH_3$	100	62
$C_6H_5N=CHC_6H_5$†	$H_2 + Cu$ Chromite	$C_6H_5NHCH_2C_6H_5$	97	23, 67
$C_6H_5N=CHC_6H_5$†	$H_2 + Ni$	$C_6H_5NHCH_2C_6H_5$		23, 24, 83
$C_6H_5N=CHC_6H_5$	$H_2 + Ni$	$C_6H_5NHCH_2C_6H_5$	Excellent	119
$C_6H_5N=CHC_6H_5$†	$H_2 + Ni$	$C_6H_5NHCH_2C_6H_5$	89	118
$C_6H_5N=CHC_6H_5$†	$Mg + CH_3OH$	$C_6H_5NHCH_2C_6H_5$	70–90	65
$C_6H_5N=CHC_6H_5$†	Electrolytic Pb cathode	$C_6H_5NHCH_2C_6H_5$	83	68
$C_6H_5N=CHC_6H_5$†	$Na—Hg + CH_3CH_2OH$	$C_6H_5NHCH_2C_6H_5$	74	120
$C_6H_5N=CHC_6H_5$†	$NaOC_5H_{11}$	$C_6H_5NHCH_2C_6H_5$	73	121
$C_6H_5N=CHC_6H_5$†	Electrolytic Cu cathode	$C_6H_5NHCH_2C_6H_5$	67	68
$C_6H_5N=CHC_6H_5$†	Electrolytic Pb cathode	$C_6H_5NHCH_2C_6H_5$	—	171
$C_6H_5N=CHC_6H_5$†	$Na—Hg + CH_3CH_2OH$	$C_6H_5NHCH_2C_6H_5$	—	172
$C_6H_5N=CHC_6H_5$†	Electrolytic Pb cathode	$C_6H_5NHCH_2C_6H_5$	—	158
$C_6H_5N=CHC_6H_5$†	$Zn + CH_3CO_2H$	$C_6H_5NHCH_2C_6H_5$	—	163
$C_6H_5N=CHC_6H_5$†	$H_2 + Ni$	$C_6H_5NHCH_2C_6H_5$	—	63
$C_6H_5N=CHC_6H_5$†	$NaOCH_2CH_3$	$C_6H_5NHCH_2C_6H_5$	—	173
$C_6H_5N=CHC_6H_5$†		$C_6H_5NHCH_2C_6H_5$	—	121
$C_6H_5N=CHC_6H_5$†	$Al—Hg$	$C_6H_5NHCH_2CH(C_6H_5)CH(C_6H_5)NHC_6H_5$	0	170
$o\text{-}C_6H_5N=CHC_6H_4CH_3$†	Electrolytic Pb cathode	$o\text{-}C_6H_5NHCH_2C_6H_4CH_3$	87	68
$m\text{-}C_6H_5N=CHC_6H_4CH_3$†	Electrolytic Pb cathode	$m\text{-}C_6H_5NHCH_2C_6H_4CH_3$	79	68
$m\text{-}C_6H_5N=CHC_6H_4CH_3$†	Electrolytic Cu cathode	$m\text{-}C_6H_5NHCH_2C_6H_4CH_3$	43	68
$p\text{-}C_6H_5N=CHC_6H_4CH_3$†	Electrolytic Pb cathode	$p\text{-}C_6H_5NHCH_2C_6H_4CH_3$	73	68
$p\text{-}C_6H_5N=CHC_6H_4CH_3$†	Electrolytic Cu cathode	$p\text{-}C_6H_5NHCH_2C_6H_4CH_3$	20	68
$p\text{-}C_6H_5N=CHC_6H_4CH(CH_3)_2$†	$Na—Hg + CH_3CH_2OH$	$p\text{-}C_6H_5NHCH_2C_6H_4CH(CH_3)_2$	—	174
$C_6H_5N=CHCH=CHC_6H_5$†	$Mg + CH_3OH$	$C_6H_5NH(CH_2)_3C_6H_5$	—	65

* References 134–180 are listed on p. 255.

† These Schiff's bases probably were purified before reduction.

TABLE X—Continued

PREPARATION OF SECONDARY AMINES

I. By Reduction of Schiff's Bases Derived from Aromatic Amines—Continued

Schiff's Base	Reducing Agent	Product	Yield, %	Ref.*
o-C₆H₅N=CHC₆H₄Cl†	Electrolytic Pb cathode	o-C₆H₅NHCH₂C₆H₄Cl	87	68
o-C₆H₅N=CHC₆H₄Cl†	Electrolytic Cu cathode	o-C₆H₅NHCH₂C₆H₄Cl	83	68
o-C₆H₅N=CHC₆H₄Cl†	Na—Hg + CH₃CH₂OH	o-C₆H₅NHCH₂C₆H₄Cl	38	175
m-C₆H₅N=CHC₆H₄Cl†	Electrolytic Pb cathode	m-C₆H₅NHCH₂C₆H₄Cl	77	68
m-C₆H₅N=CHC₆H₄Cl†	Electrolytic Cu cathode	m-C₆H₅NHCH₂C₆H₄Cl	40	68
p-C₆H₅N=CHC₆H₄Cl†	Electrolytic Pb cathode	p-C₆H₅NHCH₂C₆H₄Cl	63	68
p-C₆H₅N=CHC₆H₄Cl†	Electrolytic Cu cathode	p-C₆H₅NHCH₂C₆H₄Cl	57	68
o-C₆H₅N=CHC₆H₄OH†	Mg + CH₃OH	o-C₆H₅NHCH₂C₆H₄OH	—	65
o-C₆H₅N=CHC₆H₄OH†	Na—Hg + CH₃CH₂OH	o-C₆H₅NHCH₂C₆H₄OH	—	176
m-C₆H₅N=CHC₆H₄OH†	Na—Hg + CH₃CH₂OH	m-C₆H₅NHCH₂C₆H₄OH	88	175
p-C₆H₅N=CHC₆H₄OH†	Na—Hg + CH₃CH₂OH	p-C₆H₅NHCH₂C₆H₄OH	—	176
2',5'-C₆H₅N=CHC₆H₃(OH)(CH₃)†	Zn + CH₃CO₂H	2',5'-C₆H₅NHCH₂C₆H₃(OH)(CH₃)	—	170
2',5'-C₆H₅N=CHC₆H₃(OH)(CH₃)†	Al-Hg	2,5,2',5'-C₆H₅NHCHCH₃)C₆H₃(OH)(CH₃)]NHC₆H₅]-CH[C₆H₃OH(CH₃)]NHC₆H₅	Quantitative	170
p-C₆H₅N=CHC₆H₄OCH₃†	Na—Hg + CH₃CH₂OH	p-C₆H₅NHCH₂C₆H₄OCH₃	80	177
p-C₆H₅N=CHC₆H₄OCH₃†	Electrolytic Pb cathode	p-C₆H₅NHCH₂C₆H₄OCH₃	—	171
p-C₆H₅N=CHC₆H₄OCH₃†	Mg + CH₃OH	p-C₆H₅NHCH₂C₆H₄OCH₃	—	65
3',4'-C₆H₅N=CHC₆H₃O₂CH₂†	Mg + CH₃OH	3',4'-C₆H₅NHCH₂C₆H₃O₂CH₂	—	65
p-C₆H₅N=CHC₆H₄N(CH₃)₂†	Mg + CH₃OH	p-C₆H₅NHCH₂C₆H₄N(CH₃)₂	—	63
o-CH₃C₆H₄N=CHCH₂CH(CH₃)₂†	H₂ + Ni	o-CH₃C₆H₄NH(CH₂)₂CH(CH₃)₂	—	63
o-CH₃C₆H₄N=CHC₆H₅†	Electrolytic Pb cathode	o-CH₃C₆H₄NHCH₂C₆H₅	99	68
o-CH₃C₆H₄N=CHC₆H₅†	Electrolytic Cu cathode	o-CH₃C₆H₄NHCH₂C₆H₅	83	68
o-CH₃C₆H₄N=CHC₆H₅†	H₂ + Ni	o-CH₃C₆H₄NHCH₂C₆H₅	—	63
2,4'-CH₃C₆H₄N=CHC₆H₄CH₃†	Electrolytic Pb cathode	2,4'-CH₃C₆H₄NHCH₂C₆H₄CH₃	77	173
2,4'-CH₃C₆H₄N=CHC₆H₄CH₃†	Electrolytic Cu cathode	2,4'-CH₃C₆H₄NHCH₂C₆H₄CH₃	48	68
2,4'-CH₃C₆H₄N=CHC₆H₄Cl†	Electrolytic Pb cathode	2,4'-CH₃C₆H₄NHCH₂C₆H₄Cl	61	68

Schiff's base	Reducing agent	Product	Yield %	Reference
$2,4'\text{-}CH_3C_6H_4N{=}CHC_6H_4Cl$†	Electrolytic Cu cathode	$2,4'\text{-}CH_3C_6H_4NHCH_2C_6H_4Cl$	30	68
$2,4'\text{-}CH_3C_6H_4N{=}CHC_6H_4OCH_3$†	Na—Hg + CH_3CH_2OH	$2,4'\text{-}CH_3C_6H_4NHCH_2C_6H_4OCH_3$	—	177
$m\text{-}CH_3C_6H_4N{=}CH(CHOH)_4CH_2OH$	H_2 + Ni	$m\text{-}CH_3C_6H_4NHCH_2(CHOH)_4CH_2OH$	52	66
$m\text{-}CH_3C_6H_4N{=}CHC_6H_5$†	Electrolytic Pb cathode	$m\text{-}CH_3C_6H_4NHCH_2C_6H_5$	77	68
$m\text{-}CH_3C_6H_4N{=}CHC_6H_5$†	Electrolytic Pb cathode	$m\text{-}CH_3C_6H_4NHCH_2C_6H_5$	51	68
$m\text{-}CH_3C_6H_4N{=}CHC_6H_5$†	H_2 + Ni	$m\text{-}CH_3C_6H_4NHCH_2C_6H_5$	—	173
$3,3'\text{-}CH_3C_6H_4N{=}CHC_6H_4CH_3$†	Electrolytic Pb cathode	$3,3'\text{-}CH_3C_6H_4NHCH_2C_6H_4CH_3$	83	68
$3,3'\text{-}CH_3C_6H_4N{=}CHC_6H_4CH_3$†	Electrolytic Cu cathode	$3,3'\text{-}CH_3C_6H_4NHCH_2C_6H_4CH_3$	61	68
$3,4'\text{-}CH_3C_6H_4N{=}CHC_6H_4CH_3$†	Electrolytic Pb cathode	$3,4'\text{-}CH_3C_6H_4NHCH_2C_6H_4CH_3$	63	68
$3,4'\text{-}CH_3C_6H_4N{=}CHC_6H_4CH_3$†	Electrolytic Cu cathode	$3,4'\text{-}CH_3C_6H_4NHCH_2C_6H_4CH_3$	51	68
$3,4'\text{-}CH_3C_6H_4N{=}CHC_6H_4Cl$†	Electrolytic Pb cathode	$3,4'\text{-}CH_3C_6H_4NHCH_2C_6H_4Cl$	57	68
$3,4'\text{-}CH_3C_6H_4N{=}CHC_6H_4Cl$†	Electrolytic Cu cathode	$3,4'\text{-}CH_3C_6H_4NHCH_2C_6H_4Cl$	32	68
$p\text{-}CH_3C_6H_4N{=}CHC_6H_5$	Electrolytic Pb cathode	$p\text{-}CH_3C_6H_4NHCH_2C_6H_5$	97	68
$p\text{-}CH_3C_6H_4N{=}CHC_6H_5$†	Electrolytic Cu cathode	$p\text{-}CH_3C_6H_4NHCH_2C_6H_5$	75	68
		$p,p'\text{-}CH_3C_6H_4NHCH(C_6H_5)\text{-}CH(C_6H_5)NHC_6H_4CH_3$	10	68
$p\text{-}CH_3C_6H_4N{=}CHC_6H_4CH_3$†	Mg + CH_3OH	$p\text{-}CH_3C_6H_4NHCH_2C_6H_4CH_3$	—	65
$p\text{-}CH_3C_6H_4N{=}CHC_6H_4CH_3$†	H_2 + Ni	$p\text{-}CH_3C_6H_4NHCH_2C_6H_4CH_3$	—	173
$p\text{-}CH_3C_6H_4N{=}CHC_6H_4CH_3$†	Na—Hg + CH_3CH_2OH	$p\text{-}CH_3C_6H_4NHCH_2C_6H_4CH_3$	—	178
$4,3'\text{-}CH_3C_6H_4N{=}CHC_6H_4CH_3$†	Electrolytic Pb cathode	$4,3'\text{-}CH_3C_6H_4NHCH_2C_6H_4CH_3$	73	68
$4,3'\text{-}CH_3C_6H_4N{=}CHC_6H_4CH_3$†	Electrolytic Cu cathode	$4,3'\text{-}CH_3C_6H_4NHCH_2C_6H_4CH_3$	53	68
		$4,3,4',3'\text{-}CH_3C_6H_4NHCH(C_6H_4CH_3)\text{-}CH(C_6H_4CH_3)NHC_6H_4CH_3$	20	
$4,4'\text{-}CH_3C_6H_4N{=}CHC_6H_4CH_3$†	Electrolytic Pb cathode	$4,4'\text{-}CH_3C_6H_4NHCH_2C_6H_4CH_3$	91	68
$4,4'\text{-}CH_3C_6H_4N{=}CHC_6H_4CH_3$†	Electrolytic Cu cathode	$4,4'\text{-}CH_3C_6H_4NHCH_2C_6H_4CH_3$	57	68
		$4,4,4',4'\text{-}CH_3C_6H_4NHCH_2C_6H_4NHCH(C_6H_4CH_3)\text{-}CH(C_6H_4CH_3)NHC_6H_4CH_3$	24	
$4,4'\text{-}CH_3C_6H_4N{=}CHC_6H_4CH(CH_3)_2$†	Na—Hg + CH_3CH_2OH	$4,4,4',4'\text{-}CH_3C_6H_4NHCH_2C_6H_4CH(CH_3)_2$	—	174
$4,4'\text{-}CH_3C_6H_4N{=}CHC_6H_4Cl$†	Electrolytic Pb cathode	$4,4'\text{-}CH_3C_6H_4NHCH_2C_6H_4Cl$	59	68
		$4,4,4',4'\text{-}CH_3C_6H_4NHCH_2C_6H_4NHCH(C_6H_4Cl)\text{-}CH(C_6H_4Cl)NHC_6H_4CH_3$	10	
$4,4'\text{-}CH_3C_6H_4N{=}CHC_6H_4Cl$†	Electrolytic Cu cathode	$4,4'\text{-}CH_3C_6H_4NHCH_2C_6H_4Cl$	16	68
		$4,4,4',4'\text{-}CH_3C_6H_4NHCH_2C_6H_4NHCH(C_6H_4Cl)\text{-}CH(C_6H_4Cl)NHC_6H_4CH_3$	20	
$4,2'\text{-}CH_3C_6H_4N{=}CHC_6H_4OH$†	Na—Hg + CH_3CH_2OH	$4,2'\text{-}CH_3C_6H_4NHCH_2C_6H_4OH$	Good	176

* References 134–180 are listed on p. 255.
† These Schiff's bases probably were purified before reduction.

TABLE X—Continued

PREPARATION OF SECONDARY AMINES

I. By Reduction of Schiff's Bases Derived from Aromatic Amines—Continued

Schiff's Base	Reducing Agent	Product	Yield, %	Ref.*
4,4'-CH₃C₆H₄N=CHC₆H₄OH†	Na—Hg + CH₃CH₂OH	4,4'-CH₃C₆H₄NHCH₂C₆H₄OH	—	176
4,4'-CH₃C₆H₄N=CHC₆H₄OCH₃†	Na—Hg + CH₃CH₂OH	4,4'-CH₃C₆H₄NHCH₂C₆H₄OCH₃	—	177
4,4'-CH₃C₆H₄N=CHC₆H₄OCH₃	Mg + CH₃OH	4,4'-CH₃C₆H₄NHCH₂C₆H₄OCH₃	—	65
2,5(CH₃)₂C₆H₃N=CH(CHOH)₄CH₂OH	H₂ + Ni	2,5(CH₃)₂C₆H₃NHCH₂(CHOH)₄CH₂OH	91	66
o-HOC₆H₄N=CHCH(CH₂CH₃)₂†	H₂ + Pt	o-HOC₆H₄NHCH₂CH(CH₂CH₃)₂	83	64
m-HOC₆H₄N=CH(CHOH)₄CH₂OH	H₂ + Ni	m-HOC₆H₄NHCH₂(CHOH)₄CH₂OH	33	66
p-HOC₆H₄N=CH(CH₂)₂CH₃†	H₂ + Ni	p-HOC₆H₄NH(CH₂)₃CH₃	85	64
p-HOC₆H₄N=CHCH(CH₃)CH₂CH₃†	H₂ + Pt	p-HOC₆H₄NHCH₂CH(CH₃)CH₂CH₃	65	64
p-HOC₆H₄N=CHC(CH₃)₃†	H₂ + Pt	p-HOC₆H₄NHCH₂C(CH₃)₃	85	64
p-HOC₆H₄N=CHCH(CH₃)(CH₂)₂CH₃†	H₂ + Pt	p-HOC₆H₄NHCH₂CH(CH₃)(CH₂)₂CH₃	89	64
p-HOC₆H₄N=CHCH(CH₂CH₃)₂†	H₂ + Pt	p-HOC₆H₄NHCH₂CH(CH₂CH₃)₂	93	64
p-HOC₆H₄N=CHCH(CH₂CH₃)(CH₂)₃CH₃†	H₂ + Pt	p-HOC₆H₄NHCH₂CH(CH₂CH₃)(CH₂)₃CH₃		64
p-HOC₆H₄N=CH(CHOH)₄CH₂OH	H₂ + Ni	p-HOC₆H₄NHCH₂(CHOH)₄CH₂OH		66
p-HOC₆H₄N=CHC₆H₅†	Zn + NaOH	p-HOC₆H₄NHCH₂C₆H₅		179
4,4'-HOC₆H₄N=CHC₆H₄CH(CH₃)₂†	Na—Hg + CH₂CH₂OH	4,4'-HOC₆H₄NHCH₂C₆H₄CH(CH₃)₂		174
4,2'-HOC₆H₄N=CHC₆H₄OH†	Zn + NaOH	4,2'-HOC₆H₄NHCH₂C₆H₄OH		179
4,4'-HOC₆H₄N=CHC₆H₄OCH₃†	Zn + NaOH	4,4'-HOC₆H₄NHCH₂C₆H₄OCH₃		179

Schiff base	Reducing agent	Amine	Yield	Reference
o-CH₃OC₆H₄N=CH(CHOH)₄CH₂OH	H₂ + Ni	o-CH₃OC₆H₄NHCH₂(CHOH)₄CH₂OH	—	66
m-CH₃OC₆H₄N=CH(CHOH)₄CH₂OH	H₂ + Ni	m-CH₃OC₆H₄NHCH₂(CHOH)₄CH₂OH	—	66
p-CH₃OC₆H₄N=CHC₆H₅	H₂ + Ni	p-CH₃OC₆H₄NHCH₂C₆H₅	—	173
2-CH₃O-4-CH₃C₆H₃N=CH(CHOH)₄CH₂OH	H₂ + Ni	2-CH₃O-4-CH₃C₆H₃NHCH₂(CHOH)₄CH₂OH	—	66
2,5-(CH₃O)₂C₆H₃N=CH(CHOH)₄CH₂OH	H₂ + Ni	2,5-(CH₃O)₂C₆H₃NHCH₂(CHOH)₄CH₂OH	—	66
m-O₂NC₆H₄N=CH(CHOH)₄CH₂OH	H₂ + Ni	m-H₂NC₆H₄NHCH₂(CHOH)₄CH₂OH	—	66
p-H₂NC₆H₄N=CH(CHOH)₄CH₂OH	H₂ + Ni	p-H₂NC₆H₄NHCH₂(CHOH)₄CH₂OH	—	66
p-(CH₃)₂NC₆H₄N=CHC₆H₅†	Na—Hg + CH₃CH₂OH	p-(CH₃)₂NC₆H₄NHCH₂C₆H₅	—	178
p-CH₃CONHC₆H₄N=CH(CHOH)₄CH₂OH	H₂ + Ni	p-CH₃CONHC₆H₄NHCH₂(CHOH)₄CH₂OH	—	66
4,4'-(CH₃)₂NC₆H₄N=CHC₆H₄CH(CH₃)₂†	Na—Hg + CH₃CH₂OH	4,4'-(CH₃)₂NC₆H₄NHCH₂C₆H₄CH(CH₃)₂	—	174
4,4'-(CH₃)₂NC₆H₄N=CHC₆H₄OCH₃†	Na—Hg + CH₃CH₂OH	4,4'-(CH₃)₂NC₆H₄NHCH₂C₆H₄OCH₃	—	177
α-C₁₀H₇N=CH(CHOH)₄CH₂OH	Mg + CH₃OH	α-C₁₀H₇NHCH₂(CHOH)₄CH₂OH	—	66
α-C₁₀H₇N=CHC₆H₅†	Mg + CH₃OH	α-C₁₀H₇NHCH₂C₆H₅	—	65
1,4'-C₁₀H₇N=CHC₆H₄OCH₃†	H₂ + Ni	1,4'-C₁₀H₇NHCH₂C₆H₄OCH₃	—	65
1,1'-C₁₀H₇N=CHC₁₀H₇†	Na—Hg + CH₃CH₂OH	1,1'-C₁₀H₇NHCH₂C₁₀H₇	—	180
β-C₁₀H₇N=CHC₆H₅†	Mg + CH₃OH	β-C₁₀H₇NHCH₂C₆H₅	Nearly quantitative	178
β-C₁₀H₇N=CHC₆H₅†	Mg + CH₃OH	β-C₁₀H₇NHCH₂C₆H₅	—	65
2,2'-C₁₀H₇N=CHC₆H₄OH†	Na—Hg + CH₃CH₂OH	2,2'-C₁₀H₇NHCH₂C₆H₄OH	—	176
2,4'-C₁₀H₇N=CHC₆H₄OH†	Na—Hg + CH₃CH₂OH	2,4'-C₁₀H₇NHCH₂C₃H₄OH	—	176
2,4'-C₁₀H₇N=CHC₆H₄OCH₃†	Mg + CH₃OH	2,4'-C₁₀H₇NHCH₂C₆H₄OCH₃	—	177
2,4'-C₁₀H₇N=CHC₆H₄OCH₃†	H₂ + Ni	2,4'-C₁₀H₇NHCH₂C₆H₅C₄OCH₃	—	65
2,2'-C₁₀H₇N=CHC₁₀H₇†	H₂ + Ni	2,2'-C₁₀H₇NHCH₂C₁₀H₇	—	180

* References 134–180 are listed on p. 255.

† These Schiff's bases probably were purified before reduction.

TABLE XI

Preparation of Tertiary Amines

A. From Ammonia and Carbonyl Compounds

Amine Used	Carbonyl Compound	Reducing Agent	Products Isolated	Yield, %	Ref.*
NH_3	CH_3CHO	$H_2 + Pt$	$(CH_3CH_2)_3N$	—	20
NH_3	CH_3CH_2CHO	$H_2 + Pt$	$[CH_3(CH_2)_2]_3N$	—	20

B. From Primary Aliphatic Amines or Nitro Compounds and Aliphatic Aldehydes

Amine or Nitro Compound Used	Carbonyl Compound	Reducing Agent	Products Isolated	Yield, %	Ref.*
CH_3NO_2	CH_3CHO	$H_2 + Pt$	$CH_3N(CH_2CH_3)_2$	92	2
CH_3NO_2	CH_3CH_2CHO	$H_2 + Pt$	$CH_3N[(CH_2)_2CH_3]_2$	45	2
CH_3NO_2	$CH_3(CH_2)_2CHO$	$H_2 + Pt$	$CH_3N[(CH_2)_3CH_3]_2$	33, 38	70
CH_3NO_2	$CH_3(CH_2)_2CHO$	$H_2 + Pt$	$CH_3N[(CH_2)_3CH_3]_2$	56	2
CH_3NO_2	$CH_3(CH_2)_2CHO$	$H_2 + Pt$	$CH_3N[(CH_2)_3CH_3]_2$	39, 46, 54	70
CH_3NO_2	$CH_3(CH_2)_4CHO$	$H_2 + Pt$	$CH_3N[(CH_2)_5CH_3]_2$	30	70
$HO(CH_2)_2NH_2$	CH_2O	$H_2 + Ni$	$HO(CH_2)_2N(CH_3)_2$	78–88	71
$m\text{-}CH_3OC_6H_4CH(CH_3)CH_2NH_2$	CH_2O	$H_2 + Ni$	$m\text{-}CH_3OC_6H_4CH(CH_3)CH_2N(CH_3)_2$	64	27
$p\text{-}CH_3OC_6H_4CH(CH_3)CH_2NH_2$	CH_2O	$H_2 + Ni$	$p\text{-}CH_3OC_6H_4CH(CH_3)CH_2N(CH_3)_2$	64	27
$C_6H_5CH_2CH(CH_3)NH_2$	CH_2O	$H_2 + Ni$	$C_6H_5CH_2CH(CH_3)N(CH_3)_2$	67	27
$o\text{-}CH_3OC_6H_4CH_2CH(CH_3)NH_2$	CH_2O	$H_2 + Ni$	$o\text{-}CH_3OC_6H_4CH_2CH(CH_3)N(CH_3)_2$	80	27
$m\text{-}CH_3OC_6H_4CH_2CH(CH_3)NH_2$	CH_2O	$H_2 + Ni$	$m\text{-}CH_3OC_6H_4CH_2CH(CH_3)N(CH_3)_2$	86	27
$p\text{-}CH_3OC_6H_4CH_2CH(CH_3)NH_2$	CH_2O	$H_2 + Ni$	$p\text{-}CH_3OC_6H_4CH_2CH(CH_3)N(CH_3)_2$	51	27
$C_6H_5CHOHCH(CH_3)NH_2$	CH_2O	$H_2 + Ni$	$C_6H_5CHOHCH(CH_3)N(CH_3)_2$	84	27
$H_2NC{=\!=}CCH_3$ ring, OC—NCH_3, N—C_6H_5	CH_2O	$H_2 + Pt$	$(CH_3)_2NC{=\!=}CCH_3$ ring, OC—NCH_3, N—C_6H_5	—	18, 72

C. From Primary Aliphatic Amines and Aromatic Aldehydes

Amine Used	Carbonyl Compound	Reducing Agent	Products Isolated	Yield, %	Ref.*
$CH_3CH_2NH_2$	C_6H_5CHO CH_3CHO	$H_2 + Pt$	$C_6H_5CH_2N(CH_2CH_3)_2$	28	11

D. From Primary Aliphatic Amines and Ketones

Amine Used	Carbonyl Compound	Reducing Agent	Products Isolated	Yield, %	Ref.*
CH_3NH_2	$CH_3COCH_2COCH_3 + CH_2O$	$H_2 + Pt$	$CH_3CHOHCH_2CH(CH_3)N(CH_3)_2$	—	73
CH_3NH_2	$C_6H_5COCOCH_3 + CH_2O$	$H_2 + Pt$	$C_6H_5CHOHCH(CH_3)N(CH_3)_2$	—	74
$CH_3CH_2NH_2$	$CH_3COCH_2COCH_3 + CH_3CHO$	$H_2 + Pt$	$CH_3CHOHCH_2CH(CH_3)N(CH_2CH_3)_2$	42	73
$CH_3CH_2NH_2$	$C_6H_5COCH_2COCH_3 + CH_3CHO$	$H_2 + Pt$	$C_6H_5CHOHCH_2CH(CH_3)N(CH_2CH_3)_2$	—	73
Cyclohexylamine	$CH_3CO(CH_2)_2COCH_3$	$H_2 + Pt$	H_3CCH $CHCH_3$ ring with CH_2—CH_2 and NC_6H_{11}	27	29, 30
H_2NC=CCH_3 / OC NCH_3 / N C_6H_5	CH_3COCH_3	$H_2 + Pt$	$CH_3CHOH(CH_2)_2CH(CH_3)NHC_6H_{11}$ $[(CH_3)_2CH]_2NC$=CCH_3 / OC NCH_3 / N C_6H_5	8 —	18

* References 181–185 are listed on p. 255.

TABLE XI—Continued

PREPARATION OF TERTIARY AMINES

E. From Primary Aromatic Amines, Nitro, Nitroso or Azo Compounds and Aliphatic Aldehydes

Amine, Nitro, Nitroso or Azo Compound Used	Carbonyl Compound	Reducing Agent	Products Isolated	Yield, %	Ref.*
C_6H_5NO	CH_3CHO	$Zn + H_2SO_4$	$C_6H_5N(CH_2CH_3)_2$	90	34
$C_6H_5NO_2$	CH_3CHO	$H_2 + Pt$	$C_6H_5N(CH_2CH_3)_2$	70	2
$C_6H_5NO_2$	CH_3CH_2CHO	$H_2 + Pt$	$C_6H_5N[(CH_2)_2CH_3]_2$	34	2
$C_6H_5NO_2$	$CH_3(CH_2)_2CHO$	$H_2 + Pt$	$C_6H_5N[(CH_2)_3CH_3]_2$	69	2
$C_6H_5NO_2$	$CH_3(CH_2)_2CHO$	$H_2 + Ni$	$C_6H_5N[(CH_2)_3CH_3]_2$	63	2, 33
$p\text{-}CH_3C_6H_4NO_2$	CH_2O	Electrolytic	$p\text{-}CH_3C_6H_4N(CH_3)_2$		181
$2,4,6\text{-}(CH_3)_3C_6H_2NH_2$	CH_2O	$Zn + HCl$	$2,4,6\text{-}(CH_3)_3C_6H_2N(CH_3)_2$	70	42
$2,4,6\text{-}(CH_3)_3C_6H_2NO_2$	CH_2O	$Zn + HCl$	$2,4,6\text{-}(CH_3)_3C_6H_2N(CH_3)_2$	68	42
$2,4,6\text{-}Cl_3C_6H_2NH_2$	CH_2O	$Zn + HCl$	$2,4,6\text{-}Cl_3C_6H_2N(CH_3)_2$	—	76
$2\text{-}CH_3\text{-}4\text{-}BrC_6H_3NH_2$	CH_2O	$Zn + HCl$	$2\text{-}CH_3\text{-}4\text{-}BrC_6H_3N(CH_3)_2$	54	76
$2,4\text{-}(CH_3)_2\text{-}6\text{-}BrC_6H_2NH_2$	CH_2O	$Zn + HCl$	$2,4\text{-}(CH_3)_2\text{-}6\text{-}BrC_6H_3N(CH_3)_2$	90	76
$2\text{-}CH_3\text{-}4\text{-}Br_2C_6H_2NH_2$	CH_2O	$Zn + HCl$	$2\text{-}CH_3\text{-}4\text{-}BrC_6H_3N(CH_3)_2$	68	76
$2,6\text{-}Br_2\text{-}4\text{-}CH_3C_6H_2NH_2$	CH_2O	$Zn + HCl$	$2\text{-}Br\text{-}4\text{-}CH_3C_6H_3N(CH_3)_2$	75	76
$2,4,6\text{-}Br_3C_6H_2NH_2$	CH_2O	$Zn + HCl$	$p\text{-}BrC_6H_4N(CH_3)_2$	88	76
$2,6\text{-}Br_2\text{-}4\text{-}IC_6H_2NH_2$	CH_2O	$Zn + HCl$	$3\text{-}CH_3\text{-}4\text{-}BrC_6H_3N(CH_3)_2$	63	76
			$C_6H_5N(CH_3)_2$	81	75
$4,6\text{-}Cl_2\text{-}1,3\text{-}C_6H_2(NH_2)_2$	CH_2O	$Zn + HCl$	$4,6\text{-}Cl_2\text{-}1,3\text{-}C_6H_2[N(CH_3)_2]_2$	71	75
$p\text{-}(CH_3)_2NC_6H_4N{=}NC_6H_5$	$CH_3(CH_2)_2CHO$	$H_2 + Ni$	$p\text{-}(CH_3)_2NC_6H_4N[(CH_2)_3CH_3]_2$	76	48
			$C_6H_5NH(CH_2)_3CH_3$	73	45
$p\text{-}HOC_6H_4NO_2$	CH_3CH_2CHO	$H_2 + Pt$	$p\text{-}HOC_6H_4NH(CH_2)_2CH_3$	26	48
$p\text{-}HOC_6H_4N{=}NC_6H_5$	$CH_3(CH_2)_2CHO$	$H_2 + Ni$	$p\text{-}HOC_6H_4N[(CH_2)_2CH_3]_2$	40	48
$p\text{-}HOC_6H_4NO_2$	$CH_3(CH_2)_2CHO$	$H_2 + Ni$	$p\text{-}HOC_6H_4N[(CH_2)_3CH_3]_2$	46	33
$p\text{-}HO_2CC_6H_4NH_2$	CH_2O	$H_2 + Pt$, Ni or Co	$p\text{-}HO_2CC_6H_4N(CH_3)_2$		77
$p\text{-}CH_3CH_2O_2CC_6H_4NH_2$	CH_2O	Ni or Co	$p\text{-}CH_3CH_2O_2CC_6H_4N(CH_3)_2$		77
$\alpha\text{-}C_{10}H_7NO_2$	CH_3CHO	$H_2 + Pt$	$\alpha\text{-}C_{10}H_7N(CH_2CH_3)_2$	40	2
$2\text{-}HOC_{10}H_6N{=}NC_6H_5$	$CH_3(CH_2)_2CHO$	$H_2 + Ni$	$2\text{-}HOC_{10}H_6N[(CH_2)_3CH_3]_2$	41	48

F. From Aromatic Nitro Compounds and Aromatic Aldehydes

Nitro Compound Used	Carbonyl Compound	Reducing Agent	Products Isolated	Yield, %	Ref.*
p-HOC$_6$H$_4$NO$_2$	C$_6$H$_5$CHO	H$_2$ + Pt	p-HOC$_6$H$_4$N(CH$_2$C$_6$H$_5$)$_2$	—	52, 53, 54
p-H$_2$NC$_6$H$_4$NO$_2$	C$_6$H$_5$CHO	H$_2$ + Pt	p-C$_6$H$_4$[N(CH$_2$C$_6$H$_5$)$_2$]$_2$	50	44

G. From Secondary Aliphatic Amines and Aliphatic Aldehydes

Amine Used	Carbonyl Compound	Reducing Agent	Products Isolated	Yield, %	Ref.*
(CH$_3$)$_2$NH	(CH$_3$)$_2$CHCH$_2$CHO	H$_2$ + Pt	(CH$_3$)$_2$N(CH$_2$)$_2$CH(CH$_3$)$_2$	—	73
(CH$_3$)$_2$NH	(CH$_3$)$_2$C=CH(CH$_2$)$_2$-C(CH$_3$)=CHCHO	H$_2$ + Pt	(CH$_3$)$_2$CH(CH$_2$)$_3$CH(CH$_3$)(CH$_2$)$_2$-N(CH$_3$)$_2$	64	73
(CH$_3$CH$_2$)$_2$NH	CH$_2$O	CH$_3$CHOHCH$_3$	(CH$_3$CH$_2$)$_2$NCH$_3$	—	135
[(CH$_3$)$_2$CH]$_2$NH	CH$_3$CH$_2$CHO	H$_2$ + Ni	(CH$_3$CH$_2$)$_3$N	90	182
(CH$_3$)$_2$CH(CH$_2$)$_2$NHCH$_2$CH$_3$	CH$_2$O	H$_2$ + Pt	[(CH$_3$)$_2$CH(CH$_2$)$_2$N(CH$_3$)CH$_2$CH$_3$	26	18
(CH$_3$)$_2$CH(CH$_2$)$_2$NHCH$_2$CH$_3$	CH$_3$CHO	H$_2$ + Pt	(CH$_3$)$_2$CH(CH$_2$)$_2$N(CH$_3$)CH$_2$CH$_3$	—	73
(CH$_3$)$_2$CH(CH$_2$)$_2$NHCH$_2$CH$_3$	CH$_3$CH$_2$CHO	H$_2$ + Pt	(CH$_3$)$_2$CH(CH$_2$)$_2$N(CH$_2$CH$_3$)$_2$	40	73
(CH$_3$)$_2$CH(CH$_2$)$_2$NHCH$_2$CH$_3$			(CH$_3$)$_2$CH(CH$_2$)$_2$N(CH$_2$CH$_3$)(CH$_2$)$_2$-CH$_3$	33	73
(CH$_3$)$_2$CH(CH$_2$)$_2$NHCH$_2$CH$_3$	(CH$_3$)$_2$CHCHO	H$_2$ + Pt	(CH$_3$)$_2$CH(CH$_2$)$_2$N(CH$_2$CH$_3$)CH$_2$-CH(CH$_3$)$_2$	40	73
(CH$_3$)$_2$CH(CH$_2$)$_2$NHCH$_2$CH$_3$	(CH$_3$)$_2$CHCH$_2$CHO	H$_2$ + Pt	[(CH$_3$)$_2$CH(CH$_2$)$_2$]$_2$NCH$_2$CH$_3$	50	73
(CH$_3$)$_2$CH(CH$_2$)$_2$NHCH$_2$CH$_3$	CH$_3$(CH$_2$)$_5$CHO	H$_2$ + Pt	(CH$_3$)$_2$CH(CH$_2$)$_2$N(CH$_2$CH$_3$)(CH$_2$)$_6$-CH$_3$	10	18
(CH$_3$)$_2$CH(CH$_2$)$_2$NHCH$_2$CH$_3$	(CH$_3$)$_2$C=CH(CH$_2$)$_2$-C(CH$_3$)=CHCHO	H$_2$ + Pt	(CH$_3$)$_2$CH(CH$_2$)$_2$N(CH$_2$CH$_3$)(CH$_2$)$_2$-CH(CH$_3$)$_2$	47	18
[CH$_3$(CH$_2$)$_3$]$_2$NH	CH$_3$CHO	H$_2$ + Ni	[CH$_3$(CH$_2$)$_3$]$_2$NCH$_2$CH$_3$	—	182, 183

* References 181–185 are listed on p. 255.

TABLE XI—*Continued*

PREPARATION OF TERTIARY AMINES

G. From Secondary Aliphatic Amines and Aliphatic Aldehydes—Continued

Amine Used	Carbonyl Compound	Reducing Agent	Products Isolated	Yield, %	Ref.*
$[CH_3(CH_2)_2]_2NH$	$CH_3(CH_2)_2CHO$	$H_2 + Ni$	$[CH_3(CH_2)_3]_3N$	34	182, 183
$[CH_3CH_2CH(CH_3)]_2NH$	$CH_3(CH_2)_5CHO$	$H_2 + Pt$	$[CH_3CH_2CH(CH_3)]_2N(CH_2)_6CH_3$	6	18
$CH_3CH_2CH(CH_3)NHCH(CH_2CH_3)_2$	CH_2O	$H_2 + Pt$	$CH_3CH_2CH(CH_3)N(CH_3)CH(CH_2CH_3)_2$	73	18
$[(CH_3)_2CH(CH_2)_2]_2NH$	CH_3CHO	$H_2 + Pt$	$[(CH_3)_2CH(CH_2)_2]_2NCH_2CH_3$	34	18
$[(CH_3)_2CH(CH_2)_2]_2NH$	$CH_3CH{=}CHCHO$	$H_2 + Pt$	$[(CH_3)_2CH(CH_2)_2]_2N(CH_2)_3CH_3$	15	18
$[(CH_3)_2CH(CH_2)_2]_2NH$	$(CH_3)_2C{=}CH(CH_2)_2C(CH_3){=}CHCHO$	$H_2 + Pt$	$[(CH_3)_2CH(CH_2)_2]_2N(CH_2)_2CH(CH_3)(CH_2)_2CH(CH_3)_2$	44	18
$(CH_3)_2CH(CH_2)_3CH(CH_3)(CH_2)_2NH(CH_2)_2CH(CH_3)_2$	CH_3CHO	$H_2 + Pt$	$(CH_3)_2CH(CH_2)_3CH(CH_3)(CH_2)_2N(CH_2CH_3)(CH_2)_2CH(CH_3)_2$	34	18
$[(CH_3)_2CH(CH_2)_3CH(CH_3)(CH_2)_2]_2NH$	$(CH_3)_2CHCH_2CHO$	$H_2 + Pt$	$[(CH_3)_2CH(CH_2)_3CH(CH_3)(CH_2)_2]_2N(CH_2)_2CH(CH_3)_2$	75	18
$[(CH_3)_2CH(CH_2)_3CH(CH_3)(CH_2)_2]_2NH$	$(CH_3)_2CH(CH_2)_3CH(CH_3)CH_2CHO$	$H_2 + Pt$	$[(CH_3)_2CH(CH_2)_3CH(CH_3)(CH_2)_2]_3N$	33	18
$[(CH_3)_2CH(CH_2)_3CH(CH_3)(CH_2)_2]_2NH$	$(CH_3)_2C{=}CH(CH_2)_2C(CH_3){=}CHCHO$	$H_2 + Pt$	$[(CH_3)_2CH(CH_2)_3CH(CH_3)(CH_2)_2]_3N$	67	18
$[(CH_3)_2CH(CH_2)_3CH(CH_3)(CH_2)_2]_2NH$	CH_3CHO	$H_2 + Pt$	$[(CH_3)_2CH(CH_2)_3CH(CH_3)(CH_2)_2]_2NCH_2CH_3$	85	18
$C_6H_{11}NHCH_2CH_3$	CH_3CHO	$H_2 + Pt$	$C_6H_{11}N(CH_2CH_3)_2$	64	73
$CH_3CHOHCH_2CH(CH_3)NHCH_3$	CH_2O	$H_2 + Pt$	$CH_3CHOHCH_2CH(CH_3)N(CH_3)_2$	—	73
$CH_3CHOHCH_2CH(CH_3)NHCH_2CH_3$	CH_2O	$H_2 + Pt$	$CH_3CHOHCH_2CH(CH_3)N(CH_3)CH_2CH_3$	—	73
$CH_3CHOHCH_2CH(CH_3)NHCH_3$	CH_3CHO	$H_2 + Pt$	$CH_3CHOHCH_2CH(CH_3)N(CH_3)CH_2CH_3$	48	73
$C_6H_5CHOHCH(CH_3)NHCH_3$	CH_2O	$H_2 + Pt$	$C_6H_5CHOHCH(CH_3)N(CH_3)_2$	Quantitative	29, 30
$C_6H_5CHOHCH(CH_3)NHCH_2CH_3$	CH_2O	$H_2 + Pt$	$C_6H_5CHOHCH(CH_3)N(CH_3)CH_2CH_3$	Quantitative	73

$C_6H_5CHOHCH_2CH(CH_3)$-$NHCH_3$	CH_2O	$H_2 + Pt$	$C_6H_5CHOHCH_2CH(CH_3)N(CH_3)_2$	83	73
$C_6H_5CHOHCH_2CH(CH_3)$-$NHCH_2CH_3$	CH_3CHO	$H_2 + Pt$	$C_6H_5CHOHCH_2CH(CH_3)N$-$(CH_2CH_3)_2$	74	73
$C_6H_5CH_2NHCH_2CH_3$	CH_3CHO	$H_2 + Pt$	$C_6H_5CH_2N(CH_2CH_3)_2$	15–50	11
Piperidine	CH_2O		(structure) $NHCH_3$	60	135
			(structure)	25	
Piperidine	CH_3CHO	$CH_3CHOHCH_3$	(structure) NCH_2CH_3		136
Piperidine	$CH_3(CH_2)_2CHO$	$H_2 + Ni$	(structure) $N(CH_2)_3CH_3$	93	23, 24, 83
Piperazine	CH_2O	$Zn + HCl$	(structure) NCH_3	88	184
Piperazine	CH_3CHO	$Zn + HCl$	(structure) NCH_2CH_3	92	184

* References 181–185 are listed on p. 255.

TABLE XI—Continued
Preparation of Tertiary Amines

G. From Secondary Aliphatic Amines and Aliphatic Aldehydes—Continued

Amine Used	Carbonyl Compound	Reducing Agent	Products Isolated	Yield, %	Ref.*
CH₂—CH₂ / CH₂—N(H)—CHCHOHCH₃	CH₃CHO	—	CH₂—CH₂ / CH₂—N—CHCOCH₃	Nearly quantitative	136
CH₂—CH₂ / CH₂—N(H)—CHCHOHCH₂CH₃	CH₂O	—	CH₂CH₃ / CH₂—CH₂ / CH₂—N—CHCOCH₂CH₃	Nearly quantitative	135
CH₂—CH₂ / CH₂—N(H)—CHCH₂CHOHCH₃	CH₂O	—	CH₃ / CH₂—CH₂ / CH₂—N—CHCH₂COCH₃	—	135

H. From Secondary Aliphatic Amines and Aromatic Aldehydes

Amine Used	Carbonyl Compound	Reducing Agent	Products Isolated	Yield, %	Ref.*
(CH₃)₂NH	C₆H₅CHO	H₂ + Pt	(CH₃)₂NCH₂C₆H₅	—	73
(CH₃)₂NH	C₆H₅CH₂CHO	CH₃CHOHCH₃	(CH₃)₂N(CH₂)₂C₆H₅	Quantitative	136
(CH₃)₂NH	C₆H₅CH₂CH₂CHO	Al—Hg + H₂O	(CH₃)₂N(CH₂)₂C₆H₅	39	127

I. *From Secondary Aliphatic Amines and Ketones*

Amine Used	Carbonyl Compound	Reducing Agent	Products Isolated	Yield, %	Ref.*
$(CH_3)_2NH$	CH_3COCH_3	$H_2 + Pt$	$(CH_3)_2NCH(CH_3)_2$	—	74
$(CH_3)_2NH$	$C_6H_5COCH_3$	$H_2 + Pt$	$(CH_3)_2NCH(CH_3)C_6H_5$	—	73
$(CH_3)_2NH$	$C_6H_5COCOCH_3$	$H_2 + Pt$	$(CH_3)_2NCH(CH_3)CH_2C_6H_5$	—	149
$(CH_3)_2NH$	$CH_3(CH_2)_2COCOCH_3$	$H_2 + Pd$	$CH_3(CH_2)_2COCH(CH_3)N(CH_3)_2$	8	28
$(CH_3)_2NH$	$C_6H_5COCOCH_3$	$H_2 + Pt$	$CH_3CHOHCH(CH_3)N(CH_3)_2$	—	74
$(CH_3)_2NH$	$CH_3COCH_2COCH_3$	$H_2 + Pt$	$C_6H_5CHOHCH_2CH(CH_3)N(CH_3)_2$	0.8	29, 30
$(CH_3CH_2)_2NH$	$C_6H_5COCH_2COCH_3$	$H_2 + Pt$	$CH_3CHOHCH_2CH(CH_3)N(CH_3)_2$	—	73
$CH_3CH_2CH(CH_3)NHCH_3$	CH_3COCH_3	$H_2 + Pt$	$CH_3CH_2CH(CH_3)N(CH_3)CH(CH_3)_2$	6	73
$CH_3CH_2CH(CH_3)NHCH_3$	$CH_3COCH_2CH_3$	$H_2 + Pt$	$CH_3CH_2CH(CH_3)N(CH_3)CH(CH_3)CH_2CH_3$	47	18
$CH_3CH_2CH(CH_3)NHCH_3$	$CH_3CO(CH_2)_2CH_3$	$H_2 + Pt$	$CH_3CH_2CH(CH_3)N(CH_3)CH(CH_3)(CH_2)_2CH_3$	18	18
$CH_3CH_2CH(CH_3)NHCH_3$	$CH_3CH_2COCH_2CH_3$	$H_2 + Pt$	$CH_3CH_2CH(CH_3)N(CH_3)CH(CH_2CH_3)_2$	17	18
$CH_3CH_2CH(CH_3)NHCH_3$	$CH_3CO(CH_2)_3CH_3$	$H_2 + Pt$	$CH_3CH_2CH(CH_3)N(CH_3)CH(CH_3)(CH_2)_3CH_3$	0.02	18
$CH_3CH_2CH(CH_3)NHCH_3$	$CH_3CO(CH_2)_4CH_3$	$H_2 + Pt$	$CH_3CH_2CH(CH_3)N(CH_3)CH(CH_3)(CH_2)_4CH_3$	8	18
$CH_3CH_2CH(CH_3)NHCH_3$	$CH_3CO(CH_2)_5CH_3$	$H_2 + Pt$	$CH_3CH_2CH(CH_3)N(CH_3)CH(CH_3)(CH_2)_5CH_3$	3	18
$CH_3CH_2CH(CH_3)NHCH_3$	Cyclohexanone	$H_2 + Pt$	$CH_3CH_2CH(CH_3)N(CH_3)C_6H_{11}$	0.6	18
$CH_3CH_2CH(CH_3)NHCH_3$	(cyclohexanone, CH_2CH_2–CH_2–CO ring)	$H_2 + Pt$	$CH_3CH_2CH(CH_3)N(CH_3)C_6H_{11}$	15	18
$CH_3CH_2CH(CH_3)NHCH_3$	(methylcyclohexanone ring; CH_2CHCH_3, CH_2CH_2, CO, CH_2)	$H_2 + Pt$	None	0	18
$CH_3CH_2CH(CH_3)NHCH_3$	(methylcyclohexanone ring; CH_2, $CHCH_2CH_3$, CO)	$H_2 + Pt$	$CH_3CH_2CH(CH_3)N(CH_3)CH$ (2‑methylcyclohexyl ring; CH_2CH_2, CH_2, CH_2CH, CH_3)	5	18

* References 180–185 are listed on p. 255.

TABLE XI—*Continued*

PREPARATION OF TERTIARY AMINES

I. From Secondary Aliphatic Amines and Ketones—Continued

Amine Used	Carbonyl Compound	Reducing Agent	Products Isolated	Yield, %	Ref.*
$CH_3CH_2CH(CH_3)NHCH_3$	4-methylcyclohexanone (H_3CCH ring with CH_2CH_2, CH_2CH_2, CO)	$H_2 + Pt$	$CH_3CH_2CH(CH_3)N(CH_3)CH$ (4-methylcyclohexyl)	4	18
$(CH_3CH_2)_2CHNHCH_3$	$CH_3COCH_2CH_3$	$H_2 + Pt$	$(CH_3CH_2)_2CHN(CH_3)CH(CH_3)CH_2CH_3$	21	18
$CH_3CH_2CH(CH_3)NHCH_2-$ CH_3	CH_3COCH_3	$H_2 + Pt$	$CH_3CH_2CH(CH_3)N(CH_2CH_3)CH(CH_3)_2$	2	18
$(CH_3)_2CH(CH_2)_2NHCH_2CH_3$	CH_3COCH_3	$H_2 + Pt$	$(CH_3)_2CH(CH_2)_2N(CH_2CH_3)CH(CH_3)_2$	24	18
$[(CH_3)_2CH(CH_2)_2]_2NH$	CH_3COCH_3	$H_2 + Pt$	$[(CH_3)_2CH(CH_2)_2]_2NCH(CH_3)_2$	14	18

J. From Aryl Alkyl Amines and Aliphatic Aldehydes

Amine Used	Carbonyl Compound	Reducing Agent	Products Isolated	Yield, %	Ref.*
$C_6H_5NHCH_3$	CH_2O	$Zn + HCl$	$C_6H_5N(CH_3)_2$	80	80
$C_6H_5NHCH_2CH_3$	CH_2O	$Zn + HCl$	$C_6H_5N(CH_3)CH_2CH_3$	88	80
$C_6H_5NHCH_2CH_3$	CH_3CHO	$Zn + H_2SO_4$	$C_6H_5N(CH_2CH_3)_2$	93	185
$C_6H_5NHCH_2CH_3$	CH_3CHO	$Zn + H_2SO_4$	$C_6H_5N(CH_2CH_3)_2$	82	35

Amine Used	Carbonyl Compound	Reducing Agent	Products Isolated	Yield, %	Ref.*
$C_6H_5NH(CH_2)_2CH_3$	CH_2O	$Zn + HCl$	$C_6H_5N(CH_3)(CH_2)_2CH_3$	76	80
$C_6H_5NH(CH_2)_3CH_3$	CH_2O	$Zn + HCl$	$C_6H_5N(CH_3)(CH_2)_3CH_3$	55	80
$C_6H_5NH(CH_2)_2CH(CH_3)_2$	CH_2O	$Zn + HCl$	$C_6H_5N(CH_3)(CH_2)_2CH(CH_3)_2$	61	80
$C_6H_5NOHCH_2C_6H_5$	$CH_3(CH_2)_2CHO$	$H_2 + Pt$	$C_6H_5N(CH_2C_6H_5)(CH_2)_3CH_3$	38	2
$C_6H_5NHCH_2C_6H_5$	$CH_3(CH_2)_2CHO$	$H_2 + Pt$	$C_6H_5N(CH_2C_6H_5)(CH_2)_3CH_3$	3	2
$p\text{-}HO_2CC_6H_4NH(CH_2)_2CH_3$	CH_2O	$H_2 + Pt$, Ni or Co	$p\text{-}HO_2CC_6H_4N(CH_3)(CH_2)_2CH_3$	—	77
$p\text{-}HO_2CC_6H_4NHCH(CH_2CH_3)C_6H_5$	CH_2O	$H_2 + Pt$, Ni or Co	$p\text{-}HO_2CC_6H_4N(CH_3)CH(CH_2CH_3)C_6H_5$	—	77
$p\text{-}CH_3CH_2O_2CC_6H_4NH(CH_2)_2CH_3$	CH_3CH_2CHO	$H_2 + Pt$, Ni or Co	$p\text{-}CH_3CH_2O_2CC_6H_4N[(CH_2)_2CH_3]_2$	—	77

K. From Aryl Alkyl Amines and Ketones

Amine Used	Carbonyl Compound	Reducing Agent	Products Isolated	Yield, %	Ref.*
$C_6H_5NHCH_3$	$CH_3CH_2COCOCH_3$	$H_2 + Pt$	$CH_3CH_2COCH(CH_3)N(CH_3)C_6H_5$	7	28

L. From Diarylamines and Aldehydes

Amine Used	Carbonyl Compound	Reducing Agent	Products Isolated	Yield, %	Ref.*
$(C_6H_5)_2NH$	CH_2O	$H_2 + Pt$	$(C_6H_5)_2NCH_3$	65	18
$(C_6H_5)_2NH$	CH_3CHO	$H_2 + Pt$	$(C_6H_5)_2NCH_2CH_3$	80	18
$(C_6H_5)_2NH$	CH_3CH_2CHO	$H_2 + Pt$	$(C_6H_5)_2N(CH_2)_2CH_3$	53	18
$(C_6H_5)_2NH$	$CH_3(CH_2)_2CHO$	$H_2 + Pt$	$(C_6H_5)_2N(CH_2)_3CH_3$	33	18
$(C_6H_5)_2NH$	$(CH_3)_2CHCHO$	$H_2 + Pt$	$(C_6H_5)_2NCH_2CH(CH_3)_2$	7	18

* References 180–185 are listed on p. 255.

REFERENCES TO TABLES

[84] Takaki and Ueda, *J. Pharm. Soc. Japan*, **58**, 276 (1938) [*C. A.*, **32**, 5376 (1938)].

[85] Lycan, Puntambeker, and Marvel, *Org. Syntheses, Coll. Vol.* **2**, 318 (1943).

[86] Suter and Moffet, *J. Am. Chem. Soc.*, **56**, 487 (1934).

[87] Paul, *Bull. soc. chim. France*, [5] **4**, 1121 (1937).

[88] Tafel, *Ber.*, **19**, 1928 (1886).

[89] Hofmann, *Ber.*, **15**, 772 (1882).

[90] Wojcik and Adkins, *J. Am Chem. Soc.*, **56**, 2419 (1934).

[91] Davis and Elderfield, *J. Am Chem. Soc.*, **54**, 1503 (1932).

[92] Tseng and Chang, *Science Repts. Natl. Univ. Peking*, **1**, No. 3, 19 (1936) [*C. A.*, **31**, 95 (1937)].

[93] Hartung, U. S. pat. 1,989,093 [*C. A.*, **29**, 1941 (1935)].

[94] Ogata and Hirano, *J. Pharm. Soc. Japan*, **50**, 147 (1930) [*C. A.*, **25**, 1819 (1931)].

[95] Fabriques de Produits de Chimie Organique de Laire, Ger. pat. 541,229 [*C. A.*, **26**, 1940 (1932)].

[96] Rosenmund and Pfankuch, *Ber.*, **56**, 2258 (1923).

[97] Coleman and Forrester, *J. Am. Chem. Soc.*, **58**, 27 (1936).

[98] Sheverdina and Kocheshkov, *Bull. acad. sci. U.S.S.R., Classe sci. chim.* (1941) 75 [*C. A.*, **37**, 3066 (1943)].

[99] Galat and Elion, *J. Am. Chem. Soc.*, **61**, 3585 (1939).

[100] Knoll A.-G. and Schmidt, Fr. pat. 671,388 [*C. A.*, **24**, 2140 (1930)].

[101] Ing and Manske, *J. Chem. Soc.*, **1926**, 2348.

[102] v. Braun, *Ber.*, **70**, 979 (1937).

[103] Wenker, *J. Am. Chem. Soc.*, **57**, 772 (1935).

[104] Kindler, *Arch. Pharm.*, **265**, 389 (1927).

[105] Tafel and Pfeffermann, *Ber.*, **35**, 1513 (1902).

[106] v. Braun, Blessing, and Zobel, *Ber.*, **56**, 1988 (1923).

[107] Carothers and Jones, *J. Am. Chem. Soc.*, **47**, 3051 (1925).

[108] Rosenmund and Jordan, *Ber.*, **58**, 51 (1925).

[109] v. Braun, Kuhn, and Goll, *Ber.*, **59**, 2330 (1926).

[110] Traube and Engelhardt, *Ber.*, **44**, 3152 (1911).

[111] Hickinbottom, *J. Chem. Soc.*, **1930**, 992.

[112] Slotta and Franke, *Ber.*, **63**, 678 (1930).

[113] Reilly and Hickinbottom, *J. Chem. Soc.*, **111**, 1027 (1917).

[114] Sekera and Marvel, *J. Am. Chem. Soc.*, **55**, 345 (1933).

[115] Lazier and Adkins, *J. Am. Chem. Soc.*, **46**, 741 (1924).

[116] v. Braun and Murjahn, *Ber.*, **59**, 1202 (1926).

[117] Brown and Reid, *J. Am. Chem. Soc.*, **46**, 1836 (1924).

[118] Rupe and Hodel, *Helv. Chim. Acta*, **6**, 865 (1923).

[119] Magee and Henze, *J. Am. Chem. Soc.*, **62**, 910 (1940).

[120] Fischer, *Ann.*, **241**, 328 (1887).

[121] Diels and Rhodius, *Ber.*, **42**, 1072 (1909).

[122] Willson and Wheeler, *Org. Syntheses, Coll. Vol.* **I**, 102 (1941).

[123] Rosenmund and Joithe, *Ber.*, **58**, 2054 (1925).

[124] Wallach, *Ann.*, **343**, 71 (1905).

[125] Billman, Radike, and Mundy, *J. Am. Chem. Soc.*, **64**, 2977 (1942).

[126] Hill and Donleavy, *Ind. Eng. Chem.*, **13**, 504 (1921).

[127] Kindler, *Ann.*, **485**, 113 (1931).

[128] Loffler, *Ber.*, **43**, 2031 (1910).

[129] Rohrmann and Shonle, *J. Am. Chem. Soc.*, **66**, 1515 (1944).

[130] Gray, U. S. pat. 2,343,769 [*C. A.*, **38**, 3421 (1944)].

[131] Couturier, *Compt. rend.*, **207**, 345 (1938).

[132] Mingoia, *Ann. Chim. farm.*, **18**, 11 (1940) [*C. A.*, **34**, 6249 (1940)].

[133] Hildebrandt, U. S. pat. 2,146,475 [*C. A.*, **33**, 3402 (1939)].

[134] Knoop and Oesterlin, *Z. physiol. Chem.*, **170**, 186 (1927).
[135] Bayer and Co., Ger. pat. 287,802 [*Frdl.*, **12**, 800 (1917)].
[136] Bayer and Co., Ger. pat. 291,222 [*Frdl.*, **12**, 802 (1917)].
[137] Graf, U. S. pat. 2,317,757 [*C. A.*, **37**, 5988 (1934)].
[138] Dobke and Keil, Fr. pat. 844,230 [*C. A.*, **34**, 7297 (1940)].
[139] Hildebrandt, U. S. pat. 2,146,473 [*C. A.*, **33**, 3401 (1939)].
[140] Susie and Hass, U. S. pat. 2,243,295 [*C. A.*, **35**, 5511 (1941)].
[141] Loffler, *Ber.*, **43**, 2035 (1910).
[142] Coleman and Carnes, *Proc. Iowa Acad. Sci.*, **119**, 288 (1942) [*C. A.*, **37**, 5703 (1943)].
[143] Hildebrandt, U. S. pat. 2,146,474 [*C. A.*, **33**, 3401 (1939)].
[144] Hildebrandt, U. S. pat. 2,344,356 [*C. A.*, **38**, 3421 (1944)].
[145] Skita, Keil, and Meiner, *Ber.*, **66**, 974 (1933).
[146] Manske and Johnson, *J. Am. Chem. Soc.*, **54**, 306 (1932).
[147] Manske and Johnson, *J. Am. Chem. Soc.*, **51**, 580 (1929).
[148] Adams and Rogers, *J. Am. Chem. Soc.*, **63**, 228 (1941).
[149] Dobke and Keil, Fr. pat. 844,226 [*C. A.*, **34**, 7297 (1940)].
[150] Gabriel, *Ber.*, **42**, 1259 (1909).
[151] Frankland, Challenger, and Nicholls, *J. Chem. Soc.*, **115**, 198 (1919).
[152] Henke and Benner, Brit. pat. 514,796 [*C. A.*, **35**, 4394 (1941)].
[153] Surrey and Hammer, *J. Am. Chem. Soc.*, **66**, 2127 (1944).
[154] Bergman, Brit. pat. 547,302 [*C. A.*, **37**, 5985 (1943)].
[155] von Bramer, Davy, and Clemens, U. S. pat. 2,323,948 [*C. A.*, **38**, 116 (1944)].
[156] Carruthers and Kiefer, U. S. pat. 2,350,446 [*C. A.*, **38**, 4963 (1944)].
[157] Stoermer and Lefel, *Ber.*, **29**, 2110 (1896).
[158] Knudsen, Ger. pat. 143,197 [*Frdl.*, **3**, 24 (1905)].
[159] Zaunschirm, *Ann.*, **245**, 279 (1888).
[160] Barger and Ewins, *J. Chem. Soc.*, **97**, 2253 (1910).
[161] Mailhe, *Caoutchouc & gutta-percha*, **17**, 10,185 (1920) (*Chem. Zentr.*, **1920**, I, 565).
[162] Clark and Wilson, U. S. pat. 2,319,848 [*C. A.*, **37**, 6275 (1943)].
[163] Franzen, *J. prakt. Chem.*, (**2**) **72**, 211 (1905).
[164] Fischer, *Ber.*, **29**, 205 (1896).
[165] Shepard and Ticknor, *J. Am. Chem. Soc.*, **38**, 381 (1916).
[166] Kindler, *Ann.*, **485**, 113 (1931).
[167] Buck, *J. Am. Chem. Soc.*, **53**, 2192 (1931).
[168] Hoffmann-LaRoche, Ger. pat. 259,874 [*Frdl.*, **11**, 1011 (1915)].
[169] Kaufmann and Muller, *Ber.*, **51**, 123 (1918).
[170] Anselmino, *Ber.*, **41**, 621 (1909).
[171] Brand, *Ber.*, **42**, 3460 (1909).
[172] Fischer, *Ber.*, **19**, 748 (1886).
[173] Mailhe, *Compt. rend.*, **172**, 280 (1921).
[174] Zaunschirm and Uebel, *Ann.*, **245**, 289 (1888).
[175] Bamberger and Muller, *Ann.*, **313**, 97 (1900).
[176] Fischer and Emmerich, *Ann.*, **241**, 343 (1887).
[177] Fischer and Steinhart, *Ann.*, **241**, 328 (1887).
[178] Fischer and Kohler, *Ann.*, **241**, 358 (1887).
[179] Chemische Fabrik auf Aktien, Ger. pat. 211,869 [*Frdl.*, **9**, 154 (1911)].
[180] Rupe and Becherer, *Helv. Chim. Acta*, **6**, 880 (1923).
[181] Lob, *Z. Elektrochem.*, **4**, 428 (1898).
[182] Christ, U. S pat. 2,170,740 [*C. A.*, **34**, 115 (1940)].
[183] Christ, Ger. pat 673,017 [*C. A.*, **33**, 6874 (1939)].
[184] Forsee and Pollard. *J. Am. Chem. Soc.*, **57**, 1788 (1935).
[185] Lockemann, Ger. pat. 503,113 [*Frdl.*, **16**, 358 (1931)].

CHAPTER 4

THE ACYLOINS

S. M. McElvain

University of Wisconsin

CONTENTS

INTRODUCTION

Acyloins are α-hydroxy ketones of the general formula RCHOHCOR, in which R represents an aliphatic residue. They are, therefore, the aliphatic analogs of benzoins.

The term "acyloin" is commonly used as a class name for the symmetrical keto alcohols, and the name of the individual compound is derived by adding the suffix *oin* to the stem name of the acid to which the acyloin corresponds, e.g., acetoin, propionoin, butyroin, etc. For euphony and to avoid confusion with commonly used names of the glyceryl esters, the acyloins corresponding to caproic and capric acids are called capronoin and caprinoin. A mixed acyloin in which the two alkyl groups are different is named as a derivative of carbinol, e.g., ethylacetylcarbinol.

The commonest method of preparation of those acyloins in which the alkyl groups are identical is the reaction of sodium with esters of aliphatic acids in inert solvents. Salts of enediols are produced in this reaction; on hydrolysis they are converted into the acyloins. Acyl

$$2RC{\overset{\displaystyle O}{\underset{\displaystyle \parallel}{}}}OR' + 4Na \rightarrow \begin{array}{c} RC{-}ONa \\ \parallel \\ RC{-}ONa \end{array} + 2NaOR'$$

$$\downarrow {\scriptstyle H_2O}$$

$$\begin{bmatrix} RC{-}OH \\ \parallel \\ RC{-}OH \end{bmatrix} \rightarrow \begin{array}{c} RC{=}O \\ \mid \\ RCHOH \end{array} + 2NaOH$$

chlorides also react with sodium. The product of this reaction is an ester of the above enediol, which can be hydrolyzed to an acyloin. The

$$2RCOCl + 4Na \rightarrow 2NaCl + \begin{array}{c} RC{-}ONa \\ \parallel \\ RC{-}ONa \end{array} \xrightarrow{RCOCl} \begin{array}{c} RC{-}OCOR \\ \parallel \\ RC{-}OCOR \end{array} \xrightarrow{H_2O} \begin{array}{c} RC{=}O \\ \mid \\ RCHOH \end{array}$$

reaction of an ester with sodium is a more satisfactory as well as a more economical method of preparation of acyloins.

Other methods of preparation that have been used for the synthesis of certain acyloins are: (1) the action of the Grignard reagent on an α-hydroxy nitrile and on nickel carbonyl, (2) the hydrolysis of an α-halo ketone, (3) the oxidation of an allene with silver chlorate in the presence of osmium tetroxide, (4) the reaction of an ethynylcarbinol with acetic acid or ethylene glycol in the presence of mercuric oxide and boron trifluoride followed by hydrolysis of the resulting acetate or dioxolane, (5) the reaction of a glyoxal with an aromatic hydrocarbon in the presence of aluminum chloride, (6) the partial reduction of a 1,2-diketone, (7) the oxidation of 1,2-glycols, and (8) photochemical and biological syntheses.

ACYLOINS FROM ALIPHATIC ESTERS

The reduction of aliphatic esters in inert solvents with sodium is the most convenient method of synthesis of acyloins in which the alkyl groups are the same. The reaction was discovered by Bouveault and

Blanc during the course of their studies [1] of the sodium reduction of aliphatic esters in alcoholic solution to the corresponding primary alcohols. Their isolation of the glycol $C_7H_{15}CHOHCHOHC_7H_{15}$ instead of the expected primary alcohol from the sodium reduction of methyl caprylate *in ether solution* led Bouveault and Locquin to a survey of the reaction of sodium on aliphatic esters in inert solvents. [2] The preparation of the diacyl derivatives of the acyloins by the action of sodium on acid chlorides had been reported in the very early literature, [3] but the structures of the compounds were not established until much later. [4]

Mechanism of the Reaction. The formation of an acyloin from an ester or acid chloride is a combination reduction-condensation reaction

$$
\begin{array}{c}
X \\
| \\
RC{=}O \\
| \\
RC{=}O \\
| \\
X
\end{array}
\; + 2Na \rightarrow
\left[
\begin{array}{c}
X \\
| \\
RC{-}ONa \\
| \\
RC{-}ONa \\
| \\
X
\end{array}
\right]
\rightarrow
\begin{array}{c}
RC{=}O \\
| \\
RC{=}O
\end{array}
\; + 2NaX
$$

$$X = Cl \text{ or } OR$$

that undoubtedly involves the initial formation of the diketone. The further reduction of this diketone by the metal yields the sodium salt of the enediol form of the acyloin. [5] The reaction is similar to the reduction of a ketone to a pinacol. [6] The yellow diketone, which is usually

$$
\begin{array}{c}
RC{=}O \\
| \\
RC{=}O
\end{array}
\; + 2Na \rightarrow
\begin{array}{c}
RC{-}ONa \\
\| \\
RC{-}ONa
\end{array}
$$

present to color the acyloin, has been postulated as resulting from air oxidation of the acyloin; [2] but later work with the acid chloride [7] and the ester [5] of trimethylacetic acid has shown that this assumption is questionable, since the intermediate diketone (R is *t*-butyl), which is very resistant to further reduction, appears as a major product of the reaction.

[1] Bouveault and Blanc, *Bull. soc. chim. France*, [3] **29**, 787 (1903); [3] **31**, 666, 672 (1904); *Compt. rend.*, **136**, 1676 (1903).

[2] Bouveault and Locquin, *Compt. rend.*, **140**, 1593, 1669 (1905); *Bull. soc. chim. France*, [3] **35**, 629, 633, 637 (1906).

[3] Freund, *Ann.*, **118**, 35 (1861); Bruhl, *Ber.*, **12**, 315 (1879).

[4] Klinger and Schmitz, *Ber.*, **24**, 1271 (1891); Basse and Klinger, *Ber.*, **31**, 1218 (1898).

[5] Snell and McElvain, *J. Am. Chem. Soc.*, **53**, 750 (1931).

[6] An interesting—but nevertheless inaccurate—description of the reaction is that the ester may be considered as being reduced to an aldehyde, which then goes to the acyloin through a condensation of the benzoin type. Houben-Weyl, 3rd ed., Vol. 2, p. 931 (1925).

[7] Egorova, *J. Russ. Phys. Chem. Soc.*, **60**, 1199 (1928) [*C. A.*, **23**, 2935 (1929)].

A mechanism similar to that outlined above has been proposed for the reduction of aromatic acids to benzoins by the binary system magnesium-magnesium iodide.[8] This reagent, however, has not been applied to aliphatic esters.

Another proposal involves the sodium enolate[9] of the ester as an

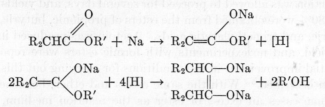

intermediate in the formation of acyloins. The most convincing objection to this mechanism is the inability to explain the ready formation of diketone and acyloin from ethyl trimethylacetate, which has no enolizable α-hydrogen.

A study of the action of sodium in liquid ammonia on a number of esters of aliphatic as well as aromatic acids has resulted in the suggestion that a series of equilibria and an intermediate free radical are involved in the formation of diketones and acyloins.[10] Even if this is a correct

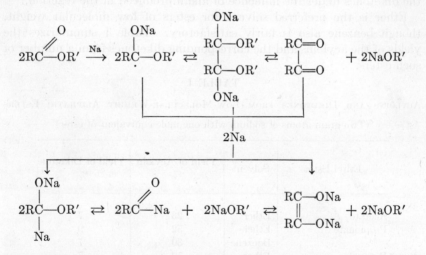

representation of the reduction of esters by sodium in liquid ammonia, it does not follow that the mechanism is similar in an inert solvent in

[8] Gomberg and Bachmann, *J. Am. Chem. Soc.*, **50**, 2762 (1928).

[9] Scheibler and Voss, *Ber.*, **53**, 388 (1920); Scheibler and Emden, *Ann.*, **434**, 265 (1923).

[10] Kharasch, Sternfeld, and Mayo, *J. Org. Chem.*, **5**, 362 (1940); see also Blicke, *J. Am. Chem. Soc.*, **47**, 229 (1925).

which one of the reactants and the final reaction product are insoluble. It also may be significant that ethyl benzoate is the only one of the esters studied that gives evidence (color) for a free radical.

Application of the Reaction. The original procedure of Bouveault and Locquin [2] consisted in treatment of the ester with sodium in ether at 0°. The reaction was allowed to proceed for several days, and yields approximating 80% were obtained from the esters of propionic, butyric, caproic, isobutyric, and trimethylacetic acids. Acetoin was produced in a much lower yield, and no experiments with formic esters were reported. A substantial improvement in the conditions for carrying out this reaction has been described.[5] With the same esters and ether, benzene, xylene, or in some cases an excess of ester as the reaction medium, the low temperature previously employed is avoided and the reaction time reduced from several days to a few hours merely by allowing the reaction to proceed at the temperature of the refluxing solvent.

Small amounts of 1,2-diketone (RCOCOR) and some higher-boiling materials generally accompany the acyloins. The presence of the diketone is a result of incomplete reduction to the sodium derivative of the acyloin; the higher-boiling materials are formed possibly from the acyloins during distillation or by polymerization or rearrangement of the diketones under the influence of alkali produced in the reaction.[5]

Ether is the preferred solvent for esters of low molecular weight, though benzene also is fairly satisfactory. Table I summarizes the yields of the acyloins and the corresponding diketones from a number of such esters.

TABLE I

ACYLOINS AND DIKETONES FROM LOW-MOLECULAR-WEIGHT ALIPHATIC ESTERS

(Two gram-atoms of sodium with one mole equivalent of ester)

Ethyl Ester	Solvent	Yield of Acyloin %	Yield of Diketone %
Acetate	Ether	23	7
Propionate	Ether	52	9
	Benzene	30	7
Butyrate	Ether	72	7
	Benzene	61	7
Isobutyrate	Ether	75	4
	Benzene	68	8
Trimethylacetate	Ether	62	32
	Benzene	63	15

There is a striking variation in the reactivities of the esters listed in Table I. In ether solution a period of twenty-four hours at the refluxing temperature is necessary to complete the reaction with ethyl acetate, whereas after two hours at the same temperature the reaction with ethyl propionate is complete. In sharp contrast to the behavior of these esters, ethyl butyrate, ethyl isobutyrate, and ethyl trimethylacetate react so vigorously with sodium that the reaction cannot be controlled if the ester is added in a single portion to sodium sand under ether. Instead the ester is added to the sodium and ether from a dropping funnel at a rate sufficient for the heat of reaction to keep the ether boiling vigorously.

With an excess of ester as the reaction medium, fair yields of acyloins are obtained from the branched-chain esters ethyl isobutyrate and trimethylacetate. Ethyl acetate and ethyl propionate under these conditions give none of the acyloin reactions but instead undergo the acetoacetic ester condensation.* With no solvent other than excess ester, the sodium will not react with ethyl acetate or with ethyl propionate until heat is applied. Even then the reaction is in no sense vigorous, and it is necessary to reflux the ester for about two hours to cause the sodium to disappear. However, the three higher esters, ethyl butyrate, ethyl isobutyrate, and ethyl trimethylacetate, react so vigorously with sodium that the metal must be added in small portions to the ester if the reaction is to be kept under control.

The use of ether as the reaction medium in the preparation of acyloins from esters of more than six carbon atoms results in much smaller yields than are obtained from the lower-molecular-weight esters.[11] This may be due to lack of proper contact of ester with the sodium because of the insolubility of the reaction product in the medium. By substituting toluene or xylene for ether this difficulty is avoided, since, at the boiling point of the medium, the sodium remains molten and in a finely dispersed state.[12] The ester must be free of organic acid or hydroxyl compounds that react with sodium and cause the reaction mixture to gel and thus stop the reaction between the ester and sodium. The toluene or xylene must be free of impurities that react with sodium. Under these conditions no diketone appears as a by-product. The acyloins from the methyl esters of the normal saturated acids from eight to eighteen carbon atoms are obtained in 80–90% yields by this method.[12] This procedure also has been applied successfully to esters of unsaturated acids. Methyl

* For a discussion of this reaction see Hauser and Hudson, *Organic Reactions*, I, 266 (1942).

[11] Corson, Benson, and Goodwin, *J. Am. Chem. Soc.*, **52**, 3988 (1930).

[12] Hansley, *J. Am. Chem. Soc.*, **57**, 2303 (1935).

10-hendecenoate and methyl 9-hendecynoate give the respective acyloins, 1,21-docosadien-11-one-12-ol and 2,20-docosadiyn-11-one-12-ol in 50% yields,[13] together with 1–2% of the corresponding diketones.

In all the conversions of esters to acyloins, the methyl or ethyl esters have been used. No data are available concerning esters derived from alcohols of higher molecular weight. With the exception of the above-mentioned unsaturated esters, the formation of acyloins from esters of acids containing other functional groups has not been reported. No mixed acyloins from simultaneous reduction of two different esters are described. Esters of alicyclic or heterocyclic acids do not appear to have been studied in this reaction.

Acyloins, when completely free from the yellow diketones, are colorless. The lower members are liquids, but those that contain sixteen or more carbon atoms are waxy, white, readily crystallized solids.[12] They are scarcely affected by sodium ethoxide. They form osazones [4, 5, 12] with phenylhydrazine, and monoacetates [12] with acetic anhydride, and the lower members reduce Fehling's solution. Reduction with hydrogen and platinum at room temperature or with nickel at 125–150° results in the formation of glycols.[12] Oxidation with Wijs solution [12] (iodine monochloride in glacial acetic acid) or with nitric acid [14] has been used to convert acyloins to the corresponding diketones.

Cyclic Acyloins from Esters of Aliphatic Dibasic Acids. The intramolecular condensation of esters of dibasic acids, $RO_2C(CH_2)_nCO_2R$, in which n is 7 or more, to cyclic acyloins, $(CH_2)_nCHOHCO$, was re-

ported [14a] in the patent literature in 1941. The reaction was carried out in xylene using sodium that had been finely dispersed in a colloid mill.

More recently this cyclization has been used with remarkable success by two groups of Swiss investigators [14b, c, d] to prepare macrocyclic acyloins containing 9–20 carbons in the cycle. These cyclic acyloins were obtained in yields of 29–96% without the use of the high dilutions that have been employed for this [14a] and other [14e] cyclizations of bifunctional open-chain compounds into large-membered rings, and without using sodium prepared in a colloid mill; dispersion of the metal by rapid stirring in hot xylene was quite sufficient.

The success of these cyclizations proved to be primarily dependent

[13] Ruzicka, Plattner and Widmer, *Helv. Chim. Acta*, **25**, 604, 1086 (1942).

[14] Fuson, Gray, and Gouza, *J. Am. Chem. Soc.*, **61**, 1937 (1939).

[14a] Hansley, U. S. pat. 2,228,268 [*C. A.*, **35**, 2534 (1941)].

[14b] Prelog, Frenkiel, Kobelt, and Barman, *Helv. Chim. Acta*, **30**, 1741 (1947).

[14c] Stoll and Hulstkamp, *Helv. Chim. Acta*, **30**, 1815 (1947).

[14d] Stoll and Rouvé, *Helv. Chim. Acta*, **30**, 1822 (1947).

[14e] Ziegler et al., *Ann.*, **504**, 94 (1933); **513**, 43 (1934); Hunsdiecker, *Ber.*, **75**, 1190 (1942).

upon the rigid exclusion of oxygen from the reaction as long as the product was in contact with alkali. The cyclic acyloins in the presence of sodium alkoxides are extremely sensitive to oxygen, and the small amount of oxygen present in commercial nitrogen is sufficient to transform the disodium enolate of the acyloin into the cyclic diketone and other secondary-reaction products. For example, the yield of sebacoin from methyl sebacate dropped from 32% to less than 5% when the reaction was run in an atmosphere of nitrogen containing 4% of oxygen instead of in pure nitrogen; also the yield of thapsoin was reduced from 73% to 31% when the reaction mixture from methyl thapsate was allowed to cool under air instead of pure nitrogen.[14c] In an atmosphere of pure nitrogen, however, the formation of the secondary-reaction products is prevented and the cyclic acyloins are obtained in good yields.

The relative ease with which these macrocyclic acyloins may be prepared and transformed into other classes of compounds indicates that intramolecular acyloin condensations of diesters may well be the preferred route to large carbocyclic ring compounds in the future.

The boiling points, melting points, and yields of the cyclic acyloins that have been prepared from diesters are listed in Table II.

TABLE II

Cyclic Acyloins, $(CH_2)_n CHOHCO$, from Esters of Aliphatic Dibasic Acids,

$RO_2C(CH_2)_n CO_2R$ (R is CH_3 or C_2H_5)

Acyloin	n Is	B.P., °C (mm.)	M.P., °C	Yield, %	Reference *
Cyclononanol-2-one (azeloin)	7	110–124 (12)	43	9	14b, 14d
Cyclodecanol-2-one (sebacoin)	8	124–127 (10)	38–39	45	14d, 14b
Cycloundecanol-2-one	9	100–105 (0.12)	29–33		14d
Cyclododecanol-2-one	10	106–109 (0.09)	78–79	76	14d, 14b
Cyclotridecanol-2-one (brassyloin)	11	126–139 (0.2)	45–46	67	14d
Cyclotetradecanol-2-one	12	116–124 (0.15)	84–85	79	14d, 14b
Cyclopentadecanol-2-one	13	123–139 (0.02)	57–58	77	14d
Cyclohexadecanol-2-one (thapsoin)	14	143–146 (0.1)	56–58	84	14d, 14b
Cycloheptadecanol-2-one	15	168–170 (0.1)	53–54	85	14d
Cyclooctadecanol-2-one	16	155–160 (0.15)	59–60	96	14d
Cycloeicosanol-2-one	18	210–225 (0.3)	——	96	14b

* The first reference listed reports the higher melting point and yield of the acyloin.

ACYLOINS FROM ACID CHLORIDES

Acyloins may be obtained by the saponification of the esters of enediols which result from the reaction of sodium and the acyl chlorides. This latter reaction is carried out in ether solution. No yields of the diesters are reported in the earlier work [4] in which butyryl, isobutyryl, and isovaleryl chlorides were used. Yields of 60–70% of the diesters are reported from lauroyl, myristoyl, palmitoyl, and stearoyl chlorides.[15] The highly branched trimethylacetyl chloride reacts with sodium to give hexamethylbiacetyl as the chief product and the monoacyl derivative of the acyloin as the secondary product.[7]

From the data thus far published there appears to be no reason to use acid chlorides in place of esters for the preparation of acyloins.

ACYLOINS FROM α-HYDROXY NITRILES, NICKEL CARBONYL, AND α-HALO KETONES

A general method for the preparation of both simple and mixed acyloins involves the reaction of an α-hydroxy nitrile (from an aldehyde and hydrogen cyanide) and a Grignard reagent.[16]

$$RCHOHCN + 2R'MgX \rightarrow R'H + \underset{\underset{OMgX}{|}}{RCH}{-}\!\!-\!\!\underset{\underset{NMgX}{\|}}{CR'} \xrightarrow{H_2O} RCHOHCOR'$$

By this procedure methylpropionylcarbinol, isopropylpropionylcarbinol, and isobutyroin have been prepared in 60–70% yields,[16] and sym-diphenylacetoin has been obtained in 45% yield.[17]

The preparation of benzoin, butyroin, isobutyroin, and valeroin in 70, 50, 35, and 50% yields respectively from the reaction of nickel carbonyl with the appropriate Grignard reagent has been reported.[18]

The hydrolysis of α-bromo ketones to the corresponding hydroxy ketones has been used to determine the structure of a variety of brominated ketones.[19] In this work the acyloins, acetoin and methyltrimethylacetylcarbinol, as well as a number of dialkylacylcarbinols, R_2-COHCOR', were obtained in 60–75% yields by hydrolysis of the corresponding bromo ketones in the presence of potassium or barium

[15] Ralston and Selby, *J. Am. Chem. Soc.*, **61**, 1019 (1939).
[16] Gauthier, *Compt. rend*, **152**, 1100 (1911).
[17] Ruggli and Hegedus, *Helv. Chim. Acta*, **25**, 1285 (1942).
[18] Benton, Voss, and McCusker, *J. Am. Chem. Soc.*, **67**, 82 (1945).
[19] Faworsky, *J. prakt. Chem.*, [2] **88**, 675 (1913).

carbonate. This procedure has been used to prepare cyclic acyloins derived from cyclopentane and from cyclohexane. Thus 2-hydroxycyclopentanone and its 3-methyl derivative are obtained in about 28% yield from the corresponding 2-chlorocyclopentanones simply by boiling with water;[20] 2-hydroxycyclohexanone (adipoin) and its 4-, 5-, and 6-methyl derivatives are obtained in 50% yields from the corresponding 2-chlorocyclohexanones by hydrolysis with aqueous potassium carbonate.[21]

ACYLOINS FROM ALLENES AND ACETYLENES

The conversion of ethylallene to ethylacetylcarbinol has been reported.[22] The reaction involves the oxidation of the allene with 10% aqueous silver chlorate in the presence of catalytic amounts of osmium

$$C_2H_5CH{=}C{=}CH_2 + 2OH \rightarrow C_2H_5CHOHC(OH){=}CH_2 \rightarrow C_2H_5CHOHCOCH_3$$

tetroxide. This method is of doubtful preparative value because the requisite allenes are difficult to obtain.

The addition of ethylene glycol or acetic acid to ethynylcarbinols in the presence of mercuric oxide and boron trifluoride results in the formation of dioxolanes or acetates which readily yield α-hydroxy ketones on hydrolysis.[23]

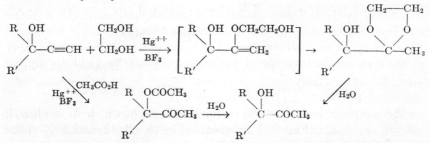

Although the reaction has been applied mainly to the preparation of acetyldialkylcarbinols, the fact that the acetates of acetoin and acetylphenylcarbinol are obtained in 41 and 50% yields and the dioxolane corresponding to acetoin in 67% yield indicates that this method should be generally applicable to the synthesis of mixed acyloins of the structure RCHOHCOCH₃.

[20] Godchot and Taboury, *Bull. soc. chim. France*, [4] **13**, 546 (1913); *Compt. rend.*, **156** 1779 (1913).
[21] Kötz et al., *Ann.*, **400**, 62 (1913); **379**, 16 (1911).
[22] Bouis, *Bull. soc. chim. France*, [4] **51**, 1177 (1932).
[23] Hennion and Murray, *J. Am. Chem. Soc.*, **64**, 1220 (1942).

ACYLOINS FROM 1,2-DIKETONES AND 1,2-GLYCOLS

Since 1,2-diketones are readily prepared from monoketones,[24] the partial reduction of such diketones, particularly the symmetrical ones, would seem to be a practical method of preparation of acyloins. No study of the sodium reduction of 1,2-diketones to acyloins from a preparative point of view appears to have been made. However, the preparations of a few acyloins from the corresponding diketones by other reducing agents are described.

Biacetyl is reduced to acetoin in 45% yield with zinc and sulfuric acid.[25] This reducing agent converts the mixed diketone acetylpropionyl into methylpropionylcarbinol.[26] The cyclic acyloin, 3-hydroxycamphor, is obtained from the reduction of camphorquinone in wet ether with aluminum amalgam.[27]

The oxidation of 1,2-glycols to acyloins has not been generally applied, primarily because the acyloins (or the 1,2-diketones) are the usual source of the glycols. The oxidation of 2,3-butylene glycol (from sucrose fermentation) by air over a copper catalyst at 270–275° has been reported.[28] Both acetoin and biacetyl are obtained, but the yields are not stated.

ACYLOINS FROM GLYOXALS

A novel method of preparation of mixed aliphatic-aromatic acyloins has been described.[14] In this preparation t-butylglyoxal is condensed with the aromatic hydrocarbons (ArH), benzene, toluene, m-xylene, or mesitylene, in the presence of aluminum chloride to yield an aryltri-

$$(CH_3)_3CCOCHO + ArH \xrightarrow{AlCl_3} (CH_3)_3CCOCHOHAr$$

methylacetylcarbinol. By this method acyloins in which Ar is phenyl, p-tolyl, m-xylyl, and mesityl are obtained in 49, 52, 42, and 30% yields respectively.

PHOTOCHEMICAL AND BIOLOGICAL PREPARATION OF ACYLOINS

Ultraviolet irradiation of an aqueous solution of acetaldehyde or pyruvic acid is reported [29] to produce acetoin in quantitative yields. It

---

[24] von Pechmann, Ber., **20**, 3162 (1887); **21**, 1411 (1888); **22**, 2115 (1889); Locquin, Bull. soc. chim. France, [3] **31**, 1173 (1904); Dieckmann, Ber. **30**, 1470 (1897); Meyerfield, Chem. Ztg., **36**, 549 (1912); Wallach and Weissenborn, Ann., **437**, 148 (1924).

[25] Diels and Stephan, Ber., **40**, 4338 (1907).

[26] Cf. von Pechmann and Dahl, Ber., **23**, 2425 (1890), and Venus-Daniloff, Bull. soc chim. France, [4] **43**, 585 (1928).

[27] Mannase, Ber., **30**, 659 (1897).

[28] McAllister and de Simo, U. S. pat. 2,051,266 [C. A., **30**, 6759 (1936)].

[29] Dirscherl, Z. physiol. Chem., **188**, 225 (1930).

is thought that pyruvic acid is decarboxylated into nascent acetaldehyde, which then is dimerized to acetoin. This method is believed [29] to have preparative possibilities for acetoin. When the ultraviolet irradiation of pyruvic acid is carried out in the presence of benzaldehyde a small yield of phenylacetylcarbinol is obtained along with the acetoin.[30] The irradiation of α-ketovaleric acid produces butyroin to the extent of 35–40% of the acid decomposed.[30]

Fermentation processes for the production of acetoin and its oxidation and reduction products, biacetyl and 2,3-butylene glycol, have been studied extensively. They are not reviewed here because they are not generally applicable to other acyloins. It may be mentioned, however, that the yeast fermentation of pyruvic acid yields an optically active acetoin.[31] The fermentation of sucrose to 2,3-butylene glycol in 90% yield is reported,[32] and in this publication references are given to previous work on the formation of this glycol and acetoin by fermentation processes.

EXPERIMENTAL PROCEDURES

Butyroin from Ethyl Butyrate. The preparation of this acyloin in 65–70% yield from ethyl butyrate is described in *Organic Syntheses*.[33] Propionoin, isobutyroin, and pivaloin (hexamethylacetoin) can be prepared similarly in 50–55, 70–75, and 52–60% yields, respectively.

Lauroin from Methyl Laurate.[12] A mixture of 115 g. (5 atoms) of sodium and 3 l. of xylene (C.P.) is charged into a 5-l., three-necked flask immersed in an oil bath at 105°. The flask is fitted with a high-speed stirrer (2000–2500 r.p.m.), and the air over the xylene is replaced by nitrogen or other inert gas. When the temperature of the xylene reaches 105° and the sodium melts, the stirrer is started and the sodium dispersed in a finely divided state in the xylene. From a separatory funnel 535 g. (2.5 moles) of methyl laurate, or the equivalent quantity of another ester, is then introduced into the reaction flask. The addition is at such a rate that the temperature does not rise above 110°. The addition of the ester requires about one hour. Stirring is continued for one-half hour after the ester has been added.

Small particles of unchanged sodium are decomposed by the addition of an excess of methanol (1–2 moles). Then, after cooling to about 80°, water (0.5 to 1 l.) is added cautiously until the alkali has dissolved, and the layers are separated by decantation. After one or two more washings

[30] Dirscherl, *Z. physiol. Chem.*, **219**, 177 (1933).
[31] Dirscherl and Schöllig, *Z. physiol. Chem.*, **252**, 53 (1938).
[32] Fulmer, Christensen, and Kendall, *Ind. Eng. Chem.*, **25**, 798 (1933).
[33] Snell and McElvain, *Org. Syntheses*, Coll. Vol. **2**, 114 (1943).

of the xylene layer with water, the remaining alkali is neutralized with a slight excess of mineral acid, and this excess acid is finally neutralized with sodium bicarbonate. The xylene is removed by steam distillation, and the residual oily layer is poured into a suitable vessel to solidify. The impure product contains 80–90% of the acyloin. The acyloins from methyl caproate, laurate, and myristate are purified by crystallization from 95% ethanol, but acyloins from methyl palmitate and stearate crystallize better from trichloroethylene or acetone.

By the above procedure butyroin, capronoin, capryloin, nonyloin, caprinoin, myristoin, palmitoin, and stearoin have been prepared in 80–90% yields.[12]

The boiling points, melting points, and yields of the acyloins that have been prepared by procedures analogous to those described above are listed in Table III.

TABLE III

BOILING POINTS, MELTING POINTS, AND YIELDS OF SYMMETRICAL ACYLOINS
(RCHOHCOR)

Acyloin	B.P., °C (mm.)	M.P., °C	Yield, %	Reference
Acetoin	140–150		23	5
Propionoin	60–65 (12)		50–55	33
Butyroin	80–86 (12)	−10	65–70	33
Isobutyroin	70–75 (14)		70–75	33
Valeroin	90–92 (3)		50	11
Isovaleroin	94–97 (12)		50	11
Pivaloin (hexamethylacetoin)	85–95 (12)	81	52–60	33
Capronoin	105–107 (3)	9	50	11
Isocapronoin	101–103 (3)		50	11
3,8-Dimethyldecan-5-one-6-ol	102–104 (3)		50	11
3,3,6,6-Tetramethyloctan-4-one-5-ol	96–97 (3)	12	50	11
Capryloin		39	80–90	12
Nonyloin		45	80–90	12
Caprinoin		52	80–90	12
1,21-Docosadien-11-one-12-ol		47	50	13
2,20-Docosadiyn-11-one-12-ol		51	50	13
Lauroin		62	80–90	12
Myristoin		72	80–90	12
Palmitoin		78	80–90	12
Stearoin		83	80–90	12

CHAPTER 5

THE SYNTHESIS OF BENZOINS

WALTER S. IDE AND JOHANNES S. BUCK *†

The Wellcome Research Laboratories

CONTENTS

* Present address: Sterling-Winthrop Research Institute, Rensselaer, N.Y.

† The invitation to write this chapter was extended to J. S. B., but circumstances compelled him to turn the work over to W. S. I., the second author's contribution being nominal.

INTRODUCTION

Benzoins are aromatic α-hydroxy ketones of the general formula
Ar'CHOHCOAr. Similar compounds containing aromatic heterocyclic
nuclei also are classed as benzoins. If the two nuclei in a molecule are
alike, the benzoin is said to be symmetrical; if different, unsymmetrical
or "mixed." The reactions for the preparation of benzoins are (1) the
condensation of two molecules of an aromatic aldehyde in the presence
of cyanide ion (benzoin condensation), (2) the conversion of an unsymmetrical benzoin into its isomer, (3) the condensation of an aryl glyoxal
with an aromatic hydrocarbon, (4) the reaction of an aryl Grignard
reagent with a mandelamide or a mandelonitrile, (5) the reduction of a
benzil, (6) the reduction of an aromatic acid or its derivative, (7) the
introduction of a hydroxyl group into a desoxybenzoin, (8) miscellaneous
methods of limited application. Through these many methods the
variety of benzoins that can be prepared is large.

The benzoins constitute convenient intermediates for the preparation
of many related compounds, such as desoxybenzoins, ArCH₂COAr';
benzils, ArCOCOAr'; hydrobenzoins, ArCHOHCHOHAr'; enediols,
ArC(OH)=C(OH)Ar'; stilbenes, ArCH=CHAr'; diphenylethylamines,
hydroxy amines, isoquinolines, etc.

The term "benzoin" is used to represent the molecule containing two
unsubstituted phenyl groups, $C_6H_5CHOHCOC_6H_5$, and substituents

are indicated in the usual way; $4\text{-}CH_3OC_6H_4CHOHCOC_6H_4OCH_3\text{-}4$ is 4,4'-dimethoxybenzoin, and $2,4,6\text{-}(CH_3)_3C_6H_2CHOHCOC_6H_2(CH_3)_3\text{-}2,4,6$ is 2,2',4,4',6,6'-hexamethylbenzoin. In a second system of nomenclature of symmetrical benzoins the suffix "ic" or "oic" of the corresponding carboxylic acid is replaced by "oin." Thus the benzoin containing two anisoyl radicals is known as anisoin, and that containing two naphthoyl radicals as naphthoin.

In unsymmetrical or mixed benzoins, which may have either of two isomeric structures, primes (') are used to indicate substitution on the ring adjacent to the carbinol carbon atom; thus the substance $4\text{-}ClC_6H_4CHOHCOC_6H_4N(CH_3)_2\text{-}4$ is called 4'-chloro-4-dimethylaminobenzoin, and the isomer, $4\text{-}ClC_6H_4COCHOHC_6H_4N(CH_3)_2\text{-}4$, is called 4-chloro-4'-dimethylaminobenzoin. Another system for naming some of the simpler unsymmetrical benzoins has been used occasionally. The terms for the two aroyl radicals present are abbreviated and combined, and the ending "oin" is added; $4\text{-}CH_3OC_6H_4COCHOHC_6H_5$ would be designated as anisbenzoin or benzanisoin. This terminology does not serve to distinguish between isomers. The letter "β" has been used to indicate the higher-melting, more stable isomer, and "α" the lower-melting, less stable one.

Some benzoins may exist not only in the normal keto form (Ar'CHOH-COAr) but also in the enediol form [ArC(OH)=C(OH)Ar']. Cis and trans forms of certain enediols have been isolated. Enediols reduce cupric acetate and Tollens' reagent, whereas benzoins do not. The enediols frequently ketonize spontaneously, and they isomerize readily when treated with methanolic hydrochloric acid. They are oxidized with ease to the corresponding diketones (benzils).

The relatively stable enediols are found almost exclusively among those in which one or both of the aryl radicals have substituents in the two positions (2,6-) adjacent to the hydroxy ketone residue.[1-15] The

[1] Fuson and Corse, J. Am. Chem. Soc., **61**, 975 (1939).

[2] Fuson, Corse, and McKeever, J. Am. Chem. Soc., **61**, 2010 (1939).

[3] Fuson, McKeever, and Corse, J. Am. Chem. Soc., **62**, 600 (1940).

[4] Fuson, Scott, Horning, and McKeever, J. Am. Chem. Soc., **62**, 2091 (1940).

[5] Fuson and Horning, J. Am. Chem. Soc., **62**, 2962 (1940).

[6] Fuson and Kelton, J. Am. Chem. Soc., **63**, 1500 (1941).

[7] Fuson, Scott, and Lindsey, J. Am. Chem. Soc., **63**, 1679 (1941).

[8] Fuson, Corse, and Welldon, J. Am. Chem. Soc., **63**, 2645 (1941).

[9] Fuson, McKeever, and Behr, J. Am. Chem. Soc., **63**, 2648 (1941).

[10] Fuson and Scott, J. Am. Chem. Soc., **64**, 2152 (1942).

[11] Fuson and Soper, J. Am. Chem. Soc., **65**, 915 (1943).

[12] Barnes and Green, J. Am. Chem. Soc., **60**, 1549 (1938).

[13] Barnes and Tulane, J. Am. Chem. Soc., **62**, 894 (1940).

[14] Barnes and Tulane, J. Am. Chem. Soc., **63**, 867 (1941).

[15] Barnes and Lucas, J. Am. Chem. Soc., **64**, 2258, 2260 (1942).

steric hindrance of such groups appears to stabilize the highly conjugated system. The symmetrical enediols containing certain aroyl radicals (2,4,6-trimethylbenzoyl, 2,4,6-triethylbenzoyl, 2,4,6-triisopropylbenzoyl, 2,6-dimethylbenzoyl, 2-methyl-1-naphthoyl, 2,3,5,6-tetramethylbenzoyl, and 2,3,4,6-tetramethylbenzoyl) are stable in an inert atmosphere and do not ketonize spontaneously. In the ketonization of unsymmetrical enediols, the hydroxyl group of the benzoin appears on the carbon *beta* to the aryl radical with the 2,4,6-substituents.

$$2,4,6\text{-}(C_3H_7)_3C_6H_2C{=\!\!=}CC_6H_5 \rightarrow 2,4,6\text{-}(C_3H_7)_3C_6H_2COCHOHC_6H_5$$
$$\underset{OH\ \ \ OH}{|\ \ \ \ \ |}$$

Unsymmetrical benzoins can exist in two isomeric forms differing in the relative positions of the carbinol and carbonyl groups:

$$ArCHOHCOAr' \quad \text{and} \quad ArCOCHOHAr'$$

In general, one isomer is more stable than the other, and many of the less stable unsymmetrical benzoins can be made to isomerize to the more stable forms. Not infrequently, isomeric benzoins of this type yield identical derivatives, since a shift from the less stable to the more stable isomer takes place during the reaction.

THE BENZOIN CONDENSATION

The benzoin condensation consists in the treatment of an aromatic aldehyde with potassium cyanide or sodium cyanide, usually in aqueous ethanolic solution. By the use of one mole of each of two different

$$ArCHO + Ar'CHO \xrightarrow{KCN} Ar'CHOHCOAr$$

aromatic aldehydes, it is possible to prepare many unsymmetrical or mixed benzoins.

The reaction is not applicable to all aromatic or aromatic-type aldehydes. The condensation is affected greatly by the nature of the substituents in the aromatic nucleus. Many substituted benzaldehydes either do not react or yield products other than benzoins.

In order that an aldehyde may form a symmetrical benzoin it must possess not only a relatively unsaturated carbonyl group but also a mobile hydrogen atom.[16-20] Two aldehydes, neither of which forms a sym-

[16] Staudinger, *Ber.*, **46**, 3530, 3535 (1913).
[17] Jenkins, Buck, and Bigelow, *J. Am. Chem. Soc.*, **52**, 4495 (1930); Jenkins, Bigelow and Buck, *ibid.*, **52**, 5198 (1930).
[18] Buck and Ide, *J. Am. Chem. Soc.*, **52**, 4107 (1930); **53**, 1912 (1931).
[19] Tiffeneau and Lévy, *Bull. soc. chim. France*, [4] **49**, 725 (1931).
[20] Hodgson and Rosenberg, *J. Chem. Soc.*, **1930**, 14.

metrical benzoin, may form an unsymmetrical benzoin if one aldehyde is an acceptor and the other a donor of the hydrogen atom. Benzaldehyde, which is both an acceptor and a donor, readily forms a benzoin. 4-Dimethylaminobenzaldehyde does not form a symmetrical benzoin; however, it condenses with other aldehydes, acting as a donor, for in the mixed benzoins that are formed the dimethylaminophenyl group is always attached to the carbonyl carbon atom. Benzaldehyde by contrast usually acts as an acceptor when it reacts with other aldehydes to form mixed benzoins. As an index to the activity of an aldehyde as an acceptor or donor of the hydrogen atom Staudinger [16] relates benzoin formation to the ease of autoxidation of the aldehyde. The mobility of the hydrogen atom is assumed to be parallel to the rate of autoxidation [21] of the aldehyde, and the unsaturation of the carbonyl group is inferred from the ease with which the aldehyde forms a symmetrical benzoin.

Mechanism of Condensation

The mechanism postulated by Lapworth [22]—two successive aldol (ionic) reactions—has been accepted generally, although the only step that is corroborated by experimental evidence is the initial one between benzaldehyde and the cyanide ion. A subsequent reaction is assumed between this addition product and another benzaldehyde molecule.[23] The work of Greene and Robinson [24, 25] on the preparation of benzoylated benzoins (p. 296) tends to confirm Lapworth's hypothesis that the initial

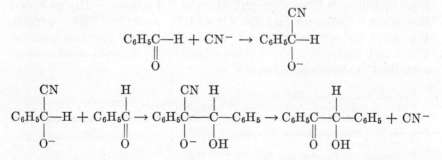

stage is the formation of mandelonitrile, which then condenses with the free aldehyde.

[21] For further work on the oxidation of aldehydes see Raiford and Talbot, *J. Am. Chem. Soc.*, **54**, 1092 (1932); Perry and Raiford, *Proc. Iowa Acad. Sci.*, **47**, 264 (1940) [*C. A.*, **35**, 7383 (1941)].

[22] Lapworth, *J. Chem. Soc.*, **83**, 995 (1903); **85**, 1206 (1904).

[23] Weiss, *Trans. Faraday Soc.*, **37**, 782 (1941); Watson, *ibid.*, **37**, 707 (1941).

[24] Greene and Robinson, *J. Chem. Soc.*, **121**, 2182 (1922).

[25] Greene, *J. Chem. Soc.*, **1926**, 328.

Most syntheses of benzoins have involved the use of a solvent which contains water, and many of the theories on mechanism of formation are based on the assumption that the reaction is ionic and that water is necessary for the reaction. Very few of the early experiments were carried out in such a way that ionization or hydrolysis could not occur. However, that water is unnecessary was shown by Smith [26] in 1899, and confirmed by other workers.[27,28] The reaction also takes place in anhydrous petroleum ether.[27] This has led to the suggestion of a nonionic mechanism. In the formation of unsymmetrical benzoins the elimina-

$$C_6H_5CHO + NaCN \rightarrow C_6H_5CH\!-\!CN$$
$$\underset{\displaystyle ONa}{|}$$

$$C_6H_5CH\!-\!ONa$$
$$|$$

$$\boxed{\begin{matrix} CN \\ | \\ H \end{matrix}}$$
$$|$$
$$C_6H_5C\!-\!ONa$$
$$|$$
$$CN$$

$$\rightarrow \quad \begin{matrix} C_6H_5CH\!-\!ONa \\ | \\ C_6H_5C\!-\!ONa \\ | \\ CN \end{matrix} \quad \xrightarrow{\text{HCN}} \quad NaCN + \quad \begin{matrix} C_6H_5CHOH \\ | \\ C_6H_5C\!-\!ONa \\ | \\ CN \end{matrix} \rightarrow$$

$$C_6H_5CHOHCOC_6H_5 + NaCN$$

tion of hydrogen cyanide in one or the other direction would determine the structure of the product.

Other important discussions of the mechanism have been given by Zincke,[29] Chalanay and Knoevenagel,[30] Bredig and Stern,[31] Staudinger,[16] Horbye,[32] Ekecrantz and Ahlqvist,[33] Lachman,[34] Hodgson and Rosenberg,[20] Tiffeneau and Lévy,[19] and Hammett.[34a] More recently Wheeler,[28] Weiss,[23] and Watson [23] have reviewed the previous theories. Weiss and Lachman make a comparison of the benzoin condensation with the Cannizzaro reaction.

[26] Smith, *Am. Chem. J.*, **22**, 249 (1899).

[27] Morton and Stevens, *J. Am. Chem. Soc.*, **52**, 2031 (1930).

[28] Nadkarni, Mehta, and Wheeler, *J. Phys. Chem.*, **39**, 727 (1935); Nadkarni and Mehta, *ibid.*, **39**, 901 (1935); Nadkarni, *ibid.*, **39**, 907 (1935).

[29] Zincke, *Ber.*, **9**, 1769 (1876).

[30] Chalanay and Knoevenagel, *Ber.*, **25**, 289 (1892).

[31] Stern, *Z. physik. Chem.*, **50**, 513 (1905); Bredig and Stern *Z. Elektrochem.*, **10**, 582 (1904).

[32] Horbye, Dissertation, Dresden, 1917.

[33] Ekecrantz and Ahlqvist, *Arkiv Kemi, Mineral. Geol.*, **3**, No. 13, 1 (1908) (*Chem. Zentr.*, **1908**, II, 1688).

[34] Lachman, *J. Am. Chem. Soc.*, **45**, 1509, 1522, 1529 (1923); **46**, 708 (1924).

[34a] L. P. Hammett, *Physical Organic Chemistry*, McGraw-Hill, 1940, pp. 348–350.

Symmetrical Benzoins

No generalization concerning the types of aromatic aldehydes that will undergo the benzoin condensation is possible. Many aldehydes that will not give symmetrical benzoins will condense with other aldehydes to give unsymmetrical benzoins.

The simple alkyl- and ethoxy-benzaldehydes, the *ortho-*, *meta-*, and *para*-chloro-, bromo-, hydroxy-, and amino-benzaldehydes do not readily form symmetrical benzoins.[35, 36, 37] The presence of a halogen atom in addition to other substituents generally prevents the condensation. Thus 5-bromo-4-hydroxy-3-methoxy-,[38] 5,6-dibromo-4-hydroxy-3-methoxy-,[38] 4-hydroxy-3-methoxy-,[21] 2-bromo-3,4-dimethoxy-,[21] 6-bromo-3,4-dimethoxy-,[21] and 4-dimethylamino-benzaldehydes[16] have been reported not to yield symmetrical benzoins.

2-Methoxybenzaldehyde (salicylaldehyde methyl ether)[35] and 3-[20] and 4-methoxybenzaldehyde[39] give yields of benzoins of 55, 20, and 60% respectively. When alkoxyl groups are present the smoothness of the reaction depends upon the absence of phenolic impurities.[35] Many methoxybenzaldehydes with additional alkoxyl or other substituents have not been condensed successfully to symmetrical benzoins; among them are 3-methoxy-4-ethoxy-,[32] 3-ethoxy-4-methoxy-,[40] and 2-ethyl-4-methoxy-benzaldehyde.[41] Benzoins have not been isolated from 3,4-dimethoxy-[21, 32, 42] and 5-bromo-3,4-dimethoxy-benzaldehyde,[21] but the reaction mixture from each aldehyde yields on oxidation nearly quantitative amounts of the corresponding benzil. A bromine atom, which usually acts as an interfering group, does not prevent the condensation of 5-bromo-2-methoxybenzaldehyde,[43] which gives a 50% yield of the benzoin.

ortho-Nitrobenzaldehyde gives a benzoin,[33, 44, 45] but with the *meta* or *para* isomer a reaction occurs which leads to the nitrophenylacetic acid and the azobenzoic acid.[44, 46] 4-Cyanobenzaldehyde reacts, but the product is the desoxybenzoin (4,4'-dicyanodesoxybenzoin).[47]

[35] Irvine, *J. Chem. Soc.*, **79**, 668 (1901).
[36] Brass and Stroebel, *Ber.*, **63**, 2617 (1930).
[37] Brass, Willig, and Hanssen, *Ber.*, **63**, 2613 (1930).
[38] Raiford and Hilman, *J. Am. Chem. Soc.*, **49**, 1571 (1927).
[39] Bösler, *Ber.*, **14**, 323 (1881).
[40] Buck and Ide, *J. Am. Chem. Soc.*, **54**, 3302 (1932).
[41] Linnell and Shaikmahamud, *Quart. J. Pharm. Pharmacol*, **15**, 384 (1942).
[42] Vanzetti, *Gazz. chim. ital.*, **57**, 162 (1927).
[43] Kuhn, Birkofer, and Möller, *Ber.*, **76**, 900 (1943).
[44] Ekecrantz and Ahlqvist, *Ber.*, **41**, 878 (1908); **43**, 2606 (1910).
[45] Popovici, *Ber.*, **40**, 2562 (1907); **41**, 1851 (1908).
[46] Homolka, *Ber.*, **17**, 1902 (1884).
[47] Ashley, Barber, Ewins, Newbery, and Self, *J. Chem. Soc.*, **1942**, 103.

Cinnamaldehyde does not undergo the benzoin condensation.[27] 2-Furaldehyde,[48] 2-picolinaldehyde,[49] and quinaldehyde,[50] 3,4-methylenedioxybenzaldehyde,[51] α-naphthaldehyde,[52] and 4-phenylbenzaldehyde,[52] condense in 38, (?), 66, 80, 13, and 95% yields respectively.

Unsymmetrical Benzoins

The benzoin condensation is more generally applicable to the preparation of unsymmetrical benzoins than to the preparation of symmetrical benzoins. No prediction can be made with respect to the aldehydes that will react with other aldehydes. Benzaldehyde and its mono- and dialkoxy and methylenedioxy derivatives give unsymmetrical benzoins. Among the substituted benzaldehydes that do not undergo symmetrical benzoin condensation but react readily with other aldehydes are 4-dimethylamino-,[16] 3-methoxy-4-ethoxy-,[40] and 3-ethoxy-4-methoxy-benzaldehyde.[40] Other substituted aldehydes that give unsatisfactory yields of symmetrical benzoins give good yields of unsymmetrical benzoins; 2-chlorobenzaldehyde, which is reported to form a symmetrical benzoin in 20–40% yield, condenses with 4-dimethylamino-,[53] 4-methoxy-,[18] 3-methoxy-4-ethoxy-,[40] 3,4-diethoxy-,[40] 3,4-dimethoxy-,[18] and 3-ethoxy-4-methoxy-benzaldehyde [40] to form unsymmetrical benzoins in yields of 36, 60, 60, 63, 70, and 81%, respectively. 2-Furaldehyde (furfural) [48, 53] and 3,4-methylenedioxybenzaldehyde [18, 19, 32, 40, 53, 54] also condense with a variety of substituted aldehydes.

Two different aldehydes might be expected to yield a mixture of two symmetrical benzoins and two unsymmetrical benzoins, but only a single unsymmetrical benzoin usually is isolable. The second unsymmetrical benzoin may be formed when the reactivity of the two aldehydes is similar.[19, 40, 53] In the products examined, the carbinol group usually is adjacent to the unsubstituted phenyl group or to the ortho, meta-, or para-halogen substituted phenyl group. The carbonyl group generally is next to the methylenedioxy-, 4-dimethylamino-, methoxy-, dimethoxy-, methoxyethoxy-, or diethoxy-substituted ring or to the furan nucleus. However, in the following products (I–IV) the carbinol group is adja-

[48] Fischer, Ber., **13**, 1334 (1880); Hartman and Dickey, J. Am. Chem. Soc., **55**, 1228 (1933); Fischer, Ann., **211**, 214 (1882).

[49] Harries and Lénárt, Ann., **410**, 95 (1915).

[50] Kaplan, J. Am. Chem. Soc., **63**, 2654 (1941).

[51] Torrey and Sumner, J. Am. Chem. Soc., **32**, 1492 (1910).

[52] Gomberg and Bachmann, J. Am. Chem. Soc., **49**, 236, 2584 (1927); Gomberg and Van Natta, ibid., **51**, 2238 (1929).

[53] Buck and Ide, J. Am. Chem. Soc., **52**, 220 (1930).

[54] Buck and Ide, J. Am. Chem. Soc., **53**, 2350 (1931).

cent to the nucleus substituted with the methylenedioxy or methoxy group.[19, 40, 54] It is interesting to note that, in the formation of I, the

$$3,4\text{-}CH_2O_2C_6H_3CHOHCOC_6H_4N(CH_3)_2\text{-}4 \qquad 4\text{-}CH_3OC_6H_4CHOHCOC_6H_3O_2CH_2\text{-}3,4$$
$$\text{I} \qquad\qquad\qquad\qquad\qquad \text{II}$$

$$2\text{-}CH_3OC_6H_4CHOHCOC_6H_4OCH_3\text{-}4 \qquad 2\text{-}CH_3OC_6H_4CHOHCOC_6H_5$$
$$\text{III} \qquad\qquad\qquad\qquad\qquad \text{IV}$$

aldehyde carrying the methylenedioxy group is the acceptor of the hydrogen atom, whereas in II it is the donor. In the formation of II, 4-methoxybenzaldehyde is the acceptor, whereas in III it is the donor. Benzaldehyde is the acceptor and 4-methoxybenzaldehyde is the donor when these aldehydes are condensed to form 4-methoxybenzoin ($C_6H_5CHOHCOC_6H_4OCH_3\text{-}4$); but benzaldehyde is the donor when condensed with 2-methoxybenzaldehyde, as shown in IV. In a benzoin condensation the carbinol group never appears next to the 4-dimethylamino-substituted ring.

Reversion Applied to Formation of Unsymmetrical Benzoins

Benzoin tends to revert to benzaldehyde in the reaction mixture in which it is synthesized. Other products, such as benzyl benzoate, benzyl alcohol, benzoic acid, ethyl benzoate, mandelonitrile, and benzylphenylcarbinol, also are formed.[31, 33, 34, 55, 56] This reactivity accounts for the poor yields of some benzoins. Although benzoin can be formed by the action of potassium cyanide on benzaldehyde in the absence of water, the decomposition and dissociation of the benzoin require water.

The reversion of the benzoin to the aldehyde has been used as a means of synthesizing unsymmetrical benzoins,[54, 57] usually with good yields. By addition to an aqueous ethanolic solution of potassium cyanide of one mole of a benzoin and two moles of an aldehyde, or one mole of each of two symmetrical benzoins, it is possible to obtain a new benzoin. The three types of reaction are shown below.

1. $XC_6H_4CHOHCOC_6H_4X + 2YC_6H_4CHO \rightarrow$
$$YC_6H_4CHOHCOC_6H_4X + XC_6H_4CHOHCOC_6H_4Y$$

2. $XC_6H_4CHOHCOC_6H_4Y + 2ZC_6H_4CHO \rightarrow$
$$XC_6H_4CHOHCOC_6H_4Z + ZC_6H_4CHOHCOC_6H_4Y$$

3. $XC_6H_4CHOHCOC_6H_4X + YC_6H_4CHOHCOC_6H_4Y \rightarrow$
$$2XC_6H_4CHOHCOC_6H_4Y$$

[55] Anderson and Jacobson, *J. Am. Chem. Soc.*, **45**, 836 (1923).
[56] Romo, *Química (Mex.)*, **2**, 8 (1944) [*C. A.*, **38**, 5214 (1944)].
[57] Buck and Ide, *J. Am. Chem. Soc.*, **53**, 2784 (1931).

To illustrate the first of these possibilities the following reactions may be cited: the conversion of benzoin with 4-dimethylamino-, 4-methoxy-, and 3,4-methylenedioxy-benzaldehyde or 2-furaldehyde, to 4-dimethyl-amino-, 4-methoxy-, and 3,4-methylenedioxy-benzoin or benzfuroin ($C_6H_5CHOHCOC_4H_3O$); the conversion of 3,4,3′,4′-dimethylenedioxy-benzoin with benzaldehyde or with 2-chloro- or 4-dimethylamino-benzaldehyde to 3,4-methylenedioxy-, 2′-chloro-3,4-methylenedioxy-, or 3′,4′-methylenedioxy-4-dimethylamino-benzoin; the conversion of furoin with benzaldehyde or 4-dimethylaminobenzaldehyde into benzfuroin ($C_6H_5CHOHCOC_4H_3O$) or 4-dimethylaminobenzfuroin (see Table I, p. 281). Examples of reaction 2 are the conversion of 3,4-methylene-dioxybenzoin with 2-chloro- or 4-dimethylamino-benzaldehyde into 2′-chloro-3,4-methylenedioxybenzoin or 4-dimethylaminobenzoin; the conversion of 4-methoxybenzoin with 4-dimethylaminobenzaldehyde into 4-dimethylaminobenzoin, and of 2′-chloro-4-methoxybenzoin with 4-dimethylaminobenzaldehyde into 2′-chloro-4-dimethylaminobenzoin (see Table I). For reaction 3, the conversion of benzoin with 3,4,3′,4′-dimethylenedioxybenzoin or with furoin into 3,4-methylenedioxybenzoin or into benzfuroin ($C_6H_5CHOHCOC_4H_3O$) serves as an illustration (see Table I).

It is not necessary to start with a pure benzoin in order to accomplish these interconversions. The reaction mixture in which a symmetrical or unsymmetrical benzoin has been formed can be treated directly with an aldehyde or another benzoin.

Determination of Structure of Unsymmetrical Benzoins

Several methods have been used to determine the structures of the un-symmetrical benzoins. Oxidative degradation and alkali fission [19, 32, 58, 59, 60] convert benzoins into substituted benzaldehydes and benzoic acids. The aldehyde is derived from the arylcarbinol portion of the benzoin.

The oxime of a benzoin can be oxidized with nitric acid to an aldehyde and an arylnitrolic acid [$ArC(NO_2)$=NOH].[61] Identification of the aldehyde determines the structure.

It is reported that on the basis of oxidation-reduction potential meas-urements the structure of a mixed benzoin can be established.[62, 63, 64]

[58] Tiffeneau and Lévy, *Compt. rend.*, **192**, 287 (1931).

[59] Luis, *J. Chem. Soc.*, **1932**, 2547.

[60] Clutterbuck and Reuter, *J. Chem. Soc.*, **1935**, 1467.

[61] Charlton, Earl, Kenner, and Luciano, *J. Chem. Soc.*, **1932**, 30.

[62] Semerano, *Gazz. chim. ital.*, **65**, 273 (1935).

[63] Semerano, *Gazz. chim. ital.*, **71**, 447 (1941).

[64] Law, *J. Chem. Soc.*, **89**, 1437, 1512, 1520 (1906).

Since the reduction of a benzoin to the corresponding desoxybenzoin is accomplished readily, a comparison of the desoxybenzoin with an authentic sample prepared by some other method [65-72] has been applied frequently. The methylene group, however, is not always found in the same position as that held by the carbinol group, and hence the procedure is of doubtful value.

Probably the most satisfactory method of determining the benzoin structure is the Beckmann rearrangement. The oxime of the benzoin is converted [18,40,73,74] into an aldehyde and a nitrile or isonitrile. The

$$\text{RCHOHC}(\text{=NOH})\text{R}' \rightarrow \text{RCHO} + \text{R}'\text{CN or R}'\text{NC}$$

structure of the aldehyde establishes the position of the carbinol group in the benzoin, and the formation of the nitrile or isonitrile discriminates between the two possible configurations of the oxime group.

Experimental Conditions

The experimental conditions used in the preparation of symmetrical and unsymmetrical benzoins are the same.[75] A solution of 0.2 mole of the aldehyde(s) in 100 ml. of 95% ethanol is mixed with a solution of 10 g. of potassium cyanide (96–98%) in 20 ml. of water, and the mixture is refluxed on a steam bath from one to one and one-half hours. Sufficient ethanol should be used to keep the aldehyde(s) in solution. Mechanical stirring is not necessary, since the ebullition of the mixture provides sufficient agitation. The products are obtained from the reaction mixture by dilution and refrigeration. There is no particular advantage in steam distillation or extraction of the reaction mixture with bisulfite to remove the unchanged aldehydes. Seeding the reaction mixture is advisable. The instantaneous crystallization of the product observed with benzoin [75] is unusual. Purification generally can be accomplished by recrystallization from ethanol, but recrystallization

[65] Buck and Ide, *J. Am. Chem. Soc.*, **54**, 3012 (1932).

[66] Collet, *Bull. soc. chim. France*, **17**, 506 (1897).

[67] Isimura, *Bull. Chem. Soc. Japan*, **16**, 196, 252 (1941) [*C. A.*, **36**, 4487 (1942)].

[68] Jenkins, *J. Am. Chem. Soc.*, **55**, 703 (1933).

[69] Jenkins and Richardson, *J. Am. Chem. Soc.*, **55**, 1618 (1933).

[70] Jenkins, *J. Am. Chem. Soc.*, **55**, 2896 (1933).

[71] Jenkins, *J. Am. Chem. Soc.*, **56**, 682 (1934).

[72] Jenkins, *J. Am. Chem. Soc.*, **56**, 1137 (1934).

[73] Werner and Piguet, *Ber.*, **37**, 4295 (1904); Werner and Detscheff, *Ber.*, **38**, 69 (1905).

[74] Gheorghiu and Cozubschi, *Ann. sci. univ. Jassy*, **26**, 575 (1940) [*C. A.*, **35**, 6246 (1941)]; Gheorghui and Cozubschi-Sciurevici, *Bull. sect. sci. acad. roumaine*, **24**, 15 (1942) [*C. A.*, **38**, 3276 (1944)].

[75] Adams and Marvel, *Org. Syntheses*, Coll. Vol. **1**, 2nd ed., 94 (1941).

from acetic acid, in which the benzoins are sparingly soluble, is advisable when catalytic reduction is to follow.[40, 76]

The catalyst for the condensation is the cyanide ion. Only alkali salts of hydrogen cyanide have proved successful. A large number of possible catalysts for the benzoin reaction have been explored, but in the absence of cyanide ion little or no benzoin has been obtained.

Both the aldehyde and the alkali cyanide may contain substances that inhibit the reaction. Aldehydes sometimes contain the corresponding acid, hydroquinone, or quinone; and alkali cyanides may contain such inhibitors as alkali halides. Other inhibitors are iodine, hydrogen sulfide, sulfur, and carbon disulfide. It has been found that a quantitative relationship sometimes exists between a specified amount of inhibitor and a definite quantity of potassium cyanide; 0.3 g. of hydroquinone renders inactive 0.7 g. of potassium cyanide. Inhibitors can be removed from the aldehyde by washing with aqueous sodium carbonate, by formation of the bisulfite compound, or by treatment with solid potassium cyanide overnight at room temperature in an atmosphere of nitrogen.[28, 34, 75] The effect of the impurities is decreased by an increase of the proportion of water and by the addition of an excess of cyanide.

Experimental Procedures

The detailed description of the preparation of benzoin is given in *Organic Syntheses*.[75]

4-Methoxybenzoin.[77] To 50 g. of potassium cyanide dissolved in 350 ml. of water in a 3-l. flask is added 272 g. (2 moles) of 4-methoxybenzaldehyde, 212 g. (2 moles) of benzaldehyde, and 700 ml. of 95% ethanol. The mixture forms a solution at the boiling temperature and is refluxed for one and one-half hours. Steam is then passed through the solution until all the ethanol and nearly all the unchanged aldehydes are removed. The water formed by condensation in the reaction flask is decanted from the product, which crystallizes on chilling. The product is then pressed as free as possible from oily material on a suction funnel and washed with cold ethanol. In this way about 250 g. (52% yield) of crude product is obtained. After recrystallization from ethanol the 4-methoxybenzoin melts at 106°.

2′-Chloro-3,4-dimethoxybenzoin.[76] A solution of 8.3 g. (0.05 mole) of 3,4-dimethoxybenzaldehyde (veratraldehyde), 7.0 g. (0.05 mole) of 2-chlorobenzaldehyde, and 4.0 g. of potassium cyanide in 75 ml. of 50% ethanol is refluxed for two and one-half hours. The product crystallizes

[76] Buck and Ide, *J. Am. Chem. Soc.*, **52**, 4107 (1930).
[77] Kinney, *J. Am. Chem. Soc.*, **51**, 1592 (1929).

TABLE I
BENZOINS PREPARED BY THE REVERSION PROCEDURE

Benzoin	Grams	Compound Added Aldehyde	Grams	Benzoin Produced R'—CHOHCO—R	Yield, grams	KCN, grams	Heating, hours	Ethanol, milliliters
*Reaction 1 * [54]*								
Benzoin	4.24	4-Dimethylaminobenz-	5.96	4-Dimethylamino-	9.18	3.0	3.0	20
Benzoin	4.24	4-Methoxybenz-	5.44	4-Methoxy-	7.36	4.0	2.0	20
Benzoin	4.24	3,4-Methylenedioxybenz-	6.00	3,4-Methylenedioxy-	2.16	2.0	0.5	30
Benzoin	4.24	2-Furaldehyde	3.84	Benzfuroin ($C_6H_5CHOHCOC_4H_2O$)	3.98	3.0	1.5	20
Piperoin	6.00	Benz-	4.24	3,4-Methylenedioxy-	1.29	4.0	2.0	30
Piperoin	3.00	2-Chlorobenz-	2.82	2'-Chloro-3,4-methylenedioxy-	2.05	2.0	3.0	15
Piperoin	3.00	4-Dimethylaminobenz-	2.98	3',4'-Methylenedioxy-4-dimethylamino-	2.12	2.0	3.0	15
Furoin	3.84	Benz-	4.24	Benzfuroin	4.06	2.0	0.16	20
Furoin	3.84	4-Dimethylaminobenz-	5.96	4-Dimethylaminobenzfuroin [$C_4H_3OCHOHCOC_6H_4N-(CH_3)_2-4$]	5.77	3.0	1.5	20
*Reaction 2 * [57]*								
3,4-Methylenedioxy-	5.12	2-Chlorobenz-	5.64	2-Chloro-3,4-methylenedioxy-	3.13	4.0	1.5	40
3,4-Methylenedioxy-	5.12	4-Dimethylaminobenz-	5.96	4-Dimethylamino-	1.93	4.0	2.0	40
4-Methoxy-	4.84	4-Dimethylaminobenz-	5.96	4-Dimethylamino-	2.04	4.0	3.0	40
2'-Chloro-4-methoxy-	5.54	4-Dimethylaminobenz-	5.96	2'-Chloro-4-dimethylamino-	3.33	4.0	2.5	40
*Reaction 3 * [57]*								
Benzoin	4.24	*Piperoin*	6.00	3,4-Methylenedioxy-	0.98	5.0	3.2	50
Benzoin	4.24	*Furoin*	3.84	Benzfuroin ($C_6H_5CHOHCOC_4H_2O$)	3.00	3.0	1.0	50

* See p. 277.

on cooling. After recrystallization from ethanol the compound forms fine white needles, m.p. 142°; yield 11 g. (70%).

Reversion Procedure. Appropriate molecular proportions of the benzoin and aldehyde are dissolved in hot ethanol, and potassium cyanide is added in saturated aqueous solution. The mixture is then boiled under a reflux condenser on a steam bath, additional water being added to keep most of the potassium cyanide in solution. After heating from ten minutes to three hours the flask is chilled and the product isolated.[54, 57] Compounds formed by this general procedure are listed in Table I, p. 281.

THE CONVERSION OF AN UNSYMMETRICAL BENZOIN INTO ITS ISOMER

The less stable isomeric form of an unsymmetrical benzoin will isomerize under relatively mild conditions to the more stable form. By indirect means the more stable isomer can be converted into the less stable one. This interconversion of isomers is useful synthetically for the preparation of certain benzoins that are difficult to obtain by one of the more general methods. Although interconversions have been recorded by many investigators,[59, 78-89] sufficient examples are not available to permit predictions concerning the relative stability of the two possible unsymmetrical benzoins in any new instance.

Less Stable to More Stable

The less stable 4'-methoxybenzoin (V), 4'-dimethylaminobenzoin (VI), and 4-chloro-4'-dimethylaminobenzoin (VII) are isomerized to the more stable products, 4-methoxybenzoin (VIII), 4-dimethylamino-benzoin (IX), and 4'-chloro-4-dimethylaminobenzoin (X), in yields of 60 to 80% by treatment with ethanolic potassium hydroxide at room temperature for three days or by heating with ethanolic potassium cyanide for thirty minutes.[59, 80, 81] The isomerization of 4'-methoxybenzoin (V) can be brought about quantitatively by distillation at 1 mm.[82]

[78] Wren, *J. Chem. Soc.*, **95**, 1583, 1593 (1909).
[79] McKenzie, Roger, and Wills, *J. Chem. Soc.*, **1926**, 779.
[80] Jenkins, *J. Am. Chem. Soc.*, **53**, 3115 (1931).
[81] Jenkins, *J. Am. Chem. Soc.*, **55**, 3048 (1933).
[82] Julian and Passler, *J. Am. Chem. Soc.*, **54**, 4756 (1932).
[83] Buck and Ide, *J. Am. Chem. Soc.*, **54**, 4359 (1932).
[84] Buck and Ide, *J. Am. Chem. Soc.*, **55**, 4312 (1933).
[85] Buck and Ide, *J. Am. Chem. Soc.*, **55**, 855 (1933).
[86] Barnes, Cooper, Tulane, and Delaney, *J. Org. Chem.*, **8**, 153 (1943).
[87] Cowper and Stevens, *J. Chem. Soc.*, **1940**, 347.
[88] Weinstock and Fuson, *J. Am. Chem. Soc.*, **58**, 1986 (1936).
[89] Weinstock and Fuson, *J. Am. Chem. Soc.*, **58**, 1233 (1936).

LESS STABLE   MORE STABLE

V $C_6H_5COCHOHC_6H_4OCH_3$-4 $\rightarrow$ $C_6H_5CHOHCOC_6H_4OCH_3$-4   VIII

VI $C_6H_5COCHOHC_6H_4N(CH_3)_2$-4 $\rightarrow$ $C_6H_5CHOHCOC_6H_4N(CH_3)_2$-4   IX

VII   4-$ClC_6H_4COCHOHC_6H_4N(CH_3)_2$-4 $\rightarrow$ 4-$ClC_6H_4CHOHCOC_6H_4N(CH_3)_2$-4   X

4-Methoxy- or 4′-methoxy-benzoin or the α-bromo derivative of 4-methoxybenzoin upon treatment with potassium acetate and acetic anhydride gives a mixture of the benzoin monoacetate and enediol diacetate, each of which on hydrolysis forms the stable isomer.[14, 86]

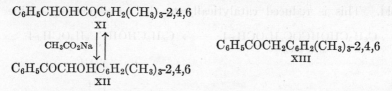

Most unsymmetrical benzoins undergo reduction to desoxybenzoins in which the carbinol group of the benzoin has been replaced by methylene. However, the isomeric desoxybenzoin or a mixture of both of the two desoxy compounds may be obtained.[17, 80, 90, 91] In this latter class may be cited 4-methoxy-, 4-dimethylamino-, 4′-chloro-4-dimethylamino-, 3′-chloro-4-methoxy-, and 2,4,6-trimethyl-benzoin.

The reduction of either 2,4,6-trimethylbenzoin (XI) or 2′,4′,6′-trimethylbenzoin (XII) results in the same desoxybenzoin, 2,4,6-trimethylbenzyl phenyl ketone (XIII).[88, 89] If either 2,4,6-trimethylbenzoin (XI)

$C_6H_5CHOHCOC_6H_2(CH_3)_3$-2,4,6
XI

CH_3CO_2Na ⇅ $C_6H_5COCH_2C_6H_2(CH_3)_3$-2,4,6
                                    XIII

$C_6H_5COCHOHC_6H_2(CH_3)_3$-2,4,6
XII

or 2′,4′,6′-trimethylbenzoin (XII) is warmed with ethanolic sodium acetate, an equilibrium mixture is formed; therefore the stabilities of the two isomers are similar. It is obvious that one of the benzoins is reduced much more readily, since a single desoxy compound entirely free from

[90] Jenkins, *J. Am. Chem. Soc.*, **54**, 1155 (1932).

[91] Jenkins and Richardson, *J. Am. Chem. Soc.*, **55**, 3874 (1933).

even traces of the isomer results. Both benzoins XI and XII on treatment with benzoyl chloride give the same monobenzoate. Presumably an equilibrium mixture of isomers is produced first; benzoylation then occurs readily with only one of the isomers.[88]

The diketone corresponding to XI or XII, when treated with zinc and acetic acid for five minutes, yields a mixture of the isomeric benzoins; but on heating for ten hours only the desoxy compound XIII is formed, and no further reduction takes place.

More Stable to Less Stable

More stable benzoins can be converted into the less stable isomers by indirect means through derivatives which have the appropriate isomeric structures and which in turn can be transformed readily into the desired benzoins. 4-Methoxybenzoin upon reduction gives the desoxy compound related to the isomeric benzoin (82% yield); the desoxybenzoin can be brominated to the bromo ketone (84% yield). This on treatment with sodium ethoxide followed by acidification is converted (74%) into the isomer of the original benzoin. Isolation of the bromo ketone is not necessary.[65, 71, 72, 81]

$$C_6H_5CHOHCOC_6H_4OCH_3\text{-}4 \xrightarrow[\text{HCl}]{\text{Sn}}$$
More stable

$$C_6H_5COCH_2C_6H_4OCH_3\text{-}4 \xrightarrow{Br_2} C_6H_5COCHBrC_6H_4OCH_3\text{-}4$$

$$\downarrow NaOC_2H_5$$

$$C_6H_5COCHOHC_6H_4OCH_3\text{-}4 \xleftarrow{HCl} C_6H_5C(OC_2H_5)_2CHC_6H_4OCH_3\text{-}4$$
Less stable

$$\underset{ONa}{|}$$

Another procedure for the conversion of the more stable isomeric benzoin into the less stable one is illustrated also with 4-methoxybenzoin.[18, 84] The more stable benzoin is converted into the oxime in 50–99% yield. This is reduced catalytically to the corresponding amine in

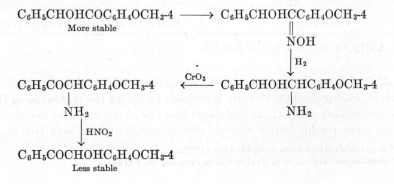

$$C_6H_5CHOHCOC_6H_4OCH_3\text{-}4 \longrightarrow C_6H_5CHOHCC_6H_4OCH_3\text{-}4$$
More stable
$$\underset{NOH}{\|}$$

$$\downarrow H_2$$

$$C_6H_5COCHC_6H_4OCH_3\text{-}4 \xleftarrow{CrO_3} C_6H_5CHOHCHC_6H_4OCH_3\text{-}4$$
$$\underset{NH_2}{|} \qquad\qquad \underset{NH_2}{|}$$

$$\downarrow HNO_2$$

$$C_6H_5COCHOHC_6H_4OCH_3\text{-}4$$
Less stable

66–86% yield. Oxidation with chromic acid converts the amino carbinol into the amino ketone in 59–70% yield. Treatment of the desylamine with nitrous acid yields the less stable benzoin [92] in 50–71% yield. This procedure should be applicable to any benzoin that does not contain substituents affected by the reagents used in the different steps.

Slight modification of the reaction series just outlined may sometimes be desirable. As an alternative procedure the desylamine can be heated with aqueous ethanolic hydrochloric acid in a sealed tube at 95° for twenty hours; a yield of 40% of the benzoin results. By heating at 130° for twenty-four hours a 100% conversion is possible. 2,4,6-Trimethyl-desylamine is difficult to convert into the benzoin by ordinary procedures; however, heating with aqueous ethanolic hydrochloric acid at 130° for twenty-four hours furnishes a 20% yield of 2,4,6-trimethylbenzoin.[93]

Experimental Procedures

The Benzoin Oxime. The benzoin oxime is prepared by any of the following methods: [18] (a) The benzoin is allowed to stand in ethanolic solution at room temperature with hydroxylamine acetate, and the product is precipitated by the gradual addition of water. (b) The benzoin is warmed on the steam bath, usually for three hours, with hydroxylamine and excess of ethanolic sodium hydroxide solution. The oxime is precipitated by carbon dioxide. This method is useful when the benzoin is sparingly soluble in ethanol. (c) The benzoin, in pyridine solution, is warmed on the steam bath for three hours with hydroxylamine hydrochloride, and the reaction mixture is then diluted gradually with water. By these methods yields varying from 50 to 99% are obtained.

The Reduction of the Benzoin Oxime to the α-Aminobenzylphenyl-carbinol.[84] The reduction is carried out in the usual Burgess-Parr apparatus, with the exception that the bottle is heated electrically and the apparatus modified so that it will accommodate from about 0.1 to 0.005 mole of material. This modification of the apparatus requires only the insertion of a second gauge in the line between the reservoir and the bottle. After the bottle is filled with hydrogen it is cut off from the reservoir by means of the needle valve. Under these conditions the bottle functions as its own reservoir, the pressure being read on the second gauge. Since the capacity of the bottle is only a fraction of that of the tank, the pressure drop accompanying the hydrogenation of 0.005 mole of a substance can be read easily.[94]

[92] McKenzie and Walker, *J. Chem. Soc.*, **1928**, 646; McKenzie and Kelman, *ibid.*, **1934**, 412; McKenzie and Pirie, *Ber.*, **69**, 861, 876 (1936).

[93] Weissberger and Glass, *J. Am. Chem. Soc.*, **64**, 1724 (1942).

[94] Buck and Jenkins, *J. Am. Chem. Soc.*, **51**, 2163 (1929).

A solution of 0.03 mole of the benzoin oxime in 50 ml. of absolute ethanol is reduced with 0.5 g. of platinum oxide catalyst (Adams) at 70–75°. The product is isolated by removal of the catalyst, partial evaporation of the solvent, and recrystallization of the solid from ethanol. The aminocarbinol is obtained in 66–86% yield.

The Oxidation of the α-Aminobenzylphenylcarbinol to the α-Aminobenzyl Phenyl Ketone.[84] The oxidation is carried out by dissolving the aminocarbinol in 7–12 parts of 20% sulfuric acid and adding chromic acid (one atomic equivalent of oxygen) in water. For example, 4.86 g. (0.02 mole) of α-amino-4-methoxybenzylphenylcarbinol is dissolved in 50 ml. of 20% sulfuric acid, and 1.33 g. of chromic acid in 10 ml. of water is added. The reaction mixture is heated slowly to 70°. The aminobenzyl phenyl ketone usually separates as the sulfate on the further addition of sulfuric acid. If the sulfate does not separate, the reaction mixture is extracted with ether to remove non-basic material. The mixture is made alkaline with aqueous ammonia, extracted with ether, and the extract is dried over anhydrous sodium sulfate. Dry hydrogen chloride is passed through the ether solution to precipitate the hydrochloride, which is filtered and recrystallized from ethanol; the yields are 59–70%.

Conversion of the α-Aminobenzyl Phenyl Ketone into the Benzoin.[84] A solution of 0.01 mole of the α-aminobenzyl phenyl ketone hydrochloride in 40 ml. of water is cooled, and 3.0 ml. of concentrated hydrochloric acid is added (in some cases 8.0 ml. of concentrated sulfuric acid is used). A solution of 0.02 mole of sodium nitrite in 15 ml. of water is introduced in portions at room temperature. The mixture is warmed on a steam bath for a few minutes or until the nitrogen is expelled. The oily product that separates solidifies on being cooled, and is filtered and recrystallized from ethanol. The yield of benzoin is 50–71%. It is not necessary to isolate the α-aminobenzyl phenyl ketone from the oxidation mixture. The ether extract may be treated directly with sodium nitrite and acid.

THE CONDENSATION OF ARYLGLYOXALS WITH AROMATIC HYDROCARBONS

Benzoins can be prepared in 35–90% yield by the condensation of phenylglyoxals with aromatic hydrocarbons in the presence of aluminum chloride.[95–97] The benzoins prepared in this way have the carbonyl group adjacent to the aromatic residue of the glyoxal.

$$\text{ArCOCHO} + \text{Ar'H} \xrightarrow{\text{AlCl}_3} \text{ArCOCHOHAr'}$$

[95] Fuson, Weinstock, and Ullyot, *J. Am. Chem. Soc.*, **57**, 1803 (1935).
[96] Arnold and Fuson, *J. Am. Chem. Soc.*, **58**, 1295 (1936).
[97] Fuson, Emerson, and Weinstock, *J. Am. Chem. Soc.*, **61**, 412 (1939).

Aliphatic glyoxals condense with aromatic compounds in a similar way to give analogs of benzoin with one aromatic and one aliphatic group. This reaction is discussed in Chapter 4.

Scope and Limitations

This method is equally successful with substituted or unsubstituted phenylglyoxals and substituted or unsubstituted hydrocarbons, and it may be used for the preparation of symmetrical or unsymmetrical benzoins. It appears especially useful for halogen- and methyl-substituted benzoins that cannot be formed satisfactorily from the appropriate aldehydes. Phenylglyoxal condenses with the following aromatic compounds to give benzoins in the yields indicated: benzene (90%), anisole (48%), naphthalene (42%), chlorobenzene (84%), bromobenzene (57%), toluene (50%), and mesitylene (62%). 4-Methyl-, 4-chloro-, and 4-bromo-phenylglyoxal condense with benzene in 42, 35, and 70% yields, respectively; and mesitylglyoxal condenses with benzene, toluene, m-xylene, and mesitylene in 57, 24, 17, and 40% yields, respectively. The method is unsatisfactory for the condensation of highly hindered arylglyoxals with certain heavily substituted aromatic compounds to form unsymmetrical benzoins: mesitylglyoxal condenses with 3,5-dimethylanisole, 3,5-dimethylphenetole, 1,3,5-triethylbenzene, durene (1,2,4,5-tetramethylbenzene), or isodurene (1,2,3,5-tetramethylbenzene) to form diarylbenzoylmethanes rather than benzoins.

$$2,4,6\text{-}(CH_3)_3C_6H_2COCHO + 1,3,5\text{-}(C_2H_5)_3C_6H_3 \rightarrow$$
$$2,4,6\text{-}(CH_3)_3C_6H_2COCH[C_6H_2(C_2H_5)_3\text{-}2,4,6]_2$$

The glyoxals are prepared readily by the oxidation of the substituted acetophenones with selenium dioxide in dioxane.[98, 99]

Experimental Conditions

In the usual procedure, an excess of the hydrocarbon reactant is employed as the solvent. Often, however, carbon disulfide has been found advantageous as a solvent.[96, 97] If an arylglyoxal is condensed with m-xylene in the presence of excess hydrocarbon as solvent, a diarylaroylmethane is formed. By the use of one mole of m-xylene with carbon disulfide as solvent, a benzoin results. Aluminum chloride (two molar equivalents) generally is used as the catalyst, although zinc chloride has been reported to be satisfactory in one instance.[96]

[98] Riley, Morley, and Friend, *J. Chem. Soc.*, **1932**, 1875.
[99] Riley and Gray, *Org. Syntheses*, Coll. Vol. **2**, 509 (1943).

The time of heating to complete the reaction varies from one-half hour to twenty hours and is determined largely by trial. In general, the time required decreases as the number of substituents in the aromatic hydrocarbon increases; for example, in the condensation of mesitylglyoxal with benzene the reaction period is twenty hours, with toluene six to ten hours, with m-xylene four to six hours, whereas with mesitylene it is but one and one-half hours. With insufficient length of heating, the glyoxal hydrate contaminates the product; with too prolonged heating the product is difficult to crystallize. The reaction is best carried out in an atmosphere of nitrogen.

Since glyoxals readily form hydrates, which may cause complications, they should be rendered as anhydrous as possible immediately before use.

Experimental Procedures

General Procedure. Anhydrous phenylglyoxal is prepared in the following way from the reaction mixture obtained by oxidizing acetophenone in dioxane solution with selenium dioxide.[98, 99] The dioxane solution is decanted from the precipitate of selenium and is distilled at atmospheric pressure until nearly all the dioxane is removed. One hundred milliliters of a suitable hydrocarbon with a boiling point about 10 to 15° above the melting point of the glyoxal hydrate is added, and the solution is again distilled at atmospheric pressure until the distillate is no longer turbid. The solution is transferred to a Claisen flask, and the distillation is continued under reduced pressure.[96]

In a 200-ml. three-necked flask equipped with a reflux condenser and drying tube, mercury-sealed stirrer, and dropping funnel are placed 0.06 mole of powdered anhydrous aluminum chloride, 0.03 mole of the hydrocarbon, and about 70 ml. of carbon disulfide. The mixture is cooled in an ice bath. The freshly distilled glyoxal (0.03 mole) in about 20 ml. of carbon disulfide is then added over a period of one-half to three-quarters of an hour. Stirring is continued at 0° for a total of one to twenty hours. In experiments where the time required is long, the ice bath is allowed to warm to room temperature after the first six hours. The reaction mixture is decomposed with ice and hydrochloric acid, and the resulting emulsion is extracted twice with ether. The ether solution is washed once with water containing a little hydrochloric acid and then twice with water. After the solution has been dried over anhydrous sodium sulfate, the ether and carbon disulfide are distilled under reduced pressure. The residual oil is placed in an Erlenmeyer flask, and a little petroleum ether is added and evaporated by means of an air blast. A little more petroleum ether is then added, and the mixture is placed in the ice box to crystallize. The crude product is collected on a filter, washed with petroleum ether, and crystallized from aqueous ethanol.

2,4,6-Trimethylbenzoin.[95] To a stirred mixture of 26.6 g. of powdered anhydrous aluminum chloride and 100 ml. of dry benzene contained in a 500-ml. three-necked flask immersed in water at a temperature of 10°, is added over a period of two hours 17.6 g. of mesitylglyoxal [98,99] dissolved in 100 ml. of dry benzene. Stirring at room temperature is continued for five hours. The mixture is poured slowly into ice and concentrated hydrochloric acid. The benzene layer, containing the benzoin, is removed. The aqueous layer is extracted once with a small amount of benzene. The benzene extract is added to the main portion of the solution. The benzene is removed at 50° by evaporation under diminished pressure; to prevent oxidation of the benzoin, nitrogen is passed through the ebullator tube during the evaporation. The residual yellow liquid is crystallized from 100 ml. of ethanol. There is obtained 16.1 g. (63% yield) of a colorless product, m.p. 97–99°. The pure compound obtained by recrystallization from ethanol melts sharply at 102°.

4-Bromobenzoin.[96] In a 500-ml. three-necked, round-bottomed flask surrounded with ice and equipped with a mercury-sealed stirrer are placed 200 ml. of dry benzene and 13.3 g. of powdered aluminum chloride. A solution of 10.65 g. of 4-bromophenylglyoxal in 50 ml. of benzene is added dropwise to the benzene-aluminum chloride solution. The addition takes approximately thirty minutes. The reaction mixture is allowed to remain at 0° for fifteen hours. It is then decomposed by the slow addition of ice-cold 20% aqueous hydrochloric acid. The benzene solution is separated and concentrated to a volume of 30 ml. by removal of the solvent under diminished pressure in the absence of air. To this concentrate is added 30 ml. of petroleum ether (b.p. 30–60°), and the solution is kept cold overnight. The precipitate is separated by filtration with suction and washed with four 25-ml. portions of cold petroleum ether. The material weighs 10.2 g. (70.2% yield). After one recrystallization from ethanol the benzoin melts at 108–109°.

THE REACTION OF MANDELAMIDES AND MANDELONITRILES WITH THE GRIGNARD REAGENT

The synthesis of benzoins from mandelonitriles or amides and aromatic magnesium halides is general. Both symmetrical and isomeric stable and less stable unsymmetrical benzoins can be prepared in this way. 4-Dimethylaminomandelamide, obtained from 4-dimethylaminobenzaldehyde, reacts with three moles of phenylmagnesium bromide to give 4'-dimethylaminobenzoin (45% yield), the less stable isomer.[17] From mandelamide and 4-dimethylaminophenylmagnesium bromide, 4-dimethylaminobenzoin, the more stable isomer, is formed in 25% yield.[17]

$$4\text{-}(CH_3)_2NC_6H_4CHO \rightarrow 4\text{-}(CH_3)_2NC_6H_4\underset{\underset{OH}{|}}{C}HCN \xrightarrow[H_2O]{H_2SO_4} 4\text{-}(CH_3)_2NC_6H_4\underset{\underset{OH}{|}}{C}HCONH_2$$

$$\xrightarrow{3C_6H_5MgBr} 4\text{-}(CH_3)_2NC_6H_4\underset{\underset{BrMgO}{|}}{\overset{\overset{OMgBr}{|}}{C}}H\underset{\underset{C_6H_5}{|}}{C}NHMgBr \xrightarrow{H_2O} \underset{\text{Less stable}}{4\text{-}(CH_3)_2NC_6H_4CHOHCOC_6H_5}$$

Extensive study of the preparation of benzoins by this procedure has revealed that, although it is time-consuming and does not result in yields better than 20–47%, it nevertheless is the best procedure for many benzoins.[17, 71, 91, 92, 93, 100–108] Symmetrical and unsymmetrical methyl- and halogen-substituted benzoins and the less stable isomers of unsymmetrical benzoins have been synthesized; 4'-chlorobenzoin (32%),[104] 4-chlorobenzoin (17%),[104] 4'-methylbenzoin (24%),[104] 4-methylbenzoin (47%),[104] and 4-chloro-4'-dimethylaminobenzoin (42%)[80] are typical. In an attempt to form 2',4',6'-trimethylbenzoin from phenylmagnesium bromide and 2,4,6-trimethylmandelonitrile only α-aminobenzyl 2,4,6-trimethylphenyl ketone[93] was obtained.

$$2,4,6\text{-}(CH_3)_3C_6H_2CHOHCN + C_6H_5MgBr \rightarrow 2,4,6\text{-}(CH_3)_3C_6H_2COC\underset{\underset{NH_2}{|}}{H}C_6H_5$$

Experimental Procedure

4'-Dimethylaminobenzoin (Less Stable Isomer).[17] Phenylmagnesium bromide is prepared from 30 g. of bromobenzene, 5.5 g. of magnesium turnings, and 50 ml. of anhydrous ether. Then 2.5 g. of finely powdered 4-dimethylaminomandelamide is added in small portions over a period of fifteen minutes. After each addition of the amide a vigorous reaction occurs and is allowed to subside before the next portion is added. The mixture is heated on the water bath for twelve hours and then poured into 200 g. of crushed ice containing 30 g. of concentrated sulfuric acid.

[100] Béis, *Compt. rend.*, **137**, 575 (1903).

[101] McKenzie and Wren, *J. Chem. Soc.*, **93**, 309 (1908).

[102] Gauthier, *Compt. rend.*, **152**, 1100, 1259 (1911).

[103] Asahina and Terasaka, *J. Pharm. Soc. Japan*, **494**, 219 (1923) [*C. A.*, **17**, 3028 (1923)]; Asahina and Ishidate, *ibid.*, **521**, 624 (1925) [*C. A.*, **20**, 409 (1926)].

[104] Weissberger, Strasser, Mainz, and Schwarze, *Ann.*, **478**, 112 (1930); Weissberger and Dym, *Ann.*, **502**, 74 (1933).

[105] McKenzie and Luis, *Ber.*, **65**, 794 (1932).

[106] McKenzie, Luis, Tiffeneau, and Weill, *Bull. soc. chim. France*, [4] **45**, 414 (1929).

[107] Smith, *Ber.*, **64**, 427 (1931).

[108] Asahina and Asano, *Ber.*, **63**, 429 (1930).

The ether is removed, and the aqueous layer is extracted with two 100-ml. portions of ether. The extracts are discarded. The acid solution is neutralized with aqueous ammonia, and the yellow precipitate which forms is separated, dissolved in 50 ml. of ethanol, and filtered while hot. On cooling, yellow needles separate, which weigh 1.5 g. (45% yield). After three recrystallizations from ethanol, a pure product results, m.p. 159–160°.

THE REDUCTION OF BENZILS

Benzils have been reduced by a variety of reagents, usually with the formation of the benzoins. Although the transformation is simple and direct, it has the serious limitation that most benzils are accessible only

$$\text{ArCOCOAr}' \;\rightarrow\; \text{ArC}\!\!=\!\!\text{CAr}' \;\rightarrow\; \text{ArCOCHOHAr}'$$
$$\underset{\text{OH}\quad\text{OH}}{|\qquad\;|}$$

through oxidation of the corresponding benzoins. The probable mechanism of reduction in the absence of certain catalysts is 1,4-addition of the hydrogen with subsequent rearrangement of the enediol intermediate. The reagent used and the conditions employed determine whether any of the following reduction products are obtained in place of or in addition to the benzoin: $\text{ArCH}_2\text{COAr}'$, $\text{ArCHOHCHOHAr}'$, $\text{ArCH}_2\text{CHOHAr}'$, $\text{ArCH}_2\text{CH}_2\text{Ar}'$. In unsymmetrical benzils the relative reactivity of the two carbonyl groups is so markedly different that usually only one of them is reduced; the stable isomeric form of the corresponding benzoin is formed.[83, 89] Catalytic hydrogenation and reduction with magnesium and magnesium iodide or bromide are the preferred procedures of the variety of systems that have been studied.

The reduction of benzil with zinc dust and sulfuric acid in the presence of acetic anhydride [109, 110] yields two stereoisomeric forms of the enediol diacetate; each is converted by hydrolysis with ethanolic potassium hydroxide into benzoin. Only one of the two stereoisomeric enediol

$$\text{C}_6\text{H}_5\text{COCOC}_6\text{H}_5 \rightarrow \underset{\underset{cis\ \text{and}\ trans}{\text{OCOCH}_3\quad\text{OCOCH}_3}}{\text{C}_6\text{H}_5\text{C}\!\!=\!\!=\!\!\text{CC}_6\text{H}_5} \rightarrow \underset{\text{OH}\quad\text{OH}}{\text{C}_6\text{H}_5\text{C}\!\!=\!\!\text{CC}_6\text{H}_5} \rightarrow$$

$$\text{C}_6\text{H}_5\text{COCHOHC}_6\text{H}_5$$

diacetates is obtained if benzil is reduced in ether solution by sodium and then treated with acetic anhydride.[110] Hydrolysis of some of the diacetates leads to enediols which can be isolated.

[109] Thiele, *Ann.*, **306**, 142 (1899).
[110] Nef, *Ann.*, **308**, 283 (1899).

Treatment with triphenylmethylmagnesium bromide or with magnesium and magnesium iodide or bromide converts a benzil into the halomagnesium salt of the enediol which on hydrolysis gives a benzoin. The following benzoins have been obtained in this way: 4,4'-toluoin (82% yield), 4,4'-anisoin (62% yield), 4,4'-dichlorobenzoin (91% yield), α-naphthoin (91% yield), 4,4'-diphenylbenzoin (88% yield), and 4-phenylbenzoin (good yield).[52, 111, 112]

$$C_6H_5COCOC_6H_5 \xrightarrow{Mg-MgI_2} \underset{\underset{OMgI}{|}}{C_6H_5C}=\!\!=\!\!=\underset{\underset{OMgI}{|}}{CC_6H_5} \rightarrow \underset{\underset{OH}{|}}{C_6H_5C}=\!\!=\underset{\underset{OH}{|}}{CC_6H_5}$$

$$\downarrow$$

$$C_6H_5COCHOHC_6H_5$$

The reduction of benzil with sodium or with tin or zinc amalgam and hydrochloric acid gives benzoin in nearly quantitative yield;[112, 113] with magnesium amalgam and hydrochloric acid or aluminum amalgam and ethanolic hydrochloric acid a 90% yield results;[113, 114] nickel aluminum alloy in sodium hydroxide, on the other hand, converts benzil into a mixture of reduction products but converts anisil into anisoin in 80% yield.[115] Furoin has been obtained from furil by enzymatic reduction.[116]

The reduction of 2,2',4,4',6,6'-hexamethylbenzil with zinc amalgam and hydrochloric acid is not successful,[117] but the benzoin can be obtained by catalytic hydrogenation.[118]

Ferrous sulfate in the presence of aqueous ammonia reduces 4,4'-dinitrobenzil to a mixture of 4,4'-diaminobenzoin and 4,4'-diaminobenzil.[119]

2,4,6-Trimethylbenzil is reduced with zinc in acetic acid to a mixture of isomeric benzoins. This appears to be the only recorded reduction in which both isomers of an unsymmetrical benzoin have been obtained simultaneously.[89]

The catalytic reduction of benzils is of more general application; the yields generally are in the range 86–93%. Platinum oxide (Adams)[120] is the usual catalyst.[94] It promotes the hydrogenation of hindered benzils, such as 2,2',4,4',6,6'-hexamethylbenzil, when other reagents are in-

[111] Gomberg and Bachmann, *J. Am. Chem. Soc.*, **50**, 2762 (1928).

[112] Bachmann, *J. Am Chem. Soc.*, **53**, 2758 (1931); **56**, 963 (1934).

[113] Pearl and Dehn, *J. Am. Chem. Soc.*, **60**, 57 (1938).

[114] Carré and Mauclère, *Bull. soc. chim. France*, [4] **49**, 1148 (1931).

[115] Papa, Schwenk, and Whitman, *J Org. Chem.*, **7**, 587 (1942).

[116] Neuberg, Lustig, and Cagan, *Arch. Biochem.*, **1**, 391 (1943).

[117] Kohler and Baltzly, *J. Am. Chem. Soc.*, **54**, 4015 (1932).

[118] Thompson, *J. Am. Chem. Soc.*, **61**, 1281 (1939).

[119] Kuhn, Möller, and Wendt, *Ber.*, **76**, 405 (1943).

[120] Voorhees and Adams, *J. Am. Chem. Soc.*, **44**, 1397 (1922).

effective.[4, 118] The *cis* and *trans* enediols are formed from such benzils; they can be separated, and on treatment with piperidine acetate or with ethanolic hydrochloric acid [1, 9] they isomerize to the benzoins.

Experimental Procedures

Catalytic Reduction (General Procedure). The catalytic reduction of benzil [94, 120] is carried out conveniently in a Burgess-Parr apparatus (with the modification described on p. 285). A solution of 0.01 mole of the substance in about 50 ml. of the appropriate solvent (ethanol, ethyl acetate, pyridine, or acetic acid), to which 0.5 g. of platinum oxide is added, is warmed to 70–75° and allowed to absorb 0.01 mole of hydrogen. The reduction is then stopped to prevent the formation of hydrobenzoin. The catalyst is removed, the solvent partially evaporated, and the product recrystallized from a suitable solvent. Anisil, benzil, furil, and piperil are reduced to the corresponding benzoins in 86–93% yield.

Reduction of 4,4′-Tolil with Magnesium–Magnesium Bromide.[52] To an ether solution containing 10 g. of anhydrous magnesium bromide in a 70-ml. test tube is added 4.76 g. of tolil and 20 ml. of benzene. A deep-yellow solution results. A weighed magnesium rod is inserted, and the tube is corked and placed on a shaking machine. A deep-brown coloration soon forms around the ends of the magnesium rod; after several hours the entire solution has become very deep brown. The reduction is apparently complete after twenty hours' shaking. The magnesium rod is removed and washed with benzene, and the solution is quickly decomposed with water. The ether-benzene solution is dried over anhydrous sodium sulfate. The product crystallizes after partial evaporation of the solvent. The yield of pure toluoin is 3.9 g. (82%), m.p. 88–89°.

THE REDUCTION OF AROMATIC ACIDS AND THEIR DERIVATIVES

The reduction of aromatic acids, their chlorides, esters, and peroxides can be accomplished by treatment with magnesium and magnesium iodide in a mixture of ether and benzene as solvents. With benzoic acid or benzoyl peroxide two steps are involved: the formation of the magnesium iodide salt and the reduction. With an acid chloride or ester the magnesium iodide derivative of the enediol forms directly and is hydrolyzed to the benzoin. Intermediate enediols have been isolated only from reduction of hindered acid chlorides. The method has been used in reducing benzoic, 4-toluic, α- and β-naphthoic, and phenyl-benzoic acid, benzyl and methyl benzoate, benzoyl peroxide, and 2,4,6-

trimethylbenzoyl, 2,4,6-triisopropylbenzoyl, and 2,6-dimethylbenzoyl chloride, the corresponding benzoins being isolated in 30 to 75% yields.[3-7, 111] Acid chlorides give the best yields. The procedure can be

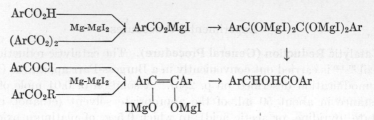

employed when the aldehyde corresponding to the symmetrical benzoin desired is not available. No unsymmetrical benzoin has been prepared by this method.

Experimental Procedures

Benzoin from Benzoic Acid.[111] A mixture of magnesium and magnesium iodide is prepared from 95 g. (0.75 atom) of iodine and 20 g. of magnesium powder in 100 ml. of dry ether and 200 ml. of benzene. To this colorless mixture 30.5 g. (0.25 mole) of benzoic acid is added in portions. When the lively evolution of gas has ceased, the mixture, protected from air by means of a mercury trap, is heated on the steam bath. After five days of heating, the dark reddish-brown solution is filtered from the undissolved magnesium and treated with water. Dilute acid is added to dissolve the copious precipitate of magnesium hydroxide. The organic solution is extracted with dilute aqueous sodium carbonate, which removes unchanged benzoic acid. Evaporation of the solvents leaves a solid contaminated with some oily by-products, which are removed by digestion with ether. The residue consists of practically pure benzoin and weighs 12.0 g. (30% yield).

Mesitoin from 2,4,6-Trimethylbenzoyl Chloride.[3] To 3 g. of magnesium turnings, 60 ml. of dry ether, and 120 ml. of dry benzene is added 15.3 g. of iodine in several portions. When the reaction mixture has become colorless and has been cooled to room temperature, the air in the flask is swept out by a stream of dry, oxygen-free nitrogen. A solution of 11 g. of 2,4,6-trimethylbenzoyl chloride in 10 ml. of dry ether is then added from a dropping funnel over a period of fifteen minutes. Stirring in a nitrogen atmosphere is continued for sixteen to eighteen hours. At the end of this time the magnesium has nearly disappeared, and the solution is dark red.

The reaction mixture is filtered through folded cheesecloth into a separatory funnel containing 8 ml. of acetic acid and 100 ml. of ice water.

The ether-benzene layer is separated and washed *rapidly* with water, with 5% aqueous sodium thiosulfate, again with water, then with 10% aqueous potassium bicarbonate, and finally once more with water. The solution is then dried for a few minutes over calcium chloride, filtered, and evaporated to a thin syrup as rapidly as possible under reduced pressure. Dilution of the brown syrup with 50 ml. of petroleum ether followed by cooling causes the enediol to precipitate as a white crystalline material, which is separated and washed with petroleum ether; yield, 3.1 g. (35%). The enediol is unstable in the presence of oxygen, being rapidly autoxidized to the benzil.

A solution of 1.3 g. of enediol and 6 ml. of methanol which has been saturated previously with dry hydrogen chloride is refluxed for forty-five minutes, allowed to cool, and poured into 70 ml. of water. The mesitoin separates as a white crystalline compound. It is collected on a filter and recrystallized from 70% aqueous methanol; yield, 1.2 g. (92%); m.p. 130–131°.

THE CONVERSION OF DESOXYBENZOINS INTO BENZOINS

Desoxybenzoins are prepared readily by a number of methods which do not involve the use of benzoins.[65–72, 121–124] Since the α-hydrogen atom in a desoxybenzoin is quite active and can be replaced easily, desoxybenzoins serve as convenient starting materials for the synthesis of benzoins.

In the presence of light, bromine converts a desoxybenzoin into an α-bromo derivative.[71, 72] (The α-chloro derivatives usually have been prepared from the benzoins.[125–128]) The α-bromodesoxybenzoins react with alkali to form benzoins,[71, 72, 126, 129, 130] and with sodium ethoxide to form the corresponding ketals, which are readily hydrolyzed with cold

$$C_6H_5CH_2COC_6H_4OCH_3\text{-}4 \xrightarrow{Br_2} C_6H_5CHBrCOC_6H_4OCH_3\text{-}4 \xrightarrow{NaOH} C_6H_5CHOHCOC_6H_4OCH_3\text{-}4$$

$$\Big\downarrow NaOC_2H_5 \qquad\qquad \Big\uparrow HCl$$

$$\underset{\substack{| \\ NaO}}{C_6H_5CHBr}\text{—}\underset{\substack{| \\ OC_2H_5}}{C}\text{—}C_6H_4OCH_3\text{-}4 \to \underset{\substack{\diagdown \\ O}}{C_6H_5CH}\text{—}\underset{\substack{| \\ OC_2H_5}}{C}\text{—}C_6H_4OCH_3\text{-}4 \to \underset{\substack{| \\ ONa}}{C_6H_5CHC(OC_2H_5)_2}C_6H_4OCH_3\text{-}4$$

[121] Fuson, Corse, and McKeever, *J. Am. Chem. Soc.*, **62**, 3250 (1940).
[122] Français, *Ann. chim.*, **11**, 212 (1939).
[123] Ruggli and Businger, *Helv. Chim. Acta*, **24**, 1112 (1941).
[124] Blau, *Monatsh.*, **26**, 1149 (1905); Weisl, *ibid.*, **26**, 977 (1905).
[125] Schroeter, *Ber.*, **42**, 2336 (1909).
[126] Ward, *J. Chem. Soc.*, **1929**, 1541.
[127] McKenzie and Wren, *J Chem. Soc.*, **97**, 473 (1910).
[128] Curtius and Lang, *J. prakt. Chem.*, [2] **44**, 544 (1891).
[129] Meisenheimer and Jochelson, *Ann.*, **355**, 249, 293 (1907).
[130] von Auwers, *Ber.*, **53**, 2271 (1920).

dilute mineral acid to the benzoins. If sodium methoxide is used in place of sodium ethoxide, benzoin methyl ether $C_6H_5CH(OCH_3)COC_6H_5$ is obtained.[131]

Scope and Limitations

Since the conversion of the α-bromodesoxybenzoins into benzoins is a reaction that results in 90% yields,[71, 72, 126, 129, 130] and the bromination of the desoxybenzoins to α-bromodesoxybenzoins usually gives 80% yields,[71, 72] the practical applicability of the general procedure for synthesis of benzoins depends on the availability of the desoxybenzoins. The desoxybenzoins are most commonly prepared (1) from an arylacetamide with an aryl Grignard reagent, (2) from an arylamide with benzyl or a substituted benzyl Grignard reagent, and (3) from an arylacetyl chloride and an aromatic or substituted aromatic hydrocarbon with anhydrous aluminum chloride. Reactions 2 and 3 are preferred to reaction 1. The yields of desoxybenzoins vary widely (30–80%) and depend on the individual components involved.[65–72, 121–124]

Experimental Procedure

General Procedure.[71, 72] A solution of 0.010 mole of the desoxybenzoin in 20–40 ml. of warm carbon tetrachloride in a 150-ml. Pyrex flask is exposed to the rays of a 500-watt tungsten lamp, and 20 ml. of a solution containing 8.00 g. of bromine per 100 ml. of carbon tetrachloride is added slowly while the flask is shaken. The reaction is quite rapid; hydrogen bromide is liberated, and the bromine color quickly disappears. The solution is concentrated under reduced pressure and cooled, and petroleum ether is added to complete crystallization of the product. The substance is dissolved in warm absolute ethanol. Three equivalents of sodium ethoxide in absolute ethanol is added, and the solution is allowed to stand until sodium bromide ceases to precipitate. The mixture is poured into 100 ml. of cold 15% hydrochloric acid. The product crystallizes on cooling; it can be recrystallized from ethanol.

MISCELLANEOUS SYNTHESES OF BENZOINS

Benzoylmandelonitriles have been obtained in nearly quantitative yields by treatment of aromatic aldehydes with benzoyl chloride and aqueous potassium cyanide.[132, 133] In the presence of ethanolic sodium

[131] Madelung and Oberwegner, *Ann.*, **526**, 195 (1936).
[132] Francis and Davis, *J. Chem. Soc.*, **95**, 1403 (1909).
[133] Davis, *J. Chem. Soc.*, **97**, 949 (1910).

ethoxide these substances generate benzoylbenzoins; [24, 25] the yields are improved by the addition of some of the aldehyde before the treatment

$$C_6H_5CHO + C_6H_5COCl + KCN \rightarrow \underset{\underset{OCOC_6H_5}{|}}{C_6H_5CHCN} \xrightarrow{NaOC_2H_5} \underset{\underset{OCOC_6H_5}{|}}{C_6H_5COCHC_6H_5}$$

with the base. If the aldehyde added at the second stage is different from that used in the preparation of the benzoylmandelonitrile, a derivative of an unsymmetrical benzoin is formed. By this method the O-

$$\underset{\underset{OCOC_6H_5}{|}}{C_6H_5CHCN} + CH_2O_2C_6H_3CHO \xrightarrow{NaOC_2H_5} \underset{\underset{OCOC_6H_5}{|}}{C_6H_5COCHC_6H_3O_2CH_2}$$

benzoyl derivatives of benzoin, furoin, 3,4,3',4'-methylenedioxybenzoin (piperoin), 4-methoxy- and 4'-methoxy-benzoin, 3,4-methylenedioxy- and 3',4'-methylenedioxy-benzoin, and furopiperoin (both isomers) have been prepared in yields of 10–53%. The hydrolysis of the benzoyl group has not been studied extensively. However, the O-benzoyl derivatives of 4-methoxy- and 4'-methoxy-benzoin are both hydrolyzed with sodium ethoxide in the cold to the more stable 4-methoxybenzoin. This method is of little practical value, since all the compounds recorded can be prepared in better yields by other methods.

Benzoins have been isolated in small amounts, usually as by-products, from various reactions, none of which has been studied sufficiently to permit evaluation for the synthesis of benzoins. [34, 110, 132-137] Other processes have furnished certain benzoins in yields often unspecified but sometimes as high as 90%; however, the recorded data concerning them are meager. These preparations are listed in the following paragraphs.

α-Hydroxydiphenylacetaldehyde (obtained from α-bromodiphenylacetaldehyde and barium carbonate) rearranges in ethanol containing a few drops of sulfuric acid to benzoin, along with a lesser amount of the ethyl ether of benzoin. [138-141] Aliphatic α-hydroxy aldehydes undergo a similar transformation. [140, 141] Diphenylacetaldehyde gives the desoxybenzoin. [67, 139]

[134] Wahl, *Compt. rend.*, **147**, 72 (1908).

[135] Blicke, *J. Am. Chem. Soc.*, **46**, 2560 (1924); **47**, 229 (1925).

[136] Shoruigin, Isagulyantz, and Guseva, *J. Gen. Chem. U.S.S.R.*, **4**, 683 (1934) [*C. A.*, **29**, 3671 (1935)].

[137] Ramage, Simonsen, and Stowe, *J. Chem. Soc.*, **1939**, 89.

[138] Danilov, *Ber.*, **60**, 2390 (1927).

[139] Danilov and Venus-Danilova, *J. Russ. Phys. Chem. Soc.*, **57**, 428 (1925) [*C. A.*, **21**, 380 (1927)]; **58**, 957 (1926) [*C. A.*, **21**, 2126 (1927)].

[140] James and Lyons, *J. Org. Chem.*, **3**, 273 (1938).

[141] Danilov and Venus-Danilova, *Ber.*, **62**, 2653 (1929); **67**, 24 (1934).

$$(C_6H_5)_2C(OH)CHO \xrightarrow{H_2SO_4} C_6H_5CHOHCOC_6H_5 + C_6H_5CHCOC_6H_5$$
$$\underset{\displaystyle OC_2H_5}{|}$$

When 2-methylquinoline (quinaldine) is treated with selenium dioxide, quinaldehyde is formed in 50% yield. However, oxidation of 2-methylquinoline with unsublimed, aged selenium dioxide furnishes quinaldoin in yields as high as 84%.[50] Under similar conditions 4-methylquinoline may give the aldehyde or it may produce the corresponding stilbene in yields as high as 84%. 1-Methylisoquinoline gives only the aldehyde.[142]

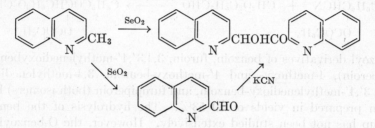

1-Methylanthraquinone can be oxidized directly with manganese dioxide to the corresponding benzoin.[143, 144]

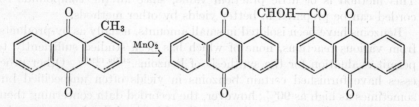

Phenylmagnesium bromide reacts with methyl cyanoformate to yield the phenyl ether of benzoin.[145]

$$CNCO_2CH_3 + 3C_6H_5MgBr \rightarrow C_6H_5CHCOC_6H_5$$
$$\underset{\displaystyle OC_6H_5}{|}$$

Diphenyl triketone (1,3-diphenyl-1,2,3-propanetrione) rearranges on treatment with phenylmagnesium bromide or phosphoric acid in acetic acid to give benzoin.[95, 146–148]

[142] Barrows and Lindwall, *J. Am. Chem. Soc.*, **64**, 2430 (1942).
[143] I. G. Farbenind. A.-G., Ger. pat. 481,291 [*C. A.*, **23**, 4951 (1929)].
[144] Scholl and Wallenstein, *Ber.*, **69**, 503 (1936).
[145] Finger and Gaul, *J. prakt. Chem.*, [2] **111**, 54 (1925).
[146] Schönberg and Azzam, *J. Chem. Soc.*, **1939**, 1428.
[147] Kohler and Erickson, *J. Am. Chem. Soc.*, **53**, 2301 (1931).
[148] de Neufville and von Pechmann, *Ber.*, **23**, 3375 (1890).

$$C_6H_5COCOCOC_6H_5 \rightarrow C_6H_5C(OH)COC_6H_5 \rightarrow C_6H_5CHOHCOC_6H_5$$
$$\underset{CO_2H}{|}$$

2-Methoxymandelonitrile and resorcinol react in the presence of zinc chloride in hydrochloric acid (Hoesch reaction) to give a ketimine hydrochloride, which can be hydrolyzed to 2′-methoxy-2,4-dihydroxybenzoin.[149] Benzoylmandelonitrile reacts similarly with resorcinol to form a non-crystalline phenolic substance, which on acetylation gives 2,4-diacetoxy-O-acetylbenzoin.[150]

$$2\text{-}CH_3OC_6H_4CH(OH)CN + C_6H_4(OH)_2 \rightarrow 2\text{-}CH_3OC_6H_4CHOHCC_6H_3(OH)_2 \rightarrow$$
$$\underset{NH \cdot HCl}{\|}$$

$$2\text{-}CH_3OC_6H_4CHOHCOC_6H_3(OH)_2\text{-}2,4$$

$$\underset{OCOC_6H_5}{\overset{C_6H_5CHCN}{|}} + C_6H_4(OH)_2 \rightarrow 2,4\text{-}(CH_3CO_2)_2C_6H_3COCHC_6H_5$$
$$\underset{OCOCH_3}{|}$$

Phenylmagnesium bromide reacts with carbon monoxide under pressure [151] or with nickel carbonyl [152] to give benzoin in 70% yield.

TABLE OF BENZOINS PREPARED BY VARIOUS METHODS

In Table II are listed the benzoins whose preparation has been described up to November, 1947. The numbers in the column headed "Method" refer to the following methods of preparation: (1) benzoin condensation; (2) from isomeric benzoin; (3) condensation of an arylglyoxal with an aromatic hydrocarbon; (4) the Grignard reaction; (5) reduction of benzils; (6) reduction of aromatic acids or their derivatives; (7) from desoxybenzoins.

[149] Ishidate, *J. Pharm. Soc. Japan*, **542**, 311 (1927) [*C. A.*, **22**, 1153 (1928)].
[150] Baker, *J. Chem. Soc.*, **1930**, 1015.
[151] Benton, Voss, and McCusker, *J. Am. Chem. Soc.*, **67**, 82 (1945).
[152] Fischer and Stoffers, *Ann.*, **500**, 253 (1933).

TABLE II

Benzoins Prepared by Various Methods

Formula	R'—CHOHCO—R Benzoin	Method	M.P., °C	Yield, %	Reference*
$C_{10}H_8O_4$	Furoin	1	135	38	48
		5		86	94
$C_{12}H_{10}O_3$	Benzfuroin ($C_6H_5CHOHCOC_4H_3O$)	1	139		19, 48, 54, 57
$C_{12}H_{10}O_3$	Benzfuroin ($C_6H_5COCHOHC_4H_3O$)	4	119		103
$C_{12}H_{10}O_2N_2$	2-Pyridoin	1	156		49
$C_{14}H_{12}O_2$	Benzoin	1	134	92	75, 154
		5		93	52, 94, 162
		3		90	95, 96
		4	137	33	103
		6		45	111
		†		70	151, 152
$C_{14}H_{12}O_3$	2'-Hydroxy-	4	148		103
$C_{14}H_{12}O_4$	2,2'-Dihydroxy-	‡	142–149	80	155
$C_{14}H_{18}O_2$	Cyclohexoylphenylcarbinol ($C_6H_5CHOHCOC_6H_{11}$)	4	62–63	26	92
$C_{14}H_{18}O_3$	1-(p-Anisyl)-2-cyclopentylethan-1-ol-2-one (4-$CH_3OC_6H_4CHOHCOC_5H_9$)	4	70–71	12	123
$C_{14}H_{24}O_2$	Dodecahydro- $C_6H_{11}CHOHCOC_6H_{11}$	6 §	B.P. 140–141.5/ 3 mm.		141
$C_{14}H_{10}O_2Cl_2$	2,2'-Dichloro-	1	62–63 56–57	20–40	20, 104
$C_{14}H_{10}O_2Cl_2$	3,3'-Dichloro-	1			33
$C_{14}H_{10}O_2Cl_2$	4,4'-Dichloro-	1	88		156
		5	85–87	91	52
$C_{14}H_{10}O_2Br_2$	3,3'-Dibromo-	1	123–124		33
$C_{14}H_{10}O_2I_2$	4,4'-Diiodo-	1	122		157
$C_{14}H_{10}O_6N_2$	2,2'-Dinitro-	1	155.5, 168–169	8	44, 45
$C_{14}H_{11}O_2Cl$	4-Chloro-	3	90–91	35	96
		4	88–89	17	104
		7		94	71
$C_{14}H_{11}O_2Cl$	4'-Chloro-	3	116	84	96
		4	110–111	32	104
		7	116–117	93	71
$C_{14}H_{11}O_2Br$	3-Bromo- (?)	1	129–130	32	53
$C_{14}H_{11}O_2Br$	4-Bromo-	3	108–109	70	96
$C_{14}H_{11}O_2Br$	4'-Bromo-	3	125–126	57	96
$C_{14}H_{14}O_2N_2$	4,4'-Diamino-	5	199		119
$C_{14}H_{15}O_3N$	4-Dimethylaminobenzfuroin [$C_4H_3OCHOHCOC_6H_4N(CH_3)_2$-4]	1	168	30	53, 54
$C_{15}H_{12}O_4$	3,4-Methylenedioxy-	1	120	32	19, 32, 53, 54, 57
$C_{15}H_{14}O_2$	2'-Methyl-	4	64–65	15	104
$C_{15}H_{14}O_2$	3-Methyl-	4	69.5–70		92
$C_{15}H_{14}O_2$	4'-Methyl-	3	116	50	96
		4	116–117	24	104

* References 153–171 are listed on pp. 303–304.
† The Grignard reagent added to carbon monoxide or nickel carbonyl.
‡ By hydrolysis of 2,2'-bis(methoxymethoxy)-benzoin.
§ From corresponding α-hydroxy acetaldehyde.

TABLE II—*Continued*

BENZOINS PREPARED BY VARIOUS METHODS

Formula	R'—CHOHCO—R Benzoin	Method	M.P., °C	Yield, %	Reference*
$C_{15}H_{14}O_2$	4-Methyl-	3	109–	42–	96
		4	110	47	104
$C_{15}H_{14}O_3$	2-Methoxy-	1	56–57	70	37
$C_{15}H_{14}O_3$	2'-Methoxy-	1	78		19
		4	58		103
$C_{15}H_{14}O_3$	4-Methoxy-	1	105.5–	25–45	19, 54, 77
		2	106.5		14, 59, 82, 86
		4			90
		7	108	94	71, 129
$C_{15}H_{14}O_3$	4'-Methoxy-	2		50	81, 84, 85
		3	100	48	96
		4	89	41	103, 105
		7	90	74	71
$C_{15}H_{14}O_3$	2-Hydroxy-5-methyl-	7			130
$C_{15}H_{14}O_5$	2'-Methoxy-2,4-dihydroxy-	†	171		149
$C_{15}H_{20}O_3$	4'-Methoxyphenyl hexahydrophenyl- ($4\text{-}CH_3OC_6H_4CHOHCOC_6H_{11}$)	4	72–73		123
$C_{15}H_{11}O_4Cl$	2'-Chloro-3,4-methylenedioxy-	1	116	50	18, 53, 54, 57
$C_{15}H_{11}O_4Cl$	4'-Chloro-3,4-methylenedioxy-	1	110	40	40, 76
$C_{15}H_{11}O_4Br$	3'-Bromo-3,4-methylenedioxy-	1	106	33	53
$C_{15}H_{13}O_3Cl$	2'-Chloro-4-methoxy-	1	84	60	76
$C_{15}H_{13}O_3Cl$	3'-Chloro-4-methoxy-	1	85.5	25–30	91
		4		20	91
$C_{15}H_{13}O_3Cl$	4'-Chloro-4-methoxy-	7	84.5– 85.5	85	72
$C_{15}H_{13}O_3Cl$	4-Chloro-4'-methoxy-	7	70.5– 71.5	70	72
$C_{15}H_{13}O_3Br$	3'-Bromo-4-methoxy (?)-	1	88	20	76
$C_{16}H_{12}O_4$	4,4'-Dialdehydo-	1	170–174		158
$C_{16}H_{12}O_6$	3,4,3',4'-Dimethylenedioxy-	1	120	80	51, 159
		5		87	94
$C_{16}H_{14}O_5$	4'-Methoxy-3,4-methylenedioxy-	1	110		19
$C_{16}H_{16}O_2$	2,2'-Dimethyl-	1	79		33
$C_{16}H_{16}O_2$	3,3'-Dimethyl-	1	Oil		33
$C_{16}H_{16}O_2$	4,4'-Dimethyl-	1	88–89		33, 160
		5		90	52
$C_{16}H_{16}O_3$	2-Ethoxy-	4	77–78	16	104
$C_{16}H_{16}O_3$	2'-Ethoxy-	4	81–82	14	104
$C_{16}H_{16}O_4$	2,2'-Dimethoxy-	1	99–100 101.5	55	35
$C_{16}H_{16}O_4$	3,4-Dimethoxy (?)-	1	Oil		36
$C_{16}H_{16}O_4$	2',4-Dimethoxy-	1	102	79	19
		4	92–93		103
$C_{16}H_{16}O_4$	3',3-Dimethoxy-	1	41–42	20	20
		1	55	70	161
$C_{16}H_{16}O_4$	3'-4-Dimethoxy-	4	60	5	108
$C_{16}H_{16}O_4$	4,4'-Dimethoxy-	1	109–110	60	39
		5	113	62–90	52, 94, 162

*References 153–171 are listed on pp. 303–304.
† The Hoesch reaction.

TABLE II—*Continued*

BENZOINS PREPARED BY VARIOUS METHODS

Formula	R'—CHOHCO—R Benzoin	Method	M.P., °C	Yield, %	Reference*
$C_{16}H_{10}O_{10}N_2$	6,6'-Dinitropiperoin	†	150–240 (dec.)		24
$C_{16}H_{11}O_8N$	6'-Nitropiperoin	†	166		24
$C_{16}H_{14}O_4Cl_2$	2,2'-Dichloro-3,3'-dimethoxy-	1	134		20
$C_{16}H_{14}O_4Br_2$	2,2'-Dimethoxy-5,5'-dibromo-	1	105	50	43
$C_{16}H_{15}O_4Cl$	2'-Chloro-3,4-dimethoxy-	1	142	70	18, 76
$C_{16}H_{17}O_2N$	4'-Dimethylamino-	4	159–160	45	17
$C_{16}H_{17}O_2N$	4-Dimethylamino-	1	163–164	86	16, 54, 57
		2			59
		5		68	17
		4		25	17
$C_{16}H_{16}O_2NCl$	2'-Chloro-4-dimethylamino-	1	173	36	18, 53, 57
$C_{16}H_{16}O_2NCl$	3'-Chloro-4-dimethylamino-	1	145	45	40, 76
$C_{16}H_{16}O_2NCl$	4'-Chloro-4-dimethylamino-	1	127–128	46	16, 80
		2		80	80
		4			80
$C_{16}H_{16}O_2NCl$	4'-Dimethylamino-4-chloro-	4	104.5	42	80
$C_{16}H_{16}O_2NBr$	4-Dimethylamino-3'-bromo-	1	145	50	53
$C_{17}H_{18}O_2$	2',4',6'-Trimethyl-	3	93.5–	62	96, 97
		5	94		89
		2			88
$C_{17}H_{18}O_2$	2,4,6-Trimethyl-	5	103.5–	57–	89
		3	104.5	63	95, 96, 97
$C_{17}H_{18}O_2$	4-Isopropyl-	1	97	Small	32
$C_{17}H_{17}O_4N$	3',4'-Methylenedioxy-4-dimethylamino-	1	136	40	40, 54
$C_{17}H_{17}O_4Cl$	2'-Chloro-3-methoxy-4-ethoxy-	1	121	60	40
$C_{17}H_{17}O_4Cl$	2'-Chloro-3-ethoxy-4-methoxy-	1	103	81	40
$C_{17}H_{19}O_3N$	4'-Methoxy-4-dimethylamino (?)-	1	144	52	76
$C_{18}H_{14}O_2$	Naphthabenzoin ($C_{10}H_7CHOHCOC_6H_5$)	3	128	42	96
$C_{18}H_{20}O_2$	2,4,4',6-Tetramethyl-	3	95–95.5	24	97
$C_{18}H_{20}O_2$	2,2',6,6'-Tetramethyl-	6	127–128		4
$C_{18}H_{20}O_2$	3,3',5,5'-Tetramethyl-	1	93–94	77	170
$C_{18}H_{20}O_3$	4'-Methoxy-4-isopropyl (?)-	1	81–82		33
$C_{18}H_{20}O_4$	2,2'-Diethoxy-	4	68.5–69		104
		1	68.5–69	5	104
$C_{18}H_{20}O_4$	4,4'-Diethoxy-	1	86–87	8	104
$C_{18}H_{20}O_6$	2,2'-Dimethoxymethoxy-	1	B.P. 200–210/ 1 mm.	50– 60	155
$C_{18}H_{20}O_6$	2,2',3,3'-Tetramethoxy-	1	86–87.3	44	165
$C_{18}H_{20}O_6$	2,2',5,5'-Tetramethoxy-	1	Oil	100	165
$C_{18}H_{20}O_6$	3,4,3',4'-Tetramethoxy-	1	Oil	60	21, 36, 42
$C_{18}H_{18}O_4N_2$	4,4'-Diacetamido-	1	244–246	30	171
$C_{18}H_{18}O_2Br_2$	4,4'-Dibromo-2,2',6,6'-tetramethyl-	6	143–144		7
$C_{18}H_{19}O_4Cl$	2'-Chloro-3,4-diethoxy-	1	106	63	40
$C_{19}H_{16}O_3$	4-Methoxynaphthabenzoin ($4\text{-}CH_3OC_{10}H_6COCHOHC_6H_5$)	‡	162–163		163

* References 153–171 are listed on pp. 303–304.
† Nitration of corresponding benzoin.
‡ Desoxybenzoin treated with thioglycolic acid followed by hydrolysis.

TABLE II—*Continued*

BENZOINS PREPARED BY VARIOUS METHODS

Formula	R'—CHOHCO—R Benzoin	Method	M.P., °C	Yield, %	Reference
$C_{19}H_{22}O_2$	2,2',4,4',6-Pentamethyl-	3	120– 120.5	17	97
$C_{20}H_{16}O_2$	4 Phenyl (?)-	5	148–151	Good	52
$C_{20}H_{24}O_2$	2,2',4,4',6,6'-Hexamethyl-	3	130.5– 131	48	96, 97
		5			118
		6			1, 3
$C_{20}H_{24}O_2$	4,4'-Diisopropyl-	1	101–102	35	39, 164
$C_{20}H_{24}O_8$	2,2',4,4',6,6'-Hexamethoxy-	*	Gum		137
$C_{20}H_{24}O_8$	3,3',4,4',5,5'-Hexamethoxy-	1	147.5– 148.6	16	165, 167
$C_{20}H_{14}O_2N_2$	2-Quinaldoin	1	269–271	66	50, 153
		5	135	36	166
		†		84	50
$C_{20}H_{22}O_2Br_2$	3,3'-Dibromo-2,2',4,4'-6,6'-hexamethyl-	6	133.5–135		7
$C_{22}H_{16}O_2$	α-Naphthoin	1	138–139	13	52
		6		35	52, 111
		5		91	52, 162
$C_{22}H_{16}O_2$	β-Naphthoin	6		70	52, 111
$C_{22}H_{28}O_2$	2,2',3,3',5,5',6,6'-Octamethyl-	5		45	6
		6	130–131		6
$C_{22}H_{28}O_2$	2,2',3,3',4,4',6,6'-Octamethyl-	6	117–118		6
$C_{23}H_{30}O_2$	2,4,6-Triisopropyl-	5	117.5– 118.5		11
$C_{24}H_{20}O_2$	2,2'-Dimethyl-1,1'-naphthoin	6	149– 151.5		9
$C_{26}H_{20}O_2$	4,4'-Diphenyl-	1	168–	95	52, 162
		5	170	88	52, 162
$C_{26}H_{36}O_2$	2,2',4,4',6,6'-Hexaethyl-	6	64–65.5		2
$C_{30}H_{16}O_6$	2,2'-Diphthaloyl- [R,R' = $C_6H_4(CO)_2C_6H_3$-]	‡			143, 144
$C_{30}H_{20}O_2$	9,9'-Phenanthroin	1	283	25	168, 169
$C_{32}H_{48}O_2$	2,2',4,4',6,6'-Hexaisopropyl-	6	126.5– 127.5		5

* Reduction of aldehyde.
† Oxidation of 2-methylquinoline.
‡ Oxidation of 1-methylanthraquinone.

REFERENCES TO TABLES

[153] Henze, *Ber.*, **67**, 750 (1934).
[154] Cass and Bordner, U. S. pat. 2,372,709 (1945).
[155] LaForge, *J. Am. Chem. Soc.*, **55**, 3040 (1933).
[156] Hantzsch and Glower, *Ber.*, **40**, 1519 (1907).
[157] Willgerodt and Ucke, *J. prakt. Chem.*, [2] **86**, 276 (1912).
[158] Oppenheimer, *Ber.*, **19**, 1814 (1886).
[159] Perkin, *J. Chem. Soc.*, **59**, 150 (1891).
[160] Stierlin, *Ber.*, **22**, 376 (1889).
[161] Schönberg and Malchow, *Ber.*, **55**, 3746 (1922).

[162] Bachmann, *J. Am. Chem. Soc.*, **56**, 963 (1934).
[163] Behaghel and Ratz, *Ber.*, **72**, 1257 (1939).
[164] Biltz and Stellbaum, *Ann.*, **339**, 294 (1905).
[165] Hartwell and Kornberg, *J. Am. Chem. Soc.*, **67**, 1606 (1945).
[166] Linsker and Evans, *J. Am. Chem. Soc.*, **68**, 947 (1946).
[167] Richtzenhain, *Ber.*, **77**, 409 (1944).
[168] Bergmann and Israelashwili, *J. Am. Chem. Soc.*, **67**, 1951 (1945).
[169] Jones, *J. Am. Chem. Soc.*, **67**, 1956 (1945).
[170] Weiler, *Ber.*, **33**, 334 (1900).
[171] Gee and Harley-Mason, *J. Chem. Soc.*, **1947**, 251.

CHAPTER 6

SYNTHESIS OF BENZOQUINONES BY OXIDATION

JAMES CASON *

Vanderbilt University

CONTENTS

* Present address: Department of Chemistry, University of California, Berkeley, Cal.

INTRODUCTION

p-Benzoquinone, or "quinone," was discovered in 1838 as a product of the action of manganese dioxide in sulfuric acid on the rare natural product quinic acid,[1] a tetrahydroxycyclohexanecarboxylic acid; however, benzoquinones generally are prepared by the oxidation of disubstituted aromatic hydrocarbon derivatives having hydroxyl or amino groups in the *ortho* or *para* positions. Thus quinone results from the oxidation of hydroquinone, p-aminophenol, or p-phenylenediamine; in the two latter instances the reaction proceeds through the formation and the rapid hydrolysis of a quinonimine or quinonediimine. When such starting

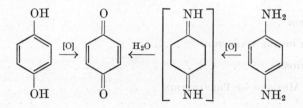

materials or intermediates are available, conditions often can be defined for the production of the desired quinone in high yield. Certain quinones are obtainable in moderate or fair yield by the oxidation of starting materials containing only one hydroxyl or amino group, as exemplified by the industrial production of quinone from aniline. Other methods that have been employed for the synthetic production of benzoquinones are of less consequence.

Oxidation of phenols and amines constitutes the chief topic for discussion in this chapter. Processes for the oxidation with dichromate in sulfuric acid solution [2,3] or with ferric chloride [4] were developed at an early date, and Nietzki [5] found that a marked increase in yield results if the substance oxidized contains an additional hydroxyl or amino group in the *para* position. This investigator was the first to employ the efficient method of introducing a *para* amino group into a phenol or an amine by the process of diazo coupling and reduction.

[1] Woskrensky, *Ann.*, **27**, 268 (1838).

[2] Nietzki, *Ber.*, **10**, 1934 (1877).

[3] Nietzki, *Ber.*, **19**, 1467 (1886).

[4] Carstanjen, *J. prakt. Chem.*, [2] **3**, 54 (1871).

[5] Nietzki, *Ber.,* **10**, 833 (1877).

MECHANISM OF THE OXIDATION

Bamberger and Tschirner[6] isolated p-aminophenol as a product of the partial oxidation of aniline, and they tentatively suggested that the conversion of aniline to quinone with dichromate may proceed through the formation and oxidation of this known product of the rearrangement of phenylhydroxylamine. However, these investigators found[7] that

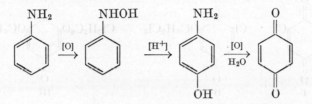

phenylhydroxylamine actually is oxidized by dichromate to nitrosobenzene; furthermore Willstätter and Dorogi[8] observed that sulfuric acid of the concentration used in the oxidizing mixture does not rearrange phenylhydroxylamine to p-aminophenol at an appreciable rate. A suggestion[9] that p-aminodiphenylamine is formed as an intermediate product is discounted by the observation[8] that oxidation of this substance gives a much poorer yield than is obtained from aniline.

Pummerer's work on the oxidation of β-dinaphthol[10] suggests that the initial product of the oxidation of any phenol is an aroxyl radical, which exists in a state of resonance with ketomethylene radicals. Further oxidation of a radical with a free electron at the *para* position would

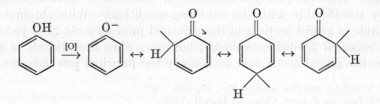

afford a *para* quinone. The oxidation of an amine can proceed through a similar radical intermediate and subsequent hydrolysis of the ketimine group; quinonimines have been isolated as products of the oxidation of

[6] Bamberger and Tschirner, *Ber.*, **31**, 1522 (1898).
[7] Bamberger and Tschirner, *Ber.*, **40**, 1893 (1907).
[8] Willstätter and Dorogi, *Ber.*, **42**, 2147 (1909).
[9] Nover, *Ber.*, **40**, 288 (1907).
[10] Pummerer and Frankfurter, *Ber.*, **47**, 1472 (1914).

aminophenols when anhydrous conditions are maintained [11] or when the imino group is very resistant to hydrolysis.[12] Free-radical mechanisms may be involved in reactions of preformed benzoquinones [13] and in the oxidation of hydroquinones.[14] Hunter [15, 16, 17] investigated the oxidation of certain halogenated phenols and isolated various products that appeared to be formed through free-radical intermediates. Thus 2,4,6-

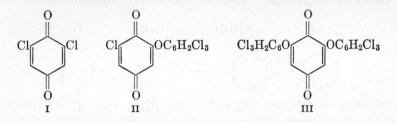

I   II   III

trichlorophenol was found to yield the products I, II, and III. Davis and Harrington [18] also suggested the formation of free radicals during the oxidation of halogenated phenols. The formation of biphenyl derivatives or of substances of higher degree of polymerization as products of the oxidation of benzene derivatives is generally attributed to free-radical intermediates of the same type.[14, 19, 20, 21]

SIDE REACTIONS

The nature of the oxidizing agent, the experimental conditions, and the character of the substituents present influence the side reactions that occur. Thus the products obtained on oxidation of trichlorophenol [15] vary considerably with the oxidizing conditions. With chromic anhydride in glacial acetic acid the principal product (only 27% yield) is the expected 2,6-dichloroquinone; however, when lead dioxide is used in either glacial acetic acid or benzene the principal products are the

[11] Willstätter and Pfannenstiel, *Ber.*, **37,** 4605 (1904).

[12] Kehrmann, *J. prakt. Chem.*, [2] **40,** 494 (1889).

[13] Wieland, Heymann, Tsatsas, Juchum, Varvoglis, Labriola, Dobbelstein, and Boyd-Barrett, *Ann.*, **514,** 145 (1934).

[14] Erdtman, *Proc. Roy. Soc. London,* **A143,** 191 (1933).

[15] Hunter and Morse, *J. Am. Chem. Soc.*, **48,** 1615 (1926).

[16] Hunter and Levine, *J. Am. Chem. Soc.*, **48,** 1608 (1926).

[17] Hunter and Woollett, *J. Am. Chem. Soc.*, **43,** 135 (1921).

[18] Davis and Harrington, *J. Am. Chem. Soc.*, **56,** 131 (1934).

[19] Erdtman, *Proc. Roy. Soc. London,* **A143,** 228 (1933).

[20] Levine, *J. Am. Chem. Soc.*, **48,** 797 (1926).

[21] Davis and Hill, *J. Am. Chem. Soc.*, **51,** 493 (1929).

aryloxyquinones represented by formulas II and III above.   Tribromo-
2,6-dimethoxyphenol gives the expected quinone [16] when treated with
chromic anhydride in glacial acetic acid, whereas weaker oxidizing agents
yield an aryloxyquinone (IV).   This compound also is obtained from the

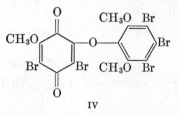

IV

oxidation with chromic anhydride when 50% acetic acid is used as
solvent.   A coupling product is formed when 4-bromopyrogallol 1,3-
dimethyl ether is oxidized in 50% acetic acid.

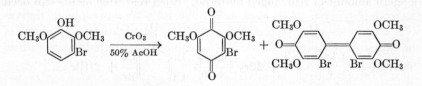

The preceding data might suggest the general use of glacial acetic acid;
however, this is not always desirable.   Oxidation of 2,4,6-tribromo-*m*-
cresol with chromic anhydride in 50% acetic acid gives the expected
product, 3,5-dibromotoluquinone, but oxidation in glacial acetic acid
yields a mixture of di- and tri-bromoquinones.[22]   Similar results are
reported in the oxidation of 4,6-dibromo-*o*-cresol.[23]   It appears that no
other such direct comparisons have been made; however, several
workers [24, 25, 26] obtained satisfactory products on oxidizing trihalogenated
phenols with chromic anhydride in dilute acetic acid.   A free-radical
mechanism has been used to explain the oxidation of a halogenated
phenol or amine to a quinone containing more than the expected number
of halogen atoms.   Thus tribromomethoxyquinone is obtained on oxidation of 2,4,6-tribromo-3-methoxyphenol.[18]   Substitution of bromine in

[22] Claus and Hirsch, *J. prakt. Chem.*, [2] **39**, 59 (1889).
[23] Claus and Jackson, *J. prakt. Chem.*, [2] **38**, 326 (1888).
[24] Kehrmann and Tiesler, *J. prakt. Chem.*, [2] **40**, 480 (1889).
[25] Conant and Fieser, *J. Am. Chem. Soc.*, **45**, 2194 (1923).
[26] Smith and Byers, *J. Am. Chem. Soc.*, **63**, 616 (1941).

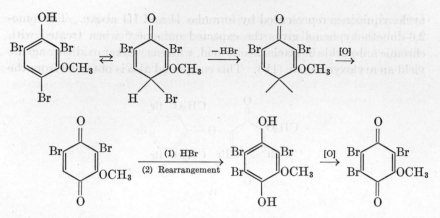

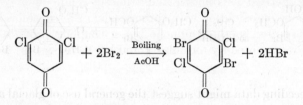

2,6-dichloroquinone,[27] with glacial acetic acid as solvent, leads to the rearranged product, 2,5-dichloro-3,6-dibromoquinone. At 10–20° the product consists chiefly of the normal substitution product, with only a small amount of rearranged material. Such rearrangements can occur

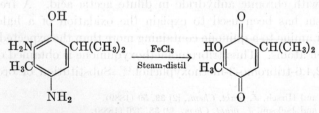

in solvents other than glacial acetic acid, however, for oxidation of 2,6-dichloro-4-nitrophenol with bromine in water at 100° gives 2,5-dichloro-3,6-dibromoquinone.[27, 28]

It has been observed by several investigators that oxidation in aqueous medium may result in hydrolysis of an amino group to a hydroxyl group. Thus in the oxidation of diaminothymol[4] a hydroxyquinone results. Other workers[29, 30, 31] have reported similar results with aqueous

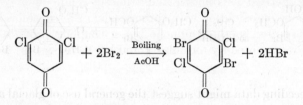

[27] Ling, *J. Chem. Soc.*, **61**, 558 (1892).
[28] Ling, *J. Chem. Soc.*, **51**, 783 (1887).
[29] Fittig and Siepermann, *Ann.*, **180**, 23 (1875).
[30] Ladenburg and Engelbrecht, *Ber.*, **10**, 1219 (1877).
[31] Mazzara, *Ber.*, **23**, 1390 (1890).

ferric chloride and with aqueous chromic acid. The amino group resists hydrolysis during oxidation in aqueous medium, however, in the preparation of 5-amino-6-chlorotoluquinone.[32] When certain alkyl-p-aminophenols are oxidized with ferric chloride (even in the absence of hydrochloric acid) the product contains, in addition to the expected quinone, some of the corresponding chloroquinone; for example:[33, 34]

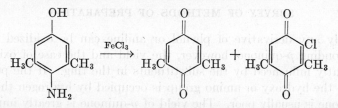

This difficulty is avoided by use of ferric sulfate.

The most generally encountered by-products in quinone preparations are dark, insoluble, amorphous materials. These materials doubtless result from coupling and from polymerization, and certain of them have been characterized as dimeric and trimeric compounds.[14] Methoxyhydroquinone on oxidation with chromic acid or ferric chloride does not give the expected methoxyquinone but a coupling product for which structures represented by formulas V and VA have been proposed. This

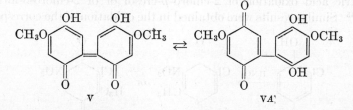

product is also formed when a trace of sulfuric acid is added to an acetic acid solution of methoxyquinone. Biphenyl derivatives are also obtained from hydroxyhydroquinone trimethyl ether and from pyrogallol. Oxidation of toluhydroquinone dimethyl ether with chromic acid, nitric acid, or manganese dioxide gives, in addition to dark materials of high molecular weight, a ditoluquinone derivative. Treatment of toluquinone with 50% sulfuric acid yields bitolyl and tritolyl derivatives and higher polymers. Benzoquinone [19] when shaken for two and one-half days with 50% acetic acid-sulfuric acid is converted into a complex mixture of amorphous products, from which a small amount of a termolecular dihydroxy compound can be isolated.

[32] Zincke and Schurman, *Ann.*, **417**, 251 (1918).
[33] Smith and Irwin, *J. Am. Chem. Soc.*, **63**, 1036 (1941).
[34] Smith and King, *J. Am. Chem. Soc.*, **63**, 1887 (1941).

Dilute alkali polymerizes quinones rapidly, and even neutral oxidizing agents sometimes cause polymerization.[14] It should also be mentioned that light often promotes polymerization. Avoidance of drastic conditions and rapidity of operation are usually important factors in the successful preparation of quinones.

SURVEY OF METHODS OF PREPARATION

Nearly any derivative of phenol or aniline can be oxidized to the corresponding p-quinone; however, the yield and the ease of oxidation are greatly influenced by the substituents in the ring. If the position *para* to the hydroxy or amino group is occupied by hydrogen the yield of quinone is usually poor. The yield of p-quinone is greatly improved by a *para* amino or hydroxyl group; an o-quinone has been prepared only rarely except from an intermediate containing *ortho* amino or hydroxyl groups. A *para* halogen atom usually improves the yield of p-quinone, and various other *para* substituents sometimes help. Any group *para* to the amino or hydroxyl group will be eliminated or oxidized under appropriate conditions, and usually some quinone can be isolated. This fact has been applied as evidence of orientation; however, the migration of a methyl group into the quinone ring has been assumed in the nitric acid oxidation of 2-chloro-p-cresol or of 2-chloro-6-nitro-p-cresol.[35] Similar results were obtained in the oxidation of the correspond-

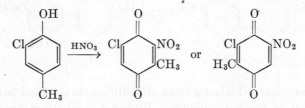

ing bromo compounds.[36] These appear to be the only examples of such a migration. Several p-toluidines have been oxidized with a chromic acid-sulfuric acid mixture; in every one the *para* methyl group was eliminated.[37]

Choice of the most suitable method for preparing a given quinone is rendered difficult not only by the variety of routes available but also by the lack of data regarding yields. Any specific quinone usually can be prepared satisfactorily by oxidation of any one of at least five compounds. The choice of compound to be oxidized will depend upon the

[35] Zincke, Schneider, and Emmerich, *Ann.*, **328**, 314 (1903).
[36] Zincke and Emmerich, *Ann.*, **341**, 313 (1905).
[37] Nölting and Baumann, *Ber.*, **18**, 1151 (1885).

availability of the various starting materials and the yields obtainable on oxidation. In addition, the relative ease of manipulation is sometimes a determining factor. In the following pages the more successful methods and oxidizing agents are discussed in some detail; less important methods and oxidizing agents are mentioned briefly. The objective is the presentation of an overall picture, not only of the final oxidation but also of the choice and preparation of starting materials. It should be emphasized that the choice of oxidizing agent and the manner of use depend largely upon the specific structure of the compound being oxidized.

o-QUINONES

o-Quinones are nearly always prepared from the corresponding catechols. Amines are usually unsatisfactory starting materials, for many o-quinones are sensitive to moisture, and oxidation of an amine in anhydrous medium leads to the quinonimine. The only preparation in which an amine has proved useful as a starting material was the oxidation of 2-amino-4,5-dimethylphenol to 4,5-dimethyl-o-quinone; with a chromic acid-sulfuric acid mixture a yield of 45% was obtained.[38, 39]

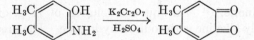

No tetramethyl-o-quinone is obtained by oxidation of tetramethyl-o-phenylenediamine; however, this unstable quinone is obtained in 81% yield by oxidation of tetramethylcatechol with silver oxide.[40]

Silver oxide is a very useful reagent for preparing sensitive quinones and is especially so in the o-quinone series. The dihydroxy compound is usually oxidized by shaking at room temperature with freshly prepared silver oxide [41, 42] in anhydrous ether in the presence of a dehydrating agent such as sodium sulfate. The method is rapid, simple, and successful; the few yields reported range from 12 to 81%.

The usual instability associated with o-quinones is not encountered in the highly halogenated derivatives, which are sufficiently stable to be prepared in good yield by oxidation of the catechol with nitric acid [43, 44, 45] in acetic acid or ethanol solution. The stability of these

[38] Diepolder, Ber., **42**, 2921 (1909).
[39] Willstätter and Müller, Ber., **44**, 2171 (1911).
[40] Smith and Hac, J. Am. Chem. Soc., **56**, 477 (1934).
[41] Willstätter and Pfannenstiel, Ber., **37**, 4744 (1904).
[42] Willstätter and Müller, Ber., **41**, 2581 (1908).
[43] Jackson and Koch, Am. Chem. J., **26**, 10 (1901).
[44] Jackson and Maclaurin, Am. Chem. J., **37**, 11 (1907).
[45] Jackson and Flint, Am. Chem. J., **39**, 83 (1908).

quinones is not due solely to the highly substituted ring, for tetramethyl-o-quinone is especially unstable.[40]

The only preparations of amino-o-quinones reported are oxidations by air in ammoniacal solution.[46,47,48] These compounds doubtless exist in equilibrium with the hydroxyquinonimines.

A method generally applicable for the preparation of catechols is the oxidation of o-hydroxybenzaldehydes with alkaline hydrogen peroxide. This procedure [49] usually gives satisfactory yields unless the aldehydo group is hindered by a large *ortho* substituent. The method is also

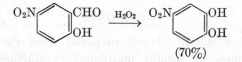

(70%)

moderately successful for oxidation of p-acetophenols [18,49,50] to the corresponding hydroquinones.

Experimental Procedure

4-o-Toluquinone.[39,51] An aqueous solution of 17 g. of silver nitrate is made slightly alkaline with sodium hydroxide. The precipitated silver oxide [42,52] is washed twelve times with water, six times with acetone, and six times with anhydrous ether, then covered with 100 ml. of anhydrous ether. After addition of 15 g. of anhydrous sodium sulfate and a solution of 3 g. of 4-methylcatechol [51] in 80 ml. of anhydrous ether the mixture is shaken for three to four minutes. The precipitate is removed by filtration from the red solution, and the filtrate is cooled in an ice-salt mixture. One gram of dark-red prisms and blades separate; they are collected and washed with dry ether. The filtrate and washings, on concentration in vacuum, yield an additional gram of quinone (total yield, 68%). 4-o-Toluquinone melts with decomposition, and the melting point has been variously reported in the range 75–84°.

[46] Kehrmann and Prunier, *Helv. Chim. Acta,* **7,** 987 (1924).
[47] Hoehn, *Helv. Chim. Acta,* **8,** 275 (1925).
[48] Kehrmann and Poehl, *Helv. Chim. Acta,* **9,** 485 (1926).
[49] Dakin, *Am. Chem. J.,* **42,** 477 (1909).
[50] Baker, *J. Chem. Soc.,* **1941,** 665.
[51] Kvalnes, *J. Am. Chem. Soc.,* **56,** 2487 (1934).
[52] Busch, Clark, Genung, Schroeder, and Evans, *J. Org. Chem.,* **1,** 2 (1936).

EXPLANATION OF TABLES *

In Table I and subsequent tables the compounds are listed for the most part in alphabetical sequence. Halo- and nitro-quinones, however, are listed as substitution products according to the method of Beilstein. Those quinones which contain more than one functional group are listed in Table V. The tables include all references found in *Chemical Abstracts* to November, 1947; some preparations appearing as minor parts of papers may well have been overlooked.

In many instances the yield is not recorded in the literature and probably was low; in other instances the result given appears to represent the yield in a single experiment and is probably far from the maximum obtainable. Where an oxidation has been reported several times the yield quoted is that reported in the reference followed by (y.). Where the yield is not based on the substance oxidized but is the overall yield from some previous intermediate the figure reporting the yield is followed by the symbol (o.). An overall yield from a phenol or an amine by the process of coupling, reduction, and oxidation is indicated by the symbol (c.). The following abbreviations are used: cr., crude; hydr., isolated as the hydroquinone.

* The system and abbreviations used in the several tables included in the chapter are explained in this section. References occurring for the first time in a table are listed at the end of that table.

TABLE I

o-QUINONES

Quinone	Substance Oxidized	Oxidizing Agent	Yield	References
4-Acetamino-o-quinone	4-Acetaminocatechol	$Na_2Cr_2O_7$ (H_2SO_4)	75%	53
3,5-Diacetamino-o-quinone	3,5-Diacetaminocatechol	$K_2Cr_2O_7$ (H_2SO_4)	78%	48
3,5-Diamino-o-quinone	3,5-Diaminocatechol	Air (ammonia solution)	Nearly quant.	46
4,5-Diamino-o-quinone	4,5-Diaminocatechol	Air (ammonia solution)	—	47
3,5-Diamino-6-hydroxy-o-quinone	4,6-Diaminopyrogallol	Air (ammonia solution)	—	48
4,5-Dianilino-o-quinone	Catechol and aniline	Ag_2O (AcOH)	—	54
4,5-Diethyl-o-quinone	4,5-Diethylcatechol	Ag_2O	—	55
3,5-Dimethyl-4,6-dichloro-o-quinone	3,5-Dimethyl-4,6-dichlorocatechol	HNO_3 (AcOH)	—	56
4,5-Dimethyl-o-quinone	4,5-Dimethylcatechol	Ag_2O	—	39, 57
	2-Amino-4,5-dimethylphenol	$Na_2Cr_2O_7$	—	39
		$K_2Cr_2O_7$ (H_2SO_4)	45%	38
4-(4-Chloro-2-hydroxyphenoxy)-o-quinone	4-Chlorocatechol	$NaNO_2$ (Ac_2O)	70%	58
3-Methoxy-o-quinone	3-Methoxycatechol	Ag_2O	Poor	39
4-Methoxy-o-quinone	4-Methoxycatechol	Ag_2O	—	51
o-Quinone (1,2-benzoquinone)	Catechol	Ag_2O	—	41, 42, 59 60, 61
	Pb salt of catechol	I_2	—	43, 62
3-Chloro-o-quinone	3-Chlorocatechol	Ag_2O or PbO_2	12%	63
4-Chloro-o-quinone	4-Chlorocatechol	Ag_2O	—	51, 63
3,5-Dichloro-o-quinone	3,5-Dichlorocatechol	Ag_2O	—	51
4,5-Dichloro-o-quinone	4,5-Dichlorocatechol	Ag_2O	—	63
Tetrachloro-o-quinone	Tetrachlorocatechol	HNO_3	81%	44 (y.), 59, 64
	Catechol	Cl_2	—	64
	Tetrachlorocatechol mono- or di-methyl ether	HNO_3	—	65
4-Bromo-o-quinone	4-Bromocatechol	Ag_2O	—	51
Tetrabromo-o-quinone	Tetrabromocatechol	HNO_3 (AcOH, EtOH)	90.5%	43, 45 (y.), 59, 64
	Catechol	Br_2	—	64
	Tetrabromocatechol mono- or di-methyl ether	HNO_3	—	65
Tetramethyl-o-quinone	Tetramethylcatechol	Ag_2O	81%	40
3-o-Toluquinone (3-methyl-o-quinone)	3-Methylcatechol	Ag_2O	—	39
5,6-Dichloro-3-o-toluquinone	5,6-Dichloro-3-methylcatechol	HNO_3	—	66
4,5,6-Trichloro-3-o-toluquinone	4,5,6-Trichloro-3-methylcatechol	HNO_3 (AcOH)	—	67
4,6-Dichloro-5-bromo-3-o-toluquinone	4,6-Dichloro-5-bromo-3-methylcatechol	HNO_3	—	68
5,6-Dibromo-3-o-toluquinone	5,6-Dibromo-3-methylcatechol	HNO_3	—	69
4-o-Toluquinone (4-methyl-o-quinone)	4-Methylcatechol	Ag_2O	68%	39 (y.), 51, 70
3,5,6-Trichloro-4-o-toluquinone	3,5,6-Trichloro-4-methylcatechol	HNO_3 (AcOH)	—	71, 72
3,5,6-Tribromo-4-o-toluquinone	3,5,6-Tribromo-4-methylcatechol	HNO_3 (AcOH)	—	72
3,5,6-Trimethyl-4-chloro-o-quinone	3,5,6-Trimethyl-4-chlorocatechol	HNO_3 (AcOH)	—	73
4-Triphenylmethyl-o-quinone	4-Triphenylmethylcatechol	PbO_2 (benzene)	—	51
		HNO_3 (EtOH)	Good	74
4-Triphenylmethyl-6-chloro-o-quinone	4-Triphenylmethyl-2,6-dichlorophenol	HNO_3 (AcOH)	8–10%	74
4-Triphenylmethyl-6-bromo-o-quinone	4-Triphenylmethyl-2,6-dibromophenol	HNO_3 (AcOH)	8%	74

REFERENCES TO TABLE I

[53] Kehrmann and Hoehn, *Helv. Chim. Acta*, **8**, 218 (1925).

[54] Kehrmann and Cordone, *Ber.*, **46**, 3011 (1913).

[55] Fries and Bestian, *Ann.*, **533**, 80 (1938).

[56] Francke, *Ann* **296**, 206 (1897).

[57] Diepolder, *Ber.*, **44**, 2502 (1911).

[58] Frejka, Sefránek, and Zika, *Collection Czechoslov. Chem. Commun.*, **9**, 238 (1937) [*C. A.*, **31**, 7047 (1937)].

[59] Conant and Fieser, *J. Am. Chem. Soc.*, **46**, 1860 (1924).

[60] Goldschmidt and Graef, *Ber.*, **61**, 1868 (1928).

[61] Dyer and Baudisch, *J. Biol. Chem.*, **95**, 483 (1932).

[62] Jackson and Koch, *Ber.*, **31**, 1457 (1898).

[63] Willstätter and Müller, *Ber.*, **44**, 2188 (1911).

[64] Zincke, *Ber.*, **20**, 1776 (1887).

[65] Cousin, *Compt. rend.*, **129**, 967 (1899).

[66] Zincke and Preiss, *Ann.*, **417**, 217 (1918).

[67] Prenntzell, *Ann.*, **296**, 185 (1897).

[68] Janney, *Ann.*, **398**, 364 (1913).

[69] Zincke and Janney, *Ann.*, **398**, 351 (1913).

[70] McPherson and Boord, *J. Am. Chem. Soc.*, **33**, 1529 (1911).

[71] Bergmann and Francke, *Ann.*, **296**, 163 (1897).

[72] Cousin, *Ann. chim. phys.*, [7] **13**, 536 (1898).

[73] Hodes, *Ann.*, **296**, 218 (1897).

[74] Zincke and Wugk, *Ann.*, **363**, 295 (1908).

p-QUINONES

Alkyl and Aryl Quinones and Their Substituted Derivatives

Oxidation of Simple Amines and Phenols. If the simple amine or the phenol is readily available, or if only a small amount of quinone is desired, it is often most convenient to oxidize directly without introducing a substituent into the position *para* to the amino or hydroxyl group.

Perhaps the most widely used agent for this type of oxidation is sodium or potassium dichromate in dilute sulfuric acid. Ordinarily the amine is dissolved in dilute sulfuric acid and the dichromate added gradually at a temperature below 20°; however, the dichromate is sometimes introduced in one portion. In the preparation of *o*-xyloquinone from 2,3-dimethylaniline (33% yield) the oxidation period is extended preferably over two and one-half days.[75] In the preparation of pseudocumoquinone [76] (trimethylquinone) from pseudocumenol-3 (2,3,6-trimethylphenol), the oxidation may be carried out advantageously in an hour or less. The dichromate oxidation of pseudocumenol-6 gives no quinone.[76]

[75] Emerson and Smith, *J. Am. Chem. Soc.*, **62**, 141 (1940).

[76] Smith, Opie, Wawzonek, and Prichard, *J. Org. Chem.*, **4**, 318 (1939).

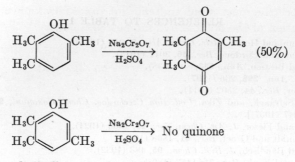

When a p-dialkylbenzene is nitrated as the first step in a quinone synthesis the mixture of nitro compounds need not be separated, for the mixture of amines obtained by reduction can be oxidized to give a single quinone. This procedure followed by dichromate oxidation furnishes 5-nonyltoluquinone in 17% yield and 5-hendecyltoluquinone in 22% yield.[77]

Manganese dioxide is a very useful and convenient reagent for oxidation of simple amines as well as other types of compounds, and it is sometimes preferred even where other methods give somewhat better yields. When a mixture of the amine, manganese dioxide, and dilute sulfuric acid is steam-distilled the quinone usually separates (or is extractable) from the distillate in the pure state. This method has been used for preparing 2-bromo-5-chloroquinone from 2-chloro-5-bromo-aniline,[78,79] and it is stated that the results are much better than those of dichromate oxidation. Manganese dioxide is preferred for oxidation of o-toluidine to toluquinone (48% yield), and detailed directions for this preparation have been reported.[80] When 2,4,5-trimethylaniline is oxidized with manganese dioxide the 4-methyl group is eliminated and p-xyloquinone is formed in 35% yield.[81]

Oxidation of Aminophenols and Diamines. Alkyl- and aryl-quinones usually are prepared from amines or phenols having favorable substituents in the *para* positions, and various methods for introducing these substituents have been developed. Perhaps the most successful is the coupling procedure perfected [82] in the naphthalene series and extensively employed [76,83,84,85] in the benzene series. This method has been de-

[77] Hasan and Stedman, *J. Chem. Soc.*, **1931**, 2112.

[78] Nef, *Am. Chem. J.*, **13**, 422 (1891).

[79] Clark, *Am. Chem. J.*, **14**, 553 (1892).

[80] Fieser, *Experiments in Organic Chemistry*, 2nd ed., Boston, Heath, 1941, p. 228.

[81] Heymann and Koenigs, *Ber.*, **20**, 2395 (1887).

[82] Fieser, *Org. Syntheses*, **17**, 9, 68 (1937).

[83] Smith, Hoehn, and Whitney, *J. Am. Chem. Soc.*, **62**, 1863 (1940).

[84] Smith and Opie, *J. Org. Chem.*, **6**, 427 (1941).

[85] Smith and Austin, *J. Am. Chem. Soc.*, **64**, 528 (1942).

scribed [76] as "the most rapid and efficient procedure known at present for preparation of the polymethylquinones in quantity." Several com-

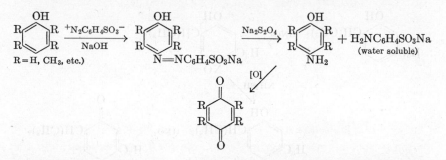

binations of coupling agents and reducing agents have been studied,[33, 76] but all are less successful than the process of coupling with diazotized sulfanilic acid and reducing with sodium hydrosulfite. The coupling should be carried out in strongly alkaline solution, and adequate time should be allowed for completion. The preferred oxidizing agent is ferric chloride, or ferric sulfate where ferric chloride causes chlorination.[33, 34] The ferric salt is added to an aqueous solution of the amine or its salt, and the mixture is steam-distilled at once. If the quinone is very sensitive (e.g., o-xyloquinone [85]) steam distillation is carried out at reduced pressure. Coupling and reduction are commonly carried out as consecutive reactions without isolation of the intermediate, and the crude amine is usually oxidized without purification. Overall yields are rarely less than 60% and occasionally, as in the preparation of pseudocumoquinone [76] from the phenol, may be as high as 95%. Even unsaturated quinones,[83] such as allylquinone and allyltrimethylquinone, are obtained in quite satisfactory yields.*

Although coupling is the most generally successful method for preparing p-aminophenols, other methods have found some application. One is the electrolytic reduction of the appropriate nitro compound.[86, 87] Nitration of a phenol, followed by reduction of the nitro group, has been used, and in representative procedures [88, 89] good results have been obtained by oxidizing the aminophenol with chromic acid-sulfuric acid at 0°. Nitrosation and reduction have also been used successfully,[90, 91, 91a]

* For another method of preparing unsaturated quinones see p. 322.

[86] Gattermann, *Ber.*, **27**, 1931 (1894).

[87] Raiford, *Am. Chem. J.*, **46**, 425 (1911).

[88] van Erp, *Rec. trav. chim.*, **30**, 284 (1911).

[89] van Erp, *Ber.*, **58**, 663 (1925).

[90] Hodgson and Moore, *J. Chem. Soc.*, **1926**, 2039.

[91] Hodgson and Nicholson, *J. Chem. Soc.*, **1942**, 375.

[91a] Karrer and Schläpfer, *Helv. Chim. Acta*, **24**, 298 (1941).

and details for the preparation of thymoquinone by this route are given in *Organic Syntheses.*[92] Nitrosophenols are isomeric with quinone

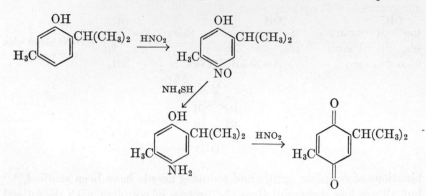

monoximes and may be hydrolyzed directly to quinones, as illustrated by the preparation of alkylquinones.[93, 94]

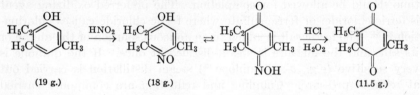

If the *p*-dinitro compound can be obtained by dinitration, it may serve as a suitable starting material. This procedure [95, 96, 97] has been developed particularly for the preparation of bromotrimethylquinone,[98] duroquinone [99, 100, 101] (tetramethylquinone), pseudocumoquinone [102] (trimethylquinone), trimethylethylquinone,[103, 104] and tetraethylquinone.[104, 105, 106] It consists in nitration with fuming nitric and sulfuric acids, reduction to the diamine with stannous chloride and hydrochloric

[92] Kremers, Wakeman, and Hixon, *Org. Syntheses, Coll. Vol.* **1**, 2nd ed., p. 511 (1941).
[93] Karrer and Hoffmann, *Helv. Chim. Acta,* **22**, 654 (1939).
[94] Karrer and Hoffmann, *Helv. Chim. Acta,* **23**, 1126 (1940).
[95] Nef, *J. Chem. Soc.,* **53**, 428 (1888).
[96] Claus, Raps, Herfeldt, and Berkfeld, *J. prakt. Chem.,* [2] **43**, 563 (1891).
[97] Nietzki and Schneider, *Ber.,* **27**, 1426 (1894).
[98] Smith and Johnson, *J. Am. Chem. Soc.,* **59**, 673 (1937).
[99] Smith and Dobrovolny, *J. Am. Chem. Soc.,* **48**, 1420 (1926).
[100] Smith, *Org. Syntheses,* **10**, 40 (1930).
[101] Smith and Denyes, *J. Am. Chem. Soc.,* **58**, 304 (1936).
[102] Smith, *J. Am. Chem. Soc.,* **56**, 472 (1934).
[103] Smith and Kiess, *J. Am. Chem. Soc.,* **61**, 993 (1939).
[104] Smith and Opie, *J. Am. Chem. Soc.,* **63**, 932 (1941).
[105] Smith and Harris, *J. Am. Chem. Soc.,* **57**, 1292 (1935).
[106] Smith and Guss, *J. Am. Chem. Soc.,* **62**, 2635 (1940).

acid, and oxidation with ferric chloride.   The yields by this procedure
are usually good.   The method is well illustrated by the preparation of
duroquinone [100, 101] (overall yield, 84%).

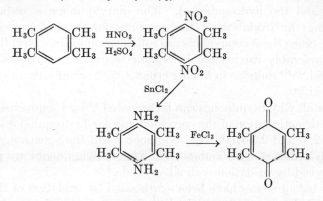

Oxidation of Hydroquinones.   Substituted hydroquinones may be
oxidized to quinones in satisfactory yield by a variety of oxidizing
agents.   Ferric chloride, chromic acid-sulfuric acid, silver oxide, and
manganese dioxide have been widely used, and in some instances benzoquinone [107-111] in boiling ethanol has proved quite successful.

Arylhydroquinones may be prepared by condensation of quinone
with benzene or various substituted benzenes.[107, 108, 110, 112, 113, 114]   Usually
aluminum chloride is the best condensing agent, but sometimes 10%
sulfuric acid is used.   The condensation* normally gives 2,5-disubstitu-
tion, but monoresorcinylhydroquinone is obtained by condensation of
quinone and resorcinol at 250° without a catalyst.[115]   The preparation of
a 2,5-diarylquinone may be represented in the following way.   Actually

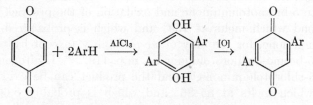

* For a detailed discussion of this type of condensation see p. 359.

[107] Browning and Adams, *J. Am. Chem. Soc.*, **52**, 4102 (1930).
[108] Shildneck and Adams, *J. Am. Chem. Soc.*, **53**, 346 (1931).
[109] Shildneck and Adams, *J. Am. Chem. Soc.*, **53**, 2208 (1931).
[110] Shildneck and Adams, *J. Am. Chem. Soc.*, **53**, 2373 (1931).
[111] Knauf, Shildneck, and Adams, *J. Am. Chem. Soc.*, **56**, 2109 (1934).
[112] Pummerer and Prell, *Ber.*, **55**, 3108 (1922).
[113] Pummerer and Fiedler, *Ber.*, **60**, 1441 (1927).
[114] Pummerer, Dally, and Reissinger, *Ber.*, **66**, 792 (1933).
[115] Pummerer and Huppmann, *Ber.*, **60**, 1442 (1927).

the initial condensation rarely gives a pure hydroquinone, for this is oxidized in part by quinone, and there results a mixture of diarylquinone, diarylhydroquinone, and the quinhydrone (molecular complex of the quinone and the hydroquinone). The diarylquinone is obtained by completing the oxidation of this mixture (for detailed procedure see p. 326). Since these compounds are rather insoluble in water, the oxidation is preferably carried out in organic media, e.g., ferric chloride in acetic acid,[112, 114] quinone in boiling ethanol,[107, 111] or chromic anhydride in acetic acid.[110]

Higher alkylhydroquinones can be prepared [116] by Clemmensen reduction and demethylation of the corresponding acylhydroquinone dimethyl ethers. 2,3- and 2,5-Diallylhydroquinone result from rearrangement of the diallyl ether of hydroquinone.[117] The diallylquinones are prepared in good yield by oxidation with silver oxide.*

Many haloquinones have been synthesized by oxidation of the corresponding halogen-substituted hydroquinones, prepared by addition of halogen acid to the appropriate quinone.[25, 59, 118] If an alkyl group or halogen is present in the quinone the halogen acid adds in such a way that the two substituents bear the 2,5-relationship.[119-121] When both

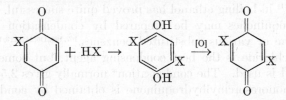

alkyl and halogen are present in a quinone the position at which a second halogen enters has not been established. The addition of hydrogen chloride to 5-bromotoluquinone and oxidation of the product [122] affords a compound which melts at 150° and which is probably 5-bromo-6-chlorotoluquinone, for the only other possibility (except by rearrangement) is 5-bromo-3-chlorotoluquinone, m.p. 119°.[123] Hydrogen chloride adds to 5-chlorotoluquinone,[124] and the product can be oxidized to a quinone which melts at 85–86° and which is probably 5,6-dichloro-

* For another method of preparing unsaturated quinones see p. 319.
[116] Asano and Hase, J. Pharm. Soc. Japan, 60, 650 (1940).
[117] Fieser, Campbell, and Fry, J. Am. Chem. Soc., 61, 2216 (1939).
[118] Schniter, Ber., 20, 1316 (1887).
[119] Sarauw, Ann., 209, 106 (1881).
[120] Levy and Schultz, Ann., 210, 138 (1881).
[121] Hantzsch and Schniter, Ber., 20, 2279 (1887).
[122] Schniter, Ber., 20, 2283 (1887).
[123] Raiford, J. Am. Chem. Soc., 36, 670 (1914).
[124] Kehrmann, Silva, and Keleti, Ber., 48, 2027 (1915).

toluquinone, for this has been reported as melting at 83°,[125] whereas the melting point of 3,5-dichlorotoluquinone is recorded as 102° [126] and as 103°.[87, 123] Addition of hydrogen chloride to 6-chlorotoluquinone gives a product that on oxidation yields a dichloroquinone entirely different from the 5,6-dichlorotoluquinone described above; it is probably 3,6-dichlorotoluquinone.[124] Work in progress by the author indicates that the melting points of dihalotoluquinones obtained via halogen acid addition may be unreliable because of contamination by very difficultly separable trihalotoluquinones. Consequently the correlations and structures assigned in this paragraph should be regarded as tentative.

Oxidation of Halophenols. A number of 2,6-dihaloquinones (and 2-alkyl-6-haloquinones) have been prepared from the corresponding 2,4,6-trihalophenols (or 2-alkyl-4,6-dihalophenols). Typical procedures are illustrated by the preparations of 3,5-dibromotoluquinone [26] (see p. 326) and 2,6-dichloroquinone.[24, 25] These oxidations were carried out with chromic anhydride in dilute acetic acid in yields of 77% and 69%. They demonstrate the beneficial effect of p-halogen substituents. Highly halogenated phenols and hydroquinones are so sparingly soluble in water that their oxidation is usually accomplished in an organic solvent. Inspection of Table II will show that haloquinones have been prepared from virtually every conceivable type of intermediate and are frequently prepared by a combination halogenation and oxidation process.

Miscellaneous Oxidations. There is little to be said about the numerous nitric acid oxidations included in Table II except that few yields have been reported and most of those are poor. Preparations in which yields are mentioned include 2-bromo-6-chloroquinone [27] (10.5%) and 2,6-diiodoquinone [127] ("poor"). Oxidation of 2,3,5-tribromo-1,4-dimethoxybenzene with fuming nitric acid results in a "small" yield of bromanil [128] (tetrabromoquinone). Nitric acid oxidations in acetic acid solutions have been carried out by several workers,[68, 129, 130] but no yields are reported. 2,6-Dichloroquinone is obtained in 49% yield by oxidation of 2,4,6-trichlorophenol with nitric acid in ethanol; [27] however, chromic anhydride in acetic acid is preferable for this oxidation. Halogenation of phenol [131] or p-phenylenediamine [132] followed by nitric acid oxidation constitutes a satisfactory preparation of chloranil [131] or bromanil.[131,132]

[125] Angeletto and Oliverio, *Gazz. chim. ital.*, **70**, 789 (1940).
[126] Raiford and Leavell, *J. Am. Chem. Soc.*, **36**, 1510 (1914).
[127] Kvalnes, *J. Am. Chem. Soc.*, **56**, 669 (1934).
[128] Kohn and Guttmann, *Monatsh.*, **45**, 573 (1924).
[129] Asahina and Yasue, *Ber.*, **69**, 647 (1936).
[130] Cruickshank and Robinson, *J. Chem. Soc.*, **1938**, 2068.
[131] Kempf and Moehrke, *Ber.*, **47**, 2620 (1914).
[132] Graebe and Weltner, *Ann.*, **263**, 31 (1891).

Nitric acid has been used repeatedly for the preparation of highly halogenated quinones;[133] however, yields are not specified. Treatment of the methyl ether of 2,3,4,6-tetrabromophenol [134] with concentrated nitric acid gives the corresponding nitroanisole, but oxidation of the acetyl derivative of this phenol gives 2,3,6-tribromo-5-nitroquinone.

Several quinones have been prepared by electrolytic oxidation. Oxidation of o-xylene [135] for ten ampere-hours gives toluquinone in 12.2% yield, while after forty ampere-hours 7.3% of toluquinone and 1.3% of m-xyloquinone are obtained. Low yields of quinones are obtained by a similar procedure [136] from benzene, phenol, toluene, and thymol under a variety of conditions. The electrolytic oxidation of ethylbenzene and of o- and p-ethylphenol has been studied.[137] By electrolysis of aniline in 10% hydrochloric acid, chloranil results,[138] whereas in 20% hydrochloric acid the product is trichloroquinone. The only good yields (77–81% [139] and 65% [140]) reported for electrolytic oxidations are obtained in the preparation of quinone by oxidation of benzene.

Of the many other methods included in Table II a few may be mentioned briefly. A variety of 2,6-disubstituted quinones [141, 142] results from oxidation of the appropriate 4-nitrophenols with one-half equivalent of lead tetraacetate in acetic acid at room temperature. It is claimed that this method gives excellent yields when alkyl and aryl substituents are

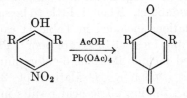

present. p-Hydroxysulfonic acids have been oxidized [143–147] with chromic acid-sulfuric acid, and satisfactory yields of quinones are claimed in

[133] Kohn and Steiner, *Monatsh.*, **58**, 92 (1931), and numerous earlier papers in this series.
[134] Kohn and Strassmann, *Monatsh.*, **45**, 597 (1924).
[135] Fichter and Rinderspacher, *Helv. Chim. Acta*, **10**, 40 (1927).
[136] Fichter and Stocker, *Ber.*, **47**, 2012 (1914).
[137] Ono, *Helv. Chim. Acta*, **10**, 45 (1927).
[138] Erdelyi, *Ber.*, **63**, 1200 (1930).
[139] Inoue and Shikata, *J. Chem. Ind. Japan*, **24**, 567 (1921).
[140] Seyewetz and Miodon, *Bull. soc. chim. France*, **33**, 449 (1923).
[141] Jones and Kenner, *J. Chem. Soc.*, **1931**, 1851.
[142] Kenner and Morton, *J. Chem. Soc.*, **1934**, 679.
[143] Kehrmann, *J. prakt. Chem.*, [2] **37**, 334 (1888).
[144] Kehrmann, *J. prakt. Chem.*, [2] **39**, 392 (1889).
[145] Kehrmann, *J. prakt. Chem.*, [2] **40**, 188 (1889).
[146] Kehrmann, *Ber.*, **22**, 3263 (1889).
[147] Kehrmann and Kruger, *Ann.*, **310**, 89 (1900).

some instances. Oxidation of sulfanilic acids [148, 149] is only moderately successful.

Experimental Procedures

Several detailed preparations have been described. These include the preparation of p-benzoquinone by oxidation of hydroquinone with sodium dichromate in sulfuric acid,[150] manganese dioxide in sulfuric acid,[80] or sodium chlorate in the presence of vanadium pentoxide.[151] Toluquinone [80] is prepared by oxidation of o-toluidine with manganese dioxide in sulfuric acid; thymoquinone [92] (2-isopropyl-5-methylquinone) is prepared by nitrosation of thymol, reduction, and oxidation with nitrous acid; duroquinone [100, 101] (tetramethylquinone) is prepared by dinitration of durene, reduction, and oxidation with ferric chloride.

Trimethylquinone.[34, 76] A solution of 105 g. of sulfanilic acid in 500 ml. of water containing 26.5 g. of sodium carbonate is cooled to 15°, and a solution of 37 g. of sodium nitrite in 100 ml. of water is added. The mixture is poured immediately into 600 g. of ice and 106 ml. of concentrated hydrochloric acid, then allowed to stand for twenty to thirty minutes. The diazo solution is introduced slowly into a well-stirred solution of 63 g. of pseudocumenol-6 (2,3,5-trimethylphenol) in 300 ml. of water containing 75 g. of sodium hydroxide. An excess of alkali must be present at this point. The mixture is allowed to stand at least two hours (preferably overnight), during which period the ice melts and the temperature rises to that of the room. After coupling is complete the solution is made strongly acid with 200–250 ml. of concentrated hydrochloric acid. Without removal of the red azo compound, 164 g. of stannous chloride * in 200 ml. of concentrated hydrochloric acid is added, and the mixture is heated almost to boiling until the precipitate dissolves and the color becomes orange-brown. The mixture is transferred to a steam-distillation flask, excess ferric sulfate (about 1400 g. of the nonahydrate) is added, and the mixture is steam-distilled at once. The product is removed from the distillate by ether extraction, which must be continued until the aqueous layer is colorless, for this quinone is fairly soluble in the large volume of water necessary for steam distillation. The combined ether solution is dried over anhydrous sodium sulfate, and the solvent is removed through a short packed column (to prevent loss of quinone). The residue, which weighs 72 g. (95%), solidifies in an ice bath and melts at 26°. Although this melting point is a

---

* In some preparations, reduction with sodium hydrosulfite is more satisfactory; see ref. 33.

[148] Hayduck, *Ann.*, **172**, 209 (1874).
[149] Heinichen, *Ann.*, **253**, 285 (1889).
[150] Vliet, *Org. Syntheses, Coll. Vol.* **1**, 2nd ed., p. 482 (1941).
[151] Underwood and Walsh, *Org. Syntheses*, **16**, 73 (1936).

few degrees low (m.p. 29–30° [102]), the quinone does not need to be purified further for most purposes. Distillation is a satisfactory method of purification; b.p. 98°/10 mm., 108°/18 mm.

2,5-Diphenylquinone.[110] To a suspension of 300 g. of finely powdered anhydrous aluminum chloride in 500 ml. of dry benzene in a 2-l., three-necked flask, equipped with a mechanical stirrer, 500-ml. separatory funnel, thermometer, and reflux condenser, is slowly added with stirring a solution of 100 g. of pure benzoquinone in 1 l. of dry benzene. The rate of addition is regulated (two to three hours required) to maintain the reaction mixture at a temperature of 35–40°. Stirring is continued for five hours, during which time the temperature is allowed to drop to that of the room. The reaction mixture is decomposed by pouring it slowly into a mechanically stirred mixture of 2 kg. of ice and 250 ml. of concentrated hydrochloric acid. Stirring is continued until a light-brown emulsion is formed and no lumps of undecomposed material remain. After the benzene has been removed by steam distillation, the residual light-brown granular solid is collected and washed with hot water and dried. The dry material (140 g.) is green and is a mixture of quinones, hydroquinones, and quinhydrones. The crude product is placed in a 5-l., round-bottomed flask with 3 l. of glacial acetic acid and 21.5 g.* of chromic anhydride, and the mixture is rapidly heated to boiling. The solution is immediately filtered through a large fluted filter and the filtrate cooled for two to three hours in running water. The yellow flakes of diphenylquinone are collected and washed first with water and then with 150 ml. of 50% ethanol. The dried material weighs 51 g. and melts at 210–212°. It is pure enough for most purposes, but a single recrystallization from benzene or glacial acetic acid yields the pure substance melting at 214°. An additional 7 g. of pure material may be obtained from the mother liquors; thus the total yield is 58 g. (72%; this figure is based on the fact that three moles of quinone are required to give one mole of diphenylquinone, if no oxidizing agent other than quinone is present).

3,5-Dibromotoluquinone.[26] A solution of 10 g. of tribromo-*m*-cresol [22] (m.p. 82–83°) in 500 ml. of 70% acetic acid is heated to 70°, 3.2 g. of chromic anhydride is added, and the temperature is maintained at 70–75° for ten minutes. After the addition of 1.5 l. of water the yellow solid is collected and recrystallized from dilute ethanol. There is obtained 6.2 g. (77%) of quinone melting at 114–115°.

---

* The amount of chromic anhydride required may be determined by boiling 1-g. samples in 25 ml. of *glacial* acetic acid with various amounts of chromic anhydride for *two to three* minutes, filtering, and cooling. The proper amount of oxidizing agent gives yellow quinone not contaminated with green quinhydrone. Excess oxidizing agent destroys the desired quinone.

TABLE II *

ALKYL AND ARYL QUINONES AND THEIR SUBSTITUTED DERIVATIVES

Quinone	Substance Oxidized	Oxidizing Agent	Yield	References†
Allylquinone	2-Allyl-4-aminophenol	FeCl₃	87%	83
Allyltrimethylquinone	2-Allyl-4-amino-3,5,6-trimethylphenol	FeCl₃	75%	83
2-Amyl-5-octylquinone	2-Amyl-5-octylhydro-quinone dimethyl ether	HNO₃ (AcOH)	—	130
n-Amylquinone	n-Amylhydroquinone	HNO₃ (AcOH)	—	129
5-Benzyl-o-xyloquinone	5-Benzyl-o-xylohydro-quinone	Fe₂(SO₄)₃ (H₂SO₄)	75% (cr.)	152
2,5-bis-(2,4-Dimethyl-phenyl)-quinone	2,5-bis-(2,4-Dimethyl-phenyl)-hydroquinone	Quinone	90%	107
2,5-bis-(2,4-Dimethyl-phenyl)-3,6-dibromo-quinone	2,5-bis-(2,4-Dimethyl-phenyl)-3,6-dibromo-hydroquinone	Quinone	70–80%	107
2,5-bis-(2,5-Dimethyl phenyl)-quinone	Quinhydrone mixture from quinone and p-xylene	FeCl₃	—	113
2,5-bis-(3-Bromomesi-tyl)-3,6-dibromo-quinone	2,5-bis-(3-Bromomesityl)-3,6-dibromohydro-quinone	Quinone	70–92%	108, 111
2,6-bis-(o-(m- and p-)Chlorophenyl)-quinone	2,6-bis-(o-(m- and p-)Chlorophenyl)-4-nitro-phenol	Pb(OAc)₄ (AcOH)	—	142
	2,6-bis-(o-(m- and p-)Chlorophenyl)-4-amino-phenol	Aqueous chromic acid	—	142
5-tert-Butyltolu-quinone	5-tert-Butyl-2-methyl-phenol	HNO₂	—	153
	4-tert-Butyl-3-methoxy-toluene	HNO₃ (sp. gr. 1.4)	22%	154
2,3-Diallylquinone	2,3-Diallylhydroquinone	Ag₂O	96% (cr.)	117
2,5-Diallylquinone	2,5-Diallylhydroquinone	Ag₂O	64%	117
2,5-Di-tert-amylquinone	2,5-Di-tert-amylhydro-quinone	FeCl₃	—	155
2,6-Dibenzylquinone	2,6-Dibenzyl-4-amino-phenol	FeCl₃	5%	215
2,5-Di-tert-butylqui-none	Hydroquinone and tert-butyl chloride	FeCl₃	—	156
	p-Di-tert-butylbenzene	CrO₃ (AcOH)	Poor	157
2,5-Diethylquinone	2,5-Diethylphenol	H₂O₂ (AcOH)	—	158
	2,5-Diethyl-4-amino-phenol	K₂Cr₂O₇ (H₂SO₄)	—	158
2,6-Diethylquinone	3,5-Diethyl-4-amino-phenol	HNO₂ (H₂SO₄)	70%	91b
	2,6-Diethyl-4-nitrophenol	Pb(OAc)₄ (AcOH)	Good	141
2,5-Diphenylquinone	Condensation product of quinone and benzene	CrO₃ (AcOH)	72% (o.)	110 (y.), 112
2,5-Diphenyl-3,6-dibromoquinone	2,5-Diphenyl-3,6-di-bromohydroquinone	Quinone	85%	110
2,6-Diphenylquinone	2,6-Diphenyl-4-nitro-phenol	Pb(OAc)₄ (AcOH)	Good	141
	2,6-Diphenyl-4-amino-phenol	K₂Cr₂O₇ (H₂SO₄)	81% (o.)	158a (y.), 159

* See p. 315 for explanation of system and abbreviations in tables.
† References 152–247 are listed on pp. 336–338.

TABLE II*—Continued

ALKYL AND ARYL QUINONES AND THEIR SUBSTITUTED DERIVATIVES

Quinone	Substance Oxidized	Oxidizing Agent	Yield	References†
2,5-Di-p-tolylquinone	2,5-Di-p-tolylhydro-quinone	Air and H_2O_2	87.5%	112
2,6-Di-o-tolylquinone	2,6-Di-o-tolyl-4-amino-phenol	$Na_2Cr_2O_7$ (H_2SO_4)	Good	141
2,6-Di-o-(m- and p-) tolylquinone	2,6-Di-o-(m- and p-) tolyl-4-nitrophenol	$Pb(OAc)_4$ (AcOH)	Good	141
Dodecylquinone	Dodecylhydroquinone	$FeCl_3$	—	116
		$Na_2Cr_2O_7$ (H_2SO_4)	—	77
Duroquinone (tetra-methylquinone)	Diaminodurene	$FeCl_3$	95% (o.)	95, 99, 100, 101(y.)
	Durenol	$Na_2Cr_2O_7$ (H_2SO_4)	50%	76
	Aminodurenol	$FeCl_3$	60% (c.)	33, 76(y.)
	Durene	H_2O_2 (AcOH)	34%	159a
Ethylquinone	Ethylhydroquinone	$Na_2Cr_2O_7$ (H_2SO_4)	—	160
	Ethylbenzene	Electrolytic ox.	—	137
	2-Ethylphenol	Electrolytic ox.	—	137
		$K_2Cr_2O_7$ (AcOH)	—	161
5-Ethyltoluquinone	2-Methyl-5-ethylphenol	$K_2Cr_2O_7$ (AcOH)	—	162
6-Ethyltoluquinone	2-Methyl-4-nitro-6-ethylphenol	$Pb(OAc)_4$ (AcOH)	Good	141
Ethyltrimethylquinone	Ethyltrimethyl-p-phenylenediamine	$FeCl_3$	—	103, 104
5-Ethyl-o-xyloquinone	2,3-Dimethyl-6-ethyl-4-aminophenol	$FeCl_3$	86% (c.)	84
3-Ethyl-m-xyloquinone	3,5-Dimethyl-2-ethyl-4-aminophenol	$FeCl_3$	66% (c.)	84
3-Ethyl-p-xyloquinone	2,5-Dimethyl-3-ethyl-hydroquinone	$FeCl_3$	73% (o.)	84
Hendecylquinone	Hendecylhydroquinone	$FeCl_3$	—	116
5-Hendecyltoluquinone	2- and 3-Amino-4-hendec-yltoluene	$Na_2Cr_2O_7$ (H_2SO_4)	22%	77
Hexadecylquinone	Hexadecylhydroquinone	$FeCl_3$	—	116
Isopropylquinone	m-Isopropylphenol or o-isopropylphenol	$K_2Cr_2O_7$ (AcOH)	—	163
5-(3-Bromomesityl)-3,6-dibromotoluqui-none	5-(3-Bromomesityl)-3,6-dibromotoluhydro-quinone	Quinone	83%	164
5-Nonyltoluquinone	2- and 3-Amino-4-nonyl-toluene	$Na_2Cr_2O_7$ (H_2SO_4)	17%	77
Octadecylquinone	Octadecylhydroquinone	$FeCl_3$	—	116
Phenylquinone	2-Phenyl-4-aminophenol	$Na_2Cr_2O_7$ (H_2SO_4)	62.5% (o.)	155a(y.), 163a
n-Propylquinone	3-Propyl-4-aminophenol	$FeCl_3$	80% (o.) (hydr.)	164a
3-Propyl-5,6-dibromo-toluquinone	2-Methyl-3-propyl-5,6-dibromo-p-phenylene-diamine	CrO_3 (AcOH)	—	96
5-Propyltoluquinone	2-Methyl-5-propylphenol	$K_2Cr_2O_7$ (AcOH)	—	217
5-Propyl-3,6-dibromo-toluquinone	2-Methyl-5-propyl-3,6-dibromo-p-phenylene-diamine	CrO_3 (AcOH)	—	96
6-Propyl-3,5-dibromo-toluquinone	2-Methyl-6-propyl-3,5-dibromo-p-phenylene-diamine	CrO_3 (AcOH)	—	96

* See p. 315 for explanation of system and abbreviations in tables.
* References 152–247 are listed on pp. 336–338.

TABLE II—*Continued*

ALKYL AND ARYL QUINONES AND THEIR SUBSTITUTED DERIVATIVES

Quinone	Substance Oxidized	Oxidizing Agent	Yield	References*
	Trimethyl-*p*-phenylene-diamine	$FeCl_3$	92–96%	97, 102 (y.)
	Pseudocumenol-3	$Na_2Cr_2O_7$ (H_2SO_4)	50%	76
Pseudocumoquinone	Pseudocumenol-6	$Na_2Cr_2O_7$ (H_2SO_4)	None	76
(trimethylquinone)	4-Aminopseudocumenol-6	$Fe_2(SO_4)_3$	95% (c.)	33, 34 (y.), 76
	2,3,4,6-Tetramethyl-aniline	CrO_3 (H_2SO_4)	—	37
Chloropseudocumo-quinone	2-Chloro-3,5,6-trimethyl-*p*-phenylenediamine	$FeCl_3$	—	97
Bromopseudocumo-quinone	2-Bromo-3,5,6-trimethyl-*p*-phenylenediamine	$FeCl_3$	82% (o.)	98
	Bromopseudocumohy-droquinone	$Fe_2(SO_4)_3$	68% (o.)	164*b*
Quinone (1,4-benzo-quinone)	Various phenols, amines, and aminophenols	Consult references 3, 8, 43, 62, 79, 80, 122, 136, 137, 139, 140, 150, 151, 165–169*b*		
Fluoroquinone	2-Fluoro-4-hydroxy-aniline	$FeCl_3$	40%	170
		$Na_2Cr_2O_7$ (H_2SO_4)	60%	170
	Chlorohydroquinone	MnO_2 (H_2SO_4)	56%	25
Chloroquinone		$Na_2Cr_2O_7$ (H_2SO_4)	88%	25, 120, 121, 171, 172 (y.)
	2-Chloro-4-aminophenol	$K_2Cr_2O_7$ (H_2SO_4)	68% (o.)	89 (y.), 173
2,3-Dichloroquinone	2,3-Dichlorohydro-quinone	MnO_2 (H_2SO_4)	88%	25 (y.), 174
		CrO_3 (AcOH)	—	171
	2,5-Dichlorohydro-quinone	Conc. HNO_3	—	120
2,5-Dichloroquinone		$K_2Cr_2O_7$ (H_2SO_4)	30.5–36.5% (o.)	25, 27 (y.), 121
	2,5-Dichlorohydroqui-none dimethyl ether	Fuming HNO_3	—	175
	2,4,6-Trichlorophenol	CrO_3 (AcOH)	69% 27%	24, 25 (y.), 27 15
		HNO_3 (EtOH)	49%	27 (y.), 176
		PbO_2 (benzene)	14%	15
	4-Bromo-2,4,6-trichloro-benzenone	Fuming HNO_3	—	177
	4,4-Dibromo-2,6-di-chlorobenzenone	Fuming HNO_3	—	178
2,6-Dichloroquinone	2,6-Dichloro-4-fluoro-phenol (and methyl ether)	HNO_3 (sp. gr. 1.5)	—	179
	2,6-Dichloro-4-amino-phenol	$K_2Cr_2O_7$ (H_2SO_4)	89.5%	89
	2,6-Dichloro-4-nitro-phenol	HNO_3 (sp. gr. 1.5)	Poor	180
	2,6-Dichlorohydroqui-none	$FeCl_3$	—	49
2,6-Dichloro-3-fluoro-quinone	2,4,6-Trichloro-3-fluoro-phenol	HNO_3 (sp. gr. 1.5)	—	181

* References 152–247 are listed on pp. 336–338.

TABLE II *—Continued

ALKYL AND ARYL QUINONES AND THEIR SUBSTITUTED DERIVATIVES

Quinone	Substance Oxidized	Oxidizing Agent	Yield	References†
Trichloroquinone	p-Hydroxybenzenesulfonic acid	$KClO_3$, HCl	—	182
	2,5-Dichlorohydroquinone	Cl_2	—	27
	Aniline	Electrolysis in 20% HCl	—	138
	p-Phenylenediamine	$KClO_3$, HCl	—	183
Chloranil (tetrachloroquinone)	p-Hydroxybenzenesulfonic acid	$KClO_3$, HCl	—	182
	2,5-Dichlorohydroquinone	Cl_2	—	27
	p-Phenylenediamine	$KClO_3$, HCl	—	183
	Phenol	HNO_3, Cl_2	42.5%	131
	Aniline	Electrolysis in 10% HCl	—	138
	Pentachlorophenol	$ClSO_3H$, Cl_2	90%	184
	Hydroquinonesulfonic acid	Cl_2	—	216
	Quinone or hydroquinone	Cl_2, HCl	Nearly quant.	184
Bromoquinone	Bromohydroquinone	Ag_2O	76%	59
		$FeCl_3$	—	119
2-Bromo-5-chloroquinone	5-Bromo-2-chloroaniline	MnO_2 (H_2SO_4)	—	78, 79
	2-Bromo-5-chlorohydroquinone	$FeCl_3$	—	185
		HNO_3	—	120
	2-Bromo-6-chloro-4-aminophenol	MnO_2 (H_2SO_4)	Nearly quant.	78 (y.), 79
2-Bromo-6-chloroquinone	2,4,4-Tribromo-6-chlorobenzenone	Fuming HNO_3	—	177, 186
	2,4-Dibromo-6-chlorophenol	HNO_3 (sp. gr. 1.5)	10.5%	27
3-Bromo-2,5-dichloroquinone	3-Bromo-2,5-dichlorohydroquinone	$K_2Cr_2O_7$ (H_2SO_4)	—	27
	4,6-Dibromo-2,5-dichlorophenol	Fuming HNO_3	—	187
3-Bromo-2,6-dichloroquinone	3-Bromo-2,6-dichlorohydroquinone	$K_2Cr_2O_7$ (H_2SO_4)	—	27
	3,4-Dibromo-2,6-dichlorophenol	Fuming HNO_3	—	178
Bromotrichloroquinone	Bromotrichlorohydroquinone	Conc. HNO_3	—	120
	3,4-Dibromo-2,5,6-trichlorophenol	Fuming HNO_3	—	188
2,5-Dibromoquinone	2,5-Dibromohydroquinone	Br_2, H_2O	—	189
		$FeCl_3$	—	119
	2,5-Dibromohydroquinone dimethyl ether	Fuming HNO_3	—	128
	2,5-Dibromo-p-phenylenediamine	$K_2Cr_2O_7$ (H_2SO_4)	—	190
	2,5-Dibromo-4-aminophenol	$K_2Cr_2O_7$ (H_2SO_4)	—	191

* See p. 315 for explanation of system and abbreviations in tables.
† References 152–247 are listed on pp. 336–338.

TABLE II—*Continued*

ALKYL AND ARYL QUINONES AND THEIR SUBSTITUTED DERIVATIVES

Quinone	Substance Oxidized	Oxidizing Agent	Yield	References*
2,6-Dibromoquinone	2,4,6-Tribromophenol	HNO_3	Poor	27 (y.), 120
	2,4,4,6-Tetrabromo-cyclohexadienone	Fuming HNO_3	—	192
		$Pb(OAc)_2$	—	193
		$AgNO_3$	—	194
	2,6-Dibromoaniline	$K_2Cr_2O_7$ (H_2SO_4)	Poor	149
	3,5-Dibromosulfanilic acid	$K_2Cr_2O_7$ (H_2SO_4)	28%	149
	2,6-Dibromo-4-amino-phenol	$K_2Cr_2O_7$, (H_2SO_4)	80%	88 (y.), 149
	2,6-Dibromo-4-bromo (chloro and fluoro) phenol	HNO_3 (sp. gr. 1.5)	—	195
2,6-Dibromo-3-fluoro-quinone	2,4,6-Tribromo-3-fluoro-phenol	HNO_3 (sp. gr. 1.5)	—	181
2,6-Dibromo-3-chloro-quinone	2,4,6-Tribromo-3-chloro-phenol	Fuming HNO_3	—	188
2,3- or 2,5-Dibromo-6-chloroquinone	2,3- or 2,5 Dibromo-4,6-dichlorophenol	Fuming HNO_3	—	178
2,5-Dibromo-3,6-di-chloroquinone †	2,6-Dichloro-4-nitro-phenol	Br_2, H_2O	—	28
2,6-Dibromo-3,5-di-chloroquinone	2,6-Dibromo-3,4,5-tri-chlorophenol	Fuming HNO_3	—	196
	3,5-Dibromo-2,6-di-chloro-4-chloro (bromo and iodo) phenol	Fuming HNO_3	—	197
Tribromoquinone	Tribromohydroquinone	$FeCl_3$ (ethanol)	—	119
	2,3,6-Tribromo-4-bromo (and chloro) phenol	Fuming HNO_3	—	178, 198
	2-Chloro-4-bromo (and chloro)-3,5,6-tribromo-phenol	Fuming HNO_3	—	197
Tribromochloroqui-none	Tribromochlorohydro-quinone	$K_2Cr_2O_7$ (H_2SO_4)	—	199
	2,4-Dichloro-6-nitro-phenol	Br_2, H_2O	—	28
Bromanil (tetra-bromoquinone)	Hydroquinone	Br_2, HNO_3	—	27, 200
	Phenol	Br_2, HNO_3	32%	131
	p-Phenylenediamine	Br_2, HNO_3	69–71.5%	132
	2,3,5,6-Tetrabromo-4-chlorophenol	Fuming HNO_3	—	197
	Tribromohydroquinone dimethyl ether	Fuming HNO_3	Poor	128
	2-Bromo-4-chloro-6-nitrophenol	Br_2, H_2O	—	28
	2,6-Dibromo-4-nitro-phenol	Br_2, H_2O	—	201
	2,4-Dibromo-6-nitro-phenol	Br_2, H_2O	—	201
	2,6-Dibromo-4-diazo-benzene-1-oxide	Br_2 (AcOH)	98%	207

* References 152–247 are listed on pp. 336–338.
† Concerning the structure of this quinone, see p. 310.

TABLE II*—*Continued*

ALKYL AND ARYL QUINONES AND THEIR SUBSTITUTED DERIVATIVES

Quinone	Substance Oxidized	Oxidizing Agent	Yield	References†
Iodoquinone	3-Iodo-4-aminophenol	$Na_2Cr_2O_7$ (H_2SO_4)	95% (cr.)	127
		$Fe_2(SO_4)_3$	—	91
2-Iodo-6-chloro-3,5-dibromoquinone	2-Iodo-4-chloro (and iodo)-6 chloro-3,5-dibromophenol	Fuming HNO_3	—	197
	3,5-Diiodo-4-hydroxy-benzenesulfonic acid	CrO_3 (H_2SO_4)	Poor	143
	p-Diacetoxybenzene	KIO_3 (H_2SO_4)	—	127, 202
	2,6-Diiodo-4-fluorophenol	HNO_3 (sp. gr. 1.5)	—	179
	Triiodophenol	Fuming HNO_3	Poor	127
2,6-Diiodoquinone		CrO_3 (AcOH)	Poor	203
	2,6-Diiodo-4-amino-phenol	$K_2Cr_2O_7$ (H_2SO_4)	Nearly quant.	204
	2,6-Diiodohydroquinone	$FeCl_3$	—	204
	2,6-Diiodo-p-phenylene-diamine	Chromic acid	—	205
2,6-Diiodo-3-fluoro-quinone	2,4,6-Triiodo-3-fluoro-phenol	HNO_3 (sp. gr. 1.5)	—	181
2,6-Diiodo-3-chloro-quinone	2,4,6-Triiodo-3-chloro-phenol	Fuming HNO_3	—	188
2,6-Diiodo-3-chloro-5-bromoquinone	2,4,6-Triiodo-3-chloro-5-bromophenol	Fuming HNO_3	—	188
2,6-Diiodo-3,5-dichloro-quinone	2,4,6-Triiodo-3,5-dichlorophenol	Fuming HNO_3	—	206
2,6-Diiodo-3,5-di-bromoquinone	2,6-Diiodo-4-chloro-3,5-dibromophenol	Fuming HNO_3	—	197
	2,4,6-Triiodo-3,5-dibromophenol	Fuming HNO_3	—	208
2- (or 6-) Nitro-3-chloro-5-bromoquinone	2,4-Dibromo-6-chloro-phenyl acetate	HNO_3 (H_2SO_4)	—	210
2-Nitro-3,5-dichloro-quinone	2,4,6-Trichlorophenyl propionate	HNO_3 (H_2SO_4)	—	209
2-Nitro-3,5-dibromo-quinone	2,4,6-Tribromophenyl propionate	HNO_3 (H_2SO_4)	—	209
2-Nitro-3,5,6-tribromo-quinone	2,3,4,6-Tetrabromo-phenyl propionate	Fuming HNO_3 (H_2SO_4)	—	134
n-Tetradecylquinone	Tetradecylhydroquinone	$FeCl_3$	—	116
Tetraethylquinone	Tetraethyl-p-phenylene-diamine	$FeCl_3$	92%	104 (y.), 105, 106
Thymoquinone (2-isopropyl-5-methylquinone)	4-Thymolsulfonic acid	MnO_2 (H_2SO_4)	25%	4 (y.), 211
	4-Aminothymol	HNO_2	73–80% (o.)	92
	Thymol	Electrolysis	—	136
3-Chlorothymo-quinone	3-Chlorothymohydro-quinone	$FeCl_3$	—	118
	4,6-Dichlorothymol	$Na_2Cr_2O_7$ (AcOH)	—	147
6-Chlorothymoquinone	4,6-Dichlorocarvacrol	$Na_2Cr_2O_7$ (AcOH)	—	147
3-Bromothymoqui-none	3-Bromothymohydroqui-none	$FeCl_3$	—	118
	4,6-Dibromothymol	$Na_2Cr_2O_7$ (AcOH)	—	146
	6-Bromo-4-thymolsul-fonic acid	$Na_2Cr_2O_7$ (AcOH)	—	146
	Thymohydroquinone	Br_2	—	212
	6-Bromo-4-aminothymol	$FeCl_3$	—	146

* See p. 315 for explanation of system and abbreviations in tables.
† References 152–247 are listed on pp. 336–338.

TABLE II—*Continued*

ALKYL AND ARYL QUINONES AND THEIR SUBSTITUTED DERIVATIVES

Quinone	Substance Oxidized	Oxidizing Agent	Yield	References*
6-Bromothymoqui-none	6-Bromo-4-carvacrolsul-fonic acid	Chromic acid	—	146
	6-Bromo-4-aminocarva-crol	Chromic acid	—	146
	4,6-Dibromocarvacrol	$Na_2Cr_2O_7$ (AcOH)	—	147
3-Bromo-6-chlorothy-moquinone	3-Bromo-6-chlorothymo-hydroquinone	$FeCl_3$	—	118
3,6-Dibromothymo-quinone	Thymohydroquinone	Br_2	—	212
	3,6-Dibromo-2-methyl-5-isopropyl-p-phenylene-diamine	Chromic acid	—	96
3-Iodothymoquinone	6-Iodo-4-thymolsulfonic acid	Chromic acid	—	144
	4,6-Diiodothymol	CrO_3 (AcOH)	—	213
6-Iodothymoquinone	6-Iodo-4-carvacrolsul-fonic acid	$Na_2Cr_2O_7$ (H_2SO_4)	50% (o.)	145, 147 (y.)
Toluquinone (2-methylquinone)	4-Hydroxy-o-toluidine	$Fe_2(SO_4)_3$	56%	33
	3-Methylsulfanilic acid	MnO_2 (H_2SO_4)	Trace	148
	o-Xylene	Electrolysis	12%	135
	Toluene	Electrolysis	Trace	136
	4-Hydroxy-m-toluidine	$Fe_2(SO_4)_3$	25% (c.)	33
	Toluhydroquinone	$Na_2Cr_2O_7$ (H_2SO_4)	—	219
	4-Amino-o- (and m-) xylene	Chromate (H_2SO_4)	Poor	37
	2-Methyl-p-phenylenedi-amine	MnO_2 (H_2SO_4), $Na_2Cr_2O_7$ (H_2SO_4), or Fe^{+++}	—	5
	o-Toluidine	MnO_2 (H_2SO_4)	48%	79, 80 (y.)
		$K_2Cr_2O_7$ (H_2SO_4)	86% (cr.)	37, 122 (y.)
	m-Toluidine	$Na_2Cr_2O_7$ (H_2SO_4)	Good	37
3-Chlorotoluquinone	3-Chloro-4-hydroxy-o-toluidine	Dichromate	60%	87
		$FeCl_3$	—	87
	5-Chlorotoluhydro-quinone	$FeCl_3$ or $K_2Cr_2O_7$ (H_2SO_4)	—	122
5-Chlorotoluquinone	5-Chloro-4-amino-o-toluidine	$K_2Cr_2O_7$ (H_2SO_4)	32%	220
	5-Chloro-4-amino-o-cresol	$FeCl_3$	60%	87
		MnO_2 (H_2SO_4)	80% ±	90
	5-Chloro-4-hydroxy-o-toluidine	MnO_2 (H_2SO_4)	80% ±	90
6-Chlorotoluquinone	4,6-Dichloro-o-cresol	$K_2Cr_2O_7$ (H_2SO_4)	Good	221
		$Na_2Cr_2O_7$ (AcOH)	—	222
	6-Chloro-4-hydroxy-o-toluidine	$Na_2Cr_2O_7$ (H_2SO_4)	—	223
	6-Chloro-4-amino-o-cresol	$K_2Cr_2O_7$ (H_2SO_4)	—	224
	6-Chloro-4-bromo-o-cresol	CrO_3 (dil. AcOH)	—	23
3,5-Dichlorotoluqui-none	2,4,6-Trichloro-m-cresol	$Na_2Cr_2O_7$ (H_2SO_4)	72% (cr.)	87 (y.), 221
	2,6-Dichloro-4-bromo-m-cresol	$Na_2Cr_2O_7$ (H_2SO_4)	65%	126
	2,6-Dichloro-4-amino-m-cresol	$Na_2Cr_2O_7$ (H_2SO_4)	—	123

* References 152–247 are listed on pp. 336–338.

TABLE II*—Continued

ALKYL AND ARYL QUINONES AND THEIR SUBSTITUTED DERIVATIVES

Quinone	Substance Oxidized	Oxidizing Agent	Yield	References†
3,6-Dichlorotoluqui-none	3,6-Dichlorotoluhydro-quinone ‡	—	—	124
5,6-Dichlorotoluqui-none	5,6-Dichlorotoluhydro-quinone ‡	$Na_2Cr_2O_7$ (H_2SO_4)	—	122, 124
	5,6-Dichloro-4-amino-o-cresol	$Na_2Cr_2O_7$ (H_2SO_4)	—	125
	Trichlorotoluhydro-quinone	—	—	223
	Crude o- and m-cresol-sulfonic acids	$KClO_3$, HCl	—	182
	o-Toluidine	$Na_2Cr_2O_7$, HCl	38–40%	225
Trichlorotoluquinone	3,5,6-Trichloro-4-amino-o-toluidine	Chromic acid	—	227
	3-Methylsulfanilic acid	$KClO_3$, HCl	—	148
	o-Cresol	$KClO_3$, HCl	—	226
	m-Cresol	Cl_2 (sunlight)	—	228
	4,6-Dichloro-o-cresol	Aqua regia	16%	229
	2,4,6-Trichloro-m-cresol	Aqua regia	25%	229
Tetrachlorotoluquinone	Beechwood creosote	$KClO_3$, HCl	—	230
5-Bromotoluquinone	5-Bromotoluhydro-quinone	$FeCl_3$ or $K_2Cr_2O_7$ (H_2SO_4)	—	122, 231
	5-Bromo-4-hydroxy-o-toluidine	MnO_2 (H_2SO_4) $FeCl_3$	80% ± —	90 86
	5-Bromo-4-amino-o-cresol	MnO_2 (H_2SO_4) $FeCl_3$	80% ± —	90 86
6-Bromotoluquinone	4,6-Dibromo-o-cresol	$Na_2Cr_2O_7$ (AcOH) CrO_3 (dil. AcOH)	— —	222 23
	6-Bromo-4-amino-o-cresol	$Na_2Cr_2O_7$ (H_2SO_4)	—	68
	6-Bromo-o-cresol-4-sulfonic acid	CrO_3	—	23
5-Bromo-3-chloro-toluquinone	5-Bromo-3-chloro-4-hydroxy-o-toluidine	$Na_2Cr_2O_7$ (H_2SO_4)	97%	123
5-Bromo-6-chlorotolu-quinone	5-Bromo-6-chlorotolu-hydroquinone ‡	$K_2Cr_2O_7$ (H_2SO_4)	—	122
6-Bromo-5-chloro-toluquinone	6-Bromo-5-chloro-toluhydroquinone ‡	$K_2Cr_2O_7$ (H_2SO_4)	—	122
5-Bromo-3,6-dichloro-toluquinone	5-Bromo-3,6-dichloro-toluhydroquinone	HNO_3 (AcOH)	—	68
3,5-Dibromotoluqui-none	2,4,6-Tribromo-m-cresol	CrO_3 (70% AcOH)	77%	22, 26 (y.), 133
	3,5-Dibromo-4-hydroxy-o-toluidine	$Na_2Cr_2O_7$ (H_2SO_4) $FeCl_3$	— Good	87 22
	2,6-Dibromo-m-cresol-4-sulfonic acid	CrO_3 (H_2SO_4)	Nearly quant.	232
3,5-Dibromo-6-chloro-toluquinone	3,5-Dibromo-4,6-di-chloro-o-cresol	Fuming HNO_3	—	233

* See p. 315 for explanation of system and abbreviations in tables.
† References 152–247 are listed on pp. 336–338.
‡ For a discussion of the probable structure of this hydroquinone, see p. 322.

TABLE II—*Continued*

ALKYL AND ARYL QUINONES AND THEIR SUBSTITUTED DERIVATIVES

Quinone	Substance Oxidized	Oxidizing Agent	Yield	References*
Tribromotoluquinone	3,5,6-Tribromo-4-chloro-o-cresol	Fuming HNO_3	—	233
	Tetrabromo-o-cresol	Fuming HNO_3	—	133, 234
	3,5,6-Tribromo-4-amino-o-cresol	$FeCl_3$	—	234
	2-Methyl-3,5,6-tribromo-4-hydroxybenzyl alcohol (and diacetate)	HNO_3	—	235
	2-Methyl-3,5,6-tribromo-4-hydroxybenzaldehyde	HNO_3 (sp. gr. 1.4)	—	236
	Tetrabromo-m-cresol	HNO_3 (sp. gr. 1.4)	—	236
	Tribromotoluhydroquinone	HNO_3	—	79
	2-Hydroxy-p-toluic acid	Br_2 (AcOH)	—	218
	2-Hydroxy-5-nitro-p-toluic acid	Br_2 (AcOH)	—	218
Tetrabromotoluquinone	2,4-bis(Acetoxymethyl)-3,5,6-tribromophenol	HNO_3	—	237
Pentabromotoluquinone	1-Dibromomethyl-3,5,6-tribromo-4-hydroxybenzaldehyde	HNO_3	—	236
5-Iodotoluquinone	5-Iodo-4-amino-o-cresol	MnO_2 (H_2SO_4)	80% ±	90
	5-Iodo-4-hydroxy-o-toluidine	MnO_2 (H_2SO_4)	80% ±	90
6-Iodotoluquinone	6-Iodo-o-cresol-4-sulfonic acid	CrO_3 (H_2SO_4)	20%	143, 144 (y.)
6-Iodo-3,5-dibromo-toluquinone	4,6-Diiodo-3,5-dibromo-o-cresol	Fuming HNO_3	—	233
3,5-Diiodotoluquinone	2,6-Diiodo-m-cresol-4-sulfonic acid	Chromic acid	15%	144
3-Nitrotoluquinone	3-Nitro-4-hydroxy-o-toluidine	PbO_2 (H_2SO_4)	—	238
3-Nitro-5- (or 6-)chloro-toluquinone	3-Nitro-4-hydroxy-o-toluidine	$Ca(OCl)_2$, HCl	—	238
3- (or 5-)Nitro-5- (or 3-)chlorotoluquinone	2-Chloro-p-cresol	HNO_3 (sp. gr. 1.5)	—	35
	6-Nitro-2-chloro-p-cresol	HNO_3 (sp. gr. 1.5)	—	35
3-(or 5-)Nitro-5-(or 3-)bromotoluquinone	2-Bromo-p-cresol	HNO_3 (sp. gr. 1.5)	—	36
	6-Nitro-2-bromo-p-cresol	HNO_3 (sp. gr. 1.5)	—	36
3-(or 5-)Nitro-5 (or 3), 6-dibromotoluquinone	6-Nitro-2,3- or 5-dibromo-p-cresol	HNO_3 (sp. gr. 1.5)	—	36
Triphenylquinone	Triphenylhydroquinone	CrO_3 (AcOH)	66%	238a
o-Xyloquinone (2,3-dimethylquinone)	vic-o-Xylidin	MnO_2 (H_2SO_4)	—	239
		$Na_2Cr_2O_7$ (H_2SO_4)	33%	75 (y.), 240
	4-Hydroxy-vic-o-xylidin	$Fe_2(SO_4)_3$	61%	85, 240a
		MnO_2 (H_2SO_4)	54%	240a
Dichloro-o-xyloquinone	2,3-Dichloro-5,6-dimethyl-p-phenylenediamine	CrO_3 (AcOH)	—	96

* References 152–247 are listed on pp. 336–338.

TABLE II*—Continued

ALKYL AND ARYL QUINONES AND THEIR SUBSTITUTED DERIVATIVES

Quinone	Substance Oxidized	Oxidizing Agent	Yield	References
m-Xyloquinone (2,6-dimethylquinone)	4-Amino-3,5-dimethyl-phenol	MnO_2 (H_2SO_4)	—	241
		$FeCl_3$ or $Fe_2(SO_4)_3$	74.5% (c.)	33, 76 (y.)
	2,4,6-Trimethylaniline	CrO_3 (H_2SO_4)	40%	37
	bis-(3,5-Dimethyl-4-hydroxyphenyl)-methane	CrO_3 (AcOH)	—	242
	o-Xylene	Electrolysis	1.3%	135
	2,6-Dimethyl-4-nitro-phenol	$Pb(OAc)_4$	Good	141
	3,5-Dimethylaniline	$Na_2Cr_2O_7$ (H_2SO_4)	30%	240
Chloro-*m*-xyloquinone	4-Amino-3,5-dimethyl-phenol	$FeCl_3$	—	33
Dichloro-*m*-xyloquinone	2,6-Dimethyl-3,5-di-chloro-*p*-phenylene-diamine	CrO_3 (dil. AcOH)	—	243
Bromo-*m*-xyloquinone	Bromo-*m*-xylohydro-quinone	$Fe_2(SO_4)_3$	84%	243a
Dibromo-*m*-xyloqui-none	2,4,6-Trimethylphenol	Br_2, H_2O	—	244
	2,4,6-Tribromo-3,5-dimethylphenol	Fuming HNO_3	—	245
p-Xyloquinone (2,5-dimethylquinone)	4-Amino-2,5-dimethyl-phenol	$FeCl_3$	82% (c.)	76, 84 (y.), 245a
	2,5-Dimethyl-*p*-phenyl-enediamine	$Na_2Cr_2O_7$ (H_2SO_4)	—	168, 246
	2,4,5-Trimethylaniline	CrO_3 (H_2SO_4)	40%	37
		MnO_2 (H_2SO_4)	35%	81
	2,5-Dimethylaniline	$K_2Cr_2O_7$ (H_2SO_4)	55%	168, 246, 247 (y.)
Chloro-*p*-xyloquinone	Chloro-*p*-xylohydro-quinone	$FeCl_3$, CrO_3 or HNO_3	—	214
Dichloro-*p*-xyloquinone	Dichloro-*p*-xylohydro-quinone	$FeCl_3$, CrO_3 or HNO_3	—	214
Dibromo-*p*-xyloquinone	*p*-Xylohydroquinone	Br_2, then HNO_3	88%	245a

* See p. 315 for explanation of system and abbreviations in tables.

REFERENCES TO TABLE II

[152] Smith and Tess, *J. Am. Chem. Soc.*, **66**, 1528 (1944).

[153] Battegay and Haeffely, *Bull. soc. chim. France*, [4] **35**, 988 (1924).

[154] Zeïde and Dubinin, *J. Gen. Chem. U.S.S.R.*, **2**, 455 (1932) [*C. A.*, **27**, 961 (1933)].

[155] Königs and Mai, *Ber.*, **25**, 2653 (1892).

[156] Gurewitsch, *Ber.*, **32**, 2427 (1899).

[157] Boedtker, *Bull. soc. chim. France*, [3] **31**, 969 (1904).

[158] Henderson and Boyd, *J. Chem. Soc.*, **97**, 1663 (1910).

[158a] Borsche, *Ber.*, **32**, 2937 (1899); *Ann.*, **312**, 220 (1900).

[159] Hill, *Am. Chem. J.*, **24**, 5 (1900).

[159a] Arnold and Larson, *J. Org. Chem.*, **5**, 250 (1940).

[160] Clemmensen, *Ber.*, **47**, 56 (1914).

[161] Bayrac, *Bull. soc. chim. France*, [3] **11**, 1131 (1894).

[162] Bayrac, *Bull. soc. chim. France*, [3] **13**, 898 (1895).

[163] Bayrac, *Bull. soc. chim. France*, [3] **13**, 984 (1895).
[163a] Hill and Hale, *Am. Chem. J.*, **33**, 11 (1905).
[164] Hill and Adams, *J. Am. Chem. Soc.*, **53**, 3457 (1931).
[164a] Baddeley and Kenner, *J. Chem. Soc.*, **1934**, 633.
[164b] Smith and Wiley, *J. Am. Chem. Soc.*, **68**, 889 (1946).
[165] Wöhler, *Ann.*, **51**, 152 (1844).
[166] Craven and Duncan, *J. Chem. Soc.*, **127**, 1489 (1925).
[167] Hofmann, *Jahresber.*, 415 (1863).
[168] Nietzki, *Ann.*, **215**, 127 (1882).
[169] Seyda, *Ber.*, **16**, 687 (1883).
[169a] Billman, Wolnak, and Barnes, *J. Am. Chem. Soc.*, **66**, 652 (1944).
[169b] Gibbs, U. S. pat. 2,343,768 [*C. A.*, **38**, 3293 (1944)].
[170] Hodgson and Nicholson, *J. Chem. Soc.*, **1941**, 645.
[171] Eckert and Ender, *J. prakt. Chem.*, [2] **104**, 81 (1922).
[172] Hollander, *Rec. trav. chim.*, **39**, 481 (1920).
[173] Kollrepp, *Ann.*, **234**, 14 (1886).
[174] Peratoner and Genco, *Gazz. chim. ital.*, **24**, 375 (1894).
[175] Kohn and Gurewitsch, *Monatsh.*, **56**, 135 (1930).
[176] Faust, *Ann.*, **149**, 153 (1869).
[177] Kohn and Rabinowitsch, *Monatsh.*, **48**, 347 (1927).
[178] Kohn and Sussmann, *Monatsh.*, **46**, 575 (1925).
[179] Hodgson and Nixon, *J. Chem. Soc.*, **1930**, 1868.
[180] Armstrong, *J. Chem. Soc.*, **24**, 1121 (1871).
[181] Hodgson and Nixon, *J. Chem. Soc.*, **1930**, 1870.
[182] Knapp and Schultze, *Ann.*, **210**, 174 (1881).
[183] Graebe, *Ann.*, **263**, 19 (1891).
[184] Schuloff and Pollak, *Chem. Ztg.*, **56**, 569 (1932).
[185] Schulz, *Ber.*, **15**, 656 (1882).
[186] Kohn and Sussmann, *Monatsh.*, **48**, 193 (1927).
[187] Kohn and Fink, *Monatsh.*, **58**, 73 (1931).
[188] Kohn and Zandman, *Monatsh.*, **47**, 357 (1926).
[189] Benedikt, *Monatsh.*, **1**, 346 (1880).
[190] Jackson and Calhane, *Am. Chem. J.*, **28**, 462 (1902).
[191] Bargellini, Monti, and Grippa, *Gazz. chim. ital.*, **60**, 559 (1930).
[192] Zincke, *Ann.*, **320**, 146 (1901).
[193] Thiele and Eichwede, *Ber.*, **33**, 673 (1900).
[194] Kastle, *Am. Chem. J.*, **27**, 42 (1902).
[195] Hodgson and Nixon, *J. Chem. Soc.*, **1930**, 1085.
[196] Kohn and Kramer, *Monatsh.*, **49**, 167 (1928).
[197] Kohn and Dömötör, *Monatsh.*, **47**, 207 (1926).
[198] Kohn and Pfeifer, *Monatsh.*, **48**, 225 (1927).
[199] Ling and Baker, *J. Chem. Soc.*, **61**, 589 (1892).
[200] Jackson and Bolton, *J. Am. Chem. Soc.*, **36**, 305 (1914).
[201] Ling, *J. Chem. Soc.*, **51**, 147 (1887).
[202] Metzeler, *Ber.*, **21**, 2555 (1888).
[203] Kehrmann and Messinger, *Ber.*, **26**, 2377 (1893).
[204] Seifert, *J. prakt. Chem.*, [2] **28**, 437 (1883).
[205] Willgerodt and Arnold, *Ber.*, **34**, 3351 (1901).
[206] Kohn and Pfeiffer, *Monatsh.*, **48**, 231 (1927).
[207] Hodgson and Foster, *J. Chem. Soc.*, **1942**, 583.
[208] Kohn and Rosenfeld, *Monatsh.*, **46**, 101 (1925).
[209] Guareschi and Daccomo, *Ber.*, **18**, 1170 (1885).
[210] Garzino, *Ber.*, **25** (ref.), 121 (1892).
[211] Carstanjen, *J. prakt. Chem.*, [2] **15**, 399 (1877).
[212] Chechik, *J. Am. Pharm. Assoc.*, **22**, 506 (1933).
[213] Bordeianu, *Arch. Pharm.*, **272**, 8 (1934).

214 Carstanjen, *J. prakt. Chem.*, **23**, 429 (1881).

215 du Feu, McQuillin, and Robinson, *J. Chem. Soc.*, **1937**, 58.

216 Datta and Bhoumik, *J. Am. Chem. Soc.*, **43**, 309 (1921).

217 Bayrac, *Bull. soc. chim. France*, [3] **13**, 979 (1895).

218 Gibbs and Robertson, *J. Chem Soc.*, **105**, 1887 (1914).

219 Kumagai and Wolffenstein, *Ber.*, **41**, 299 (1908).

220 Vorländer and Schrödter, *Ber.*, **34**, 1653 (1901).

221 Claus and Schweitzer, *Ber.*, **19**, 927 (1886).

222 Kehrmann, Mussmann, and Facchinetti, *Ber.*, **48**, 2021 (1915).

223 Angeletti and Oliverio, *Gazz. chim. ital.*, **70**, 342 (1940).

224 Kehrmann, *Ber.*, **49**, 1212 (1916).

225 Elbs and Brunnschweiler, *J. prakt. Chem.*, [2] **52**, 559 (1895).

226 Southworth, *Ann.*, **168**, 273 (1873).

227 Seelig, *Ann.*, **237**, 145 (1887).

228 Bureš, *Chem. Listy*, **21**, 108 (1927) [*C. A.*, **22**, 63 (1928)].

229 Chulkov, Parine, and Barshev, *Org. Chem. Ind. U.S.S.R.*, **3**, 410 (1937).

230 Gorup-Besanez, *Ann.*, **143**, 159 (1867); Bräuninger, *Ann.*, **185**, 352 (1877); Richter, *Ber.*, **34**, 4296 (1901).

231 Kehrmann and Rüst, *Ann.*, **303**, 24 (1898).

232 Claus and Dreher, *J. prakt. Chem.*, [2] **39**, 370 (1889).

233 Kohn and Rabinowitsch, *Monatsh.*, **48**, 361 (1927).

234 Zincke and Klostermann, *Ber.*, **40**, 679 (1907).

235 Auwers and Erggelet, *Ber.*, **32**, 3033 (1899).

236 Auwers and Burrows, *Ber.*, **32**, 3038 (1899).

237 Auwers and Hampe, *Ber.*, **32**, 3015 (1899).

238 Cohen and Marshall, *J. Chem. Soc.*, **85**, 527 (1904).

233a Koelsch and Wawzonek, *J. Am. Chem. Soc.*, **65**, 755 (1943).

239 Fieser and Chang, *J. Am. Chem. Soc.*, **64**, 2048 (1942).

240 Nölting and Forel, *Ber.*, **18**, 2673 (1885).

240a Smith and Tess, *J. Am. Chem. Soc.*, **66**, 1523 (1944).

241 Auwers and Borsche, *Ber.*, **48**, 1699 (footnote 3) (1915).

242 Auwers, *Ber.*, **40**, 2528 (1907).

243 Claus and Runschke, *J. prakt. Chem.*, [2] **42**, 110 (1890).

243a Smith and Wiley, *J. Am. Chem. Soc.*, **68**, 894 (1946).

244 Jacobsen, *Ann.*, **195**, 271 (1879).

245 Kohn and Feldmann, *Monatsh.*, **49**, 169 (1928).

245a Smith and Nichols, *J. Am. Chem. Soc.*, **65**, 1742 (1943).

246 Nölting, Witt, and Forel, *Ber.*, **18**, 2667 (1885).

247 Kehrmann and Stiller, *Ber.*, **45**, 3348 (1912).

HYDROXYQUINONES AND DERIVATIVES

Many hydroxyquinones have been prepared by the general methods discussed for alkylquinones, and the most common oxidizing agents are those previously mentioned; however, since hydroxyquinones are not sufficiently volatile to be steam-distilled they are usually isolated by crystallization or extraction from the reaction mixture.

A very successful preparation of hydroxyquinones is that introduced in 1900 by Thiele and Winter.[248] When a quinone is treated with acetic anhydride and sulfuric acid a triacetoxybenzene is formed; the hydroxy-

248 Thiele and Winter, *Ann.*, **311**, 341 (1900).

quinone is obtained from this by hydrolysis and oxidation. This reaction has been applied extensively.[249-252] Ferric chloride can be used as

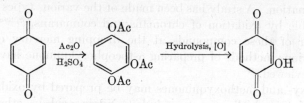

the oxidizing agent,[249, 250] but oxidation by air in a buffered solution of pH 8 is usually preferable.[252] The yields by this procedure vary from 78 to 95%, most of them being near 90% (e.g., 2-hydroxy-5-methoxyquinone, 2-hydroxy-5,6-dimethoxyquinone, 3-hydroxy-6-methoxytoluquinone, and 3-hydroxy-5,6-dimethoxytoluquinone). In the acetoxylation of 3-methoxytoluquinone and 5-methoxytoluquinone substitution occurs in the position *meta* to the methoxyl group.[249]

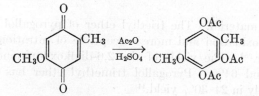

Quinones containing a hydroxyl group in the side chain have been prepared by oxidation of the appropriate 6-hydroxychroman or 5-hydroxycoumaran. Thus, oxidation of 6-hydroxy-2,5,7,8-tetramethyl-chroman yields 2,3,5-trimethyl-6-(3'-hydroxybutyl)-quinone.[253] Ferric

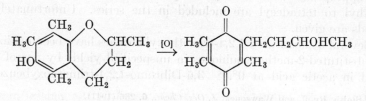

chloride or silver nitrate in ethanol oxidizes chromans to quinones in yields of 60–80%;[253] silver acetate in methanol is reported[254, 255] to be

[249] Anslow, Ashley, and Raistrick, *J. Chem. Soc.*, **1938**, 439.
[250] Raistrick, *Chemistry & Industry*, **1938**, 293.
[251] Anslow and Raistrick, *Biochem. J.*, **32**, 694 (1938).
[252] Anslow and Raistrick, *J. Chem. Soc.*, **1939**, 1446.
[253] John, Dietzel, and Emte, *Z. physiol. Chem.*, **257**, 180 (1939).
[254] John and Schmeil, *Ber.*, **72**, 1653 (1939).
[255] John, Gunther, and Rathmann, *Z. physiol. Chem.*, **268**, 104 (1941).

an even better agent for this oxidation. The oxidation of chromans by use of ceric sulfate in aqueous ethanol [256] may be adapted to volumetric determination. A study has been made of the various types of quinones obtainable by oxidation of chromans and coumarans,[152, 240a] and of the behavior of these compounds at the dropping mercury electrode.[256a] The various methods of preparing α-tocopherylquinone have been critically reviewed.[257]

Ethoxy- and methoxyquinones may be prepared by oxidation of the appropriate polyalkoxy compounds. Nitric acid in ethanol [50, 258] or acetic acid [259, 260] has proved useful, although there is some nitration of

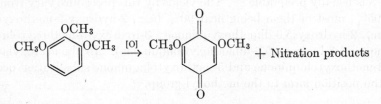

the starting material. The triethyl ether of pyrogallol is much more resistant to oxidation and more susceptible of nitration than the trimethyl ether.[259] The yields of the 2,6-dialkoxyquinones are, respectively, 16 and 64%. Pyrogallol trimethyl ether has been oxidized electrolytically in 24–30% yield.[14]

2,6-Dialkoxyquinones may also be obtained in 20–39% yield by oxidation of ethers of phloroglucinol with chromic anhydride in acetic acid.[261] Chromic anhydride or sodium dichromate in acetic acid at 100° also has been used for the preparation of 2-methoxy-6-alkylquinones from the appropriate 1,3-dimethoxy-5-alkylbenzenes.[262-265] Alkyl groups from methyl to tetradecyl are included in the series. Unfortunately, no yields are given.

Several 5-substituted-1,2,4-trimethoxybenzenes have been oxidized to 5-substituted-2-methoxyquinones in unspecified yields by use of nitric acid in acetic acid at 0°.[266] 3,6-Dibromo-1,2,4-trimethoxybenzene is

[256] Smith, Ruoff, and Wawzonek, J. Org. Chem., 6, 236 (1941).
[256a] Smith, Kolthoff, Wawzonek, and Ruoff, J. Am. Chem. Soc., 63, 1018 (1941).
[257] Tishler and Wendler, J. Am. Chem. Soc., 63, 1532 (1941).
[258] Graebe and Hess, Ann., 340, 232 (1905).
[259] Pollak and Goldstein, Monatsh., 29, 135 (1908).
[260] Majima and Okazaki, Ber., 49, 1489 (1916).
[261] Späth and Wesseley, Monatsh., 49, 229 (1928).
[262] Fuzikawa, Ber., 68, 72 (1935).
[263] Asahina, Miyasaka, and Sekizawa, Ber., 69, 1643 (1936).
[264] Asano and Yamaguti, J. Pharm. Soc. Japan, 60, 105 (1940).
[265] Asano and Yamaguti, J. Pharm. Soc. Japan, 60, 585 (1940).
[266] Szeki, Ber., 62, 1373 (1929).

oxidized [267] by warm concentrated nitric acid to 3,6-dibromo-2-methoxy-quinone in 84% yield. Nitric acid also has proved useful for the preparation of nitranilic acid (2,5-dihydroxy-3,6-dinitroquinone) by nitration and oxidation of quinone [268] or hydroquinone diacetate [269, 270] (yields of 72–80%). The oxidation is carried out at 0° or lower.

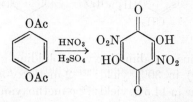

Ferric chloride appears to have been used less frequently than in the alkylquinone series but in several instances has afforded good yields. A 40% yield of 2-hydroxy-6-methoxyquinone results on oxidation of 2,4-dihydroxy-6-methoxyaniline,[271] and a "nearly quantitative" yield of 2,6-dihydroxy-m-xyloquinone on oxidation of 2,4,6-trihydroxy-3,5-dimethylaniline.[272] Hydroxyhydroquinones and methoxyhydroquinones have been oxidized with ferric chloride [249, 252] in yields varying from 47% to "nearly quantitative." In one instance,[273] 2,3,4-trimethoxyaniline, oxidation by ferric chloride gives a poor yield, whereas use of aqueous chromic acid gives a 72% yield. As a matter of fact, inspection of

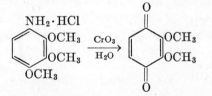

Tables I–V reveals only one instance (oxidation of aniline to 2,5-di-anilinoquinone in 16% yield, Table IV) in which an amine or a phenol with no *para* substituent has been oxidized with ferric chloride; and in the few cases where the *para* substituent is some group other than amino or hydroxy the yield (if reported) is poor. Thus 2,4-diaminomesity-lene [29] gives a 5% yield of hydroxy-m-xyloquinone. Several amines with

[267] Dorn, Warren, and Bullock, J. Am. Chem. Soc., **61**, 145 (1939).
[268] Meyer, Ber., **57**, 327 (1924).
[269] Nietzki, Ber., **43**, 3458 (1910).
[270] Town, Biochem. J., **30**, 1834 (1936).
[271] Pollak and Gans, Monatsh., **23**, 954 (1902).
[272] Brunmayr, Monatsh., **21**, 9 (1900).
[273] Baker and Smith, J. Chem. Soc., **1931**, 2547.

no *para* substituent have been oxidized by chromic acid-sulfuric acid mixture. As usual with starting materials of this type, the yields are

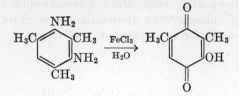

relatively low. Thus, 5,6-dimethoxy-*m*-toluidine gives 5,6-dimethoxytoluquinone (crude) in 30% yield; [274] 2-methoxy-*m*-toluidine gives 3-methoxytoluquinone in 14.5% yield; [249] *o*-methoxyaniline gives methoxyquinone in 20% yield; [275, 276] and 5-methoxy-6-ethoxy-*m*-toluidine gives 5-ethoxy-6-methoxytoluquinone (crude) in 29% yield. [251] Chromic acid-sulfuric acid appears unsuited to the preparation of quinones containing a free hydroxyl group. None of the expected quinone is obtained on oxidation of 4,6-dihydroxy-*o*-toluidine, [277] although a 65% yield of 6-methoxytoluquinone results on oxidation of 4-hydroxy-6-methoxy-*o*-toluidine. [278] Other *p*-disubstituted compounds (2-ethoxy-

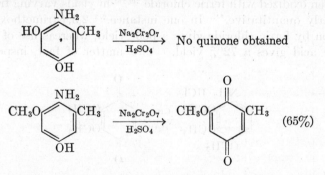

4-hydroxyaniline, 2,4'-dimethoxy-4-amino-5-ethoxydiphenylamine) have been oxidized in moderate to good yields with dichromate.

Experimental Procedures

2-Hydroxy-5-methoxyquinone.[252] For acetoxylation of methoxyquinone by the Thiele-Winter procedure, 4.0 g. of this quinone [276, 279] is

[274] Pollak and Solomonica, *Monatsh.*, **22**, 1008 (1901).
[275] Mühlhäuser, *Ann.*, **207**, 251 (1881).
[276] Will, *Ber.*, **21**, 605 (1888).
[277] Henrich, Taubert, and Birkner, *Ber.*, **45**, 303 (1912).
[278] Henrich and Nachtigall, *Ber.*, **36**, 894 (1903).
[279] Erdtman, *Proc. Roy. Soc. London*, **A143**, 186 (1933).

dissolved with shaking in a mixture of 30 ml. of acetic anhydride and 1.5 ml. of concentrated sulfuric acid. After the mixture has stood for twenty-four hours at room temperature, it is poured on 100 g. of ice and water. The 1,2,4-triacetoxy-5-methoxybenzene separates as crystals or as an oil which soon solidifies. The material is collected, washed with a few milliliters of cold water and a like amount of anhydrous ether, then dried in vacuum. The crude product, 5–5.5 g., is suitable for the next step.

Five grams of 1,2,4-triacetoxy-5-methoxybenzene, prepared by Thiele-Winter acetylation of methoxyquinone,[276, 279] is boiled for forty-five minutes in an atmosphere of nitrogen with a mixture of 36 ml. of methanol and 1.2 ml. of concentrated sulfuric acid. After dilution with water the methanol is removed by distillation in vacuum, and the hydroquinone (2.56 g.) is extracted with ether. For oxidation, 1.1 g. of the crude hydroquinone is dissolved in 110 ml. of pH 8.0 buffer solution (molar potassium dihydrogen phosphate, 50 ml.; normal sodium hydroxide, 46.8 ml.; water to 100 ml.) and aerated vigorously for ten minutes. The intensely blood-red solution is acidified with 16.5 ml. of concentrated hydrochloric acid. 2-Hydroxy-5-methoxyquinone quickly crystallizes (0.60 g.), and an additional 0.45 g. of slightly impure quinone may be obtained by ether extraction of the filtrate; total yield, 1.05 g. (95%). The substance forms large, orange-brown, rectangular leaflets from ethanol, m.p. 179° (dec.), after softening at 171°. This quinone may be sublimed in high vacuum at 100°.

2,6-Dimethoxyquinone.[50, 258] In a 3-l, round-bottomed flask are placed 155 g. of pyrogallol trimethyl ether, 775 ml. of 95% ethanol, and 775 ml. of nitric acid (sp. gr. 1.2). The mixture is warmed carefully to 35° and then allowed to stand until a vigorous reaction sets in. By external cooling the temperature is maintained just below 50° until the main heat evolution ceases (about fifteen minutes). The mixture is then allowed to stand for about four hours (after prolonged standing, the nitro derivative of the starting material may crystallize), and the crystals of yellow quinone which separate are collected, washed with several portions of ethanol (400 ml. in all) and several portions of water (800 ml. in all), and dried. There is obtained 124 g. (80%) of material melting at 255°.

TABLE III *

HYDROXYQUINONES AND DERIVATIVES

Quinone	Substance Oxidized	Oxidizing Agent	Yield	References†
2,6-*bis*(Benzyloxy)-quinone	1,2,3-*tris*(Benzyloxy)-benzene	HNO₃ (sp. gr. 1.19)	46% (cr.)	280
2,5-*bis*(p-n-Butoxy-phenyl)-quinone	Condensation product of quinone and phenyl butyl ether	Quinone	20% (o.)	110
2,5-*bis*(2,4-Dihydroxy-phenyl)-quinone	2,5-*bis*(2,4-Dihydroxy-phenyl)-quinhydrone	Quinone	70%	115
2,5-*bis*(4-Hydroxy-2-methylphenyl)-qui-none	2,5-*bis*(4-Hydroxy-2-methylphenyl)-quin-hydrone	FeCl₃ (AcOH)	—	114
2,5-*bis*(4-Hydroxy-3-methylphenyl)-qui-none	2,5-*bis*(4-Hydroxy-3-methylphenyl)-quin-hydrone	FeCl₃ (AcOH)	31% (cr.)	114
2,5-*bis*(p-Hydroxy-phenyl)-quinone	Condensation product of phenol and quinone	FeCl₃ (AcOH)	20% (cr.)	112
2,5-*bis*(3-Bromomesi-tyl)-3,6-dihydroxy-quinone	2,5-*bis*(3-Bromomesi-tyl)-1,3,4,6-tetra-hydroxybenzene	Quinone	—	109
2,6-*bis*(2,4,6-Trichloro-phenoxy)-quinone	2,4,6-Trichlorophenol	PbO₂ (benzene)	25%	15
2,5-Dianisylquinone	Condensation product of anisole and quinone	FeCl₃ (AcOH)	13.5% (cr.)	112
2,5-Dianisyl-3,6-di-bromoquinone	2,5-Dianisylhydroqui-none	Br₂	44%	110
2,5-Diethoxyquinone	2,5-Diethoxy-p-phenyl-enediamine	FeCl₃	—	281
2,6-Diethoxyquinone	3,5-Diethoxyphenol	CrO₃ (AcOH)	22%	261
	2,6-Diethoxy-4-hy-droxyaniline	FeCl₃	—	282
	Pyrogallol triethyl ether	HNO₃ (AcOH)	16%	259
	Phenyl-(2,6-Diethoxy-4-methoxyphenyl)-carbinol	CrO₃ (AcOH)	39%	261
3,6-Dihydroxy-5-meth-oxytoluquinone	2,3,5,6-Tetrahydroxy-4-methoxytoluene	Air (alkaline sol.)	55% (cr.) (o.)	250, 251 (y.)
2-Diacetoxymethyl-5-methoxyquinone	2,4,5-Trimethoxybenz-aldehyde	HNO₃ (H₂SO₄, Ac₂O)	—	283
2-(2,4-Dihydroxy-phenyl)-quinone	2-(2,4-Dihydroxy-phenyl)-hydroquinone	FeCl₃	—	115
2,5-Dihydroxy-3-phenyl-6-p-tolyl-quinone	2-Phenyl-5-p-tolylhy-droquinone	Br₂	—	284
Dihydroxythymoqui-none	3-Hydroxycarvacrol	O₂ (alkaline sol.)	—	285
	Tetrahydroxy-p-cymene	Air	—	286
	2-Methyl-4-ethoxy-5-isopropyl-m-phenyl-enediamine	FeCl₃	—	30
3,5-Dihydroxy-m-xylo-quinone	2,4,6-Trihydroxy-3,5-dimethylaniline	FeCl₃	Nearly quant.	272
3,6-Dimethoxy-2-hydroxyquinone	1,2-Dihydroxy-3,4,6-trimethoxybenzene	FeCl₃	70.5%	50

* See p. 315 for explanation of system and abbreviations in tables.
† References 280–323 are listed on p. 350.

TABLE III—*Continued*

HYDROXYQUINONES AND DERIVATIVES

Quinone	Substance Oxidized	Oxidizing Agent	Yield	References*
5,6-Dimethoxy-2-hydroxyquinone	2-Hydroxy-5,6-dimethoxyhydroquinone	Air (pH 8)	78% (o.)	252
5,6-Dimethoxy-3-hydroxytoluquinone	3-Hydroxy-5,6-dimethoxytoluhydroquinone	Air (pH 8)	87% (cr., o.)	252
2,3-Dimethoxyquinone	2,3,4-Trimethoxyaniline	Aqueous chromic acid	72%	273
		FeCl$_3$	Poor	273
	2,3-Dimethoxyhydroquinone	FeCl$_3$	79%	252
2,3-Dimethoxy-5,6-dibromoquinone	1,2-Dibromo-3,4,5,6-tetramethoxybenzene	HNO$_3$ (sp. gr. 1.4)	—	287
2,5-Dimethoxyquinone	2,5-Dimethoxy-p-phenylenediamine	FeCl$_3$	—	281
	2,5-Dimethoxy-4-aminophenol	HNO$_3$ (50%)	—	288
2,6-Dimethoxyquinone	Pyrogallol trimethyl ether	HNO$_3$ (AcOH)	64%	259 (y.) 276
		HNO$_3$ (EtOH)	80%	50 (y.), 258, 289
		Electrolysis	24–30%	14
	3,5-Dimethoxy-4-hydroxybenzoic acid	Na$_2$Cr$_2$O$_7$ (H$_2$SO$_4$)	60%	290, 291(y.)
	2,6-Dimethoxy-4-hydroxyaniline	FeCl$_3$	—	282
	2,6-Dimethoxy-4-isovalerophenol	CrO$_3$ (AcOH)	—	292
	2,6-Dimethoxy-4-valerophenol	K$_2$Cr$_2$O$_7$ (H$_2$SO$_4$)	—	293
	2,6-Dimethoxy-4-ethylphenol	K$_2$Cr$_2$O$_7$ (H$_2$SO$_4$)	63% (cr.)	294
2,6-Dimethoxy-3,5-dichloroquinone	2,6-Dimethoxy-3,4,5-trichlorophenol	CrO$_3$ (AcOH)	43.5%	16 (y.), 295
2,6-Dimethoxy-3-bromoquinone	2,6-Dimethoxy-3-bromophenol	CrO$_3$ (50% AcOH)	5%	20
	3,5-Dimethoxy-4-hydroxy-6-bromobenzoic acid	CrO$_3$ (H$_2$SO$_4$)	62%	20
2,6-Dimethoxy-3-bromo-5-chloroquinone	2,6-Dimethoxy-3-bromo-4,5-dichlorophenol	CrO$_3$ (AcOH)	45%	20
2,6-Dimethoxy-3,5-dibromoquinone	2,6-Dimethoxy-3,5-dibromohydroquinone	CrO$_3$ or FeCl$_3$	—	287
	2,6-Dimethoxy-3,4,5-tribromophenol	CrO$_3$ (AcOH)	30%	16 (y.), 295
	1,2,4,6-Tetramethoxy-3,5-dibromobenzene	HNO$_3$	—	276
3,5-Dimethoxytoluquinone	2,3,4,6-Tetramethoxytoluene	HNO$_3$ (AcOH) or CrO$_3$ (AcOH, H$_2$SO$_4$)	—	296
5,6-Dimethoxytoluquinone	5,6-Dimethoxy-m-toluidine	K$_2$Cr$_2$O$_7$ (H$_2$SO$_4$)	30% (cr.)	274

* References 280–323 are listed on p. p. 350.

TABLE III*—Continued

HYDROXYQUINONES AND DERIVATIVES

Quinone	Substance Oxidized	Oxidizing Agent	Yield	References†
2,5-Di-p-phenetyl-quinone	Condensation product of quinone and phene-tole	FeCl₃	—	113
2,5-Diphenoxyquinone	2,5-Diphenoxyhydro-quinone	CrO₃ (AcOH)	—	297
2-(α,α-Diphenylethyl)-5-methoxyquinone	2-(α,α-Diphenylethyl)-1,4,5-trimethoxyben-zene	HNO₃ (AcOH)	—	266
2-(α,β-Diphenyliso-propyl)-5-methoxy-quinone	2-(α,β-Diphenyliso-propyl)-1,4,5-trimeth-oxybenzene	HNO₃ (AcOH)	—	266
2,5-Di-p-toloxyquinone	2,5-Di-p-toloxyhydro-quinone	CrO₃ (dil. AcOH)	—	133
Ethoxyquinone	2,4-Diethoxyaniline	K₂Cr₂O₇ (H₂SO₄)	Nearly quant.	298
	2-Ethoxy-4-hydroxy-aniline	Na₂Cr₂O₇ (H₂SO₄)	—	299
2-Ethoxy-6-methoxy-quinone	Phenyl-(2,4-dimethoxy-6-ethoxyphenyl)-car-binol	CrO₃ (AcOH)	—	261
	3-Methoxy-5-ethoxy-phenol	CrO₃ (AcOH)	20% (cr.)	261
5-Ethoxy-6-methoxy-toluquinone	5-Methoxy-6-ethoxy-m-toluidine	Na₂Cr₂O₇ (H₂SO₄)	29% (cr.)	251
2-Ethoxy-6-propyl-quinone	1,2,4-Triethoxy-6-propylbenzene	HNO₃ (25%)	—	311
5-Ethoxytoluquinone	2,4'-Dimethyl-4-amino-5-ethoxydiphenyl-amine	K₂Cr₂O₇ (H₂SO₄)	48%	300
3-Ethoxy-m-xyloqui-none	2,4',6-Trimethyl-4-amino-5-ethoxy-di-phenylamine	K₂Cr₂O₇ (H₂SO₄)	—	301
2-Hydroxy-5-methoxy-quinone	2-Hydroxy-5-methoxy-hydroquinone	Air (pH 8)	95%	252
2-Hydroxy-6-methoxy-quinone	2,4-Dihydroxy-6-meth-oxyaniline	FeCl₃	40%	271
3-Hydroxy-5-meth-oxytoluquinone	3-Hydroxy-5-methoxy-toluhydroquinone	FeCl₃	Nearly quant.	249 (y.), 250, 296
	3-Hydroxy-4-amino-5-methoxy-o-cresol	FeCl₃	—	302
	2-Hydroxy-3-amino-4,6-dimethoxytoluene	FeCl₃	—	274
3-Hydroxy-6-methoxy-toluquinone	3-Hydroxy-6-methoxy-toluhydroquinone	Air (pH 8)	92% (o.)	252
5-Hydroxy-3-methoxy-toluquinone	5-Hydroxy-3-methoxy-toluhydroquinone	FeCl₃	47%	249
6-Hydroxy-5-methoxy-toluquinone	4-Amino-5-hydroxy-6-methoxy-m-cresol	FeCl₃	—	312
3-Hydroxy-5-methoxy-m-xyloquinone	3-Hydroxy-4-amino-5-methoxy-vic.-m-xylol	FeCl₃	80%	303
Hydroxymethylquinone	Gentisylalcohol	Pb(OAc)₄	70%	303a
Hydroxyquinone	Hydroxyhydroquinone	Ag₂O	60%	39, 59 (y.)

* See p. 315 for explanation of system and abbreviations in tables.
† References 280–323 are listed on p. 350.

TABLE III—*Continued*

HYDROXYQUINONES AND DERIVATIVES

Quinone	Substance Oxidized	Oxidizing Agent	Yield	References*
3-Hydroxythymoquinone	3-Hydroxycarvacrol	HNO_3 or H_2O_2	—	285
	3-Hydroxy-6-amino-carvacrol	HNO_3	—	285
	4,6-Diaminothymol	$FeCl_3$	—	4
	2,6-Diamino-3-ethoxy-*p*-cymene	$FeCl_3$	—	30
	Menthone, 2,3-dihydro-menthone or menthol	SeO_2	2–8%	304
	2,6-Diamino-3-chloro-*p*-cymene	$Na_2Cr_2O_7$ (H_2SO_4)	Poor	30
3-Hydroxy-6-chloro-thymoquinone	2,6-Diamino-3-chloro-*p*-cymene	$Na_2Cr_2O_7$ (H_2SO_4)	Very poor	30
6-Hydroxythymoquinone	4,6-Diaminocarvacrol	$FeCl_3$	—	31
3-Hydroxy-6-chloro-toluquinone	3-Hydroxy-6-chloro-toluhydroquinone	HNO_3 (sp. gr. 1.4)	—	66
5-Hydroxytoluquinone	5-Hydroxytoluhydro-quinone	$FeCl_3$	90%	248, 309*a* (y.)
5-Hydroxy-3,6-dichloro-toluquinone	5-Hydroxy-3,6-dichloro-toluhydroquinone	HNO_3 (sp. gr. 1.4)	Poor	32
6-Hydroxy-3-chloro-toluquinone	4,6-Dihydroxy-3-chloro-*o*-toluidine	$K_2Cr_2O_7$ (H_2SO_4)	—	277
6-Hydroxy-5-chloro-toluquinone	4,6-Dihydroxy-*o*-toluidine hydrochloride	$K_2Cr_2O_7$ (H_2SO_4)	6%	277
6-Hydroxy-3,5-dichloro-toluquinone	2,4,6-Trichloro-5-meth-ylresorcinol	Alkaline potassium ferrocyanide	—	305
Hydroxytriphenylquinone	Ethyl triphenylgentisate	Air in alkaline medium	12%	238*a*
3-Hydroxy-*m*-xyloquinone	2,4-Diaminomesitylene	$K_2Cr_2O_7$ (H_2SO_4) or $FeCl_3$	5%	29
	3,5-Dimethyl-Δ^2-cyclo-hexenone	SeO_2 (AcOH)	—	306
2-Methoxy-6-amylquinone	1-Amyl-3,5-dimethoxy-benzene	$Na_2Cr_2O_7$ (AcOH)	—	262, 263
2-Methoxy-6-amyl-5-bromoquinone	1-Amyl-2-bromo-3,5-dimethoxybenzene	$Na_2Cr_2O_7$ (AcOH)	30% (o.)	262
	1',4',3-Tribromo-3'-methyl-2-amyl-1,4,5'-trimethoxydiphenyl ether	$Na_2Cr_2O_7$ (AcOH)	23%	310
2-Methoxy-6-(3,4,5-tri-chloro-2,6-dimethoxy-phenoxy)-3,5-di-chloroquinone	2,6-Dimethoxy-3,4,5-trichlorophenol	CrO_3 (50% AcOH)	50%	16
2-Methoxy-6-(3,4,5-tri-bromo-2,6-dimeth-oxyphenoxy)-3,5-di-bromoquinone	2,6-Dimethoxy-3,4,5-tribromophenol	CrO_3 (50% AcOH)	40%	16
		PbO_2 (AcOH)	60%	16
		$NaNO_2$ (AcOH)	25%	16
		PbO_2 (benzene)	70%	16
2-Methoxy-6-dodecyl-quinone	1,3-Dimethoxy-5-dodec-ylbenzene	CrO_3	45%	264
2-Methoxy-6-hendecyl-quinone	1,3-Dimethoxy-5-hen-decylbenzene	CrO_3	—	264

* References 280–323 are listed on p. 350.

TABLE III*—Continued

HYDROXYQUINONES AND DERIVATIVES

Quinone	Substance Oxidized	Oxidizing Agent	Yield	References†
2-Methoxy-6-heptyl-quinone	1,3-Dimethoxy-5-heptylbenzene	$Na_2Cr_2O_7$ (AcOH) or CrO_3 (AcOH)	—	262, 263
2-Methoxy-5-propyl-quinone	2-Propyl-4,5-dimethoxyaniline	HNO_2 (H_2SO_4) or chromic acid	—	314
	1,4,5-Trimethoxy-2-propylbenzene	Chromyl chloride	—	315
		HNO_3	—	313
2-Methoxy-6-propyl-quinone	1,3-Dimethoxy-5-propylbenzene	$Na_2Cr_2O_7$ (AcOH)	—	262
	1,3,6-Trimethoxy-5-propylbenzene	HNO_3 (25%)	—	311
2-Methoxy-6-propyl-5-bromoquinone	1,3-Dimethoxy-4-bromo-5-propylbenzene	$Na_2Cr_2O_7$ (AcOH)	30% (o.)	262
Methoxyquinone	o-Methoxyaniline	$Na_2Cr_2O_7$ (H_2SO_4)	20%	275, 276 (y.)
	2,4-Dimethoxyaniline	$Na_2Cr_2O_7$ (H_2SO_4)	—	307
	Methoxyhydroquinone	PbO_2 (benzene)	50–57%	279 (y.), 308
Methoxytrichloro-quinone	2,4-Dimethoxy-3,5,6-trichlorophenol	HNO_3 (sp. gr. 1.4)	—	309
2-Methoxy-3,6-di-bromoquinone	1,2,4-Trimethoxy-3,6-dibromobenzene	HNO_3 (sp. gr. 1.4)	84%	267
Methoxytribromo-quinone	Methoxyhydroquinone	Br_2	90%	18
	2,4,6-Tribromo-3-methoxyphenol	CrO_3 (AcOH)	47%	18
2-Methoxy-6-tetradec-ylquinone	1,3-Dimethoxy-5-tetra-decylbenzene	$Na_2Cr_2O_7$ (AcOH)	—	265
3-Methoxytoluquinone	2-Methoxy-m-toluidine	$Na_2Cr_2O_7$ (H_2SO_4)	14.5%	249 (y.), 260
5-Methoxytoluqui-none	2-Methyl-4,5-dimethoxyaniline	$FeCl_3$	—	296, 316
	2,4,5-Trimethoxy-toluene	CrO_3 (AcOH, H_2SO_4)	—	296
5-Methoxy-3,6-di-bromotoluquinone	2,4,5-Trimethoxy-3,6-dibromotoluene	HNO_3 (sp. gr. 1.4)	—	296
6-Methoxytoluqui-none	2,3-Dimethoxytoluene	HNO_3 (AcOH)	—	260
	6-Methoxytoluhydro-quinone	$FeCl_3$	—	260
	4,5-Dimethoxy-m-toluidine	$Na_2Cr_2O_7$ (H_2SO_4) and PbO_2	10%	260
	4,5-Dimethoxy-m-cresol	$Na_2Cr_2O_7$ (H_2SO_4) and PbO_2	50%	260
	4-Amino-5-methoxy-m-cresol	$K_2Cr_2O_7$ (H_2SO_4)	65% (cr.)	278 (y.), 317
	2,4,5′-Trimethoxy-3′,6-dimethyldiphenyl ether	$Na_2Cr_2O_7$ (AcOH)	26%	317
	2,4,5′-Trimethoxy-6-amyl-3′-methyldi-phenyl ether	$Na_2Cr_2O_7$ (AcOH)	36%	310
	3,5-Dimethoxytoluene	$Na_2Cr_2O_7$ (AcOH)	60%	317
6-Methoxy-3-bromo-toluquinone	3,5-Dimethoxy-2-bromotoluene	$Na_2Cr_2O_7$ (AcOH)	75%	262
	2,3′,4-Trimethoxy-5′,6-dimethyl-4′,5,6′-tri-bromodiphenyl ether	$Na_2Cr_2O_7$ (AcOH)	7.5%	262

* See p. 315 for explanation of system and abbreviations in tables.
† References 280–323 are listed on p. 350.

TABLE III—*Continued*

HYDROXYQUINONES AND DERIVATIVES

Quinone	Substance Oxidized	Oxidizing Agent	Yield	References*
2-Methoxy-6-tridecyl-quinone	1,3-Dimethoxy-5-tri-decylbenzene	$Na_2Cr_2O_7$ (AcOH)	—	265
Methoxy-*p*-xyloquinone	2,3′,4-Trimethoxy-2′,3,5′,6-tetramethyl-diphenyl ether	$Na_2Cr_2O_7$ (AcOH)	35%	262
	2,5-Dimethyl-3-meth-oxy-4-aminophenol	$Na_2Cr_2O_7$ (H_2SO_4)	—	262
Nitranilic acid (2,5-dihydroxy-3,6-di-nitroquinone)	Hydroquinone diacetate	HNO_3 (H_2SO_4)	75–80% (as salt)	269
		HNO_3 (H_2SO_4)	45%	270
	Quinone	HNO_3	72–78%	268
2-(2,4,6-Trichloro-phenoxy)-6-chloro-quinone	Trichlorophenol	CrO_3 (AcOH)	1.5%	15
		PbO_2 (AcOH)	—	15
		PbO_2 (benzene)	35%	15
2-Propoxy-6-propyl-quinone	1,2,4-Tripropoxy-6-propylbenzene	HNO_3 (25%)	—	311
Tetrahydroxyquinone	Inositol	HNO_3	29–33%	318
α-Tocopherylquinone	α-Tocopherol	$FeCl_3$, $AgNO_3$, or gold chloride	—	319–321
	α-Tocopherylhydro-quinone	Ag_2O	31% (o.)	257 (contains earlier refs.), 322
2,3,5-Trimethyl-6-(2′-hydroxybutyl)-quinone	5-Hydroxy-2-ethyl-4,6,7-trimethylcou-maran	Ceric sulfate	49 % (hydr.)	256
2,3,5-Trimethyl-6-(3′-hydroxybutyl)-quinone	6-Hydroxy-2,5,7,8-tetramethylchroman	Ceric sulfate	64%	256
		$FeCl_3$	80%	253 (y.), 319
		$AgNO_3$ (EtOH)	60%	253
		AgOAc (MeOH)	>80%	254
2,3,5-Trimethyl-6-(3′-hydroxy-3′-methyl-butyl)-quinone	6-Hydroxy-2,2,5,7,8-pentamethylchroman	$AgNO_3$ or $FeCl_3$	48%	253
		Ceric sulfate	40% (hydr.)	256
2,3,5-Trimethyl-6-(2′-hydroxy-3′-methyl-butyl)-quinone	2-Isopropyl-5-hydroxy-4,6,7-trimethylcou-maran	$AuCl_3$	89%	323
		$FeCl_3$	70%	323
2,3,5-Trimethyl-6-(3′-hydroxy-3′-methyl-nonadecyl)-quinone	2,5,6-Trimethyl-4-meth-oxy-3-(3′-hydroxy-3′-methylnonadecyl)-phenol	AgOAc	—	255
2,3,5-Trimethyl-6-(2′-hydroxy-2′-methyl-propyl)-quinone	5-Hydroxy-2,2,4,6,7-pentamethylcoumaran	$AuCl_3$	48%	256
2,3,5-Trimethyl-6-(2′-hydroxypropyl)-quinone	5-Hydroxy-2,4,6,7-tetra-methylcoumaran	Ceric sulfate	40%	256
		AgOAc	—	83
		$AuCl_3$	—	319
	5-Amino-2,4,6,7-tetra-methylcoumaran	$FeCl_3$	50%	83

* References 280–323 are listed on p. 350.

REFERENCES TO TABLE III

[280] Baker, Nodzu, and Robinson, *J. Chem. Soc.*, **1929**, 77.

[281] Nietzki and Rechberg, *Ber.*, **23**, 1213 (1890).

[282] Weidel and Pollak, *Monatsh.*, **21**, 33 (1900).

[283] van Alphen, *Rec. trav. chim.*, **47**, 174 (1928).

[284] Asano and Kameda, *J. Pharm. Soc. Japan*, **59**, 768 (1939) [*C. A.*, **34**, 2345 (1940)].

[285] Treibs, *J. prakt. Chem.*, [2] **138**, 284 (1933).

[286] Wakeman, *J. Am. Chem. Soc.*, **41**, 1873 (1919).

[287] Aulin and Erdtman, *Svensk Kem. Tid.*, **49**, 208 (1937) [*C. A.*, **32**, 4552 (1938)].

[288] Fabinyi and Széki, *Ber.*, **44**, 2296 (1911).

[289] Oxford, *J. Chem. Soc.*, **1942**, 583.

[290] Alimchandani and Meldrum, *J. Chem. Soc.*, **117**, 967 (1920).

[291] Graebe and Martz, *Ann.*, **340**, 221 (1905).

[292] Hurd and Winberg, *J. Am. Chem. Soc.*, **64**, 2085 (1942).

[293] Asahina and Kusaka, *Ber.*, **69**, 454 (1936).

[294] Schultes, *Ber.*, **69**, 1872 (1936).

[295] Kohn and Gurewitsch, *Monatsh.*, **49**, 173 (1928).

[296] Aulin and Erdtman, *Svensk. Kem. Tid.*, **50**, 42 (1938).

[297] Kohn and Sussmann, *Monatsh.*, **48**, 203 (1927).

[298] Will and Pukall, *Ber.*, **20**, 1132 (1887).

[299] Kietaibl, *Monatsh.*, **19**, 552 (1898); Henrich, *Ber.*, **35**, 4194 (1902).

[300] Jacobson and Jankowski, *Ann.*, **369**, 20 (1909).

[301] Jacobson and Fulda, *Ann.*, **369**, 28 (1909).

[302] Konya, *Monatsh.*, **21**, 422 (1900).

[303] Bosse, *Monatsh.*, **21**, 1027 (1900).

[303a] Brack, *Helv. Chim. Acta*, **30**, 1 (1947).

[304] Hirayama, *J. Chem. Soc. Japan*, **58**, 1383 (1937) [*C.A.*, **32**, 4157 (1938)]; **59**, 67, 229 (1938) [*C.A.*, **32**, 4969, 9072 (1938)].

[305] Stenhouse and Groves, *Ber.*, **13**, 1306 (1880).

[306] Dane and Schmitt, *Ann.*, **536**, 200 (1938).

[307] Bechhold, *Ber.*, **22**, 2381 (1889).

[308] Erdtman, *Svensk. Kem. Tid.*, **44**, 135 (1932).

[309] Zincke and Schaum, *Ber.*, **27**, 555 (1894).

[309a] Butz and Butz, *J. Org. Chem.*, **8**, 497 (1943).

[310] Asahina and Nogami, *Ber.*, **68**, 77 (1935).

[311] Thoms, *Ber.*, **36**, 1718 (1903).

[312] Posternak and Ruelius, *Helv. Chim. Acta*, **26**, 2045 (1943).

[313] Ciamician and Silber, *Ber.*, **23**, 2294 (1890).

[314] Thoms, *Ber.*, **36**, 861 (1903).

[315] Beckstroem, *Arch. Pharm.*, **242**, 99 (1904).

[316] Luff, Perkin, and Robinson, *J. Chem. Soc.*, **97**, 1137 (1910).

[317] Asahina and Fuzikawa, *Ber.*, **67**, 167 (1934).

[318] Preisler and Berger, *J. Am. Chem. Soc.*, **64**, 67 (1942).

[319] Karrer, Escher, Fritzsche, Keller, Ringier, and Salomon, *Helv. Chim. Acta*, **21**, 939 (1938).

[320] Karrer and Geiger, *Helv. Chim. Acta*, **23**, 455 (1940).

[321] Smith, Kolthoff, and Spillane, *J. Am. Chem. Soc.*, **64**, 646 (1942).

[322] Smith, Spillane, and Kolthoff, *J. Am. Chem. Soc.*, **64**, 644 (1942).

[323] Smith and King, *J. Am. Chem. Soc.*, **65**, 443 (1943).

AMINOQUINONES AND DERIVATIVES

Relatively few aminoquinones have been prepared, and most of these have been obtained only as the acetyl derivatives. The amino group is susceptible of both oxidation and hydrolysis (refer to section on side reactions) if aqueous oxidizing agents are used. An exception is 5-amino-6-chlorotoluquinone,[32] which can be prepared by the action of

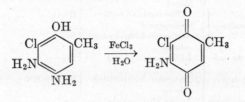

aqueous ferric chloride on 2-amino-5-hydroxy-6-chloro-p-toluidine. Several oxidizing agents have been employed, but very few yields have been reported. It is interesting that aniline may be oxidized with ferric chloride to give a mixture of aniline black and 2,5-dianilinoquinone, from which the quinone may be separated in 16% yield.[324]

[324] Willstätter and Majima, *Ber.*, **43**, 2590 (1910).

TABLE IV *

Aminoquinones and Derivatives

Quinone	Substance Oxidized	Oxidizing Agent	Yield	References
2-Acetamino-6-bromoquinone	2,4-Diacetamino-6-bromo-phenol	HNO_3	—	325
2-Acetamino-5,6-dibromo-quinone	2,4-Diacetamino-5,6-di-bromophenol	HNO_3	—	325
	2-Acetamino-5-nitrohydro-quinone	Br_2	—	325
2-Acetamino-3,5,6-tribromo-quinone	2,4-Diacetaminophenol	Br_2	—	325
2-Acetamino-3,6-dihydroxy-5-nitroquinone	2-Acetamino-5-nitrohydro-quinone	Fuming HNO_3	—	326
5-Amino-6-chlorotoluquinone	2-Amino-5-hydroxy-6-chloro-p-toluidine	$FeCl_3$	—	32
5-(3-Amino-5-bromomesityl)-3,6-dibromotoluquinone	5-(3-Amino-5-bromomesityl)-3,6-dibromotoluhydroqui-none	Quinone	70%	164
2-Anilinoquinone	2-Anilinohydroquinone	$FeCl_3$	—	324
2,5-Diacetamino-3,6-dihy-droxyquinone	2,3,5,6-Tetraacetoxy-1,4-di-acetaminobenzene	Br_2	—	325
		Air (OH^-)	—	329
2,5-Diacetaminoquinone	2,5-Diacetaminophenol	$Na_2Cr_2O_7$ (AcOH)	—	327
2,5-Diacetamino-3-chloro-quinone	2,5-Diacetamino-3-chlorohy-droquinone	$FeCl_3$	—	24
2,5-Diacetamino-3,6-dichloro-quinone	2,5-Diacetamino-3,6-di-chlorohydroquinone	$FeCl_3$	80% (o.)	328
2,6-Diacetaminoquinone	2,6-Diacetaminophenol	HNO_3	—	325
	2,4,6-Triacetaminophenol	HNO_3	72% (cr.)	325
	2,6-Diacetaminohydroqui-none	$FeCl_3$	—	325
2,6-Diacetamino-3,5-dibro-moquinone	2,6-Diacetaminohydroqui-none	Br_2	—	325
2,5-Dianilinoquinone	Aniline	$FeCl_3$ (H_2SO_4)	16%	324

* See p. 315 for explanation of system and abbreviations in tables.

MISCELLANEOUS QUINONES

The substances listed in this section include quinones substituted with nearly all the common functional groups and some rather uncommon groups. The oxidizing agents which have been found applicable include silver oxide, ferric chloride, air, chromic acid-sulfuric acid, and nitric acid. Substituted hydroquinones have been successfully oxidized with

[325] Heller, Dietrich, Hemmer, Kätzel, Rottsahl, and Zambalos, J. prakt. Chem., [2] 129, 232 (1931).
[326] Heller and Hemmer, J. prakt. Chem., [2] 129, 209 (1931).
[327] Kehrmann and Betsch, Ber., 30, 2099 (1897).
[328] Fieser and Martin, J. Am. Chem. Soc., 57, 1847 (1935).
[329] Nietzki and Schmidt, Ber., 21, 1852 (1888).

silver oxide to give such varied types as d-camphor-10-sulfonylquinone [330] (30–80% yield), 2,5-dibenzoylquinone [331] (70% crude yield), and carbomethoxyquinone [332] (60% yield). Carbomethoxyquinone is so sensitive that it can be prepared with no other oxidizing agent.

Only two benzoquinones with a free carboxyl group attached directly to the quinone nucleus have been obtained. Durylic acid quinone,[95, 333] results in quantitative yield from oxidation of 2,4,5-trimethyl-3,6-diaminobenzoic acid with ferric chloride. Triphenylquinonecarboxylic acid [238a] is obtained by oxidation of the corresponding hydroquinone with ferric chloride. The instability of such acids is probably due in

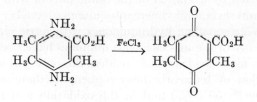

part to the β-keto acid grouping.[333a] Attempted preparations of quinone acids and esters have been published.[95, 332]

A variety of dialkylaminoquinonedisulfonates has been prepared by oxidizing a mixture of hydroquinone, the appropriate amine, and sulfur dioxide with air in the presence of cupric hydroxide.[334-338] No yields are reported.

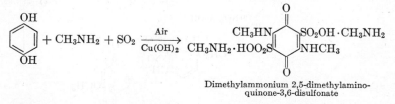

Dimethylammonium 2,5-dimethylamino-
quinone-3,6-disulfonate

Chromic acid-sulfuric acid mixture has been useful for preparing a number of rather sensitive quinones. Oxidation of benzoylhydroquinone gives benzoylquinone in 77% yield,[339] and dibenzoylhydroquinone gives

[330] Hunter and Kvalnes, *J. Am. Chem. Soc.*, **54**, 2880 (1932).
[331] Pummerer and Buchta, *Ber.*, **69**, 1021 (1936).
[332] Brunner, *Monatsh.*, **34**, 913 (1913).
[333] Smith and Denyes, *J. Am. Chem. Soc.*, **56**, 475 (1934).
[333a] Loewy, *Ber.*, **19**, 2387 (1886).
[334] Garreau, *Compt. rend.*, **202**, 1186 (1936).
[335] Garreau, *Compt. rend.*, **203**, 1073 (1936).
[336] Garreau, *Compt. rend.*, **204**, 692 (1937).
[337] Garreau, *Compt. rend.*, **204**, 1570 (1937).
[338] Garreau, *Ann. chim.*, **10**, 485 (1938).
[339] Bogert and Howells, *J. Am. Chem. Soc.*, **52**, 844 (1930).

2,6-dibenzoylquinone (originally reported as the 2,5-isomer) [331, 340] in 60% yield. Quinone acids prepared by use of chromic acid-sulfuric acid include quinonesulfonic acid [341, 342] (90% yield from the hydroquinone), quinonylacetic acid [343] (65–70% from the hydroquinone), γ-quinonyl-butyric acid [344] [83% overall yield from γ-(o-hydroxyphenyl)-butyric acid], and ε-quinonylcaproic acid [344] (83% yield from the aminophenol). The last two preparations illustrate the wide applicability of the coupling procedure for the synthesis of p-aminophenols. Although quinonylacetic acid is unstable in warm water, the oxidation in aqueous medium is successfully carried out at 0°. Methylmercaptoquinone [345] has been prepared by oxidation of the aminophenol with chromic acid-sulfuric acid, and several alkylmercaptoquinones have been prepared by oxidizing the corresponding hydroquinones with ferric chloride.[346a]

Although many of the miscellaneous quinones have been prepared by oxidation with nitric acid or nitric oxides, the only yields reported are in the oxidation of tetracarbethoxy-p-phenylenediamine to tetracarbethoxyquinone [95] (50–55%) and in the oxidation and nitration of 2-meconyl-1,4,5-trimethoxybenzene [266] (83%, crude).

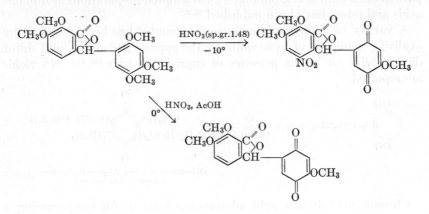

Experimental Procedures

Carbomethoxyquinone.[332] To a solution of 5 g. of methyl gentisate in 50 ml. of dry benzene are added 5 g. of anhydrous potassium carbonate and 15 g. of silver oxide (prepared as for the oxidation of 4-methyl-

[340] Dischendorfer and Verdino, *Monatsh.*, **66**, 255 (1935).
[341] Schultz and Stäble, *J. prakt. Chem.* [2] **69**, 334 (1904).
[342] Seyewetz and Poizat, *Bull. soc. chim. France* [4] **13**, 49 (1913).
[343] Mörner, *Z. physiol. Chem.*, **78**, 306 (1912).
[344] Fieser, Gates, and Kilmer, *J. Am. Chem. Soc.*, **62**, 2966 (1940).
[345] Zincke and Müller, *Ber.*, **46**, 1780 (1913).

catechol, p. 314). The mixture is warmed to 40–50°, shaken for five minutes, allowed to stand an additional five minutes, then filtered. The precipitate of silver is extracted with 30 ml. of warm benzene, and the total benzene solution is dried in the dark for three hours with anhydrous potassium carbonate. The benzene is then removed in vacuum at 40° and the residue dried in vacuum in the dark at room temperature. The resultant yellow-brown crystal mass is treated with boiling carbon disulfide, and the quinone solution is decanted from a viscous brown residue. Crystallization is allowed to continue for several hours in the dark at 0°. The yellow-red crystals of carbomethoxyquinone are collected, washed with a little cold carbon disulfide, and dried in vacuum in the dark. The yield is 3 g. (60%), m.p. 53.5–54°. The melting point is not raised by recrystallization. This quinone is very sensitive to moisture.

γ-Quinonylbutyric Acid.[344] For preparation of a diazonium reagent, a mixture of 3.14 g. of sulfanilic acid dihydrate, 0.79 g. of anhydrous sodium carbonate, and 15 ml. of water is heated and stirred until the sulfanilic acid has dissolved. This solution is cooled in an ice bath to 15° (sodium sulfanilate begins to crystallize at this temperature) and treated with a solution of 1.11 g. of sodium nitrite in 3 ml. of water. The resulting solution is poured at once into a mixture of 3.2 ml. of concentrated hydrochloric acid (sp. gr. 1.18) and 18 g. of ice contained in a 50-ml. beaker. The solution, from which p-benzenediazonium sulfonate separates on stirring, is allowed to stand in an ice bath for about fifteen minutes before use.

A solution of 2.6 g. of crude γ-(o-hydroxyphenyl)-butyric acid[344] in 15 ml. of water containing 3 g. of sodium hydroxide is treated at 0° with the diazonium reagent prepared as above. After fifty minutes the solution is warmed to 70° and treated with 6.9 g. of sodium hydrosulfite. The resulting pale-yellow solution is saturated with salt and cooled to 5°. The grayish precipitate which separates is collected and washed with brine containing hydrosulfite, then dissolved in 30 ml. of 25% sulfuric acid. A little gummy material is removed by filtration, and the filtrate is treated at 5° with 8 ml. of 4 N sodium dichromate solution. After the dark-purple solution has stood at 5° for eleven hours it is diluted with an equal volume of water and extracted five times with ether. The combined extracts are washed twice with saturated brine, concentrated on the steam bath to a volume of 250 ml., and then evaporated in vacuum to half that volume. After Norit treatment the ether is removed in vacuum, and 1.6 g. (57%) of a bright-yellow powder, m.p. 99–100°, separates. The substance crystallizes from ether-petroleum ether as yellow plates; the melting point of the pure substance is 104.9–105.3°.

TABLE V *

Miscellaneous Quinones

Quinone	Substance Oxidized	Oxidizing Agent	Yield	References†
2-Acetyl-3,5-6-trimethoxy-quinone	2-Hydroxy-3,4,6-trimeth-oxyacetophenone	CrO_3 (AcOH)	—	346
Benzoylquinone	Benzoylhydroquinone	$Na_2Cr_2O_7$ (AcOH, H_2SO_4)	77%	339
Benzylmercaptoquinone	Benzylmercaptohydroqui-none	$FeCl_3$	—	346a
5-Benzylmercaptotoluqui-none	5-Benzylmercaptotolu-hydroquinone	$FeCl_3$	—	346a
2,6-bis-(2,5-Dihydro-2,5-diketo-1-pyrryl)-quinone	2,4,6-tris-(2,5-Dihydro-2,5-diketopyrryl)-phenol	HNO_3 (sp. gr. 1.48)	—	347
2,6-bis-(2,5-Diketo-1-pyrrolidyl)-quinone	2,4,6-tris-(2,5-Diketo-1-pyrrolidyl)-phenol	HNO_3 (sp. gr. 1.43)	—	348
2,5-bis-(2,4-Dimethyl-1-pyrryl)-3,6-dibromo-quinone	2,5-bis-(2,4-Dimethyl-1-pyrryl)-3,6-dibromo-hydroquinone	Benzoyl peroxide	—	349
2,5-bis-(o- and p-Nitro-phenylmercapto)-qui-none	2,5-bis-(o- and p-Nitro-phenylmercapto)-hydro-quinone	$FeCl_3$	—	350
Butylammonium 2,5-di-butylaminoquinone-3-sulfonate	Hydroquinone, butylamine, and SO_2	Air, $Cu(OH)_2$	—	337
n-Butylmercaptoquinone	n-Butylmercaptohydro-quinone	$FeCl_3$	—	346a
d-Camphor-10-sulfonyl-quinone	d-Camphor-10-sulfonyl-hydroquinone	Ag_2O or PbO_2 $Pb(OAc)_4$	30–80% —	330 51
d-Camphor-10-sulfonyl-p-xyloquinone	d-Camphor-10-sulfonyl-p-xylohydroquinone	Ag_2O or PbO_2	—	330
Carbethoxyquinone	Ethyl gentisate	Ag_2O	80% (cr.)	332
Carbethoxytriphenylqui-none	Ethyl triphenylgentisate	CrO_3 (AcOH)	50%	238a
Carbomethoxyquinone	Methyl gentisate	Ag_2O	60%	332
5-Carbomethoxytoluqui-none	Methyl 4-methylgentisate	Ag_2O	60%	350a
6-Carbomethoxytoluqui-none	Methyl 3-methylgentisate	Ag_2O	84%	350a
Diammonium 2,5-diamino-quinone-3,6-disulfonate	Hydroquinone, ammonia, and SO_2	Air, $Cu(OH)_2$	—	334
Diamylammonium 2,5-diamylaminoquinone-3,6-disulfonate	Hydroquinone, amylamine, and SO_2	Air, $Cu(OH)_2$	—	338
2,5-Dibenzoylquinone	2,5-Dibenzoylhydroquinone	Ag_2O	70% (cr.)	331
2,6-Dibenzoylquinone	2,6-Dibenzoylhydroquinone	$Na_2Cr_2O_7$ (AcOH, H_2SO_4)	60%	339
	2,6-Dibenzoyl-4-amino-phenol	$K_2S_2O_8$	Trace	340
Dibutylammonium 2,5-di-butylaminoquinone-3,6-disulfonate	Hydroquinone, butylamine, and SO_2	Air, $Cu(OH)_2$	—	337

* See p. 315 for explanation of system and abbreviations in tables.
† References 346–355 are listed on p. 359.

TABLE V—*Continued*

MISCELLANEOUS QUINONES

Quinone	Substance Oxidized	Oxidizing Agent	Yield	References*
2,5-Dicarbethoxy-3,6-di-hydroxyquinone	2,5-Dicarbethoxytetrahy-droquinone	HNO_2	30%	351
2-(β,β-Dicarbomethoxy-ethyl)-3-bromo-5,6-di-methylbenzoquinone	3-Carbomethoxy-3,4-di-hydro-5-bromo-6-hy-droxy-7,8-dimethylcou-marin	$FeCl_3$ (MeOH)	89%	164*b*
2,3-Dicyanoquinone	2,3-Dicyanohydroquinone	Oxides from HNO_3	—	352
2,3-Dicyano-5-chloroqui-none	2,3-Dicyano-5-chlorohydro-quinone	Oxides from HNO_3	—	352
2,3-Dicyano-5,6-dichloro-quinone	2,3-Dicyano-5,6-dichloro-hydroquinone	Oxides from HNO_3	—	352
2,3-Dicyano-5,6-dibromo-quinone	2,3-Dicyano-5,6-dibromo-hydroquinone	Oxides from HNO_3	—	352
Dicyclohexylammonium 2,5-dicyclohexylamino-quinone-3,6-disulfonate	Hydroquinone, cyclohexyl-amine, and SO_2	Air, $Cu(OH)_2$	—	336
Diisoamylammonium 2,5-diisoamylaminoquinone-3,6-disulfonate	Hydroquinone, isoamyl-amine, and SO_2	Air, $Cu(OH)_2$	—	338
Diisobutylammonium 2,5-diisobutylaminoquinone-3,6-disulfonate	Hydroquinone, isobutyl-amine, and SO_2	Air, $Cu(OH)_2$	—	338
Dimethylammonium 2,5-dimethylaminoquinone-3,6-disulfonate	Hydroquinone, methyl-amine, and SO_2	Air, $Cu(OH)_2$	—	335
2-(Diphenylbenzoyl-methyl)-5-methoxyqui-none	2-(Diphenylbenzoyl-methyl)-1,4,5-trimethoxy-benzene	HNO_3 (AcOH)	—	266
2,3-, 2,5-, and 2,6-Diphthal-imidoquinone	2,3-, 2,5-, and 2,6-Diphthal-imidohydroquinone	HNO_3 (sp. gr. 1.4)	—	353
Durylic acid quinone	2,4,5-Trimethyl-3,6-diam-inobenzoic acid	$FeCl_3$	100% (cr.)	95 (y.) 333 (y.)
Ethylmercaptoquinone	Ethylmercaptohydro-quinone	$FeCl_3$	62% (o.)	346*a*
Ethyl β-pseudocumoqui-nonylpropionate	3,4-Dihydro-5,7,8-tri-methyl-6-hydroxycou-marin	$AgNO_3$ (EtOH)	Good	253
Isobutylmercaptoquinone	Isobutylmercaptohydro-quinone	$FeCl_3$	—	346*a*
2-Meconyl-5-methoxyqui-none	2-Meconyl-1,4,5-trimeth-oxybenzene	HNO_3 (AcOH)	—	266
2-(4′-Nitromeconyl)-5-methoxyquinone	2-Meconyl-1,4,5-trimeth-oxybenzene	HNO_3 (sp. gr. 1.4)	83% (cr.)	266
2-Methylmercapto-5-phenylquinone	2-Methylmercapto-5-phenylhydroquinone	$FeCl_3$	—	346*a*
2-Methylmercapto-quinone	2-Methylmercapto-4-hydroxyaniline	$Na_2Cr_2O_7$ (H_2SO_4)	—	345
	Methylmercaptohydro-quinone	$FeCl_3$	71% (o.)	346*a*

* References 346–355 are listed on p. 359.

TABLE V *—Continued

MISCELLANEOUS QUINONES

Quinone	Substance Oxidized	Oxidizing Agent	Yield	References
2-Methylmercapto-3,5-di-chloroquinone	2-Methylmercapto-3,5-di-chlorohydroquinone	$FeCl_3$	—	346a
5-Methylmercaptotolu-quinone	5-Methylmercaptotolu-hydroquinone	$FeCl_3$	—	346a
2-Phenylazoxyquinone	2-Phenylazoxyhydroqui-none	PbO_2 (AcOH)	—	354
2-(o-Nitrophenylmer-capto)-quinone	2-(o-Nitrophenylmer-capto)-hydroquinone	$FeCl_3$	—	350
Phthalic anhydride quinone	3,6-Dihydroxyphthalic anhydride	Oxides from HNO_3	—	352
2-Phthalidyl-5-methoxy-quinone	2-Phthalidyl-1,4,5-trimeth-oxybenzene	HNO_3 (AcOH)	—	266
Phthalimidoquinone	3,6-Dihydroxyphthalimide	Oxides from HNO_3	—	352
Potassium S-2-(5-phenyl-quinonyl)-thiosulfate	Potassium S-2-(5-phenyl-hydroquinonyl)-thio-sulfate	CrO_3	—	346a
Potassium S-2-quinonyl-thiosulfate	Potassium S-2-hydro-quinonylthiosulfate	CrO_3	—	346a
n-Propylmercaptoquinone	n-Propylmercaptohydro-quinone	$FeCl_3$	80% (o.)	346a
β-Pseudocumoquinonyl-propionic acid	β-(2,4,5-Trimethyl-3,6-di-aminophenyl)-propionic acid	$FeCl_3$	56%	101
Quinonesulfonic acid	Barium hydroquinone sul-fonate	PbO_2 (H_2SO_4)	Poor	341
	Hydroquinonesulfonic acid	$Na_2Cr_2O_7$ (H_2SO_4)	90% (as Na salt)	342
Quinone tetrathioglycolic acid	Hydroquinone tetrathio-glycolic acid	HNO_3 (dil.)	60%	353a
Quinonylacetic acid	Homogentisic acid	$Na_2Cr_2O_7$ (H_2SO_4)	65–70%	343
γ-Quinonylbutyric acid	2-Hydroxy-5-amino-γ-phenylbutyric acid	$Na_2Cr_2O_7$ (H_2SO_4)	57% (c.)	344
ε-Quinonylcaproic acid	2-Hydroxy-5-amino-ε-phenylcaproic acid	$Na_2Cr_2O_7$ (H_2SO_4)	83%	344
2,5-Quinonyldiacetic acid	2,5-Hydroquinonyldiacetic acid	$K_2Cr_2O_7$ (H_2SO_4)	85%	354a
Tetracarbethoxyquinone	Tetracarbethoxy-p-phenyl-enediamine	HNO_3 (conc.)	50–55%	95
2,3,5-Trimethyl-6-(3′-keto-butyl)-quinone	2,3,5-Trimethyl-6-(3′-keto-butyl)-p-phenylenedi-amine	—	—	255
2,3,5-Trimethylquinone-α-thioacetic acid	2,3,5-Trimethylhydroqui-none-α-thioacetic acid	$FeCl_3$	—	355
Triphenylquinonecar-boxylic acid	Triphenylgentisic acid	$FeCl_3$	55%	238a

* See p. 315 for explanation of system and abbreviations in tables.

REFERENCES TO TABLE V

[346] Nierenstein, *J. Chem. Soc.*, **111**, 8 (1917).

[346a] Alcalay, *Helv. Chim. Acta*, **30**, 578 (1947).

[347] Covello, *Gazz. chim. ital.*, **63**, 517 (1933).

[348] Covello and Gabrieli, *Rend. accad. sci. Napoli* (iii), **32**, 147 (1926) [*C. A.*, **22**, 1762 (1928)].

[349] Pratesi, *Gazz. chim. ital.*, **66**, 215 (1936).

[350] Dimroth, Kraft, and Aichinger, *Ann.*, **545**, 124 (1940).

[350a] Nudenberg, Gaddis, and Butz, *J. Org. Chem.*, **8**, 500 (1943).

[351] Hantzsch and Loewy, *Ber.*, **19**, 27 (1886).

[352] Thiele and Günther, *Ann.*, **349**, 45 (1906).

[353] Covello, *Rend. accad. sci. Napoli* (iii), **34**, 149 (1928) [*C. A.*, **23**, 2430 (1929)].

[353a] Schubert, *J. Am. Chem. Soc.*, **69**, 712 (1947).

[354] Bigiavi and Benedetti, *Gazz. chim. ital.*, **54**, 363 (1924).

[354a] Wood, Colburn, Cox, and Garland, *J. Am. Chem. Soc.*, **66**, 1540 (1944).

[355] Snell and Weissberger, *J. Am. Chem. Soc.*, **61**, 450 (1939).

PREPARATIVE METHODS DEPENDING INDIRECTLY UPON OXIDATION

Halogenation of some quinones apparently proceeds by addition to the double bond and elimination of halogen acid.[79, 356] Halogenation of other quinones, however, involves a dihalohydroquinone as an intermediate. Halogenation of this latter group of quinones therefore serves as an indirect route to halogenated quinones since the halohydroquinones can be oxidized to the corresponding quinones. 3,5-Dibromo-2,6-dimethoxyhydroquinone is obtained by addition of one mole of bromine to 2,6-dimethoxyquinone.[287] The hydroquinone can be oxidized to the quinone by chromic acid, ferric chloride, or a second mole of bromine. In the preparation of dibromo-*o*-xyloquinone by bromination of *o*-xyloquinone, the dibromohydroquinone is an intermediate.[85]

Treatment of quinone with a primary alcohol of low molecular weight in the presence of zinc chloride gives the 2,5-dialkoxyquinone and hydro-

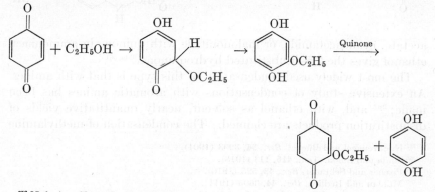

[356] Nef, *Am. Chem. J.*, **12**, 463 (1890).

quinone.[357] It seems established [355, 358] that this reaction involves the 1,4-addition of the alcohol, rearrangement to the hydroquinone, and oxidation by a second molecule of quinone. A repetition of this process gives one mole of 2,5-dialkoxyquinone and two moles of hydroqu none from two moles of alcohol and three moles of quinone.

By similar condensations a variety of monosubstituted or 2,5-disub-stituted quinones has been prepared. Thiols condense with quinones on mixing the reactants in ethanol to give mono- or di-substituted qui-nones in yields of 21–92.5%.[355] Esters of amino acids [359] react similarly to give disubstitution products (51–64% yield). Indoles give a conden-

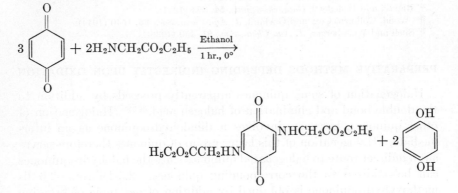

$$3 \quad + 2H_2NCH_2CO_2C_2H_5 \xrightarrow[\text{1 hr., 0°}]{\text{Ethanol}}$$

sation involving the beta carbon atom; nearly quantitative yields of monosubstitution products result.[360] The condensation of ethyl cyano-

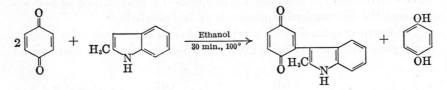

acetate, cyanoacetamide, or malononitrile with quinone in ammoniacal ethanol gives the 2,5-disubstituted hydroquinone.[354a, 361]

The most widely used condensation of this type is that with amines. An extensive study of condensations with aromatic amines has been made; [358] and, with ethanol as solvent, nearly quantitative yields of disubstitution products are claimed. The condensation of methylamine

[357] Knoevenagel and Bückel, *Ber.*, **34**, 3993 (1901).
[358] Suida and Suida, *Ann.*, **416**, 113 (1918).
[359] Fischer and Schrader, *Ber.*, **43**, 525 (1910).
[360] Möhlau and Redlich, *Ber.*, **44**, 3605 (1911).
[361] Wood and Cox, *Org. Syntheses*, **26**, 24 (1946).

with a variety of quinones [77, 116, 252, 265] has been studied (yields 34–90% [252]). Methoxyl groups may be replaced by methylamino groups.[252]

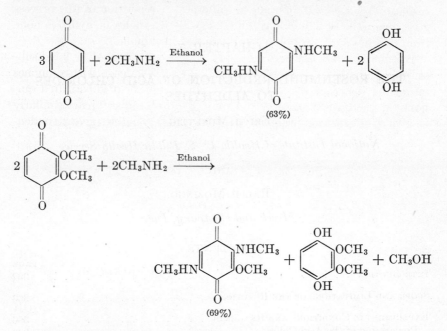

Since oxidation is only an incidental part of the reactions discussed in this section, experimental procedures and a table of compounds are not included.

CHAPTER 7

THE ROSENMUND REDUCTION OF ACID CHLORIDES TO ALDEHYDES

Erich Mosettig

National Institute of Health, U. S. Public Health Service

AND

Ralph Mozingo

Merck and Company, Inc.

CONTENTS

INTRODUCTION

In the synthesis of complex molecules, particularly in connection with natural products, it is occasionally desirable to prepare an aldehyde when the readily available starting material is the corresponding acid.

For accomplishing this transformation, $RCO_2H \rightarrow RCHO$, the Rosenmund reduction [1] is probably the most useful method for application to a large number of aldehydes of varied types.

The Rosenmund reduction consists in the selective hydrogenation of an acid chloride in the presence of a suitable catalyst, usually supported palladium, to the corresponding aldehyde. The reduction

$$RCOCl + H_2 \xrightarrow{\text{Pd-BaSO}_4} RCHO + HCl$$

is carried out by bubbling hydrogen through a hot solution of the acid chloride in which the catalyst is suspended.

SCOPE AND LIMITATIONS OF THE REACTION

The success of the method is dependent upon the resistance of the aldehyde to reduction under the conditions which permit its formation from the acid chloride. Since the reduction is effected by hydrogen in the presence of a catalyst, the aldehyde so formed may be reduced further to the corresponding alcohol and hydrocarbon.

$$RCHO + H_2 \xrightarrow{\text{Catalyst}} RCH_2OH$$

$$RCH_2OH + H_2 \xrightarrow{\text{Catalyst}} RCH_3 + H_2O$$

The reduction of the aldehyde can be prevented by the use of an appropriate catalyst "poison" or "regulator" which inactivates the catalyst towards reduction of aldehyde but not of acid chloride. The addition of a regulator was the result of an early observation of Rosenmund and Zetzsche.[2] These authors obtained nearly quantitative yields of benzaldehyde in their first experiments on the reduction of benzoyl chloride but later experienced difficulty in repeating the preparation. It has been supposed that the success of the early experiments was due to the presence of impurities, either in the solvents or in the acid chloride, which acted as the poison. Consequently much attention has been paid to the development of such regulators.[3-10] They usually contain sulfur

[1] Rosenmund, *Ber.*, **51**, 585 (1918).
[2] Rosenmund and Zetzsche, *Ber.*, **54**, 425 (1921).
[3] Rosenmund, Zetzsche, and Heise, *Ber.*, **54**, 638 (1921).
[4] Rosenmund, Zetzsche, and Heise, *Ber.*, **54**, 2038 (1921).
[5] Abel, *Ber* , **54**, 1407 (1921).
[6] Rosenmund and Zetzsche, *Ber.*, **54**, 2885 (1921).
[7] Abel, *Ber.*, **55**, 322 (1922).
[8] Rosenmund and Zetzsche, *Ber.*, **55**, 2774 (1922).
[9] Weygand and Meusel, *Ber.*, **76**, 503 (1943).
[10] Weygand and Meusel, *Ber.*, **76**, 498 (1943).

("quinoline-S," thioquinanthrene, phenylisothiocyanate, thiourea). In many reductions, however, it is not necessary to use a regulator, and in some the use of the poison appears to be definitely disadvantageous. Moreover, it has been reported [11] that the decisive factor in the acid chloride reduction is the temperature; if it is kept near the lowest point at which hydrogen chloride is evolved, the aldehydes are obtained in optimal yields.

If further reduction of the aldehyde to alcohol and hydrocarbon does take place, both the alcohol and the water react with the acid chloride, yielding the ester and the acid anhydride, respectively. The formation

$$RCOCl + RCH_2OH \rightarrow RCO_2CH_2R + HCl$$

$$RCOCl + H_2O \rightarrow RCO_2H + HCl$$

$$RCOCl + RCO_2H \rightarrow (RCO)_2O + HCl$$

of the acid anhydride is said to be an important side reaction in the reduction of certain heterocyclic acid chlorides when traces of oxygen and water are present in the hydrogen used.[12] Other reductions which may occur as side reactions involve the formation of the ether, RCH_2OCH_2R; and the cleavage of the ester, RCO_2CH_2R, to the acid, RCO_2H, and the hydrocarbon, RCH_3.[3,4] These appear to be of no practical significance, however.

Some acid chlorides undergo reductive removal of the —COCl group according to the following scheme:

$$RCOCl + H_2 \rightarrow RH + CO + HCl$$

This cleavage occurs as a side reaction in the reduction of many heterocyclic acid chlorides and has been observed in the preparation of aldehydes from p-anisoyl,[3] 3,4,5-trimethoxybenzoyl,[13] and 2-naphthoyl chloride.[14] Triphenylacetyl chloride is converted quantitatively to triphenylmethane.[15]

The Rosenmund method appears to be generally applicable to the preparation of aliphatic and aromatic monoaldehydes when the corresponding acid chlorides are available. There have been fewer occasions to use it in the aliphatic series than in the aromatic and heterocyclic groups; however, the preparation of chaulmoogryl aldehyde [16] from the

[11] Boehm, Schumann, and Hansen, *Arch. Pharm.*, **271**, 490 (1933).
[12] Rojahn and Fahr, *Ann.*, **434**, 252 (1923).
[13] Späth, *Monatsh.*, **40**, 129 (1919).
[14] Hershberg and Cason, *Org. Syntheses*, **21**, 84 (1941).
[15] Daniloff and Venus-Danilova, *Ber.*, **59**, 377 (1926).
[16] Wagner-Jauregg and Voigt, *Ber.*, **71**, 1973 (1938).

acid in almost quantitative yield, and the preparation of several triterpene aldehydes,[17-24] indicate its value in the conversion of naturally occurring acids to aldehydes.

The chlorides of dibasic acids do not ordinarily give good yields of dialdehydes. For example, succinyl chloride is converted largely to butyrolactone,[25] and o-phthalyl chloride yields phthalide.[26, 27] From the reduction of adipyl chloride the corresponding aldehyde-acid and cyclopentenecarboxylic acid have been isolated.[25] Apparently, part of the difficulty in preparing higher aliphatic dialdehydes lies in the ease with which the products polymerize during attempted purification.[25, 26, 28, 29] Dialdehydes are obtained from m- and p-phthalyl chloride in yields of about 80%,[25, 26] but the preparation of 1,8-naphthalaldehyde from naphthalic acid dichloride fails completely.[30]

It is not yet possible to generalize concerning the extent to which reducible groups other than —COCl may interfere with the Rosenmund reduction. In the presence of a regulator, p-nitrobenzoyl chloride [2] and o-chlorobenzoyl chloride [2] can be converted to the aldehydes without reduction of the nitro group or removal of the nuclear chlorine atom. Certain acid chlorides containing chlorine atoms attached to a pyridine ring give the chloro aldehydes [31, 32] in the absence of a regulator. Cinnamoyl chloride can be reduced to cinnamic aldehyde by operating at slightly reduced pressures in the presence of a regulator, but the yield is only fair (50–60%).[33]

The yield of aldehyde in the Rosenmund reduction varies greatly. While some acid chlorides give none or very little of the aldehyde, most acid chlorides give over 50%, and yields over 80% are not uncommon.

The method has been used with small quantities [14] of acid chloride as

[17] Ruzicka and Schellenberg, *Helv. Chim. Acta*, **20**, 1553 (1937).
[18] Ruzicka and Marxer, *Helv. Chim. Acta*, **22**, 195 (1939).
[19] Ruzicka and Wirz, *Helv. Chim. Acta*, **22**, 948 (1939).
[20] Ruzicka and Wirz, *Helv. Chim. Acta*, **23**, 132 (1940).
[21] Ruzicka and Marxer, *Helv. Chim. Acta*, **23**, 144 (1940).
[22] Ruzicka and Häusermann, *Helv. Chim. Acta*, **25**, 439 (1942).
[22a] Ruzicka, Rey, Spillmann, and Baumgartner, *Helv. Chim. Acta*, **26**, 1638 (1943).
[23] Ruzicka and Marxer, *Helv. Chim. Acta*, **25**, 1561 (1942).
[24] Ruzicka, Rey, Spillmann, and Baumgartner, *Helv. Chim. Acta*, **26**, 1659 (1943).
[25] Fröschl, Maier, and Heuberger, *Monatsh.*, **59**, 256 (1932).
[26] Rosenmund, Zetzsche, and Flütsch, *Ber.*, **54**, 2888 (1921).
[27] Zetzsche, Flütsch, Enderlin, and Loosli, *Helv. Chim. Acta*, **9**, 182 (1926).
[28] Waser, *Helv. Chim. Acta*, **8**, 117 (1925)
[29] Rosenmund, Zetzsche, and Enderlin, *Ber.*, **55**, 609 (1922).
[30] Davies and Leeper, *J. Chem. Soc.*, **1927**, 1124.
[31] Graf and Weinberg, *J. prakt. Chem.*, [2] **134**, 177 (1932).
[32] Graf and László, *J. prakt. Chem.*, [2] **138**, 231 (1933).
[33] Rosenmund, Zetzsche, and Weiler, *Ber.*, **56**, 1481 (1923).

well as on the usual preparative scale.[14, 34]   No variation in the yield with
the quantity of reactants has been reported.

A few acid chlorides have been converted to aldehydes by vapor-
phase catalytic reduction. Excellent yields of benzaldehyde and isovaleraldehyde have been obtained [35] by passing the acid chlorides and
hydrogen at atmospheric pressure over palladinized asbestos at about
200°. Phenylacetyl chloride, however, gave phenylethyl alcohol and
ethylbenzene, and succinyl chloride gave butyrolactone. Aromatic and
higher aliphatic chlorides have been reduced [36, 37] to aldehydes by operating at reduced pressures with nickel, nickel chloride, and platinum as
catalysts. These methods appear to present no definite advantage.

EXPERIMENTAL CONDITIONS AND REAGENTS

Preparation of the Acid Chloride. The acid chloride may be prepared
by any one of the usual methods,[38-57] but it should be purified by distillation or crystallization immediately before use. The thionyl chloride
method is to be preferred to those using phosphorus halides. Though
traces of thionyl chloride do not affect the Rosenmund reduction appreciably, phosphorus compounds are more serious poisons, and even traces
may retard or prevent the reduction.[58, 59]

[34] Barnes, *Org. Syntheses*, **21**, 110 (1941).
[35] Fröschl and Danoff, *J. prakt. Chem.*, [2] **144**, 217 (1936).
[36] Grignard and Mingasson, *Compt. rend.*, **185**, 1173 (1927).
[37] Escourrou, *Bull. soc. chim. France*, (5), **6**, 1173 (1939).
[38] Clark and Bell, *Trans. Roy. Soc. Can.*, [3] **27**, 97 (1933).
[39] Meyer, *Monatsh.*, **22**, 415 (1901).
[40] Silberrad, *J. Soc. Chem. Ind.*, **45**, 36, 55 (1926).
[41] McMaster and Ahmann, *J. Am. Chem. Soc.*, **50**, 145 (1928).
[42] Späth and Spitzer, *Ber.*, **59**, 1477 (1926).
[43] Meyer and Graf, *Ber.*, **61**, 2202 (1928).
[44] Fuson and Walker, *Org. Syntheses, Coll. Vol.* **2**, 169.
[45] Helferich and Schaefer, *Org. Syntheses, Coll. Vol.* **1**, 147, 2nd ed.
[46] Martin and Fieser, *Org. Syntheses, Coll. Vol.* **2**, 569.
[47] Fieser and Peters, *J. Am. Chem. Soc.*, **54**, 4373 (1932).
[48] Carré and Libermann, *Compt. rend.*, **199**, 1422 (1934).
[49] Kissling, Ger. pat., 701,953 [*C. A.*, **36**, 99 (1942)].
[50] Kyrides, *J. Am. Chem. Soc.*, **59**, 206 (1937).
[51] Kyrides, *Org. Syntheses*, **20**, 51 (1940).
[52] Ruggli and Maeder, *Helv. Chim. Acta*, **26**, 1476 (1943).
[53] Carré and Libermann, *Compt. rend.*, **201**, 147 (1935).
[54] Webb and Corwin, *J. Am. Chem. Soc.*, **66**, 1456 (1944).
[55] Boon, *J. Chem. Soc.*, **1945**, 601.
[56] Wood, Jackson, Baldwin, and Longenecker, *J. Am. Chem. Soc.*, **66**, 287 (1944).
[57] Adams and Ulich, *J. Am. Chem. Soc.*, **42**, 599 (1920).
[58] Zetzsche and Arnd, *Helv. Chim. Acta*, **8**, 591 (1925).
[59] Zetzsche and Arnd, *Helv. Chim. Acta*, **9**, 173 (1926).

The Hydrogen. Commercial electrolytic hydrogen directly from the cylinder is most satisfactory. When it is necessary to remove traces of oxygen, as in the preparation of heterocyclic aldehydes, the hydrogen is passed over a hot copper spiral [12, 31, 60, 61] and dried. Drying has been accomplished by passing the hydrogen over Dehydrite [62] or Drierite.[14]

The Solvent. The solvents which have been used most frequently are xylene and toluene. To a lesser extent benzene, tetralin, and decalin have been employed. The use of other hydrocarbons and of ethers has been reported.[1, 63] Although aromatic hydrocarbons of commercial grade have often been used for the Rosenmund reduction, it is preferable to use highly purified solvents (with a known amount of regulator where necessary) so that the preparation of a given aldehyde is reproducible.

The purification of the solvent has been generally accomplished by distillation over sodium. Impurities containing sulfur can be destroyed by distillation of the solvent from Raney nickel catalyst.[64, 65]

The solvent in the Rosenmund reduction is used in amounts of three to six times the weight of the acid chloride.

The Catalyst. As catalyst, palladium on barium sulfate is commonly used, ordinarily with a palladium content of 5%, occasionally of 2–3%. Generally, 1 part of the catalyst is used for 5–10 parts of acid chloride. Other carriers, as kieselguhr,[2, 61] charcoal, [25, 61] and calcium carbonate,[28] have been reported. Other metals, such as osmium,[25] platinum,[9, 36, 37] and nickel,[1, 36, 37, 66, 67] have been used.

The Regulator. The poison most commonly used is the crude preparation of thioquinanthrene, called "quinoline-sulfur" or "quinoline-S."[2] Whenever the necessity of a regulator is indicated, it is advisable, for the sake of reproducibility, to use freshly prepared "quinoline-S"[10, 33] or pure thioquinanthrene[2, 33] (for preparation and structure, see Edinger and associates[68-72]) or other pure sulfur-containing compounds.[2] Of the latter thiourea has been recommended.[9] The amount of regulator reported varies widely. About 10 mg. of "quinoline-S" per gram of catalyst will usually be found satisfactory.[14]

[60] Rojahn and Trieloff, *Ann.*, **445**, 296 (1925).

[61] Rojahn and Seitz, *Ann.*, **437**, 297 (1924).

[62] Mosettig and van de Kamp, *J. Am. Chem. Soc.*, **55**, 2995 (1933).

[63] Zetzsche, Enderlin, Flütsch, and Menzi, *Helv. Chim. Acta*, **9**, 177 (1926).

[64] Mozingo, Wolf, Harris, and Folkers, *J. Am. Chem. Soc.*, **65**, 1013 (1943).

[65] Adkins, *Reactions of Hydrogen*, University of Wisconsin Press, p. 28, 1937.

[66] Schliewienski, *Z. angew. Chem.*, **35**, 483 (1922).

[67] Rosenmund, *Z. angew. Chem.*, **35**, 483 (1922).

[68] Edinger, *Ber.*, **33**, 3769 (1900).

[69] Edinger and Lubberger, *J. prakt. Chem.*, [2] **54**, 340 (1896).

[70] Edinger, *J. prakt. Chem.*, [2] **56**, 273 (1897).

[71] Edinger and Ekeley, *Ber.*, **35**, 96 (1902).

[72] Edinger and Ekeley, *J. prakt. Chem.*, [2] **66**, 209 (1902).

General Precautions. The apparatus employed in the reduction must be carefully dried. Catalyst and solvent too must be free from water. When one of the lower-boiling hydrocarbon solvents is used, it is convenient to exclude moisture completely by placing the solvent, catalyst, and regulator in the reduction apparatus and distilling part of the solvent. The reflux condenser jacket is left empty, and, while a *slow* stream of hydrogen is passed through the stirred catalyst suspension, the solvent is heated to boiling and some solvent allowed to distil through the condenser. This fraction of solvent, which may be condensed by an auxiliary condenser, carries with it any water present. Heating is then interrupted, the circulation of water through the condenser is started carefully, and the acid chloride is added.

The apparatus used in the Rosenmund reduction should be as nearly all glass as possible. A Kyrides stirrer seal [73] made with Neoprene tubing is convenient. When mercury-sealed stirrers are used, mercury must not be allowed to splash into the reaction mixture. A Hershberg stirrer made with tantalum wire [14] is preferable to a glass stirrer, as it is much less likely to break during the rapid stirring which is necessary.

EXPERIMENTAL PROCEDURES

Excellent directions for the Rosenmund reduction under the usual conditions are those of Hershberg and Cason for β-naphthaldehyde, published in *Organic Syntheses*; [14] these are complete, detailed, and involve the use of the poison. Directions are given also for the preparation of an aldehyde (2,4,6-trimethylbenzaldehyde) without the use of the poison. [34]

Preparation of the Regulator (Quinoline-Sulfur [14]). Six grams of freshly distilled quinoline and 1 g. of sulfur are heated under reflux for five hours. After cooling, the mixture is diluted to 70 ml. with xylene to permit convenient measurement of an aliquot containing the desired amount of the regulator. This solution, which contains 0.1 g. of the regulator per milliliter, may be diluted to larger volumes if small quantities of the regulator are desired.

Preparation of Palladium-Barium Sulfate.[74, 75, 75a] A suspension of 1.7 g. of dry palladium chloride in 100 ml. of water containing 1 ml. of concentrated hydrochloric acid is heated on a steam bath or is allowed to stand (several days) until a clear, dark red solution is obtained. A

[73] Wayne and Adkins, *Org. Syntheses*, **21**, 39 (1941).

[74] Schmidt, *Ber.*, **52**, 409 (1919).

[75] Mozingo, Harris, Wolf, Hoffhine, Easton, and Folkers, *J. Am. Chem. Soc.*, **67**, 2092 (1945).

[75a] Mozingo, *Org. Syntheses*, **26**, 77 (1946.)

solution of 15 g. of anhydrous sodium sulfate in 200 ml. of water is added in the course of five minutes to a mechanically stirred solution of 21 g. of barium chloride dihydrate in 200 ml. of water at 70°. The precipitate is washed by decantation with hot water until the washings do not give a precipitate with aqueous silver nitrate. The barium sulfate is then suspended in 300 ml. of water containing 1 ml. of 40% aqueous formaldehyde. The suspension is heated to 80°, and the solution of palladium chloride is added. The well-stirred mixture is neutralized to litmus by the addition of 1 N sodium hydroxide solution over a period of fifteen to thirty minutes. Heating and stirring are continued for twenty minutes after a weakly alkaline reaction has been observed. The gray precipitate is allowed to settle and is then washed by decantation until the washings are chloride free. The precipitate is filtered by gentle suction and is dried in a desiccator over calcium chloride. The dry catalyst contains 5% of palladium.

Preparation of 1-Acenaphthaldehyde.[76] In a 200-ml. round-bottomed flask equipped with a reflux condenser, a sealed stirrer, and a gas inlet tube reaching to the bottom of the flask are placed 75 ml. of xylene, 0.35 g. of 2% palladium-barium sulfate catalyst, and 0.075 g. of quinoline-sulfur. A slow stream of hydrogen is passed through the stirred mixture while the temperature is raised to reflux and any water is co-distilled. The condenser water is turned on, and 7.5 g. of 1-acenaphthoyl chloride is added to the hot mixture. The mixture is rapidly stirred at reflux temperature (bath at about 160°) while hydrogen is passed through the mixture. The exit gases are passed through a Drierite tube and bubbled through water. The hydrogen chloride is titrated from time to time. After about five and one-half hours no more hydrogen chloride is formed; about 88% of the theoretical amount is evolved. After cooling, the catalyst is removed by centrifuging and the solvent is distilled under reduced pressure. The residue is distilled to give about 5 g. of crude aldehyde, b.p. 150–165°/2 mm. The aldehyde is dissolved in ether-benzene and shaken overnight with 75 ml. of saturated sodium bisulfite solution, and the bisulfite addition product is separated by centrifuging and decomposed with sodium carbonate solution to give 4.5 g. (72%) of 1-acenaphthaldehyde, m.p. 93–99°. The product may be recrystallized from ether-petroleum ether to give faintly yellow needles melting at 99.5–100.5°.

Preparation of 3-Phenanthraldehyde.[62] One hundred grams of freshly distilled 3-phenanthroyl chloride is dissolved with warming in 200 ml. of decalin (distilled over sodium) in an apparatus (Fig. 1) of 400-ml. capacity. Eight grams of 5% palladium-barium sulfate catalyst is

---

[76] Fieser and Hershberg, *J. Am. Chem. Soc.*, **62**, 49 (1940).

added. The reaction vessel is placed in an oil bath, and a rapid stream of hydrogen is passed into the solution. A faint development of hydrogen chloride commences at 70°; the rate of evolution increases with rise in temperature and reaches a maximum at 180°, at which temperature the reduction is carried out. The hydrogen chloride formation drops off quite suddenly after five to ten hours, and at the point where it becomes faint the reaction is interrupted.

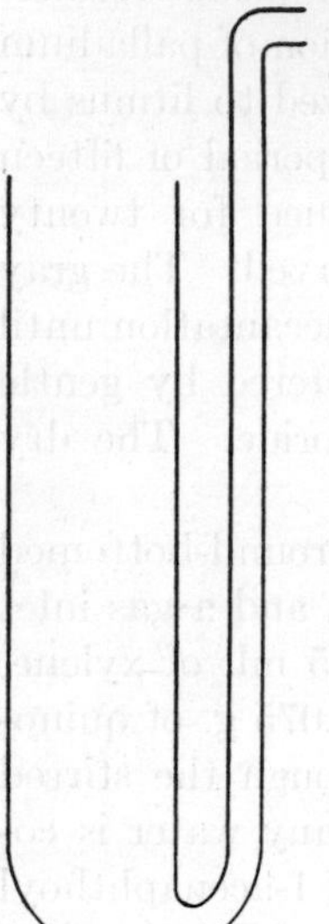

After the reaction mixture has cooled to room temperature, the decalin solution is decanted from the catalyst, diluted with 600 ml. of ether, and shaken with an equal volume of saturated sodium bisulfite solution for twelve hours. The voluminous precipitate of bisulfite compound is filtered and is washed thoroughly with ether. The bisulfite compound is decomposed by boiling with excess dilute aqueous sodium carbonate, and the aldehyde is extracted with ether. The ether solution is dried, and the ether is evaporated. The aldehyde crystallizes immediately. It contains traces of decalin, which are washed out with petroleum ether. It is distilled at reduced pressure (oil pump). The average yield is 90%. The aldehyde can be recrystallized from benzene by the addition of petroleum ether to give a product that melts at 79.5–80°.

Fig. 1

2- and 9-Phenanthraldehydes. These are prepared in the same manner as the 3-aldehyde except that 4 parts of decalin are employed in the reduction of 1 part of acid chloride. The yield of the 2-isomer, m.p. 59–59.5°, recrystallized from benzene-petroleum ether, is 70%. The yield of the 9-isomer, m.p. 100.5–101°, recrystallized from ethanol, is 90%.

TABLES OF ACID CHLORIDES REDUCED BY THE ROSENMUND METHOD

In the following tables are summarized the compounds whose reduction by the Rosenmund method is reported in the literature to November, 1947. Acid chlorides in which the functional group is attached to an aliphatic or hydroaromatic residue are listed in Table I; aromatic and heterocyclic acid chlorides are listed in Tables II and III, respectively.

TABLE I

ALIPHATIC, HYDROAROMATIC, AND ALIPHATIC-AROMATIC ALDEHYDES

Acid Chloride	Solvent	Temperature, °C	Catalyst	Regulator	Yield of Aldehyde, %	Reference*
Butyryl chloride	Ether	—	Pd-BaSO₄ (5%)	None	50 [a]	1
Isovaleryl chloride	(In gas phase)	190–200	Pd-asbestos	None	Quantitative	35
α-Ethylisovaleryl chloride	Xylene	130–140	Pd-BaSO₄	None	7	77
Stearoyl chloride	Xylene	150	Pd-BaSO₄ (5%)	None	17–21 [b]	1, 78
Undecylenoyl chloride	Xylene	—	Pd-BaSO₄	Thiourea	— [c]	79
β-Carbomethoxypropionyl chloride	Xylene	110	Pd-BaSO₄ (5%)	Quinoline-S	65	14
γ-Carbomethoxybutyryl chloride	Xylene	140–150	Pd-BaSO₄ (5%)	Quinoline-S	52	80
rac.-Pilopic acid chloride	Benzene	Room temperature	Pd-BaSO₄ (5%)	None	73	81(a)
rac.-Isopilopic acid chloride	Xylene	Reflux	Pd-BaSO₄	None	75	81(b)
d,l-Homoisopilopic acid chloride	Xylene	Reflux	Pd-BaSO₄	None	—	81(c)
Sebacic ethyl ester chloride	Xylene	—	Pd-BaSO₄ (5%)	None	70–80	82
"Hydnochaulic acid" chloride [d]	Xylene	160	Pd-BaSO₄	None	94.5	16
Acetyloleanolyl chloride	Xylene	—	Pd-BaSO₄ (5%)	Quinoline-S	64	17
Acetyldesoxoglycyrrhetinyl chloride	Xylene	155	Pd-BaSO₄ (5%)	Quinoline-S	79	18
Acetyl-β-boswellinyl chloride	Toluene	—	Pd-BaSO₄ (5%)	None	—	19
Acetyl-α-boswellinyl chloride	Toluene	—	Pd-BaSO₄ (5%)	None	—	20
Diacetylhederagenin chloride	Xylene	150	Pd-BaSO₄ (5%)	Quinoline-S	—	21
Acetylpielemenolic acid chloride	Toluene	80	Pd-BaSO₄ (5%)	None	59	22, 22a
Acetylquinovayl dichloride	Benzene	85	Pt	None	— [e]	23
Novayl chloride	Xylene	—	Pd-BaSO₄	None	—	23
Acetylpyroquinovayl chloride	Xylene	150	Pd-BaSO₄	None	—	23
Elemenoyl chloride	Toluene	90–100	Pd-BaSO₄	None	—	24
Isoelemenoyl chloride	Toluene	—	Pd-BaSO₄	None	58	24
Diacetylechinocystic acid chloride	Xylene	85	Pd-BaSO₄ (5%)	None	—	82a
O-Methylpodocarpic acid chloride	Xylene	—	Pd-BaSO₄ (10%)	None	80 [f]	83
O-Methyl-7-isopropyl podocarpic acid chloride	Xylene	—	Pd-BaSO₄ (10%)	None	88	83
Dehydroabietic acid chloride	Xylene	—	Pd-BaSO₄ (10%)	None	38 [g]	83
6-Methoxydehydroabietic acid chloride	Xylene	—	Pd-BaSO₄ (10%)	None	56	83
rac.-α-7-Methyl bisdehydrodoisynolic acid chloride	Xylene	125	Pd-charcoal (10%)	None	—	83a
rac.-β-7-Methyl bisdehydrodoisynolic acid chloride	Xylene	125	Pd-charcoal (10%)	None	—	83a
(+)7-Methyl doisynolic acid chloride	Xylene	100–120	Pd-charcoal (10%)	None	—	83a
Δ⁹,¹⁴-2,13-Dimethyl-2-carbomethoxy-7β-acetoxydodecahydrophenanthryl-1-acetyl chloride	Toluene	100–120	Pd-charcoal (10%)	None	—	83b
2,13-Dimethyl-2-carbomethoxy-7α-acetoxyperhydrophenanthryl-1-acetyl chloride	Toluene	110–120	Pd-charcoal (10%)	None	—	83b

* References 77–84 are listed on p. 376.

TABLE I—*Continued*

ALIPHATIC, HYDROAROMATIC, AND ALIPHATIC-AROMATIC ALDEHYDES

Acid Chloride	Solvent	Temperature, °C	Catalyst	Regulator	Yield of Aldehyde, %	Reference*
Phenylacetyl chloride	Toluene	125	Pd-BaSO₄	Thioquin-anthrene	80	2
Triphenylacetyl chloride	Benzene, toluene, xylene	—	Pd-BaSO₄	None	0 [h]	15
β-o-Methoxyphenylpropionyl chloride	Xylene	—	Pd	None	—	84
Phenoxyacetyl chloride	Xylene	150	Pd-BaSO₄	Quinoline-S	72 [a]	33
Cinnamoyl chloride	Xylene	122/560 mm.	Pd-BaSO₄	Thioquin-anthrene, quinoline-S	50–60 [a]	33
o-Chlorocinnamoyl chloride	Xylene	125/560 mm.	Pd-BaSO₄	Quinoline-S	61–92 [a]	33
Oxalyl chloride	Benzene	40–50	Pd-BaSO₄ (5%)	—	0 [i]	25
Malonyl chloride [j]	Benzene	90	Pd-BaSO₄ (5%)	—	0	25
Succinyl chloride	Benzene, toluene, tetralin	—	Pd-BaSO₄ (5%)	Quinoline-S	0 [k]	25
Adipyl chloride	Toluene	—	Os-charcoal Pd-BaSO₄ (5%)	None	0 [l]	25
Suberyl chloride	Xylene	155	Pd-kieselguhr (2.5%)	Quinoline-S	76 [m]	26, 25
Sebacyl chloride	Xylene	—	Pd-CaCO₃ (2%)	None	—[n]	28, 29
Tetraacetyl-D-ribonyl chloride [o]	Xylene	—	Pd-BaSO₄ (5%)	—	—	84a

* References 77–84 are listed on p. 376.

[a] Yield calculated from bisulfite compound.

[b] Yield from stearic acid calculated on the basis of the purest semithiocarbazone obtained.

[c] During the Rosenmund reduction both partial reduction and extensive migration of the double bond takes place. Addition of bromine to undecylenoyl chloride removes the possibility of rearrangement and allows reduction of the acyl chloride group to the aldehyde. By treating the resulting dibromoundecylenyl aldehyde diethyl acetal with ethanolic potassium hydroxide, undecyne-10-al-1 diethyl acetal has been obtained.

[d] The authors did not employ the chloride of a homogeneous chaulmoogric acid but a mixture of chlorides obtained from a mixture of chaulmoogric acid and hydnocarpic acid which they named hydnochaulic acid. During the reaction, migration of the alicyclic double bond took place. The use of "quinoline-S" reduced the yield somewhat.

[e] In the Rosenmund reduction of this dichloride only one acyl chloride group is converted to the aldehyde group. Carbon monoxide and hydrogen chloride are eliminated with the formation of a new olefinic bond.

[f] Calculated from the employed acid.

[g] Calculated from isolated semicarbazone.

[h] Triphenylmethane is formed quantitatively.

[i] Only gaseous products were formed; carbon monoxide was absorbed in ammoniacal cuprous chloride solution.

[j] Benzylmalonyl chloride, methylbenzylmalonyl chloride, and diethylmalonyl chloride gave also only amorphous products.[27]

[k] Main product, butyrolactone; by-products, β-formylpropionic acid and succinic anhydride.

[l] From the reaction products were isolated δ-formylvaleric acid and cyclopentenecarboxylic acid.

[m] Calculated from isolated dioxime.[26]

[n] The dialdehyde was obtained first in monomeric form and converted into the bisulfite compound, from which the dioxime was prepared. In an attempted vacuum distillation of the aldehyde, spontaneous polymerization occurred.[28] Rosenmund, Zetzsche, and Enderlin[29] reported an 80% yield (calculated on bisulfite compound) using xylene, Pd-kieselguhr (2.5%), and quinoline-sulfur.

[o] For the reduction of other acetylated hydroxy acid chlorides see ref. 127.

TABLE II

Aromatic Aldehydes

Acid Chloride	Solvent	Temperature, °C	Catalyst	Regulator	Yield of Aldehyde, %	Reference*
Benzoyl chloride					80–100	1, 2, 9, 35
p-Carbomethoxyoxybenzoyl chloride	Isopropyl benzene	—	Pd-BaSO$_4$ (5%)	None	—	1
Anisoyl chloride	—	—	—	—	81	33
m-Methoxybenzoyl chloride	Xylene	—	Pd-BaSO$_4$ (5%)	Quinoline-S	67	85
Chlorocarbonyl-(C^{14})-p-methoxybenzoyl chloride	Xylene	140–150	Pd-BaSO$_4$ (5%)	Quinoline-S	73 [a]	85a
3,4-Dimethylbenzoyl chloride	—	—	—	—	33	86
2-Methyl-5-methoxybenzoyl chloride	Xylene	—	Pd-BaSO$_4$ (5%)	None	13	87
3,5-Dimethoxybenzoyl chloride	Xylene	—	Pd-BaSO$_4$ (5%)	Quinoline-S	73	85
3,5-Diacetoxybenzoyl chloride	Xylene	160	Pd-BaSO$_4$ (4%)	None	—[b]	88
3-Methoxy-4-acetoxybenzoyl chloride	Xylene	—	Pd-BaSO$_4$	Quinoline-S	—[c]	33
2,5-Dicarbomethoxyoxy-3-ethylbenzoyl chloride	Toluene	110	Pd-BaSO$_4$ (5%)	Quinoline-S	—[d]	88a
2,5-Dicarbomethoxyoxy-4-ethylbenzoyl chloride	Toluene	110	Pd-BaSO$_4$ (5%)	—	—[d]	88a
2,5-Diacetoxy-3-hexylbenzoyl chloride	Toluene	110	Pd-BaSO$_4$ (5%)	Quinoline-S	—[d]	88a
2,5-Diacetoxy-4-hexylbenzoyl chloride	Toluene	110	Pd-BaSO$_4$ (5%)	Quinoline-S	—[d]	88a
2,4,6-Trimethylbenzoyl chloride	Xylene	—	Pd-BaSO$_4$	None	70–80	34
3,4,5-Tricarbomethoxyoxy-benzoyl chloride	Xylene	100	Pd-BaSO$_4$	None	80	11, 89
3,5-Dimethoxy-4-carbethoxy-oxybenzoyl chloride	Toluene	120–125	Pd-BaSO$_4$ (5%)	None	49 [a]	90
3,4-Dimethoxy-5-carbometh-oxyoxybenzoyl chloride	Toluene	110	Pd-BaSO$_4$	None	—	91
3,4-Dimethoxy-5-carbethoxy-oxybenzoyl chloride	Toluene	—	Pd-BaSO$_4$ (2%)	Quinoline-S	36–50	92
4-Methoxy-3,5-dicarbometh-oxyoxybenzoyl chloride	Toluene	110	Pd-BaSO$_4$	None	—	93, 94
3,4,5-Triacetoxybenzoyl chloride	Xylene	—	Pd-BaSO$_4$	Quinoline-S	70–90	95, 89
3,4,5-Trimethoxybenzoyl chloride [e]	Xylene	—	Pd-BaSO$_4$ (3%)	None	80	96, 13, 97, 98, 99, 100, 101, 101a
3,4,5-Triethoxybenzoyl chloride	Xylene	150	Pd-BaSO$_4$ (5%)	None	—	99
2-Ethoxy-3,4-dimethoxyben-zoyl chloride	Toluene	—	Pd-BaSO$_4$	None	72	102
o-Chlorobenzoyl chloride	Toluene	—	Pd-kieselguhr (2%)	Quinoline-S	70	2
m-Fluorobenzoyl chloride	Xylene [f]	—	Pd-BaSO$_4$	None	60	103
3,5-Difluoro-4-methoxyben-zoyl chloride	Xylene	—	Pd-BaSO$_4$ (5%)	Quinoline-S	—	104
p-Nitrobenzoyl chloride	Xylene	150	Pd-kieselguhr (2%)	Quinoline-S	91	2
β-Naphthoyl chloride	Xylene	150	Pd-BaSO$_4$ (2%)	Quinoline-S	84	14, 76
3-Methoxy-1-naphthoyl chloride	Xylene	—	Pd-BaSO$_4$	None	—	105
5-Methoxy-1-naphthoyl chloride	Xylene	170	Pd-BaSO$_4$	None	30–40	106, 105

* References 85–118 are listed on pp. 376–377.

TABLE II—*Continued*

AROMATIC ALDEHYDES

Acid Chloride	Solvent	Temperature, °C	Catalyst	Regulator	Yield of Aldehyde, %	Reference*
1-Acetoxy-3-naphthoyl chloride	Xylene	150	Pd-BaSO$_4$ (5%)	Quinoline-S	70	14, 107
4-Chloro-1-naphthoyl chloride	Xylene	160	Pd-BaSO$_4$ (5%)	Quinoline-S	73	107a
6-Chloro-1-naphthoyl chloride	Xylene	150	Pd-BaSO$_4$ (5%)	Quinoline-S	63 [a]	107a
5-Bromo-1-naphthoyl chloride	Xylene	—	Pd-BaSO$_4$	None	—	105
1,2,3,4-Tetrahydro-6-naphthoyl chloride	Cymene	—	Pd-BaSO$_4$ [g]	—	65–70	108
1,2,3,4-Tetrahydro-6-acetoxy-7-naphthoyl chloride	Xylene	—	Pd-BaSO$_4$	None	—[h]	110
1-Acenaphthoyl chloride	Xylene	150–160	Pd-BaSO$_4$ (2%)	Quinoline-S	72	76
2-Phenanthroyl chloride	Decalin	180–185	Pd-BaSO$_4$ (5%)	None	70	62
3-Phenanthroyl chloride	Decalin	180–185	Pd-BaSO$_4$ (5%)	None	90	62
9-Phenanthroyl chloride	Decalin	180–185	Pd-BaSO$_4$ (5%)	None	90	62
9,10-Dihydro-2-phenanthroyl chloride	Decalin	180–185	Pd-BaSO$_4$ (5%)	None	70	111
2-Methoxy-9,10-dihydro-7-phenanthroyl chloride	Decalin	180–185	Pd-BaSO$_4$ (5%)	None	67 [a]	111
2-Anthraquinonecarbonyl chloride	Xylene	150–160	Pd-BaSO$_4$ (5%)	None [i]	57	112
1,8-Diacetoxy-3-anthraquinonecarbonyl chloride	Xylene	150–160	Pd-BaSO$_4$ (5%)	None	—[j]	112
1-Acetoxy-6-anthraquinonecarbonyl chloride	Xylene	130–140	Pd-BaSO$_4$ (5%)	None	—[k]	113
1-Acetoxy-3-anthraquinonecarbonyl chloride	Xylene	140–150	Pd-BaSO$_4$ (5%)	None	—	113
p-Phthalyl chloride	Xylene	150	Pd-kieselguhr (2.5%)	Quinoline-S	81	26, 25, 58
m-Phthalyl chloride	Xylene	150	Pd-kieselguhr (2.5%)	Quinoline-S	83	26
o-Phthalyl chloride [l]	Tetralin	150	Pd-kieselguhr (2.5%)	Quinoline-S	5–6 [m]	27, 26
1,8-Naphthalyl chloride	—	—	—	—	0 [n]	30

* References 85–118 are listed on pp. 376–377.

[a] Yield calculated on the acid employed.

[b] The corresponding dihydroxyaldehyde was isolated in a yield of 81%.

[c] Yield of vanillin 82%.

[d] Isolated as the dihydroxy compound.

[e] Reduction was carried out with 100 g. of acid chloride.

[f] Commercial xylene.

[g] The same batch of catalyst was used five times. It was then reactivated by heating in a casserole for one hour over a strong flame. On the other hand, Pd-BaSO$_4$ has been heated to 600° for twenty minutes in order to deactivate it partially (hydrogenation of acetylenic to olefinic bond).[109]

[h] The corresponding hydroxyaldehyde was isolated in a yield of about 40%.

[i] When "quinoline-S" was employed, the yield was poor.

[j] The corresponding dihydroxyaldehyde was isolated in a yield of 50%.

[k] The corresponding hydroxyaldehyde was isolated in a yield of 50%.

[l] For the preparation and structure of phthalyl chloride, succinyl chloride, and related compounds, see the papers of Ott,[114] Kirpal, Galuschka, and Lassak,[115] Martin and Partington,[116] Ott, Langenohl, and Zerweck,[117] Kyrides,[50] and French and Kircher.[118]

[m] The aldehyde was isolated as phthalazine derivative; by-products, phthalide and biphthalyl; main product, resinous mass.

[n] The reaction product consisted of a complex mixture from which only naphthalic acid anhydride could be isolated. The reaction was carried out under the conditions given by Rosenmund and Zetzsche.[2]

TABLE III

HETEROCYCLIC ALDEHYDES

Acid Chloride	Solvent	Temperature, °C	Catalyst	Regulator	Yield of Aldehyde, %	Reference*
3-Furoic-	Xylene	—	Pd-BaSO$_4$	None	55	119
4-Carbomethoxy-2-furoic-	Xylene	125	Pd-BaSO$_4$	None	99	120
2-Carbethoxy-5-furoic-	Xylene	—	Pd-BaSO$_4$	None	—	121
2,5-Dimethyl-4-carbethoxy-3-furoic-	Xylene	—	Pd-BaSO$_4$	None	—	121
1-Phenyl-3-methyl-5-chloropyrazole-4-carboxylic-	Xylene	150–160	Pd-BaSO$_4$ (5%)	None	63 [a,b,c]	12
1-Phenyl-3-chloro-5-methylpyrazole-4-carboxylic-	Xylene	150–160	Pd-BaSO$_4$ (5%)	Quinoline-S	65 [a,b]	12
1-Phenyl-3,5-dimethylpyrazole-4-carboxylic-	Xylene	150	Pd-BaSO$_4$ (5%)	None	96 [a]	12
1,3-Diphenyl-5-methylpyrazole-4-carboxylic-	Xylene	150–160	Pd-BaSO$_4$ (5%)	—	57 [a]	12
1-Phenyl-5-methylpyrazole-4-carboxylic-	Xylene	—	Pd-BaSO$_4$(5%)	Quinoline-S	18 [d,e]	12
1-Phenyl-5-methylpyrazole-3-carboxylic-	Xylene	—	Pd-BaSO$_4$ (5%)	Quinoline-S[f]	60–70	61
1-Phenylpyrazole-5-carboxylic-	Xylene	—	Pd-BaSO$_4$ (5%)	None	—[a,g]	61
1-Phenyl-3-methylpyrazole-5-carboxylic-	Xylene	—	Pd-BaSO$_4$ (5%)	None	18 [a,h]	61
1-Phenyl-4-bromo-5-methylpyrazole-3-carboxylic-	Xylene	—	Pd-BaSO$_4$(5%)	None	37 [i]	61
1,3,5-Trimethylpyrazole-4-carboxylic-	Xylene	125–130	Pd-BaSO$_4$ (5%)	None	Traces [a,j]	122
1,5-Dimethylpyrazole-3-carboxylic-	Xylene	—	Pd-BaSO$_4$ (5%)	None	ca. 75 [a]	122
1,3-Dimethylpyrazole-5-carboxylic-	Xylene	120–125	Pd-BaSO$_4$ (5%)	None	57 [a,k]	122
1,4-Dimethylpyrazole-3-carboxylic-	Xylene	135	Pd-BaSO$_4$ (5%)	None	68 [a,l]	122
1-Phenyl-5-methyl-1,2,3-triazole-4-carboxylic-	Xylene	—	Pd-BaSO$_4$(5%)	None	50–80 [a,m]	60
1,5-Diphenyl-1,2,3-triazole-4-carboxylic-	Xylene	—	Pd-BaSO$_4$ (5%)	None	70 [a]	60
4,6-Dichloropyridine-2-carboxylic-	Xylene	150–160	Pd-BaSO$_4$	None	ca. 50 [a,n]	31
5,6-Dichloropyridine-3-carboxylic-	Xylene	160–170	Pd-BaSO$_4$	None	65 [a,o]	31
2,6-Dichloropyridine-4-carboxylic-	Xylene	160–170	Pd-BaSO$_4$	None	ca. 60 [a,n]	31, 123, 124
4,5,6-Trichloropyridine-2-carboxylic- [p]	Xylene	170–180	Pd-BaSO$_4$ (5%)	None	—[q]	32
Thiophene-2-carboxylic-	Toluene	—	Pd-BaSO$_4$ [r]	None	20	125, 126
Coumarin-3-carboxylic-	Xylene	100	Pd-BaSO$_4$ (5%)	None	70–75 [s]	11
Coumarin-3-acrylic-	Xylene	100	Pd-BaSO$_4$ (2.5%)	None	25–30	11
7-Acetoxycoumarin-3-carboxylic-	Xylene	120	Pd-BaSO$_4$ (5%)	None	75	11
7-(Carbethoxyoxy)-coumarin-3-carboxylic-	Xylene	100–110	Pd-BaSO$_4$ (5%)	None	60–80	11

* References 119–126 are listed on p. 377.
[a] The hydrogen was passed over a red-hot copper spiral.
[b] Yield calculated from bisulfite compound.
[c] If hydrogen was not passed over a copper spiral (and quinoline-S was employed), the acid anhydride was obtained as the main product.
[d] The hydrogen was not passed over copper; main product, acid anhydride.
[e] Yield calculated from phenylhydrazone.
[f] Reduction time in the presence of the regulator twice that in its absence.
[g] A considerable amount of 1-phenylpyrazole was formed in the reduction.
[h] A considerable amount of 1-phenyl-3-methylpyrazole was formed.

[i] Main product formed in the reduction, 1-phenyl-4-bromo-5-methylpyrazole; by-product, 1-phenyl-3-hydroxymethyl-4-bromo-5-methylpyrazole.

[j] Main product, the anhydride; by-product, 1,3,4,5-tetramethylpyrazole.

[k] By-product, 1,3,5-trimethylpyrazole.

[l] By-product, 1,4-dimethylpyrazole.

[m] By-products, 1-phenyl-5-methyl-1,2,3-triazole and 1-phenyl-4,5-dimethyl-1,2,3-triazole.

[n] Yield calculated from acid employed.

[o] Yield of crude product calculated from acid employed.

[p] The reductions of the chlorides of 5-chloropyridine-3-carboxylic acid and 5-bromopyridine-3-carboxylic acid yielded only very small amounts of aldehydes. The reductions of the following acid chlorides were entirely without success: 4-chloropyridine-2-carboxylic acid, 2,6-dibromopyridine-4-carboxylic acid, 2-chloroquinoline-4-carboxylic acid, pyridine-3-carboxylic acid, pyridine-2,5-dicarboxylic acid, pyridine-2,6-dicarboxylic acid, and quinoline-2-carboxylic acid (see Refs. 31, 123, 32).

[q] By-product, 2,3,4-trichloropyridine.

[r] An "unreduced Pd-BaSO$_4$" was employed.

[s] When the reduction was carried out at 175–180°, the yield of aldehyde was 25% (coumarin being formed in a yield of 60%) irrespective of whether purified or technical xylene was employed.

REFERENCES TO TABLES

[77] Dirscherl and Nahm, *Ber.*, **76**, 635 (1943).

[78] Feulgen and Behrens, *Z. physiol. Chem.*, **177**, 221 (1928).

[79] English and Velick, *J. Am. Chem. Soc.*, **67**, 1413 (1945).

[80] Harris, Wolf, Mozingo, Arth, Anderson, Easton, and Folkers, *J. Am. Chem. Soc.*, **67**, 2096 (1945).

[81] (a) Preobrashenski, Poljakowa, and Preobrashenski, *Ber.*, **68**, 844 (1935); (b) Preobrashenski, Poljakowa, and Preobrashenski, *Ber.*, **67**, 710 (1934); (c) Preobrashenski and Kuleshova, *J. Gen. Chem. U.S.S.R.*, **15**, 237 (1945) [*C. A.*, **40**, 2147 (1946)].

[82] English, *J. Am. Chem. Soc.*, **63**, 941 (1941).

[82a] Jeger, Nisoli, and Ruzicka, *Helv. Chim. Acta*, **29**, 1183 (1946).

[83] Campbell and Todd, *J. Am. Chem. Soc.*, **64**, 928 (1942).

[83a] Heer and Miescher, *Helv. Chim. Acta*, **30**, 777 (1947).

[83b] Heer and Miescher, *Helv. Chim. Acta*, **30**, 786 (1947).

[84] Zaki and Fahim, *J. Chem. Soc.*, **1942**, 182.

[84a] Pasternack and Brown, U. S. pat. 2,237,263 [*C. A.*, **35**, 4394 (1941)].

[85] Hartwell and Kornberg, *J. Am. Chem. Soc.*, **67**, 1606 (1945).

[85a] Reid, *Science*, **105**, 208 (1947).

[86] Sugasawa and Sugimoto, *J. Pharm. Soc. Japan*, **61**, No. 2, 29 (1941).

[87] Higginbottom, Hill, and Short, *J. Chem. Soc.*, **1937**, 263.

[88] Späth and Liebherr, *Ber.*, **74**, 869 (1941).

[88a] Renz, *Helv. Chim. Acta*, **30**, 124 (1947).

[89] Rosenmund and Zetzsche, *Ber.*, **51**, 594 (1918).

[90] Späth, *Monatsh.*, **41**, 271 (1920).

[91] Mauthner, *Ann.*, **449**, 102 (1926).

[92] Späth and Röder, *Monatsh.*, **43**, 93 (1922).

[93] Mauthner, *J. prakt. Chem.*, [2] **119**, 306 (1928).

[94] Posternak and Ruelius, *Helv. Chim. Acta*, **26**, 2045 (1943).

[95] Rosenmund and Pfannkuch, *Ber.*, **55**, 2357 (1922).

[96] Slotta and Heller, *Ber.*, **63**, 3029 (1930).

[97] Baker and Robinson, *J. Chem. Soc.*, **1929**, 152.

[98] Nierenstein, *J. prakt. Chem.*, [2] **132**, 200 (1931).

[99] Slotta and Szyszka, *J. prakt. Chem.*, [2] **137**, 339 (1933).

[100] Sharp, *J. Chem. Soc.*, **1936**, 1234.

[101] Cook, Graham, Cohen, Lapsley, and Lawrence, *J. Chem. Soc.*, **1944**, 322.

[101a] Hey, *Quart. J. Pharm. Pharmacol.*, **20**, 129 (1947).

[102] Manske, Ledingham, and Holmes, *Can. J. Research*, **23B**, 100 (1945).

[103] Shoesmith, Sosson, and Slater, *J. Chem. Soc.*, **1926**, 2760.

[104] English, Mead, and Niemann, *J. Am. Chem. Soc.*, **62**, 350 (1940).

[105] Shoesmith and Rubli, *J. Chem. Soc.*, **1927**, 3098.

[106] Shoesmith and Rubli, *J. Chem. Soc.*, **1926**, 3241.

[107] Cason, *J. Am. Chem. Soc.*, **63**, 828 (1941).

[107a] Jacobs, Winstein, Henderson, Bond, Ralls, Seymour, and Florsheim, *J. Org. Chem.*, **11**, 236 (1946).

[108] Newman and Zahm, *J. Am. Chem. Soc.*, **65**, 1097 (1943).

[109] Gibson, *J. Chem. Soc.*, **1945**, 713.

[110] Arnold, Zaugg, and Sprung, *J. Am. Chem. Soc.*, **63**, 1314 (1941).

[111] Stuart and Mosettig, *J. Am. Chem. Soc.*, **62**, 1110 (1940).

[112] Mitter and Banerjee, *J. Indian Chem. Soc.*, **9**, 375 (1932).

[113] Mitter, Das-Gupta, and Bachhwat, *J. Indian Chem. Soc.*, **11**, 893 (1934).

[114] Ott, *Ann.*, **392**, 245 (1912).

[115] Kirpal, Galuschka, and Lassak, *Ber.*, **68**, 1330 (1935).

[116] Martin and Partington, *J. Chem. Soc.*, **1936**, 1178.

[117] Ott, Langenohl, and Zerweck, *Ber.*, **70**, 2360 (1937).

[118] French and Kircher, *J. Am. Chem. Soc.*, **63**, 3270 (1941).

[119] Gilman and Burtner, *J. Am. Chem. Soc.*, **55**, 2903 (1933).

[120] Gilman, Burtner, and Smith, *J. Am. Chem. Soc.*, **55**, 403 (1933).

[121] Gilman, Burtner, and Vanderwal, *Rec. trav. chim.*, **52**, 151 (1933).

[122] Rojahn and Kühling, *Arch. Pharm.*, **264**, 337 (1926).

[123] Levelt and Wibaut, *Rec. trav. chim.*, **48**, 466 (1929).

[124] Wibaut, *Rec. trav. chim.*, **63**, 141 (1944).

[125] Barger and Easson, *J. Chem. Soc.*, **1938**, 2100.

[126] Rojahn and Schulten, *Arch. Pharm.*, **264**, 348 (1926).

[127] The Rosenmund reduction has been applied to the following acetylated hydroxy acid chlorides with the results indicated: DL-erythro-α,β-diacetoxybutyryl chloride in xylene at 150° with Pd-BaSO$_4$ (5%) gave an 87% yield of the aldehyde, Glattfield and Straitiff, *J. Am. Chem. Soc.*, **60**, 1384 (1938); DL-α,β-diacetoxyisobutyryl chloride in benzene with PdO(PtO$_2$) gave a 74% yield of the aldehyde, Glattfield and Mochel, *J. Am. Chem. Soc.*, **60**, 1011 (1938); DL-triacetylerythronyl chloride in xylene at 135° with Pd-BaSO$_4$ (5%) gave a 20% yield of DL-diacetylerythrose, Glattfield and Kribben, *J. Am. Chem. Soc.*, **61**, 1720 (1939); β-carbomethoxy-L-threo-α,β-diacetoxypropionyl chloride in xylene at 130–135° with Pd-BaSO$_4$ (5%) gave a 65–70% yield of the aldehyde, Lucas and Baumgarten, *J. Am. Chem. Soc.*, **63**, 1653 (1941); pentaacetyl-D-gluconyl chloride in xylene at about 150° with Pd-BaSO$_4$ (5%) gave an almost quantitative yield of the aldehyde, Cook and Major, *J. Am. Chem. Soc.*, **58**, 2410 (1936). No regulator was used in these reductions.

CHAPTER 8

THE WOLFF-KISHNER REDUCTION

DAVID TODD

Amherst College

CONTENTS

INTRODUCTION

The oxygen atom of the carbonyl group in aldehydes and ketones can be replaced by hydrogen by heating the semicarbazone, the hydrazone, or the azine in the presence of an alkaline catalyst—a reaction known as the Wolff-Kishner reduction. Two slightly different variations of the method were discovered independently by Kishner[1] in 1911 and by Wolff[2] in 1912. Kishner found that by dropping a hydrazone slowly upon hot potassium hydroxide, with which some platinized porous plate had been mixed, the corresponding hydrocarbon was formed. Wolff accomplished the same result by heating a semicarbazone or hydrazone in a sealed tube to about 180° in the presence of sodium ethoxide. The reduction is illustrated by the following equations. Though the Kishner

$$\frac{R'}{R}C=O \xrightarrow{H_2NNH_2} \frac{R'}{R}C=NNH_2 + H_2O$$

$$\frac{R'}{R}C=NNH_2 \xrightarrow[\text{or KOH}]{NaOC_2H_5} \frac{R'}{R}CH_2 + N_2$$

method has the obvious advantage of avoiding the necessity of a sealed tube, the Wolff method has been modified to obviate both this necessity and that of isolating the intermediate carbonyl derivative.

The first step in the Wolff reduction of a semicarbazone has been shown to be the conversion of the semicarbazone to the hydrazone.[2] Wolff pictured this reaction as a hydrolysis.* That hydrazone formation

$$\frac{R}{R'}C=NNHCONH_2 + H_2O \rightarrow \frac{R}{R'}C=NNH_2 + NH_3 + CO_2$$

is the first step in the reduction of a semicarbazone is proved by the isolation of the hydrazone from the semicarbazone if the temperature employed is not sufficiently high to produce reduction. There seems to be no appreciable difference in the yield of hydrocarbon from the two derivatives.

* Because of this conception of the mechanism of semicarbazone decomposition, Wolff ·suggested the use of 96–98% ethanol in the preparation of sodium ethoxide for the reduction of semicarbazones. For the reduction of hydrazones he used 100% ethanol. However, Eisenlohr and Polenske[3] have found that the reduction of trans-β-decalone semicarbazone proceeds smoothly in the presence of rigorously dry ethanol. An investigation into the mechanism of this step is certainly in order.

[1] Kishner, J. Russ. Phys. Chem. Soc., **43**, 582 (1911) [C. A., **6**, 347 (1912)].

[2] Wolff, Ann., **394**, 86 (1912).

[3] Eisenlohr and Polenske, Ber., **57**, 1639 (1924).

The mechanism of the Wolff-Kishner reduction nas been studied by Balandin and Vaskevich.[3a] A detailed investigation of the kinetics of the decomposition of cyclohexanone hydrazone indicated that two steps are involved, and the isomeric azo compound is suggested as the short-lived intermediate.

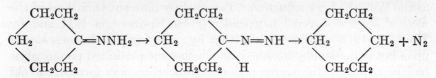

Although one can employ the azine for the Wolff-Kishner reduction it is only rarely desirable to do so. Generally the azine is so insoluble that it is brought to react only with great difficulty. When the azine is used it must be treated with alkali in the presence of excess hydrazine hydrate, since it must be first converted to the hydrazone before reduction occurs.

$$\begin{array}{c}R' \\ \diagdown \\ \diagup \\ R\end{array}\!\!C{=}N{-}N{=}C\!\!\begin{array}{c}R' \\ \diagup \\ \diagdown \\ R\end{array} + H_2NNH_2 \rightarrow 2 \begin{array}{c}R' \\ \diagdown \\ \diagup \\ R\end{array}\!\!C{=}NNH_2$$

SCOPE AND LIMITATIONS

Although the Clemmensen reduction is the most common method for reducing aldehydes and ketones to the corresponding hydrocarbons,[4] the Wolff-Kishner method is a valuable complementary tool. For instance, the Clemmensen method cannot be used to reduce pyrrole derivatives since pyrroles are sensitive to acids. The same applies to the furan field. The Wolff-Kishner method generally succeeds with compounds of high molecular weight where the Clemmensen technique fails, presumably because of the insolubility of the carbonyl compound.

Side Reactions and Abnormal Reductions

There are two principal side reactions that may take place when a compound is submitted to the Wolff-Kishner reduction; both are largely preventable by proper precautions. First there is the possibility of azine formation by the reaction of one molecule of hydrazone with one

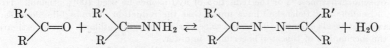

[3a] Balandin and Vaskevich, *J. Gen. Chem. U.S.S.R.*, **6**, 1878 (1936) [*C.A.*, **31**, 4575 (1937)].
[4] Martin, *Organic Reactions*, **1**, 155, John Wiley & Sons, 1942.

molecule of the carbonyl compound. Since the ketone can be formed only by hydrolysis of the hydrazone, its formation can be suppressed by the rigid exclusion of water. It was to avoid azine formation that Wolff used sodium ethoxide prepared from absolute ethanol.

The other side reaction is the formation of the secondary alcohol from the ketone, or of the primary alcohol from the aldehyde. This seems to be brought about entirely by hydrolysis of the carbonyl derivative to the free carbonyl compound followed by sodium alkoxide reduction to the carbinol. Alcohol formation may be repressed either by the exclusion of water or by the addition of hydrazine, since water is necessary for hydrolysis and the presence of hydrazine shifts the equilibrium in favor of the hydrazone. Apparently the complete absence of water is more important in some cases than in others. Eisenlohr and Polenske [3] obtained a large amount of decalol and only a small amount of decalin when they reduced the semicarbazone of *trans*-β-decalone with sodium and 99.9% ethanol; when 100% ethanol was used the fraction of decalol formed fell to one-fourth of the total product. Dutcher and Wintersteiner [5] have shown that in the steroid field the often-observed formation of alcohols in Wolff-Kishner reductions can be suppressed by employing excess hydrazine hydrate. Cholestanone semicarbazone with sodium ethoxide at 180° gave only 3(α)- and 3(β)-cholestanol; when hydrazine hydrate was added to the reaction mixture cholestane was formed in 75% yield. The same authors also showed that the semicarbazone, the hydrazone, and the azine of cholestanone were all converted principally to the carbinol in the absence of hydrazine hydrate.

Aside from the reactions normally expected to take place in the presence of alkali, such as hydrolysis of esters, cleavage of ethers, and dehydration, several abnormal reactions may occur. Complete removal of an acyl group has been observed; for example, the reduction of 2,4-diethyl-3,5-dipropionylpyrrole gives 2,4-diethyl-3-propylpyrrole.[6] A rather remarkable deacylation was found by Hess and Fink.[7] Both forms of the hydrazone of cuskhygrin were isolated, and both were submitted to Wolff-Kishner reduction under the same conditions. The α-hydrazone gave the normal product; the β-hydrazone was converted to desacetylcuskhygrin. Removal of an acyl group followed by alkylation by the sodium alkoxide may occur, as in the formation of 2-methylpyrrole from 2-acetylpyrrole when sodium methoxide is used as the reduction catalyst.[8] Direct reduction of 1-acetylanthracene with

[5] Dutcher and Wintersteiner, *J. Am. Chem. Soc.*, **61**, 1992 (1939).
[6] Fischer, Siedel, and d'Ennequin, *Ann.*, **500**, 137 (1933).
[7] Hess and Fink, *Ber.*, **53**, 781 (1920).
[8] Knorr and Hess, *Ber.*, **45**, 2631 (1912).

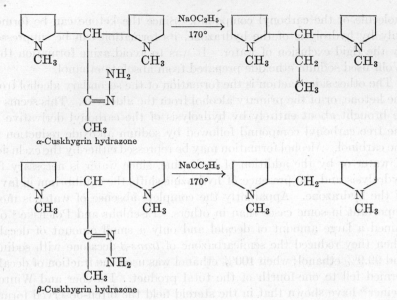

α-Cuskhygrin hydrazone

β-Cuskhygrin hydrazone

hydrazine hydrate and sodium ethoxide at 180° for eight hours gives
2-ethylanthracene, whereas reduction of the semicarbazone under the
same conditions for only four hours gives the expected 1-ethylanthra-
cene.[9]

Thielepape [10,11] has found that the Wolff-Kishner reduction of 2-
pyridone hydrazone and 2-lepidone hydrazone yields pyridine and lepidine respectively. Presumably the normal products, dihydropyridine
and dihydrolepidine, undergo air oxidation to the aromatic products.

Occasionally the intermediate carbonyl derivative will undergo some
internal condensation before it has an opportunity to undergo normal
reduction. When 5-methyl-3-carbethoxy-2-acetylpyrrole is submitted
to direct reduction there is obtained a pyridazine formed by loss of
ethyl alcohol from the intermediate hydrazone ester.[12] There is the

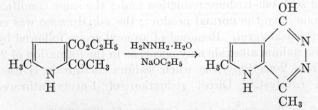

[9] Waldmann and Marmorstein, *Ber.*, **70**, 106 (1937).
[10] Thielepape, *Ber.*, **55**, 136 (1922).
[11] Thielepape and Spreckelsen, *Ber.*, **55**, 2929 (1922).
[12] Fischer, Beyer, and Zaucker, *Ann.*, **486**, 55 (1931).

danger of triazine formation from the monosemicarbazones of α-diketones,[13] but this can be avoided by employing instead the monohydrazones.[14]

α,β-Unsaturated carbonyl compounds require special consideration. These compounds usually react with hydrazine hydrate to form the pyrazoline instead of the normal hydrazone. The pyrazoline on treatment with hot alkali is converted to a cyclopropane derivative.[15] Py-

$$C_6H_5CH{=}CH{-}\overset{\displaystyle O}{\overset{\|}{C}}{-}CH_3 \xrightarrow{\;H_2NNH_2 \cdot H_2O\;} C_6H_5{-}\underset{\underset{\displaystyle NH}{|}}{CH}{-}CH_2{-}\underset{\underset{\displaystyle N}{\|}}{C}{-}CH_3 \xrightarrow{\;KOH\;}$$

$$\underset{\displaystyle C_6H_5CH{-\!-\!-}CHCH_3 \;+\; N_2}{\overset{\displaystyle CH_2}{\diagup\;\;\diagdown}}$$

razoline formation seems to be a necessary step in this synthesis of cyclopropanes. Citral hydrazone when reduced by Kishner's method gives the normal hydrocarbon, 1,7-dimethyl-2,6-octadiene. When the hydrazone is distilled it is converted to the pyrazoline, which under the conditions of the Kishner reduction yields 1-methyl-1-isohexenyl-cyclopropane.[16] Merejkowsky[17] has found that carvenone, carvone, and cyclopentenone-3 react normally instead of forming cyclopropanes, from which it is concluded that cyclopropane formation does not take place if the process requires the formation of one ring within another.

Variations in the Wolff-Kishner Method

In considering variations of the Wolff-Kishner method it should be borne in mind that the minimal conditions for reduction vary greatly with the type of compound to be reduced.

Temperature. In general, heating at 180° for six to eight hours is adequate to achieve complete reduction. The hydrazones of furan derivatives,[18, 19] of substituted benzaldehydes,[20] and of substituted acetophenones[21] undergo rapid reduction at 90–100°, but camphor

[13] Bergstrom and Haslewood, *J. Chem. Soc.*, **1939**, 540.

[14] Ishidate, Kawahata, and Nakazawa, *Ber.*, **74**, 1707 (1941).

[15] Kishner, *J. Russ. Phys. Chem. Soc.*, **44**, 849 (1912) [*C. A.*, **6**, 2915 (1912)].

[16] Kishner, *J. Russ. Phys. Chem. Soc.*, **50**, 1 (1918) [*C. A.*, **18**, 1485 (1924)].

[17] Merejkowsky, *Bull. soc. chim. France*, (4) **37**, 1174 (1925).

[18] Reichstein and Zschokke, *Helv. Chim. Acta*, **15**, 249 (1932).

[19] Zelinsky and Shuikin, *Compt. rend. acad. sci. U.R.S.S.*, **1933**, 60 [*C. A.*, **28**, 2002 (1934)].

[20] Lock and Stach, *Ber.*, **76**, 1252 (1943).

[21] Lock and Stach, *Ber.*, **77**, 293 (1944).

hydrazone [2] must be heated to 190–200° before reduction will occur. When the semicarbazone of 3-hydroxy-6-ketocholanic acid was heated for five hours at 185°, satisfactory reduction took place, whereas no crystalline compound could be isolated after only two hours of heating.[22] On the other hand heating the semicarbazone of 7-keto-12-hydroxycholanic acid for more than two hours lowers the yield of product.[23] Ruzicka found that the semicarbazone of cyclopentadecanone was in part still undecomposed after being heated for eight hours at 190°.[24]

Catalyst. It seems to be taken for granted that an alkaline catalyst is necessary to promote the Wolff-Kishner reduction, but it is not at all clear in just which reactions a catalyst is essential. Curtius and Thun early found that distillation of benzil monohydrazone gave an almost quantitative yield of desoxybenzoin.[25] Staudinger and Kupfer found that heating fluorenone at 200° with hydrazine hydrate gives fluorene, and that similar treatment of Michler's ketone, benzophenone, and benzaldehyde gives good yields of the corresponding hydrocarbons.[26] Pyrene-3-aldehyde can be reduced by the Staudinger-Kupfer method in 90% yield.[27] The fluorenones as a group do not seem to require a catalyst,[28] and Borsche has been able to reduce α- and β-benzoylnaphthalene by heating the ketones for twenty-four hours at 230° with hydrazine hydrate.[29]

The commonly used catalysts are sodium methoxide and ethoxide in the Wolff variation, and sodium and potassium hydroxides in the Kishner method. Kishner did not begin to use platinized porous plate habitually with his alkaline catalyst until he had found that the reduction of menthone hydrazone would not proceed when either potassium hydroxide or platinized plate was present alone but only when they were present together.[30] However, Wolff was able to obtain smooth reduction of menthone hydrazone with sodium ethoxide at 170°.[2] The Kishner method has frequently been used with good results without any platinum to supplement the alkali.[31, 32, 33] Palladium-barium sulfate has been used with the alkali in the Kishner method.[34]

[22] Wieland and Dane, *Z. physiol. Chem.*, **212**, 41 (1932).
[23] Wieland and Dane, *Z. physiol. Chem.*, **210**, 268 (1932).
[24] Ruzicka, Brugger, Pfeiffer, Schinz, and Stoll, *Helv. Chim. Acta*, **9**, 499 (1926).
[25] Curtius and Thun, *J. prakt. Chem.*, [2], **44**, 161 (1891).
[26] Staudinger and Kupfer, *Ber.*, **44**, 2197 (1911).
[27] Vollmann, Becker, Corell, Streeck, and Langbein, *Ann.*, **531**, 1 (1937).
[28] Borsche and Sinn, *Ann.*, **532**, 146 (1937).
[29] Borsche, Hofmann, and Kühn, *Ann.*, **554**, 23 (1943).
[30] Kishner, *J. Russ. Phys. Chem. Soc.*, **44**, 1754 (1912) [*C. A.*, **7**, 1171 (1913)].
[31] Cook and Linstead, *J. Chem. Soc.*, **1934**, 946.
[32] Barrett and Linstead, *J. Chem. Soc.*, **1935**, 436.
[33] Asahina and Nogami, *Ber.*, **68**, 1500 (1935).
[34] Linstead and Meade, *J. Chem. Soc.*, **1934**, 935.

Sodium dissolved in amyl alcohol has been used as a reduction catalyst to help prevent excessive pressure from developing in the bomb tube during the reduction.[35]

Reduction at Atmospheric Pressure. Although the Kishner reduction has always been carried out at atmospheric pressure, it was not until 1935 that a Wolff reduction was carried out in an open flask with the aid of a high-boiling solvent. Ruzicka and Goldberg [36] found that reduction proceeded when the semicarbazone was heated in benzyl alcohol to which some sodium had been added. This method has been extended by Soffer and co-workers,[37, 38] who bring about direct reduction of the ketone or aldehyde by refluxing the carbonyl compound, hydrazine hydrate, and sodium in any of several high-boiling solvents such as octyl alcohol, triethanolamine, and the ethylene glycols. Whitmore and co-workers [39] worked out essentially the same procedure but felt it desirable to prepare the crude hydrazone before adding the alkaline catalyst. Soffer employed excess metallic sodium (12 moles), excess high-boiling solvent, and 100% hydrazine hydrate to offset the temperature-lowering effect of the water formed in the first step. Huang-Minlon [40] introduced the following simple expedient: after hydrazone formation is complete (one hour), water and excess hydrazine are removed by distillation until a temperature favorable for the decomposition reaction is attained (190–200°). When this is done, no excess of solvent is required, sodium hydroxide or potassium hydroxide (2–3 moles) can be used in place of metallic sodium, cheap aqueous hydrazine is adequate, and the reaction time is reduced from fifty to one hundred hours to three to five hours. The simple procedure is applicable to large-scale reductions, and the yields are excellent.

Comparison with Other Methods

As has been pointed out the Clemmensen method has certain inescapable drawbacks that render it of little practical value for certain types of compounds. In general, compounds of high molecular weight show great resistance to Clemmensen reduction. Neither 8-keto-17-octadecenoic nor 8-keto-16-octadecenoic acid can be reduced by Clemmensen's method whereas reduction proceeds satisfactorily by the Wolff-

[35] Ruzicka and Meldahl, *Helv. Chim. Acta*, **23**, 364 (1940).

[36] Ruzicka and Goldberg, *Helv. Chim. Acta*, **18**, 668 (1935).

[37] Soffer, Soffer, and Sherk, *J. Am. Chem. Soc.*, **67**, 1435 (1945).

[38] Sherk, Augur, and Soffer, *J. Am. Chem. Soc.*, **67**, 2239 (1945).

[39] Herr, Whitmore, and Schiessler, *J. Am. Chem. Soc.*, **67**, 2061 (1945).

[40] Huang-Minlon, *J. Am. Chem. Soc.*, **68**, 2487 (1946).

Kishner method.[41] Similarly Marker found that the former method failed to reduce all five of a series of steroid ketones while the latter method succeeded.[42] It is well known that the Clemmensen method often unavoidably gives carbinols and unsaturated compounds. Though such by-products are occasionally found in Wolff-Kishner reductions, the reasons for their formation are known and precautions may be taken to prevent such side reactions. In the reduction of a series of alkyl phenyl ketones the Clemmensen method was found to be useless because of the unsaturated compounds and polymers formed;[43] here the Wolff-Kishner method made possible the preparation of pure hydrocarbons.

Table I illustrates the different results obtained when both Clemmensen and Wolff-Kishner reductions were applied to the same compounds. The list is not all-inclusive, and, because of improvements in the techniques of both reduction methods, many of the reported yields are doubtless subject to improvement.

A third method, catalytic hydrogenation, is available for the reduction of the carbonyl group to a methylene group. This method is quite limited in its application and suffers from the defect that points of unsaturation elsewhere in the molecule may be reduced simultaneously.[44, 45] The carbonyl group must be conjugated with an aromatic system to be reduced catalytically.[46] This method has been used in the pyrrole field in place of the Wolff-Kishner reduction. By the use of copper-chromium oxide and nickel catalysts, carbethoxyacylpyrroles can be reduced to carbethoxyalkylpyrroles whereas the carbethoxyl group is invariably lost during Wolff-Kishner reduction.[47, 48] By controlling the conditions 2,4-dimethyl-3,5-diacetylpyrrole can be catalytically reduced to either 2,4-dimethyl-3-ethyl-5-acetylpyrrole or to 2,4-dimethyl-3,5-diethylpyrrole.[47]

Hydrogenation with palladium-charcoal catalyst at normal temperature and pressure has been found to be an effective means for the complete reduction of the conjugated carbonyl group.[44, 46, 49-52]

[41] Kapp and Knoll, J. Am. Chem. Soc., 65, 2062 (1943).
[42] Marker et al., J. Am. Chem. Soc., 65, 1199 (1943).
[43] Schmidt, Hopp, and Schoeller, Ber., 72, 1893 (1939).
[44] Foster and Robertson, J. Chem. Soc., 1939, 921.
[45] Späth and Schläger, Ber., 73, 1 (1940).
[46] Zelinsky, Packendorff, and Leder-Packendorff, Ber., 66, 872 (1933).
[47] Signaigo and Adkins, J. Am. Chem. Soc., 58, 709 (1936).
[48] Fischer and Höfelmann, Ann., 533, 216 (1938).
[49] Zelinsky, Packendorff, and Leder-Packendorff, Ber., 67, 300 (1934).
[50] Hartung and Crossley, J. Am. Chem. Soc., 56, 158 (1934).
[51] Miller, Hartung, Rock, and Crossley, J. Am. Chem. Soc., 60, 7 (1938).
[52] Ju, Shen, and Wood, J. Inst. Petroleum, 26, 514 (1940) [C. A., 35, 1386 (1941)].

TABLE I

COMPARISON OF WOLFF-KISHNER AND CLEMMENSEN REDUCTIONS

Compound	Wolff-Kishner Product	Yield	Clemmensen Product	Yield	References[*]
β-(3-Methoxybenzoyl)-propionic acid	Normal	64.5%	Normal	42%	52a
2-Acetylanthracene	Normal	—	Normal	—	9
β-(3-Acenaphthoyl)-propionic acid	Normal	81%	Normal	50%	52a
β-(p-Phenoxybenzoyl)-propionic acid	Normal	95%	Normal	54%	52a
2-Acetyldihydroretene	Normal	Poor	Normal	79%	53
α-Benzoylcoumarin	Normal	—	Polymer	—	54
β-(2-Chrysenoyl)-propionic acid	Normal	—	Normal	—	55
2,3-Diethyl-1,4-dianisyl-1-butanone	Normal	44%	Normal	72%	56
α-(3,4-Dimethoxybenzoyl)-β-(3′,4′-dimethoxybenzyl)-butyrophenone	None	0%	None	0%	57
3,5-Dimethoxyvalerophenone	Normal	85%	Normal	Poor	33
6,7-Dimethoxy-1-veratrylnaphthalene-3-aldehyde	Normal	Small	None	0%	58
α-Diphenyltruxone	Normal	—	α-Diphenyltruxadiol	—	59
Estrone	Normal	35%	Normal	—	60
Isobilianic acid	Normal	—	Normal	Varies	61
α-Isostrophanthic acid	Normal	Poor	Carbinol	—	62
24-Ketocholesterol	Normal	—	Tar	—	63
4-Ketodecahydroquinoline	Normal	33%	Normal	—	64
4-Keto-5,5′-dimethyldi-(1,2)-pyrrolidine	Normal	65%	Carbinol	—	65
6-Ketoisolithobilianic acid	Normal	—	None	0%	66
1-Keto-8-methyloctahydropyridocoline	Normal (A cpd)	74%	Normal (B cpd)	—	64
8-Keto-17-octadecenoic acid	Normal	65%	None	0%	41
2-Ketooctahydropyrrocoline	Normal	20%	Normal and carbinol	—	67
Ketopinic acid	Normal	62%	Normal	50%	68
2-Ketoquinuclidine	Normal	25%	Normal	—	69
23-Ketosarsasapogenin	Normal	39%	Tetrahydrosarsasapogenin	—	70
3-Ketotetrahydro-1,2-cyclopentenophenanthrene	Normal	—	Hexahydrocyclopentenophenanthrene	—	71
Lupenone	α-Lupene	28%	β-Lupene	Small	72
Manogenin	Normal	—	None	0%	42
6-Methoxy-Δ^{1,9}-2-octalone	Normal	54%	Normal	—	73
2-Methyl-3-acetylpyridine	Normal	63%	Normal	18%	74
2-Methyl-5-acetylthiophene	Normal	40%	Normal	10%	75
2-Methylcyclohexanone	Normal	—	Normal and unsat'd cpds.	—	76
2-Methyl-1-isovaleroylfuran	Normal	—	None	0%	77
Perisuccinoylacenaphthene	Normal	—	None	0%	78
Pregnanol-20(α)-one-3 acetate	Pregnanediol-3(α), 20(α)	85%	Pregnanol-20(α)	—	79
d-Verbanone	Normal	—	o-Menthane	—	80

* References 52a–80 are listed on p. 388.

REFERENCES TO TABLE I

[52a] Private communication from Professor Louis F. Fieser.

[53] Nyman, *Ann. Acad. Sci. Fennicae*, **A41**, No. 5 (1934) [*C. A.*, **30**, 2958 (1936)].

[54] Stoermer, Chydenius, and Schinn, *Ber.*, **57**, 72 (1924).

[55] Beyer, *Ber.*, **71**, 915 (1938).

[56] Baker, *J. Am. Chem. Soc.*, **65**, 1572 (1943).

[57] Haworth, Kelly, and Richardson, *J. Chem. Soc.*, **1936**, 725.

[58] Haworth and Woodcock, *J. Chem. Soc.*, **1938**, 809.

[59] Stoermer and Foerster, *Ber.*, **52**, 1255 (1919).

[60] Danielli, Marrian, and Haslewood, *Biochem. J.*, **27**, 311 (1933).

[61] Borsche and Hallwasz, *Ber.*, **55**, 3324 (1922).

[62] Jacobs, Elderfield, Grave, and Wignall, *J. Biol. Chem.*, **91**, 617 (1931).

[63] Riegel and Kaye, *J. Am. Chem. Soc.*, **66**, 723 (1944).

[64] Clemo, Cook, and Raper, *J. Chem. Soc.*, **1938**, 1183.

[65] Clemo and Metcalfe, *J. Chem. Soc.*, **1936**, 606.

[66] Windaus and Grimmel, *Z. physiol. Chem.*, **117**, 146 (1921).

[67] Clemo and Metcalfe, *J. Chem. Soc.*, **1937**, 1518.

[68] Bartlett and Knox, *J. Am. Chem. Soc.*, **61**, 3184 (1939).

[69] Clemo and Metcalfe, *J. Chem. Soc.*, **1937**, 1989.

[70] Marker and Shabica, *J. Am. Chem. Soc.*, **64**, 813 (1942).

[71] Hawthorne and Robinson, *J. Chem. Soc.*, **1936**, 763.

[72] Heilbron, Kennedy, and Spring, *J. Chem. Soc.*, **1938**, 329.

[73] Cook and Robinson, *J. Chem. Soc.*, **1941**, 391.

[74] Dornow and Machens, *Ber.*, **73**, 355 (1940).

[75] Shepard, *J. Am. Chem. Soc.*, **54**, 2951 (1932).

[76] Cowan, Jeffery, and Vogel, *J. Chem. Soc.*, **1939**, 1862.

[77] Asano, *J. Pharm. Soc. Japan*, **454**, 999 (1919) [*C. A.*, **14**, 1317 (1920)].

[78] Fieser and Peters, *J. Am. Chem. Soc.*, **54**, 4347 (1932).

[79] Marker and Lawson, *J. Am. Chem. Soc.*, **61**, 852 (1939).

[80] Wienhaus and Schumm, *Ann.*, **439**, 20 (1924).

A recently developed process for accomplishing the desired reduction is the reductive removal of the two —SR groups in thioacetals by means of Raney nickel.[81] This method is practicable for small-scale work only. It has been shown to be very useful in the steroid field.[82, 83]

EXPERIMENTAL PROCEDURES

Wolff Reduction of a Hydrazone

Reduction of Camphor.[2] Ten grams of well-dried camphor hydrazone is heated in a sealed tube with 0.8 g. of sodium in 10 ml. of absolute ethanol for eighteen hours at 190°. Crude crystalline camphane separates on the addition of 750 ml. of water to the reaction mixture. The camphane is separated from the small amount of azine present by steam distillation. The steam-distilled camphane melts at 156–157° and boils at 161°/757 mm. The yield is 7 g. (84%).

[81] Wolfram and Karabinos, *J. Am. Chem. Soc.*, **66**, 909 (1944).

[82] Bernstein and Dorfman, *J. Am. Chem. Soc.*, **68**, 1152 (1946).

[83] Hauptmann, *J. Am. Chem. Soc.*, **69**, 562 (1947).

Reduction of 1-Keto-8-methyloctahydropyridocoline.[64] One-half gram of 1-keto-8-methyloctahydropyridocoline is refluxed eighteen hours with 3 ml. of hydrazine hydrate. The hydrazone is isolated by ether extraction and heated for eighteen hours at 170° in a sealed tube with a sodium ethoxide solution prepared by the addition of 0.4 g. of sodium to 2 ml. of ethanol. Water is added to the reaction mixture; the solution is acidified with concentrated hydrochloric acid, taken to dryness, and the residue made basic with saturated potassium carbonate solution. After extraction with ether the product is distilled. There is thus obtained 0.34 g. (74%) of 8-methyloctahydropyridocoline-A as a colorless oil, b.p. 47–48°/1 mm.

The Direct Wolff Reduction

Reduction of 2,4-Dimethyl-3-acetyl-5-carbethoxypyrrole. Detailed directions for the reduction of 2,4-dimethyl-3-acetyl-5-carbethoxypyrrole to 2,4-dimethyl-3-ethylpyrrole (kryptopyrrole) in 50–58% yield are given in *Organic Syntheses*.[84]

Kishner Reduction of a Hydrazone

Reduction of Ethyl Cyclobutyl Ketone.[85] The hydrazone is prepared by heating 18 g. of the ketone and 18 g. of 90% hydrazine hydrate in 50 ml. of absolute ethanol for three hours at 110–130° in an oil bath. By the end of this time the ethanol has distilled, and the residue is dried over solid potassium hydroxide. The hydrazone is poured off the potassium hydroxide and dropped slowly from a separatory funnel onto a mixture of 2 g. of potassium hydroxide and two small pieces of platinized porous plate heated to 120–140° in a Claisen flask. The platinized plate is prepared by igniting pieces of plate that have been immersed in chloroplatinic acid solution. The product that distils from the Claisen flask is treated with dilute acetic acid, and the hydrocarbon layer that separates is washed with water. After having been dried over potassium hydroxide, the product is twice distilled from sodium. There is obtained 7 g. (44%) of *n*-propylcyclobutane boiling at 99–100°/736 mm.

Reduction of 4-Methylacetophenone.[21] The hydrazone is prepared by vigorously refluxing for one hour a mixture of 4-methylacetophenone and twice its weight of 85% hydrazine hydrate. The cooled solution is extracted with ether; the ether solution is dried over potassium hydroxide and distilled in vacuum. There is obtained an 88% yield of the hydra-

[84] Fischer, *Org. Syntheses*, **21**, 67 (1941).
[85] Zelinsky and Kasansky, *Ber.*, **60**, 1101 (1927).

zone of boiling point 166–168°/16 mm. It solidifies in the receiver and melts at 34° after crystallization from petroleum ether.

Five grams of the hydrazone is mixed with 2 g. of powdered potassium hydroxide in a flask equipped with a reflux condenser, the top of which is connected with a gas buret. The flask is gently heated to 90–100°, and this temperature maintained until most of the calculated amount of nitrogen has been evolved. The flask is then heated to 150°, cooled, the contents treated with water and extracted with ether. The ether extract is distilled to give 3.25 g. (80%) of 4-ethyltoluene, b.p. 157–160°.

Kishner Reduction of a Semicarbazone

Reduction of cis-β-Bicyclooctanone.[31] Five grams of pure cis-β-bicloöctanone is converted into the semicarbazone, which is thoroughly washed, roughly dried, and heated with a free flame in a distilling flask with 7.5 g. of potassium hydroxide. The mass fuses, and ammonia is given off. At 200–210° a second reaction sets in, nitrogen being evolved, and oily droplets of hydrocarbon begin to distil. There is no charring, the residue being colorless. The distillate is shaken with sodium bisulfite solution, taken up in ether, dried with calcium chloride, and evaporated. The yield of crude cis-bicyclooctane is 4.0 g. (90%), 2.8 g. of which boils sharply at 137–138°.

Wolff-Kishner Reduction without an Alkaline Catalyst

Reduction of 2,3-Benzo-1-azafluorenone.[86] Seven-tenths of a gram of 2,3-benzo-1-azafluorenone and 1 ml. of hydrazine hydrate are heated in a sealed tube for sixteen hours at 180°. The crude crystalline product is almost colorless. On distillation in vacuum the product goes over as a violet fluorescent oil (b.p. 240°/25 mm.) which quickly solidifies. Crystallization from methanol gives colorless prisms, m.p. 140°. The yield is 0.53 g. (80%).

Reduction of Pyrene-3-aldehyde.[27] Twenty grams of pyrene-3-aldehyde and 100 g. of hydrazine hydrate are heated at 200° in a 1-l. iron autoclave for eight hours. About 100 atmospheres pressure is developed. The clear solid product is washed, dried, and distilled in vacuum. There is obtained 17 g. (91%) of almost pure 3-methylpyrene melting at 70–71°.

[86] Borsche and Noll, *Ann.*, **532**, 127 (1937).

Direct Wolff-Kishner Reduction at Atmospheric Pressure

Reduction of 5-Keto-8-methylnonanoic Acid.[37] A mixture prepared from a solution of 113 g. of sodium in 1750 ml. of diethylene glycol, 168 g. of 5-keto-8-methylnonanoic acid, and 125 ml. of 85% hydrazine hydrate is refluxed for forty-eight hours. An additional 75 ml. of the hydrazine solution is then added and heating is continued for forty-eight hours. The product is isolated by acidification and extraction with benzene and ether. Distillation at reduced pressure gives 143 g. (92%) of isodecanoic acid, b.p. 93–95/0.3 mm., n_D^{25} 1.4318.

An average yield of 85% was obtained in several repetitions of the reduction carried out in monoethylene glycol without the second addition of hydrazine hydrate.

Reduction of β-(p-Phenoxybenzoyl)-propionic Acid.[40] A mixture of 500 g. (1.85 moles) of the keto acid, 350 g. of potassium hydroxide, and 250 ml. of 85% hydrazine hydrate in 2500 ml. of triethylene (or diethylene) glycol is refluxed for one and one-half hours, the water formed is removed by a take-off condenser, and the temperature of the solution is allowed to rise to 195°, when refluxing is continued for four hours more. The cooled solution is diluted with 2.5 l. of water and poured slowly into 1.5 l. of 6 N hydrochloric acid, and the light cream-colored solid is dried. The average yield of material of m.p. 64–66° is 451 g. (95%). The pure product melts at 71–72°.

TABLE OF COMPOUNDS REDUCED BY THE WOLFF-KISHNER METHOD

In Table II are listed all those compounds cited in *Chemical Abstracts* through 1947 that have been reduced by the Wolff-Kishner method. They are arranged in the order of increasing number of carbon atoms in the molecule. The key to the abbreviations used under the "Method" column is as follows:

K = the normal Kishner method from the hydrazone.
KS = the Kishner method from the semicarbazone.
KP = the Kishner method from the pyrazoline.
WS = the Wolff method from the semicarbazone.
WH = the Wolff method from the hydrazone.
WA = the Wolff method from the azine.
WD = direct Wolff reduction of the carbonyl compound.
? = no clue given as to the variation used.

It will be observed that the figures for the yield of product are followed by the letter 'A' or "B." "76A" indicates a yield of 76% from the original carbonyl compound; "42B" indicates a yield of 42% from the carbonyl derivative used. The notation (cr.) means that the yield given is for crude product.

TABLE II

Compounds Reduced by the Wolff-Kishner Method

C₄ and C₅

Formula	Compound	Product	Method	Yield	Reference*
$C_4H_6ON_2$	3-Methylpyrazolone	n-Butyric acid †	WH	41B	86a
C_5H_6O	Cyclopentenone	Normal	KP	Small	17
C_5H_8O	Acetylcyclopropane	Normal	K	—	87
	Acetylcyclopropane	Normal	K	75B	88
	Acetylcyclopropane	Normal	K	—	89
	Acetylcyclopropane	Normal	WD	60A	39
	Cyclobutylaldehyde	Normal	K	—	87
	Cyclobutylaldehyde	Normal	K	—	89
$C_5H_4O_2$	Furfural	Normal	K	—	90
	Furfural	Normal	WH	—	2
	Furfural	Normal	K	69B	91
	Furfural	Normal	WH	76A	19
	3-Furfural	Normal	WH	72A	92
$C_5H_{10}O_2$	Pentan-2-one-5-ol	Normal	K	—	93
$C_5H_8O_3$	Levulinic acid	Normal	WH	85–90B	2
C_5H_5ON	α-Pyridone	Pyridine ‡		75A	11
C_5H_5ON	2-Formylpyrrole	Normal	WD	—	94

C₆

$C_6H_{10}O$	Cyclohexanone	Normal and cyclohexanol	K	—	1
	Cyclohexanone	Normal	WH	63A	39
	Cyclohexanone	Normal	WD	80A	40
	Mesityl oxide	1,1,2-Trimethylcyclopropane	KP	—	95
	Allylacetone	Normal	K	—	93
	Methyl cyclobutyl ketone	Normal	K	—	93
$C_6H_{12}O$	Methyl n-butyl ketone	Normal	WH	83B	2
	Methyl tert-butyl ketone	Normal	K	—	96
$C_6H_4O_2$	Quinone	§	—	—	97a
$C_6H_6O_2$	4-Methyl-3-furaldehyde	Normal	WH	29B	97
$C_6H_6O_3$	5-Hydroxymethylfurfural	Normal	WD ‖	95A	18
$C_6H_4O_4$	α-Furoylformic acid	Normal	WH	100A	98
C_6H_7ON	3-Methyl-5-formylpyrrole	Normal	WD	—	99
	{ 2-Acetylpyrrole	2-Methylpyrrole	WA ¶	—	8
		Normal	WD	50–60A	12
		Normal	WA, WS	Small	100

C₇

C_7H_6O	Benzaldehyde	Normal	WD ‖	100	26
	Benzaldehyde	Normal	K	79B	20
$C_7H_{12}O$	2-Methyl-3-hexen-5-one	1-Methyl-2-isopropylcyclopropane	KP	—	100a

* References 86a–413 are listed on pp. 416–422.

† There was also formed 39% of 2,3-dimethylpyrazolone.

‡ This reaction was carried out by boiling the pyridone hydrazone in alkaline solution with copper sulfate or ferric chloride as catalyst.

§ The monosemicarbazone and monoaminoguanidine derivative gave phenol on boiling with potassium hydroxide. The di-derivatives gave phenylhydrazine under the same conditions.

‖ No alkaline catalyst was used.

¶ Catalyst used was sodium methoxide.

TABLE II—*Continued*

COMPOUNDS REDUCED BY THE WOLFF-KISHNER METHOD

Formula	Compound	Product	Method	Yield	Reference*
$C_7H_{12}O$	Ethyl cyclobutyl ketone	Normal	K	45B	85
	2,2-Dimethylcyclopentanone	Normal	K	—	93
	2-Methylcyclohexanone	Normal	WS	—	76
	3-Methylcyclohexanone	Normal	K	—	1
	4-Methylcyclohexanone	Normal	WS	—	76
$C_7H_{14}O$	n-Heptaldehyde	Normal	WH	54A	39
	Diisopropyl ketone	Normal	WH	35A	39
$C_7H_6O_2$	o-Hydroxybenzaldehyde	Normal	K	86B	20
$C_7H_8O_2$	2,4-Dimethyl-3-furaldehyde	Normal	WH	53B	101
	α-Propionylfuran	Normal	K	44B	102
$C_7H_6O_4$	Methyl 5-formyl-2-furoate	5-Methyl-2-furoic acid	WH	—	103
	5-Methyl-2-furoylformic acid	Normal	WD	63A	18
C_7H_7ON	β-Acetylpyridine	Normal	WS	48B	104
	o-Aminobenzaldehyde	Normal	K	66B	20
C_7H_9ON	4-Methyl-3-acetylpyrrole	Normal	WD	70A	105
$C_7H_{11}ON$	2-Ketoquinuclidine	Normal	WH	25A	69
$C_7H_{15}ON$	1-Methyl-3-acetylpiperidine	Normal	WD	—	106
$C_7H_5O_3N$	p-Nitrobenzaldehyde	Normal	WH	Small	2
	p-Nitrobenzaldehyde	None	K	0	20
C_7H_6OCl	o-Chlorobenzaldehyde	Normal	K	82B	20
$C_7H_4OCl_2$	2,6-Dichlorobenzaldehyde	Normal	K	80B	20
C_7H_8OS	2-Methyl-5-acetylthiophene	Normal	KS	40B	75

C_8

C_8H_8O	Acetophenone	Normal	WH	80B	2
	Acetophenone	Normal	WD	40–50A	43
	Acetophenone	Normal	K	91B	21
$C_8H_{10}O$	Endomethylenetetrahydro-benzaldehyde	Normal	K	72A	107
$C_8H_{12}O$	cis-α-(0.3.3)Bicycloöctanone	Normal	KS	90A	31
	cis-β-(0.3.3)Bicycloöctanone	Normal	WS	60B	34
	cis-β-(0.3.3)Bicycloöctanone	Normal	KS	47B	32
	trans-β-(0.3.3)Bicycloöctanone	Normal †	WS	—	32
	Bicyclo-(2.2.2)octanone	Normal	WS	—	108
	Bicyclo-(1.2.3)octanone-2	Normal	WS	—	109
	Endomethylenehexahydro-benzaldehyde	Normal	K	—	107
	2-Isopropylidenecyclopenta-none	6,6-Dimethyl-(3.1.0)bicyclo-hexane	KP	—	110
$C_8H_{14}O$	5-Methylhepten-4-one-3	1-Methyl-1,2-diethylcyclo-propane	KP	—	95
	2-Methylhepten-2-one-6	Normal	K	—	93
	Cycloöctanone	Normal	K	58B	111
	Cycloöctanone	Normal	K	—	112
$C_8H_{16}O$	Octanone-2	Normal	WD	75A	37
	Octanone-2	Normal	WH	66A	39
	2,3,3-Trimethyl-4-pentanone	Normal	WH	62A	39
$C_8H_8O_2$	Anisaldehyde	Normal	WS	66B	2
	Furfurylideneacetone	1-(α-Furyl)2-methylcyclo-propane	KP	—	113

* References 86a–413 are listed on pp. 416–422.
† As by-product there was formed a compound whose analysis is close to that of the ethylated ketone.

TABLE II—*Continued*

COMPOUNDS REDUCED BY THE WOLFF-KISHNER METHOD

Formula	Compound	Product	Method	Yield	Reference*
$C_8H_8O_2$	o-Hydroxyacetophenone	Normal	K	71B	21
	p-Hydroxyacetophenone	Normal	K	91B	21
$C_8H_{10}O_2$	Trimethylfurfural	Normal	WH	Small	101
	α-Methyl-α'-acetylfuran	Normal	K	—	102
	Bicyclo-(2.2.2)octan-2,6-dione	Normal	WS	57B	114
$C_8H_8O_3$	Vanillin	Normal	WS, WH	67B, 88A	2
$C_8H_{12}O_4$	2,5-Dimethyl-2,5-dihydroxy-1,4-cyclohexadione	$C_8H_{12}N_2$	K	—	115
C_8H_9ON	p-Aminoacetophenone	Normal	WH	—	2
	2-Methyl-3-acetylpyridine	Normal	K	63A	74
	4-Methyl-3-acetylpyridine	Normal	K	84A	116
$C_8H_{11}ON$	2,4-Dimethyl-3-acetylpyrrole	2,4-Dimethyl-5-ethylpyrrole	W	—	8
	2,4-Dimethyl-3-acetylpyrrole	Normal	WD	23A	117
	2,3-Dimethyl-4-acetylpyrrole	Normal	WH	—	118
	2,4,5-Trimethyl-3-formylpyrrole	Normal	WS	63B	119
	2,3,4-Trimethyl-5-formylpyrrole	Normal	WD	92A	120
	3-Methyl-4-ethyl-2-formylpyrrole	Normal	WD	100A	121
	3-Methyl-4-ethyl-2-formylpyrrole	Normal	WD	90A	122
	3-Methyl-4-ethyl-5-formylpyrrole	Normal	WD	—	99
	2-Butyrylpyrrole	Normal	WD	70A	123
$C_8H_{13}ON$	2-Ketoöctahydropyrrocoline	Normal	WH	20A	67
$C_8H_{15}ON$	Pelletierine	Normal	WH	—	124
	2-(1-Butanone-2)pyrrolidine	Normal	WH	—	125
C_8H_7OCl	p-Chloroacetophenone	Normal	K	90B	21
$C_8H_8ON_2$	2,4-Dimethyl-3-cyano-5-formylpyrrole	Normal †	WD	—	126
$C_8H_8O_2N_2$	Oxime anhydride of 2-methyl-5-acetylpyrrole-4-carboxylic acid	Azine of 5-methyl-2-acetyl-3-pyrrole carboxylic acid	WD	—	12
$C_8H_9O_3N$	4-Methyl-3-acetylpyrrole-2-carboxylic acid	3-Ethyl-4-methylpyrrole ‡	WD	Little	105
	2-Methyl-5-acetylpyrrole-4-carboxylic acid	A pyridazine	WD	—	12
	2,4-Dimethyl-3-oxalylpyrrole	2,3,4-Trimethylpyrrole	WD	70A	105
$C_8H_{10}OS$	2-Ethyl-5-acetylthiophene	Normal §	WH	—	127

C₉

C_9H_8O	Cinnamaldehyde	Phenylcyclopropane	KP	—	128
$C_9H_{10}O$	p-Tolyl methyl ketone	Normal	WD	—	129
	Propiophenone	Normal	WD	40–50A	43
	Propiophenone	Normal	WD	79A	37

* References 86a–413 are listed on pp. 416–422.
† There was also formed some 2,4,5-trimethylpyrrole.
‡ The main product was $C_8H_9ON_3$.
§ There was also formed some 2,5,2',5',-tetraethyl-3,3'-bithienyl.

TABLE II—*Continued*

COMPOUNDS REDUCED BY THE WOLFF-KISHNER METHOD

Formula	Compound	Product	Method	Yield	Reference*
$C_9H_{10}O$	Propiophenone	Normal	WD	82A	40
	p-Methylacetophenone	Normal	WD	83A	130
	p-Methylacetophenone	Normal	K	80B	21
$C_9H_{12}O$	Endoethylenetetrahydrobenz-aldehyde	Normal	K	46A	131
$C_9H_{14}O$	Camphophorone	2,6,6-Trimethylbicyclo-(3.1.0)hexane	KP	—	15
	Camphenilone	Normal	K	—	132
	Camphenilone	Normal	WH	—	133
	Camphenilone	Normal	K	70B	134
	α-Isocamphenilone	Normal	K	—	135
	Phorone	α,α-Dimethyl-β-(2,2-di-methyl)cyclopropylethylene	KP	—	136
	Spiro[4,4]nonan-1-one	Normal	K	69B	137
	Santenone	Normal	WH	—	133
	Nopinone	Normal	WH	46B	138
	α-Fenchocamphorone	Normal	WH	—	133
	β-Fenchocamphorone	Normal	WH	—	133
$C_9H_{16}O$	Dihydrocamphorphorone	Normal	K	—	139
$C_9H_{18}O$	2,6-Dimethylheptanone-4	Normal	WD	70A	37
$C_9H_{12}O_2$	β-(5-Methyl-2-furyl)butyral-dehyde	Normal	K	72A	140
$C_9H_{14}O_3$	Camphononic acid	Normal	WS	83B	141
$C_9H_{11}ON$	3-Amino-4-methylaceto-phenone	Normal	WD	75A	130
$C_9H_{11}ON$	2,6-Dimethyl-3-acetylpyridine	Normal	K	35–40A	74
$C_9H_{13}ON$	2,4,5-Trimethyl-3-acetyl-pyrrole	Normal	WA	—	142
	2,4,5-Trimethyl-3-acetyl-pyrrole	2,3,5-Trimethylpyrrole	WD	Mainly	117
	2,3,4-Trimethyl-5-acetylpyrrole	Normal	WD	50A	120
	2,4-Dimethyl-3-ethyl-5-formyl-pyrrole	Normal	WS	27A	143
	2,4-Dimethyl-5-ethyl-3-formyl-pyrrole	Normal	WD	70A	144
	2-Methyl-4-ethyl-3-acetyl-pyrrole	Normal	WD	—	145
	3-Methyl-4-ethyl-2-acetyl-pyrrole	Normal	WD	—	99
	2-Methyl-5-butyrylpyrrole	Normal	WD	73A	123
$C_9H_{15}ON$	2-Keto-3-methyloctahydro-pyrrocoline	Normal	WH	31A	146
	7-Keto-3-methyloctahydro-pyrrocoline	Normal	WH	9B	147
	4-Keto-5,5'-dimethyldi(1,2)-pyrrolidine	Normal	WH	65B	65
	1-Ketoöctahydropyridocoline	Normal	WH	16A	147
	4-Ketotetrahydroquinoline	Normal	WH	33A	64
	1,4-Dimethyl-3-acetyl-1,2,5,6-tetrahydropyridine	Normal	WD	31A	148
$C_9H_{17}ON$	N-Methylisopelletierine	Normal	WH	Almost 100B	149

* References 86a–413 are listed on pp. 416–422.

TABLE II—*Continued*

Compounds Reduced by the Wolff-Kishner Method

Formula	Compound	Product	Method	Yield	Reference*
$C_9H_{17}ON$	*dl*-Methylconhydrinone	Normal	WH	50B	125
	dl-Methylconhydrinone	Normal	WD †	40A	150
$C_9H_{11}O_2N$	2,4-Dimethyl-3-acetyl-5-formylpyrrole	The azine	WS ‡	—	117
$C_9H_{10}O_2N_2$	Imine of β-(4-methyl-5-formyl-3-pyrrole)propionic acid	Normal	WD	Good	151
	Imine of β-(4-methyl-5-formyl-3-pyrrole)propionic acid	Normal	WD	67–73A	152
$C_9H_9O_3N$	3-Nitro-4-ethylbenzaldehyde	Normal	WD	64A	130
$C_9H_{11}O_3N$	2-Methyl-5-carbethoxy-3-formylpyrrole	2,3-Dimethylpyrrole	WD	57A	94
	3-Methyl-4-carbethoxy-2-formylpyrrole	2,3-Dimethylpyrrole	WD	—	153
	β-(3-Methyl-2-formyl-4-pyrrole) propionic acid	Normal	WD	98A	152
$C_9H_{10}N_2$	Myosmine	Normal §	WH	26A	154

C_{10}

Formula	Compound	Product	Method	Yield	Reference*
$C_{10}H_{10}O$	Benzalacetone	1-Phenyl-2-methylcyclopropane	KP	—	15
	Benzalacetone	1-Phenyl-2-methylcyclopropane	KP	57A	155
$C_{10}H_{12}O$	Butyrophenone	Normal	WD	40–50A	43
	Butyrophenone	Normal	WD	66A	39
	p-Tolyl ethyl ketone	Normal	WD	—	129
	Phenyl *n*-propyl ketone	Normal	WD	40–50A	43
$C_{10}H_{14}O$	Carvone	Normal	K	—	30
	Carvone	Isolimonene	KP	15B	17
	β-Pericyclocamphenone	Normal	WH	90B	156
	Tricyclal	Normal	WA	—	157
	Teresantalicaldehyde	Normal	WS	—	158
	Cyclopentylidenecyclopenta-none-2	6,6-Tetramethylene-bicyclo(3.1.0)hexane	KP	—	159
	4-Methylisocyclenone-2	Normal	WH	60B	160
	6-Camphenone	Normal	WS	—	161, 162
	Piperitenone (mixture)	Normal	K ‖	29A	163, 164
$C_{10}H_{16}O$	Camphor	Normal	K	—	1
	Camphor	Normal	WH	84B	2
	Camphor	Normal	K	—	165
	Camphor	Normal	WH	—	166
	Epicamphor	Normal	WS	—	166
	Thujone	Normal	K	—	1
	Thujone	Normal	WH	—	167

* References 86a–413 are listed on pp. 416–422.

† No alkaline catalyst was used.

‡ Direct reduction of the ketone with hydrazine hydrate and sodium ethoxide gave a product that formed two unidentified picrates.

§ Myosmine, 2-(3-pyridyl)-Δ²-pyrroline, on treatment with hydrazine hydrate was converted to the hydrazone of 4-keto-4(3-pyridyl)-butylamine which was then reduced normally.

‖ The hydrazone was placed in aqueous potassium hydroxide, a little copper sulfate added, and the solution evaporated to dryness. The residue was distilled in vacuum to complete the reaction.

TABLE II—*Continued*

COMPOUNDS REDUCED BY THE WOLFF-KISHNER METHOD

Formula	Compound	Product	Method	Yield	Reference*
$C_{10}H_{16}O$	Isothujone	Normal and $C_{10}H_{16}$	K	—	30
	Fenchone	Normal	K	—	1
	Fenchone	Normal	WH	100B	2
	Fenchone	Normal	K	—	168
	Isofenchone	Normal	WH	—	133
	Dihydrocarvone	Normal	K	—	169
	Dihydrocarvone	Normal	WH	17A	138
	Carvenone	Normal	K	—	169
	Carvenone	Normal	KP	80B	17
	Citral	Normal	K	—	169, 170
	Citral	Normal †	K	—	16
	d-Carone	Normal	K	—	171
	d-Carone	Normal	WH	22A	138
	Pinocamphone	Normal	K, WH	50B, 68B	172
	Pinocamphone	Normal	WD	—	173
	Isopinocamphone	Normal	WD	—	173
	β-Methylcamphenilone	Normal	WH	—	174, 175
	β-Methylcamphenilone	Normal	WH	—	176
	cis-β-Decalone	Normal ‡	WS	55B	3
	trans-β-Decalone	Normal §	WS	—	3
	trans-β-Decalone	Normal ‖	WS	58B	177
	Thujamenthone	Normal	K	—	139
	1,1-Tetramethylene-2-cyclo-hexanone	Normal	K	—	178
	2-Cyclopentylcyclopentanone	Normal	K	—	159
	Pulegone	Normal	WH	—	138
	Isopulegone	Normal	WS	—	179
	Tanacetone	Normal	WH	—	138
	d-Verbanone	Normal	WH	—	80
	dl-Verbanone	Normal	?	—	180
$C_{10}H_{18}O$	Citronellal	Normal	K	—	169
	Citronellal	Normal	WH	—	2
	Menthone	Normal	WH	90B	2
	Menthone	Normal	K	—	30
$C_{10}H_6O_2$	1,2-Naphthoquinone	¶	—	—	97a
	1,4-Naphthoquinone	**	—	—	97a
$C_{10}H_{14}O_2$	Elsholtzia ketone	Normal	WD	—	77
	5-Ketocamphor	Normal	WS	Almost 100B	181
	5-Ketocamphor	d-Borneol ††	WS	—	181a
	6-Ketocamphor	Normal	WS	—	182

* References 86a–413 are listed on pp. 416–422.

† The undistilled hydrazone gave the normal reaction with potassium hydroxide. On distillation the hydrazone was converted into the pyrazoline which with potassium hydroxide was converted to 1-methyl-1-isohexenylcyclopropane.

‡ Besides the normal product there was formed 30% of β-decalol.

§ With 100% ethanol there was formed a mixture consisting of 3 parts of decalin and 1 part of decalol. With 99.9% ethanol there was formed almost exclusively decalol.

‖ Besides the normal product there was formed 19% of decalol.

¶ The mono-2-semicarbazone and mono-2-aminoguanidine derivatives gave α-naphthol on boiling with potassium hydroxide.

** The monosemicarbazone and monoguanidine derivative gave α-naphthol on boiling with potassium hydroxide.

†† Since the mono-5-semicarbazone was used the product corresponds to a normal reduction accompanied by sodium alkoxide reduction of the other carbonyl group.

TABLE II—*Continued*

Compounds Reduced by the Wolff-Kishner Method

Formula	Compound	Product	Method	Yield	Reference*
$C_{10}H_{16}O_2$	5-Hydroxycamphor	Normal	WS	—	181
	5-Hydroxycamphor	Normal	WS	—	181a
	trans-π-Hydroxycamphor	Normal	WS	—	181a
	cis-π-Hydroxycamphor	Normal	WS	—	181a
	d-10-Hydroxycamphor	Normal	WS	95B	183
$C_{10}H_{20}O_2$	2,6-Dimethyloctanone-3-ol-2	2,6-Dimethyloctene-2	K	—	93
$C_{10}H_{14}O_3$	Ketopinic acid	Normal	WS	Good	184
	Ketopinic acid	Normal	?	62A	68
	Isoketopinic acid	Normal	WS	—	185
	2-Keto-7-π-apocamphanecarboxylic acid	Normal	WS	—	186
$C_{10}H_{16}O_3$	dl-α-Camphalonic acid	Normal	WS	—	187
	o-Carboxypropiophenone	4-Hydroxy-1-ethylphthalazine	WD	66A	188
$C_{10}H_{18}O_3$	5-Keto-8-methylnonanoic acid	Normal	WD	92A	37
$C_{10}H_6O_4$	Coumaroylformic acid	Normal	WD	—	189
$C_{10}H_{12}O_4$	3,4,5-Trimethylbenzaldehyde	Normal	K	77A	190
	3-Ketoisoketopinic acid	Isoketopinic acid †	K	—	14
$C_{10}H_9ON$	2-Lepidone	Lepidine ‡	K	30B	10
$C_{10}H_{13}ON$	3,5-Diacetyl-2,4-dimethylpyrrole	Normal	WD	—	191
$C_{10}H_{17}ON$	1-Keto-2-methyloctahydropyridocoline	Normal	WH	28B	67
	1-Keto-8-methyloctahydropyridocoline	Normal	WH	74A	64
$C_{10}H_{13}O_3N$	2,5-Dimethyl-4-carbethoxy-3-formylpyrrole	2,3,5-Trimethylpyrrole	WS	Trace	119
	2,4-Dimethyl-5-carbethoxy-3-formylpyrrole	2,3,4-Trimethylpyrrole	WS	—	192
	2,4-Dimethyl-5-carbethoxy-3-formylpyrrole	2,3,4-Trimethylpyrrole	WD	80A	120
	2,4-Dimethyl-5-carbethoxy-3-formylpyrrole	2,3,4-Trimethylpyrrole	WD	71A	144
	2-Ethyl-5-carbethoxy-3-formylpyrrole	2-Ethyl-3-methylpyrrole	WD	—	94
	3-Methyl-4-carbethoxy-2-acetylpyrrole	2-Ethyl-3-methylpyrrole	WD	—	153
	2-Methyl-4-carbethoxy-5-acetylpyrrole	A pyridazine	WD	—	12
$C_{10}H_{12}O_5S$	β-(3,4-Dimethoxythienoyl)-propionic acid	None	?	0	193
$C_{10}H_{14}OS$	2,5-Diethyl-3-acetylthiophene	Normal	WH	55B	127

C_{11}

Formula	Compound	Product	Method	Yield	Reference*
$C_{11}H_{12}O$	Benzalmethyl ethyl ketone	1-Ethyl-2-phenylcyclopropane	KP	57A	155
$C_{11}H_{14}O$	p-Tolyl n-propyl ketone	Normal	WD	—	129
	Phenyl n-butyl ketone	Normal	WD	40–50A	43

* References 86a–413 are listed on pp. 416–422.

† The 3-monohydrazone was used, hence isoketopinic acid is the normal product. When the Wolff method was used the carbonyl group at C_3 was reduced normally and that at C_2 reduced to the carbinol, giving trans-π-apoborneolcarboxylic acid.

‡ The normal product, 1,2-dihydrolepidine, was oxidized by the air to lepidine.

TABLE II—*Continued*

Compounds Reduced by the Wolff-Kishner Method

Formula	Compound	Product	Method	Yield	Reference*
$C_{11}H_{16}O$	4-Methylisocyclenone	Normal	WH	59B	194
$C_{11}H_{18}O$	4-Methylcamphor	Normal	WH	—	175
$C_{11}H_{16}O_2$	6-Methoxy-$\Delta^{1,9}$-2-octalone	Normal	WH	54A	73
	5-Methyl-2-(3-ketohexyl)furan	Normal	WH	28A	194a
$C_{11}H_{18}O_2$	1,3-Dimethylbicyclo(3.3.1)non-anol-5-one-7	Normal	WH †	54B	195
$C_{11}H_{16}O_3$	2-Keto-1-apocamphane-1-acetic acid	Normal	WS	83B	196
$C_{11}H_{12}O_4$	β-(3-Methoxybenzoyl)-pro-pionic acid	Normal	WD	89A (cr.)	40
$C_{11}H_{14}O_4$	2-Hydroxy-3-methoxy-5-(ω-hydroxypropyl)benzalde-hyde	"Little success"	?	—	197
$C_{11}H_{15}ON$	3,6,6-Trimethyl-4,5,6,7-tetra-hydro-4-ketoindole	Normal	?	—	198
$C_{11}H_{15}O_2N$	2-Methyl-4-ethyl-3-formyl-5-propionylpyrrole	2,3-Dimethyl-4-ethylpyrrole	WD	50A	99
$C_{11}H_{15}O_3N$	2,4-Dimethyl-5-carbethoxy-3-acetylpyrrole	2,4-Dimethyl-3-ethylpyrrole ‡	WD	53A	143
	2,4-Dimethyl-5-carbethoxy-3-acetylpyrrole	2,4-Dimethyl-3-ethylpyrrole	WD	61–66A	199
	2,4-Dimethyl-5-carbethoxy-3-acetylpyrrole	2,4-Dimethyl-3-ethylpyrrole	WD	65A	99
	2,4-Dimethyl-5-carbethoxy-3-acetylpyrrole	2,4-Dimethyl-3-ethylpyrrole	WD	50–58A	84
	2,3-Dimethyl-5-carbethoxy-4-acetylpyrrole	2,3-Dimethyl-4-ethylpyrrole	WD	Less than 60A	200
	2-Methyl-4-ethyl-5-carbeth-oxy-3-formylpyrrole	2,3-Dimethyl-4-ethylpyrrole	WD	77A	201
	2-Methyl-4-ethyl-5-carbeth-oxy-3-formylpyrrole	2,3-Dimethyl-4-ethylpyrrole	WD	—	202
	2-Ethyl-4-methyl-5-carbeth-oxy-3-formylpyrrole	2-Ethyl-3,4-dimethylpyrrole	WD	54A	203
	Ethyl 2,3,4-trimethylpyrrole-5-glyoxylate	2,3,4-Trimethylpyrrole §	WD	Small	120

C_{12}

Formula	Compound	Product	Method	Yield	Reference*
$C_{12}H_{14}O$	Benzalmethyl isopropyl ketone	1-Isopropyl-2-phenylcyclo-propane	KP	57A	155
$C_{12}H_{16}O$	Phenyl *n*-amyl ketone	Normal	WD	40–50A	43
	p-Tolyl *n*-butyl ketone	Normal	WD	—	129
	1,4,5,8-*bis-endo*-Methylene-β-decalone	Normal	WS	—	204
$C_{12}H_{18}O$	Cyclohexylidenecyclohexane-2-one	Normal	K	—	205
$C_{12}H_6O_2$	Acenaphthene quinone	Normal	WS	50B	206

* References 86a–413 are listed on pp. 416–422.
† No alkaline catalyst was used.
‡ There was also formed considerable 2,4-dimethyl-3-acetylpyrrole azine.
§ On warming the crude acidified product there was formed some 2,3,4,5-tetramethylpyrrole, presumably by loss of carbon dioxide from 2,3,4-trimethylpyrrole-5-acetic acid.

TABLE II—*Continued*

Compounds Reduced by the Wolff-Kishner Method

Formula	Compound	Product	Method	Yield	Reference*
$C_{12}H_{16}O_3$	2-Hydroxy-5-methoxyiso-valerophenone	The azine	WS	—	207
	2-Carbomethoxy-5(or 6)-keto-bornylene	Bornylene-2-carboxylic acid	WS	—	166
$C_{12}H_{18}O_3$	*d-trans-π*-Apobornyl acetate-7-aldehyde	*d*-Borneol	WS	52B	208
	d-trans-π-Apoisobornyl acetate-7-aldehyde	Isoborneol	WS	—	208
	cis-π-Apobornyl acetate-7-aldehyde	*d*-Borneol	WS	50B	208
	5-Acetoxycamphor	Epiborneol	WS	—	181a
	Methyl 2-methyl-γ-keto-1-cyclohexenebutyrate	2-Methyl-1-cyclohexenebutyric acid	WD	58A	209
$C_{12}H_{22}O_3$	5-Keto-10-methylundecanoic acid	Normal	WD	80A	37
$C_{12}H_{20}O_2N_2$	Aspergillic acid	Normal	WD	—	210
$C_{12}H_7O_2N_3$	Phenylazimidoquinone	Phenylazimidophenol	†	—	211
$C_{12}H_{17}O_3N$	2,4-Diethyl-5-carbethoxy-3-formylpyrrole	3-Methyl-2,4-diethylpyrrole	WD	—	202
	2-Ethyl-4-methyl-5-carbeth-oxy-3-acetylpyrrole	4-Methyl-2,3-diethylpyrrole	WD	—	203
	2-Methyl-4-ethyl-5-carbeth-oxy-3-acetylpyrrole	2-Methyl-3,4-diethylpyrrole	WD	—	145
	3-Ethyl-4-methyl-5-carbeth-oxy-2-acetylpyrrole	4-Methyl-2,3-diethylpyrrole	WD	58A	212
	2-Methyl-4-propyl-5-carbeth-oxy-3-formylpyrrole	2,3-Dimethyl-4-propylpyrrole	WD	70A	213
	2,4-Dimethyl-5-carbethoxy-3-propionylpyrrole	2,4-Dimethyl-3-propylpyrrole	WD	40A	213
	1,2,4-Trimethyl-5-carbethoxy-3-acetylpyrrole	1,2,4-Trimethyl-3-ethylpyrrole	WD	55A	214
	2-Butyl-5-carbethoxy-3 (or 4)-formylpyrrole	2-Butyl-3 (or 4)-methylpyrrole	WD	41A	123
$C_{12}H_{15}O_5N$	4-Methyl-3,5-dicarbethoxy-2-formylpyrrole	2,4-Dimethylpyrrole	WD	Good	215

C_{13}

Formula	Compound	Product	Method	Yield	Reference*
$C_{13}H_8O$	Fluorenone	Normal	WD, WA ‡	—	26
$C_{13}H_{10}O$	Benzophenone	Normal	WD ‡	100A	26
	Benzophenone	Normal	K	84B	2
	Benzophenone	Normal	WD	83A	40
	3-Acenaphthaldehyde	Normal	WD ‡	63A	216
$C_{13}H_{14}O$	8-Keto-5,6,7,8-tetrahydro-2,3-cyclopentenonaphthalene	Normal	KS	100B (cr.)	217
$C_{13}H_{18}O$	Phenyl *n*-hexyl ketone	Normal	WD	40–50A	43
	p-Tolyl *n*-amyl ketone	Normal	WD	—	129
$C_{13}H_{20}O$	Ionone	Normal	K	—	218
	ψ-Ionone	Normal	K	—	218

* References 86a–413 are listed on pp. 416–422.
† The monosemicarbazone on long boiling in 3% sodium hydroxide gave phenylazimidophenol, the enol form of the normal reduction product.
‡ No alkaline catalyst was used.

TABLE II—*Continued*

COMPOUNDS REDUCED BY THE WOLFF-KISHNER METHOD

Formula	Compound	Product	Method	Yield	Reference*
$C_{13}H_{22}O$	4-*n*-Propylcamphor	Normal	WH	69B	219
$C_{13}H_{10}O_3$	4-Acetoxy-2-naphthaldehyde	None	WS	—	220
$C_{13}H_{18}O_3$	3,5-Dimethoxyphenyl *n*-butyl ketone	Normal	K	85A	33
$C_{13}H_{15}ON$	1-Keto-5,6-benzo-1,2,3,4,7,8-hexahydropyridocoline	Normal	WH	37A	221
$C_{13}H_{17}ON$	6-Phenyl-2,2-dimethyl-4-piperidone	Normal	WD	93A	222
$C_{13}H_{21}ON$	1-Keto-5,6-benzododecahydro-pyridocoline	Normal	WH	40A	221
$C_{13}H_{9}O_2N$	7-Amino-2-hydroxyfluorenone	Normal	WD	100A	223
$C_{13}H_{19}O_3N$	2-Ethyl-4-methyl-3-propionyl-5-carbethoxypyrrole	2-Ethyl-3-propyl-4-methyl-pyrrole	WD	—	224
	2,4-Diethyl-5-carbethoxy-3-acetylpyrrole	2,3,4-Triethylpyrrole	WD	30A	225
	2,4-Dimethyl-5-carbobutoxy-3-acetylpyrrole	2,4-Dimethyl-3-ethylpyrrole	WD	48A	99
	2,4-Dimethyl-3-*n*-butyryl-5-carbethoxypyrrole	2,4-Dimethyl-3-*n*-butylpyrrole	WD	—	226
	2,4-Dimethyl-3-isobutyryl-5-carbethoxypyrrole	2,4-Dimethyl-3-isobutylpyr-role	WD	9A	226
$C_{13}H_{24}ON_2$	Cuskhygrin	Normal †	WH	10B	7
$C_{13}H_{16}O_3N_2$	2,4-Dimethyl-5-carbethoxy-3-(β-cyanopropionyl)-pyrrole	2,4-Dimethyl-3-(γ-keto-butyric acid)-pyrrole	WD	10A	200
$C_{13}H_{19}O_4N_2Cl$	Imide hydrochloride of ethyl 2,4-dimethyl-5-carbethoxy-pyrrole-3-glyoxylate	Normal	WD	—	227
$C_{13}H_{8}OCl_2$	*p,p′*-Dichlorobenzophenone	Normal	WH	21B	228

C_{14}

Formula	Compound	Product	Method	Yield	Reference*
$C_{14}H_{20}O$	Phenyl *n*-heptyl ketone	Normal	WD	40–50A	43
	p-Tolyl *n*-hexyl ketone	Normal	WD	—	129
$C_{14}H_{22}O$	1,1,6,10-Tetramethyl-Δ^5-octalone-2	Normal	WS	90B	229
$C_{14}H_{10}O_2$	Benzil	Normal	WH ‡	Almost 100B	25
	Benzil	Normal	WH §	Little	26
$C_{14}H_{11}ON$	1,3-Dimethyl-2-azafluorenone	Normal	WD ‖	80A	230
$C_{14}H_{21}O_2N$	2,4-Diethyl-3,5-dipropionyl-pyrrole	2,4-Diethyl-3-propylpyrrole	WD	—	6
$C_{14}H_{21}O_3N$	2-Methyl-4-propyl-3-propi-onyl-5-carbethoxypyrrole	2-Methyl-3,4-dipropylpyrrole	WD	16A	213

* References 86*a*–413 are listed on pp. 416–422.

† Though the α-hydrazone gave a small yield of the normal product, the β-hydrazone under the some conditions gave a 33% yield of desacetylcuskhygrin; that is, di-(N-methyl-α-pyrrolidyl)methane.

‡ This reaction was carried out on the monohydrazone in the absence of any alkaline catalyst. Under the same conditions the dihydrazone gave only a compound $C_{28}H_{24}N_2$, probably the azine of desoxybenzoin.

§ The monohydrazone heated in vacuum gave a little desoxybenzoin and mostly benzilazine. No alkaline catalyst was used.

‖ No alkaline catalyst was used.

TABLE II—*Continued*

COMPOUNDS REDUCED BY THE WOLFF-KISHNER METHOD

C_{15}

Formula	Compound	Product	Method	Yield	Reference*
$C_{15}H_8O$	1-Perinaphthindenone	Normal	K	19B	231
$C_{15}H_{10}O$	9-Anthraldehyde	Normal	WH	38B	232
	9-Anthraldehyde	Normal	K	79B	20
	9-Phenanthraldehyde	Normal	WS	—	232a
$C_{15}H_{12}O$	Benzalacetophenone	1,2-Diphenylcyclopropane	KP	—	233
	3(2′-Naphthyl)-cyclopenten-2-one-1	Normal	WS	49B	234
$C_{15}H_{14}O$	Dibenzyl ketone	Normal	WH	82B	2
$C_{15}H_{18}O$	9-Keto-12-methyl-1,2,3,4,9,10,11,12-octahydrophenanthrene	Normal	WS	—	235
	1-Keto-11-methyloctahydrophenanthrene	Normal	WS	—	236
$C_{15}H_{22}O$	Gurgunene ketone	Normal	WS	—	237
	Cedrone	Normal	WS	29B	238
	α-Cyperone	Normal	WS	—	239
	α-Vetivone	Normal	WS †	42B	240
	β-Vetivone	Normal	WS †	50B	240
	β-Vetivone	Normal	WS †	44B	241
	Ketones from *Zingiber* root	Normal	WS	81B	242
	p-Tolyl n-heptyl ketone	Normal	WD	—	129
	p-Tolyl n-heptyl ketone	Normal	WD, WS	—	130
$C_{15}H_{28}O$	Cyclopentadecanone	Normal	WS	62B	24
$C_{15}H_{10}O_2$	α-Benzoylcoumarone	Normal	WH	—	54
$C_{15}H_{14}O_2$	6-Methoxy-1-keto-1,2,3,4-tetrahydrophenanthrene	Normal	WS	—	242a
$C_{15}H_{20}O_2$	2-Keto-4-furyl-10-methyl-decalin	Normal	WS	50B	243
$C_{15}H_{14}O_3$	Di-p-anisyl ketone	Normal	WK ‡	—	26
$C_{15}H_{23}ON$	4-Methyl-3-aminophenyl n-heptyl ketone	Normal	WD	—	130

C_{16}

Formula	Compound	Product	Method	Yield	Reference*
$C_{16}H_{12}O$	9-Methyl-10-anthraldehyde	Normal	WH	74B	216
	1-Acetylanthracene	Normal §	WS	100B	9
	2-Acetylanthracene	Normal	WD	Good	9
$C_{16}H_{14}O$	2-Methyl-3-phenylindone	Normal	WH	100B	244
	1-Keto-1,2,3,4-tetrahydro-8,9-acephenanthrene	Normal	WD	Poor	245
$C_{16}H_{20}O$	4-Phenylcamphor	Normal	WH	85B	246
	9-Phenyl-3-decalone	Normal	K	70A	246a
$C_{16}H_{24}O$	p-Tolyl n-octyl ketone	Normal	WD	—	129
$C_{16}H_{12}O_2$	Perisuccinoylacenaphthene	Normal	WD	—	78

* References 86a–413 are listed on pp. 416–422.

† The semicarbazone was added to aqueous potassium hydroxide containing a little copper sulfate and the solution heated slowly in vacuum until both the water and the product had distilled.

‡ No alkaline catalyst was used.

§ The reaction proceeded normally when the semicarbazone was reduced for four hours at 180° when the ketone was reduced directly at 180° for eight hours, 2-ethylanthracene was formed.

TABLE II—*Continued*

Compounds Reduced by the Wolff-Kishner Method

Formula	Compound	Product	Method	Yield	Reference*
$C_{16}H_{14}O_2$	3-(6′-Methoxy-2′-naphthyl)-cyclopenten-2-one-1	Normal	WS	37B	234
$C_{16}H_{14}O_3$	β-(3-Acenaphthoyl)-propionic acid	Normal	WD	99A (cr.)	40
$C_{16}H_{24}O_3$	3,5-Dimethoxyphenyl n-heptyl ketone	Normal	?	—	247
$C_{16}H_{30}O_3$	Mixture of methyl 2-ethyl-2-butyl-5-ketonononoate and methyl 4-ethyl-4-butyl-5-ketonononoate	Mixture of normally reduced acids	WH	—	247a
$C_{16}H_{14}O_4$	β-(p-Phenoxybenzoyl)-propionic acid	Normal	WD	95A (cr.)	40
$C_{16}H_9ON$	1,2-Benzo-3-azafluorenone	Normal	WD †	—	86
	2,3-Benzo-1-azafluorenone	Normal	WD †	80A	86
	3,4-Benzo-2-azafluorenone	Normal	WD †	—	248
$C_{16}H_{13}ON$	3-Acetyl-2-phenylpyrrocoline	Normal ‡	WD	35A	249
$C_{16}H_8ONCl$	4-Chloro-1,2-benzo-3-aza-fluorenone	4-Hydroxy-1,2-benzo-3-aza-fluorene	WD †	85A	28

C_{17}

Formula	Compound	Product	Method	Yield	Reference*
$C_{17}H_{10}O$	Pyrene-3-aldehyde	Normal	WD	90A	27
	Pyrene-3-aldehyde	Normal	K	84B	20
$C_{17}H_{12}O$	α-Benzoylnaphthalene	Normal	WD †	55A	29
	β-Benzoylnaphthalene	Normal	WD †	96A	29
$C_{17}H_{14}O$	β-Propionylanthracene	Normal	WD	Good	9
	Dibenzalacetone	§	K	—	250
$C_{17}H_{18}O$	3-Keto-1,2,3,9,10,11-hexahydro-1,2-cyclopentenophenanthrene	Normal	?	—	71
	3-Keto-1,2,3,9,10,11-hexahydro-1,2-cyclopentenophenanthrene	Normal	WS	—	250a
	1-Methyl-4-keto-1,2,3,4-tetrahydro-7-ethylphenanthrene	Normal	?	—	251
$C_{17}H_{30}O$	Civetone	Normal ‖	WS	65B	252
$C_{17}H_{32}O$	Dihydrocivetone	Normal	WS	—	24
$C_{17}H_{10}O_2$	2-Methylacenthrenequinone	None	?	—	253
	?-Methylacenthrenequinone	None	?	—	253
$C_{17}H_{12}O_2$	p-Hydroxyphenyl β-naphthyl ketone	Normal	WD †	—	29
$C_{17}H_{16}O_3$	3-(2-Naphthyl)cyclopentan-1-one-2-acetic acid	Normal	WS	79A	253a
$C_{17}H_{26}O_3$	3,5-Dimethoxyphenyl n-octyl ketone	Normal	?	85A	254

* References 86a–413 are listed on pp. 416–422.
† No alkaline catalyst was used.
‡ There was also formed 45% of 2-phenylpyrrocoline.
§ With one mole of hydrazine there was formed the pyrazoline which on warming was converted to 3,4-diphenylcyclopentene. When the ketone was treated with excess hydrazine there was formed a dimeric product, converted by the action of potassium hydroxide into 1-phenyl-2-(β-phenylethyl) cyclopropane.
‖ There was also formed 31% of civetol.

TABLE II—*Continued*

Compounds Reduced by the Wolff-Kishner Method

Formula	Compound	Product	Method	Yield	Reference*
$C_{17}H_{16}O_4$	γ-(p-Phenoxybenzoyl)-butyric acid	Normal	WD	96A (cr.)	40
$C_{17}H_{11}ON$	4-Methyl-1,2-benzo-3-aza-fluorenone	Normal	WD †	—	255
$C_{17}H_{11}O_2N$	4-Methoxy-1,2-benzo-3-aza-fluorenone	4-Hydroxy-1,2-benzo-3-aza-fluorene	WD †	94A	28
$C_{17}H_{19}O_2N$	β-(Tetrahydro-4-pyranyl)-ethyl 4'-quinolyl ketone	Normal	WS	80B	256
$C_{17}H_{18}ON_2$	9-Rubanone	Normal	K	63A	257
$C_{17}H_{20}ON_2$	Michler's ketone	Normal	WA	—	26
	Michler's ketone	Normal	WH	97B	2
$C_{17}H_{24}ON_2$	3,3',5,5'-Tetramethyl-4,4'-diethylpyrroketone	2,4-Dimethyl-3-ethylpyrrole	WD	—	258

$$C_{18}$$

Formula	Compound	Product	Method	Yield	Reference*
$C_{18}H_{14}O$	2-Phenylacetylnaphthalene	Normal	WS	—	259
$C_{18}H_{16}O$	2-Keto-1,2,9,10,11,12-hexa-hydro-3,4-benzophenanthrene	Normal	WS	88A	260
$C_{18}H_{18}O$	16-Equilenone	Normal	WS	22B (cr.)	261
	β-17-Equilenone	Normal	WS	53B (cr.)	261
$C_{18}H_{20}O$	5-Keto-1,2,3,4-tetramethyl-5,6,7,8-tetrahydroanthracene	Normal	WS	76B	262
$C_{18}H_{22}O$	2-Ketododecahydrochrysene	Normal	WS	35A	263, 264
$C_{18}H_{28}O$	Phenyl n-undecyl ketone	Normal	WD	40–50A	43
	p-Tolyl n-decyl ketone	Normal	WD	—	129
$C_{18}H_{14}O_2$	cis-Diketohexahydrochrysene	Normal	WH	34A	265
	$trans$-Diketohexahydrochrysene	Normal	WH	44A	265
$C_{18}H_{22}O_2$	Estrone	Normal	WS	—	266
	Estrone	Normal	WS	35B	60
	Estrone	Normal	?	—	267
	Estrone	Normal	WS	73B	268
	Lumiestrone	Normal	WS	—	269
$C_{18}H_{24}O_2$	O-Methylpodocarpinal	6-Hydroxypodocarpane	WS	51B	270
$C_{18}H_{14}O_3$	β-(9-Phenanthroyl)propionic acid	Normal	WS	76B	271
$C_{18}H_{20}O_3$	7-Ketoestrone	Normal	WS	48B	268
	2-Hydroxy-5-benzyloxyisoval-erophenone	None	WA	—	207
$C_{18}H_{22}O_3$	β-(5 or 6)Cyclohexane-1-spiro-hydrindoylpropionic acid	Normal	WS	—	272
$C_{18}H_{26}O_3$	10-Keto-12-phenyldodecanoic acid	Normal	WD	78A	273
$C_{18}H_{30}O_3$	12-Keto-13-(3-cyclopentene)-tridecylic acid	Normal	WD	70A	274
$C_{18}H_{32}O_3$	8-Keto-17-octadecenoic acid	Normal	WD	65A (cr.)	41
	8-Keto-16-octadecenoic acid	Normal	WD	—	41
$C_{18}H_{34}O_3$	Ethyl 5-keto-3-methyl-3-amyldecanoate	None	?	—	275
$C_{18}H_{22}O_6$	Diethyl α-acetyl-β-(p-anisyl)-glutaconate	None	?	—	276

* References 86a–413 are listed on pp. 416–422.
† No alkaline catalyst was used.

TABLE II—*Continued*

COMPOUNDS REDUCED BY THE WOLFF-KISHNER METHOD

Formula	Compound	Product	Method	Yield	Reference*
$C_{18}H_{13}ON$	4-Ethyl-1,2-benzo-3-azafluor-enone	Normal	WD †	—	255
$C_{18}H_{21}O_3N$	Metathebainone	Normal	WD	56–63A	277
$C_{18}H_{19}O_4N$	Hydroxycodeinone	None	WH	—	278
		C_{19}			
$C_{19}H_{12}O$	1,2-Benzanthracene-10-alde-hyde	Normal	WH	100B	232
	3,4-Benzo-1-phenanthralde-hyde	Normal	WS	63B (cr.)	262
	3,4-Benzo-2-phenanthralde-hyde	Normal	WS	—	279
	Chrysene-5-aldehyde	Normal	WS	17B	280
$C_{19}H_{20}O$	Methyl β-9-fluorenyl-β-methyl-propyl ketone	Normal	WS	49B	281
$C_{19}H_{22}O$	1-Methyl-4-keto-1,2,3,4-tetra-hydro-7-*sec*-butylphenan-threne	Normal	?	—	251
	α-Bisdehydrodoisynolaldehyde	Normal	WS	—	281a
	β-Bisdehydrodoisynolaldehyde	Normal	WS	—	281a
$C_{19}H_{24}O$	2-Keto-16-methyldodecahy-drochrysene-a	Normal	WS	—	264
$C_{19}H_{28}O$	Δ^{16}-Androstene-3-one	Normal	WD	53A	282
$C_{19}H_{30}O$	Androstanone	Normal	WS	100B	283
	Etiocholanone-17	Normal	WS	57B	283
	A propeimin derivative	Normal	WS	—	284
$C_{19}H_{20}O_2$	Equilenin methyl ether	Desoxoequilenin	WS	61A	285
$C_{19}H_{24}O_2$	3-Keto-7-methoxy-2-methyl-3,4,9,10,11,12-hexahydrocy-clopentenophenanthrene	Normal	WS	63B	264
$C_{19}H_{28}O_2$	Norcafestanedione	Normal	WS	79B	286
	Norcafestonal	Normal	WS	Poor	287
	Androstane-3,17-dione	Normal	WS	>80B	286
	Dehydroandrosterone	Normal	WS	98A	288
	Dehydroandrosterone	Normal	WS	16B	289
$C_{19}H_{30}O_2$	Androstan-3(β)-ol-17-one	Normal	WD	81A	290
$C_{19}H_{16}O_3$	β-3-Phenanthroylisobutyric acid	Normal	WS	98B (cr.)	291
$C_{19}H_{15}ON$	4-Isopropyl-1,2-benzo-3-aza-fluorenone	Normal	WD †	81A	28
$C_{19}H_9O_2N$	2,3,5,6-Dibenzoylenepyridine	Normal	WD †	—	230
$C_{19}H_{25}O_3N$	Ketoazodehydroabietic acid	Normal	WD	—	292
		C_{20}			
$C_{20}H_{14}O$	1-Acetyl-3,4-benzophenan-threne	Normal	WS	—	279
	2-Acetyl-3,4-benzophenan-threne	Normal	WS	—	279

* References 86a–413 are listed on pp. 416–422.
† No alkaline catalyst was used.

TABLE II—*Continued*

Compounds Reduced by the Wolff-Kishner Method

Formula	Compound	Product	Method	Yield	Reference*
$C_{20}H_{16}O$	γ,γ-Diphenyl-α-hydrindone	Normal	WH, WS	Good	293
$C_{20}H_{20}O$	3-Acetylretene	Normal	WS	50B	294
$C_{20}H_{22}O$	2-Acetyldihydroretene	Normal	WS	Poor	53
$C_{20}H_{28}O$	Dehydroabietinal	Normal	WS	70B	270
	Dehydroabietinal	Normal	WS	82A	294a
$C_{20}H_{30}O$	Abietinal	Normal	WS	81B	295
$C_{20}H_{32}O$	Phenyl n-tridecyl ketone	Normal	WD	40–50A	43
	p-Tolyl n-dodecyl ketone	Normal	WD	—	129
$C_{20}H_{40}O$	3-Eicosanone	Normal	WD	40A	38
$C_{20}H_{18}O_2$	2,11-Diketo-9,18-dimethyl-1,2,9,10,11,18-hexahydro-chrysene-a	Normal	WH	66A	265
	2,11-Diketo-9,18-dimethyl-1,2,9,10,11,18-hexahydro-chrysene-b	Normal	WH	55A	265
$C_{20}H_{32}O_2$	Ketomanoyloxide	Normal	WS	83B	296
$C_{20}H_{22}O_4$	1,4-Di-p-anisoylbutane	Normal	K	82A	56
	Methyl bisdehydromarriano-late aldehyde 7-methyl ether	Bisdehydrodoisynolic acid †	WD	50A	297
$C_{20}H_{26}O_4$	Methyl marrianolate aldehyde 7-methyl ether	Doisynolic acid 7-methyl ether	WD	50A	297
	Methyl lumimarrianolate alde-hyde 7-methyl ether	Lumidoisynolic acid	WS	—	297
$C_{20}H_{30}O_4$	Diketocassanic acid	Normal	WH	82A	298
$C_{20}H_{30}O_5$	3(α),12-Dihydroxy-11-keto-etiocholanic acid	3(α),11,12-Trihydroxyetiocho-lanic acid	WD	—	298a
$C_{20}H_{11}ON$	1,2(1,2)-Naphtho-3-azafluore-none	Normal	WD ‡	100A	28
$C_{20}H_{25}O_3N$	6-(4-Benzyloxy-3-methoxy-phenyl)-2,2-dimethyl-4-pi-peridone	None	WD	0	222

C_{21}

Formula	Compound	Product	Method	Yield	Reference*
$C_{21}H_{12}O$	1,2,6,7-Dibenzofluorenone	Normal	WD	90A	299
	1,2,7,8-Dibenzofluorenone	Normal	WD ‡	—	300
	2,3,5,6-Dibenzofluorenone	Normal and some of the difluorene	WD	—	300a
	2,3,6,7-Dibenzofluorenone	Normal	WD ‡	—	300
	2,3,6,7-Dibenzofluorenone	Normal §	WD	39A	299
	3,4,5,6-Dibenzofluorenone	Normal	WD ‡	—	300
	3,4-Benzopyrene-5-aldehyde	Normal	WH	70B	301
$C_{21}H_{16}O$	2-Phenylacetylfluorene	Normal	WD, WS	—	299
	1-Propionyl-3,4-benzophenan-threne	Normal	WS	—	279
	2-Propionyl-3,4-benzophenan-threne	Normal	WS	—	279

* References 86a–413 are listed on pp. 416–422.
† The crude product was treated with hydrochloric acid to remove the methoxyl group.
‡ No alkaline catalyst was used.
§ Some of the azine and some 2,2′,3,3′,6,6′,7,7′-tetrabenzo-9,9′-bifluorenyl were also formed.

TABLE II—*Continued*

COMPOUNDS REDUCED BY THE WOLFF-KISHNER METHOD

Formula	Compound	Product	Method	Yield	Reference*
$C_{21}H_{34}O$	Allopregnan-3-one	Normal	WH	98B	302
	17a-Methyl-D-homo-3-andro-stanone	Normal	WD	—	303
$C_{21}H_{30}O_2$	O-Methyl-7-isopropylpodocar-pinal	Ferruginol †	WS	—	270
	6-Methoxydehydroabietinal	Ferruginol †	WS	—	270
	Methylhinokione	Normal (not isolated)	?	—	304
$C_{21}H_{32}O_2$	17a-Methyl-D-homoandrostan-3,17-dione	Normal	WH	30B	35
	17a-Methyl-D-etiochola-3,17-dione	Normal	WD	100A	305
	Diketodiginane	Normal	WD	45A	306
$C_{21}H_{34}O_2$	Pregnan-3(α)-ol-20-one	Normal	WS	85B	307
$C_{21}H_{30}O_3$	Dehydroandrosterone acetate	Unknown compound	WS	89B (cr.)	308
	Dehydroisoandrosterone acetate	— ‡	WS	—	308a
	Dihydrodehydrodesoxodigini-genin	Normal	WD	84A	306
$C_{21}H_{32}O_3$	Dihydrodesoxodiginigenin	None	WS	—	306
	Methyl 3-ketoetioallocholanate	Etioallocholanic acid §	WD	48A	309
$C_{21}H_{34}O_3$	3(β),17a-Dihydroxy-17a-methyl-D-homo-17-androstanone	$C_{21}H_{34}O$	WD	—	303
$C_{21}H_{36}O_3$	Pregnanol-20(α)-on-3 acetate	Pregnanediol-3(α),20(α)	WS	85B	79
$C_{21}H_{22}O_4$	Half methyl ester of bisde-hydromarrianolic half alde-hyde methyl ether	Normal ‖	WD	—	309a
$C_{21}H_{28}O_4$	Diginigenin	Desoxodiginigenin ¶	WS	24B	306
$C_{21}H_{32}O_4$	Methyl 3-keto-12(α)-hydroxy-etiocholanate	12(α)-Hydroxyetiocholanic acid	WD	—	309b
$C_{21}H_{32}O_5$	Methyl 3(α),7(α)-dihydroxy-12-ketoetiocholanic acid	3(α),7(α)-Dihydroxyetiocho-lanic acid	WD	—	309b
$C_{21}H_{15}ON$	3-Benzoyl-2-phenylpyrrocoline	Normal **	WD	26A	249

C_{22}

Formula	Compound	Product	Method	Yield	Reference*
$C_{22}H_{16}O$	6'-Keto-4',5-dimethylene-1',2',-3',4'-tetrahydro-3,4-benzo-pyrene	None	?	—	312
$C_{22}H_{20}O$	Di-o-tolylphenylmethane-o-carboxaldehyde	Normal	WD	83A	313
$C_{22}H_{22}O$	1'-Keto-1',2',3',4'-tetrahydro-3,4-benzoretene	Normal	WS	71B	314

* References 86a–413 are listed on pp. 416–422.
† This is the normal product in which the methoxyl group has undergone cleavage.
‡ A mixture of etiocholan-3(α)-ol, Δ^5-androsten-3(β)-ol, and androstan-3(β)-ol was formed.
§ There was also formed a small amount of a second acid, probably the 17-iso acid.
‖ After methylation of the crude product.
¶ Aside from the normal product (one carbonyl group reduced) there was formed dihydroxyketo-diginene, $C_{21}H_{32}O_3$, and a compound $C_{21}H_{34}O_2$ (not isolated) presumably formed by the reduction of two carbonyl groups and the reductive cleavage of an ether link.
** 2-Phenylpyrrocoline was also formed to the extent of 49%.

TABLE II—*Continued*

Compounds Reduced by the Wolff-Kishner Method

Formula	Compound	Product	Method	Yield	Reference*
$C_{22}H_{30}O$	16-Isopropylidene-$\Delta^{3,5}$-andro-stadien-17-one	Normal	WD	—	310
$C_{22}H_{36}O$	Phenyl *n*-pentadecyl ketone	Normal	WD	40–50A	43
	p-Tolyl *n*-tetradecyl ketone	Normal	WD	—	129
$C_{22}H_{32}O_2$	16-Isopropylidene-Δ^5-andro-sten-3-ol-17-one	Unknown compound	WD	—	310
$C_{22}H_{16}O_3$	β-(2-Chrysenoyl)propionic acid	Normal	WS	—	55
$C_{22}H_{28}O_3$	2,3-Diethyl-1,4-di-*p*-anisyl-1-butanone	Normal	WD	44A	56
$C_{22}H_{34}O_3$	Methyl 3-ketoallopregnane-21-carboxylate	Normal †	WH	57B	311
	D-Homoandrostan-3(β)-acetoxy-17a-one	3(β)-Hydroxy-D-homoandro-stane	WD	59A	290
$C_{22}H_{32}O_5$	$\Delta^{9,14}$-2,13-Dimethyl-2-carbo-methoxy-7(β)-acetoxy-dodecahydrophenanthryl-1-acetaldehyde	Normal hydroxy acid	WD	79A	314a
$C_{22}H_{34}O_5$	2,13-Dimethyl-2-carbometh-oxy-7(α)-acetoxyperhydro-phenanthryl-1-acetaldehyde	Normal hydroxy acid	WD	69A	314a
$C_{22}H_{24}O_7$	α-(3,4-Dimethoxybenzoyl)β-(3',4'-dimethoxybenzyl)-butyrolactone	None	?	—	57
$C_{22}H_{32}O_9$	A monoketo acid from cholic acid	Normal	WS	28A	315
$C_{22}H_{13}ON$	4-Phenyl-1,2-benzo-3-aza-fluorenone	Normal	WD ‡	—	255
$C_{22}H_{15}ON$	2-Phenyl-4-benzoylquinoline	Normal	WD ‡	—	28

C_{23}

Formula	Compound	Product	Method	Yield	Reference*
$C_{23}H_{36}O_3$	Acetate of a D-homo steroid	$C_{21}H_{36}O$	WD	—	316
$C_{23}H_{34}O_4$	3(β)-Acetoxy-17a(α)-hydroxy-17a-methyl-17-D-homoetio-cholanone	3(β)-Hydroxy-17a-methyl-17-D-homoetiocholene	WD	98A	305
	A steroid diketo monoacetate	$C_{21}H_{36}O$	WS	17B	317
$C_{23}H_{36}O_4$	3-Hydroxy-12-ketonorcholanic acid	Normal	WS	44B	318
$C_{23}H_{34}O_5$	3(α),12(β)-Diacetoxycholan-17-one	3(α)-12(β)-Dihydroxycholane	WD	82A (cr.)	319
$C_{23}H_{32}O_6$	Methyl 3(α)-acetoxy-7,12-di-ketoetiocholanate	3(α)-Hydroxyetiocholanic acid	WD	80A	309b
	Methyl 7(α)-acetoxy-3,12-di-ketoetiocholanate	7(α)-Hydroxyetiocholanic acid	WD	—	309b
$C_{23}H_{34}O_6$	Methyl 3-acetoxy-11-hydroxy-12-ketoetiocholanate	3(α),11(α)-Dihydroxyetiocho-lanic acid and 3(α),11,12-tri-hydroxyetiocholanic acid	WS	—	298a

* References 86a–413 are listed on pp. 416–422.
† Not isolated as such; methylation gave 57% of methyl ester. Also, 15% of the 3(β)-OH ester was formed.
‡ No alkaline catalyst was used.

TABLE II—*Continued*

COMPOUNDS REDUCED BY THE WOLFF-KISHNER METHOD

Formula	Compound	Product	Method	Yield	Reference*
$C_{23}H_{32}O_7$	α-Isostrophanthic acid	Normal	WS	Poor	62
$C_{23}H_{17}ON$	4-Isopropyl-1,2(1,2)-naphtho-3-azafluorenone	Normal	WD †	100A	28

C_{24}

Formula	Compound	Product	Method	Yield	Reference*
$C_{24}H_{36}O_3$	12-Keto-$\Delta^{9,11}$-cholenic acid	Normal	WS	Good	320
$C_{24}H_{38}O_3$	3-Ketocholanic acid	Normal ‡	WS	8B	5
$C_{24}H_{36}O_4$	3,7-Diketocholanic acid	3-Hydroxycholanic acid	WS	—	321
	3,12-Diketocholanic acid	Normal §	WS	31B	5
	11,12-Diketocholanic acid	A triazine	WS	—	13
	3(α)-Hydroxy-12-keto-$\Delta^{9,11}$-cholenic acid	Normal	WS	—	322
	3(α)-Hydroxy-12-keto-$\Delta^{9,11}$-cholenic acid	Normal	?	—	323
	3(α)-Hydroxy-12-keto-$\Delta^{9,11}$-cholenic acid	Normal	WS	70B (cr.)	324
$C_{24}H_{38}O_4$	3-Hydroxy-6-ketocholanic acid	Normal ‖	WS	—	22
	3(β)-Hydroxy-6-ketoallocholanic acid	Normal	WS	30B	325
	6(β)-Hydroxy-3-ketocholanic acid	Normal	WD	95A	326
	12-Hydroxy-7-ketocholanic acid	Normal	WS	71–83B (cr.)	23
	3(α)-Hydroxy-12-ketocholanic acid	Normal	WS	28B (cr.)	327
	3(α)-Hydroxy-12-ketocholanic acid	Normal	WS	47A	13
	3(α)-Hydroxy-12-ketocholanic acid	¶	WS	—	5
	3(α)-Hydroxy-12-ketocholanic acid	Normal	WD	—	328
	11-Hydroxy-12-ketocholanic acid	11,12-Dihydroxycholanic acid	WD	70A	329
$C_{24}H_{34}O_5$	3,7,12-Triketocholanic acid	Normal	WS	—	61
	3,7,12-Triketocholanic acid	Normal **	WS	22B	5
$C_{24}H_{36}O_5$	3-Hydroxy-7,12-diketocholanic acid	Normal	WS	20B	61
	3-Hydroxy-7,12-diketocholanic acid	Normal	WS	28B	36
	3-Hydroxy-7,12-diketocholanic acid	Normal	WS	—	13

* References 86a–413 are listed on pp. 416–422.

† No alkaline catalyst was used.

‡ In addition to the small amount of normal product there was formed 3(α)- and 3(β)-hydroxycholanic acid in 73% total yield.

§ There were also formed 3(α)- and 3(β)-hydroxycholanic acid (total yield, 38%) and 3(α)- and 3(β)-hydroxy-12-ketocholanic acid (total yield, 9%).

‖ There was also formed 3-hydroxyallocholanic acid.

¶ There were formed 3(α)- and 3(β)-hydroxycholanic acid (total yield, 70%) and 3(α)- and 3(β)-hydroxy-12-ketocholanic acid (total yield, 10%).

** There were also formed 38% of 3(α)-hydroxycholanic acid and a small amount of the β-isomer.

TABLE II—*Continued*

COMPOUNDS REDUCED BY THE WOLFF-KISHNER METHOD

Formula	Compound	Product	Method	Yield	Reference*
$C_{24}H_{36}O_5$	3(α)-Hydroxy-7,12-diketocholanic acid	Normal	WD	—	328
$C_{24}H_{38}O_5$	3,7-Dihydroxy-12-ketocholanic acid	Normal	WS	91B (cr.)	330
	3(α),11-Dihydroxy-12-ketocholanic acid	3(α)-Hydroxy-9-cholenic acid	WD	13A	331
	3(α),11-Dihydroxy-12-ketocholanic acid	3(α),11,12-Trihydroxycholanic acid	WD	28A	329
	3(α),11(α)-Dihydroxy-12-ketocholanic acid	Normal †	WH	33B	332
	3(α),11(β)-Dihydroxy-12-ketocholanic acid	3(α),11(α)-Dihydroxycholanic acid †	WH	20–30B	333
	3(α),12(α)-Dihydroxy-11-ketocholanic acid	3(α)-Hydroxy-Δ^{11}-cholenic acid ‡	WH	—	334
	3(α),12(β)-Dihydroxy-11-ketocholanic acid	3(α)-Hydroxy-Δ^{11}-cholenic acid ‡	WH	27B	334
	3(α),12(β)-Dihydroxy-11-ketocholanic acid	3(α)-Hydroxy-Δ^{11}-cholenic acid §	WD	—	335
	7,12-Dihydroxy-3-ketocholanic acid	Normal	WD	—	336
$C_{24}H_{30}O_7$	Lobariol	None	WH	—	337
$C_{24}H_{36}O_7$	Hyodesoxybilianic acid	Normal	WH	—	338
	Desoxybilianic acid	Normal	WS	20B	61
	Desoxybilianic acid	Normal ‖	WS	60B	315
	β-Desoxybilianic acid	Normal	WS	40A	315
$C_{24}H_{34}O_8$	Bilianic acid	Normal	WS	7B	61
	Isobilianic acid	Normal	WS	—	61

C₂₅ and C₂₆

$C_{25}H_{38}O_3$	Methyl 12-keto-9-cholenate	Δ^9-Cholenic and Δ^{11}-cholenic acids	WD	—	338a
$C_{25}H_{38}O_4$	Methyl 3(β)-hydroxy-12-keto-9-cholenate	Normal	—	—	323
$C_{25}H_{38}O_5$	3(β),17(α)-Diacetoxyallo-20-pregnanone	3(β)-Hydroxy-17a-methyl-D-homo-17-androstene	WD	100A (cr.)	303
$C_{25}H_{40}O_5$	Methyl 3-keto-7(α),12(α)-dihydroxycholanate	7(α),12(α)-Dihydroxycholanic acid	K	—	338b
$C_{25}H_{36}O_7$	Methyl 3(α),12(α)-diacetoxy-7-ketoetiocholanate	3(α),12(α)-Dihydroxyetiocholanic acid	WD	—	309b
	Methyl 3(α),6-diacetoxy-7-ketoetiocholanate	3(α),6-Dihydroxyetiocholanic acid	WD	—	309b

* References 86a–413 are listed on pp. 416–422.
† Not isolated as such.
‡ Isolated as the methyl ester. There were also formed 3(α),11(α),12(α)- and 3(α),11(α),12(β)-trihydroxycholanic acids.
§ There were also formed the two trihydroxycholanic acids mentioned before as well as some 3(α),11(β),12(β)-trihydroxycholanic acid.
‖ The product consisted of both lithobilianic and allolithobilianic acids.

TABLE II—*Continued*

COMPOUNDS REDUCED BY THE WOLFF-KISHNER METHOD

Formula	Compound	Product	Method	Yield	Reference*
$C_{25}H_{40}O_7$	Methyl 3(α),12(β)-dihydroxy-11-ketocholanate	†	WD	—	335
$C_{26}H_{16}O$	9,9-Biphenylenophenanthrone	Normal	WH ‡	—	339
$C_{26}H_{44}O$	A ketone from Diels' acid	Normal	WS	—	340
	A pyroketone from coprostanol	Normal	WS	—	341
	1-Phenyleicosanone-3	Normal	WD	§	37
	1-Phenyleicosanone-3	Normal	WD	65A	38
	1-Phenyleicosanone-3	Normal	WD	67A	342
$C_{26}H_{50}O$	1-Cyclopentyl-4-heneicosanone	Normal	WD	79A	342
$C_{26}H_{52}O$	9-Hexacosanone	Normal	WD	51A	342
$C_{26}H_{16}O_2$	Tetrabenzocyclodecan-1,6-dione	Tetrabenzonaphthalene	WH ‡	—	339
$C_{26}H_{34}O_2$	1,14-Diphenyltetradecadione-3,12	Normal	WD	‖	37
$C_{26}H_{42}O_3$	Acetylnorlithocholyl methyl ketone	Norlithocholyl methyl carbinol	WS	—	343
$C_{26}H_{40}O_5$	3-Acetoxy-12-ketocholanic acid	Normal	WS	—	36
	Ethyl 12-hydroxy-3,7-diketocholanate	12-Hydroxycholanic acid ¶	WD	—	336
$C_{26}H_{38}O_6$	3,12-Diketo-7-acetoxycholanic acid	7-Hydroxycholanic acid	WS	—	344
$C_{26}H_9ON$	2,3-Benzo-4-azafluorenone	Normal	WD ‡	Smoothly	28
$C_{26}H_{16}ON_2$	4-(2'-Aminophenyl)1,2,1',2'-naphtho-3-azafluorenone	Normal	WD ‡	—	248

C_{27}

Formula	Compound	Product	Method	Yield	Reference*
$C_{27}H_{42}O$	3-Keto-4,6-cholestadiene	Inseparable mixture	WS	—	345
	7-Keto-3,5-cholestadiene	Normal	WS	Small	348
$C_{27}H_{44}O$	Cholestenone	Normal **	WS	79B	340
	Cholestenone	Normal ††	WS	40B	5
	Cholestenone	Normal	WA	64B	5
	Δ^2-Cholesten-6-one	Normal	WD	94A (cr.)	346
	Δ^5-Cholesten-4-one	Normal ‡‡	?	—	347
$C_{27}H_{46}O$	Cholestanone	§§	WS	—	5

* References 86*a*–413 are listed on pp. 416–422.
† There were isolated 3(α)-hydroxy-Δ^{11}-cholenic acid and three 3,11,12-trihydroxycholanic acids.
‡ No alkaline catalyst was used.
§ The yield was 32%, 78%, and 83% in triethanolamine, diethylene glycol, and octyl alcohol respectively.
‖ The yield was 5%, 47%, and 60% in triethanolamine, diethylene glycol, and triethylene glycol respectively.
¶ Not isolated as such.
** There were also formed some cholesterol and some β-cholestanol.
†† There were also formed lesser amounts of α-coprostanol, β-cholestanol, cholesterol, and allocholesterol.
‡‡ Not isolated as such.
§§ By the Wolff reduction of the semicarbazone at 180° with either sodium ethoxide or sodium benzylate as catalyst there were formed only α- and β-cholestanols. At 200° the semicarbazone, hydrazone or azine yielded 75% of cholestanols and 15% of cholestane. The semicarbazone on treatment with sodium ethoxide and hydrazine hydrate gave 75% of cholestane; the azine under the same conditions gave 98% of cholestane.

TABLE II—*Continued*

COMPOUNDS REDUCED BY THE WOLFF-KISHNER METHOD

Formula	Compound	Product	Method	Yield	Reference*
$C_{27}H_{46}O$	Coprostanone	α-Coprostanol	WS	64B	5
	1-Cholestanone	Normal	WD	—	349
	2-Cholestanone	Normal	WD	—	349
$C_{27}H_{42}O_2$	3,6-Diketo-4-cholestene	Normal	WS	—	350
	4,7-Diketo-5-cholestene	Normal	WS	—	345
$C_{27}H_{44}O_2$	6-Hydroxy-4-keto-3-cholestene	Cholestandiol-3,6 †	WS	—	350
	Cholestan-3,6-dione	3(β)-Cholestanol	WS	—	351
	24-Ketocholesterol	Normal	WD	—	63
$C_{27}H_{46}O_2$	Epicoprostanol-3-one-24	Epicoprostanolone pinacol	WH, WS	—	343
$C_{27}H_{38}O_3$	3,5-Dehydro-7-ketodesoxy-tigogenin	Normal	WD	—	351a
$C_{27}H_{42}O_3$	Sarsasapogenone	Normal ‡	WS	10B	352
	7-Ketodesoxytigogenin	Normal	WD	—	351a
$C_{27}H_{40}O_4$	Chlorogenone	Tigogenin ($C_{27}H_{44}O_3$)	WS	—	351
$C_{27}H_{42}O_4$	23-Ketosarsasapogenin	Normal	WS	39B	70
	Hecogenin	Normal	?	—	42
	Furcogenin	Normal	?	—	42
$C_{27}H_{40}O_5$	Kammogenin	Normal	?	—	42
	Kammogenin	Normal	WD	—	351a
	Methyl 3(α)-acetoxy-12-keto-9-cholenate	Normal §	WD	23A	323
$C_{27}H_{42}O_5$	Manogenin	Normal	?	—	42
	Methyl 3-keto-12-acetoxy-cholanate	Normal	K	80A	354
	Methyl 3-keto-12(α)-acetoxy-cholanate	12(α)-Hydroxycholanic acid	WD	78A	355
	Mexogenin	Normal	?	—	42
	Mexogenin	Normal	WD	62A	351a
$C_{27}H_{44}O_5$	Acid from cholestan-3,6-dione	Normal	WS	—	66
$C_{27}H_{40}O_6$	Methyl 3(α)-acetoxy-7,12-di-ketocholanate	3(α)-Hydroxycholanic acid	WD	85A	353
$C_{27}H_{40}O_7$	Chlorogenonic acid	Normal	WD	75A (cr.)	356
	Digitogenic acid	Normal	WS	12A	357
$C_{27}H_{38}O_9$	Methyl 3(α),6,12(α)-triacetoxy-7-ketoetiocholanate	3(α),6,12(α)-Trihydroxyetio-cholanic acid	WD	—	309b
	Isomeric methyl 3(α),6,12(α)-triacetoxy-7-ketoetiocholanate	3(α),6,12(α)-Trihydroxyetio-cholanic acid	WD	—	309b

C_{28} and C_{29}

Formula	Compound	Product	Method	Yield	Reference*
$C_{28}H_{42}O_6$	Ethyl 12-acetoxy-3,7-diketo-cholanate	12-Hydroxycholanic acid ‖	WD	—	358
$C_{28}H_{42}O_7$	3,6-Diacetoxy-12-ketocholanic acid	Normal	WS	—	359
$C_{29}H_{46}O$	Oleanone	Normal	WD	Almost 100A	360

* References 86a–413 are listed on pp. 416–422.
† There was also formed some $C_{28}H_{43}ON_3$, probably a hydroxytriazine.
‡ The main reaction product was sarsasapogenin, $C_{27}H_{44}O_3$.
§ There was also formed some of the Δ^{11}-isomer.
‖ Not isolated as such.

TABLE II—*Continued*

COMPOUNDS REDUCED BY THE WOLFF-KISHNER METHOD

Formula	Compound	Product	Method	Yield	Reference*
$C_{29}H_{46}O$	*cis*-$\Delta^{12,13}$-Oleanenone-16	Normal	WD	—	360
	trans-$\Delta^{12,13}$-Oleanenone-16	Normal	WD	—	360
	Nor-α-amyrenone	Normal	WD	73A	361
$C_{29}H_{46}O_2$	7-Ketoepicholesteryl acetate	Normal	WS	—	362
$C_{29}H_{48}O_3$	2-Acetoxy-3-cholestanone	†	WH	—	349
	3(β)-Acetoxy-2-cholestanone	Cholestane	WD	83A	349
$C_{29}H_{42}O_5$	7-Ketodiosgenin acetate	Dehydrodesoxytigogenin	WS	Small	363
$C_{29}H_{44}O_5$	Hecogenin acetate	Tigogenin	WD	60A	351a
$C_{29}H_{44}O_7$	Methyl 7-keto-3,12-diacetoxy-cholanate	3,12-Dihydroxycholanic acid	WS	77B	364
	Methyl 3(α),7(α)-diacetoxy-12-ketocholanate	3(α),7(α)-Dihydroxycholanic acid	WD	100A (cr.)	365
	Methyl 3(α),11(β)-diacetoxy-12-ketocholanate	‡	WH	—	366
	Methyl 3(α),12(β)-diacetoxy-11-ketocholanate	§	WH	—	335
	Methyl 3-keto-7(α),12(β)-diacetoxycholanate	7(α),12(β)-Dihydroxycholanic acid	WD	—	353
$C_{29}H_{42}O_8$	3-Acid succinate of methyl 3(α)-hydroxy-11,12-diketo-cholanate	‖	WD	—	367

C_{30}

Formula	Compound	Product	Method	Yield	Reference*
$C_{30}H_{48}O$	Agnostadienone	Normal	WS	—	368
	α-Amyrone	Normal	WS	60B	369
	β-Amyrone	Normal	WS	80B	370
	Lupenone	Normal	WH	28B	72
	Lupenal	Normal	WD	13A	371
	γ-Lanostenone	Normal	WS	—	372
	2-Desoxyheterobetulinaldehyde	Normal	WD	90A	367a
$C_{30}H_{50}O$	Cryptostenone	Normal	WS	76B	373
	Cryptostenone	Normal	WS	—	376
	Artostenone	Normal	WS	Small	374
	Lupanone	Normal	WH	30B	72
	β-Amyranone	Normal	WD	88A	375
	Dihydrolanostenone	Normal	WS	—	372
	Elemenal	Normal	WD	60A	377
	Friedelin	Normal	WD	—	378
	Isoelemenal	Normal	WH	59A	377
$C_{30}H_{52}O$	Dihydroartostenone	Normal	WS	54B	374
$C_{30}H_{20}O_2$	α-Diphenyltruxone	Normal	WD	Smoothly	59
	γ-Diphenyltruxone	Normal ¶	WD	—	59

* References 86a–413 are listed on pp. 416–422.

† From the reaction mixture there were isolated two azines, cholestane, 4-cholestanol, 1-cholestanol, and some 2-cholestanol (?).

‡ There was formed a mixture of 3(α)-hydroxy-Δ^{11}-cholenic acid and 3(α),11(α)-dihydroxycholanic acid.

§ There was isolated 3(α)-hydroxy-Δ^{11}-cholenic acid and three 3,11,12-trihydroxycholanic acids.

‖ There was formed a mixture of 3(α),11-dihydroxycholanic acid and 3(α)-hydroxy-Δ^{11}-cholenic acid, not isolated as such.

¶ The principal product was α-diphenyltruxane.

TABLE II—*Continued*

Compounds Reduced by the Wolff-Kishner Method

Formula	Compound	Product	Method	Yield	Reference*
$C_{30}H_{46}O_2$	Betulonaldehyde	Normal	WH	95A	379
	Heterobetulinaldehyde	Normal	WD	75A	367a
$C_{30}H_{48}O_2$	Allobetulinone	Normal	WH	87B	380
	Manilaonol	Normal	WD	86A	381
$C_{30}H_{44}O_3$	Novaldehyde	Normal	WS	100B (cr.)	382
	Elemadienonic acid	Normal	WH	—	377
$C_{30}H_{46}O_3$	A keto methyl ester from betulin	$C_{28}H_{46}$	WD	Almost 100A	383
	α-Elemonic acid	Normal	WH	—	384
	β-Elemonic acid	Normal	WH	—	385
	Diketodihydrolanostenone	None	WS	—	372
$C_{30}H_{46}O_4$	$\Delta^{12,13}$-2-Hydroxy-x-keto-28-oleanolic acid	None	?	—	386
	An oleanolic acid derivative	None	—	0	387
$C_{30}H_{46}O_5$	Quillaic acid	Normal	WD	100A	360

C_{31}

Formula	Compound	Product	Method	Yield	Reference*
$C_{31}H_{46}O_3$	Acetylnorquinovadienolal	†	WS	—	382
	Methyl oleanolate	Normal	WS	—	388
$C_{31}H_{48}O_3$	Methyl 16-ketoöleanolate	$trans$-$\Delta^{12,13}$-Oleanene	WD	Almost 100A	360
	Methyl betulonate	Normal	WD	—	379
	Methyl β-elemonate	Desoxoelemonic acid	WS	27A	385
	Acetylnorquinovenolal	Norquinovenol	WS	—	382
	Acetylnorechinocystenolone	Norechinocystenol A	WD	—	389
$C_{31}H_{48}O_4$	Methyl $\Delta^{12,13}$-2-keto-19-hydroxy-28-oleanolate	Normal	WS	71A (cr.)	390
$C_{31}H_{48}O_5$	Methyl quillaate	Desoxyquillaic acid	WS	68B	391
$C_{31}H_{46}O_7$	Manogenin diacetate	Gitogenin	WD	80A	351a
	7-Ketogitogenin diacetate	Gitogenin	WD	57A	351a

C_{32}

Formula	Compound	Product	Method	Yield	Reference*
$C_{32}H_{50}O_3$	Acetyloleanolaldehyde	β-Amyrin ‡	WS	40B	392
	Acetylursolaldehyde	α-Amyrin	WS	—	393
	Acetyldesoxoglycyrrhetinaldehyde	β-Amyrin §	WS	27B	394
	Acetyl-α-boswellic aldehyde	β-Amyrin ‖	WH	13B	395, 396
	Acetyl-β-boswellic aldehyde	α-Amyrin	WS	90B	397
	Acetylbetulinaldehyde	Desoxybetulin (lupeol)	WS	31B	398
	Lupenalyl acetate	Lupeol	WH	29A	371

* References 86a–413 are listed on pp. 416–422.
† Three products were formed: two norquinovadienols ($C_{29}H_{46}O$) and a norquinovadiendiol ($C_{29}H_{46}O_2$).
‡ There was also formed 25% of erythrodiol.
§ There was also formed some hydroxy-β-amyrin.
‖ There was also formed 73% of an isomer, epi-β-amyrin.

TABLE II—*Continued*

COMPOUNDS REDUCED BY THE WOLFF-KISHNER METHOD

Formula	Compound	Product	Method	Yield	Reference*
$C_{32}H_{52}O_3$	β-Amyranonol acetate	β-Amyranol	WD	100A (cr.)	375
	2-Acetoxy-7-keto-α-amyrane	None	?	0	399
	Acetyldihydro-β-elemolaldehyde	$C_{30}H_{52}O$	WS	73B	385
$C_{32}H_{46}O_4$	A β-amyrin derivative	The pyridazine	?	100A	400
$C_{32}H_{50}O_4$	Methyl hederagonate	Normal †	WS	—	388
$C_{32}H_{44}O_5$	Methyl 3-benzoxy-12-keto-cholanate	3-Hydroxycholanic acid	WS	65B	401
$C_{32}H_{48}O_5$	Acetylgypsogenin	Oleanolic acid	WS	41B	402
	Dimethyl quinovenondicarboxylate	Quinovenic acid	WS	—	382
$C_{32}H_{42}O_6$	Methyl 3-benzoxy-7,12-diketo-cholanate	3-Hydroxycholanic acid	WS	63B	401
$C_{32}H_{46}O_3N_2$	Derivative of β-amyradienonal acetate	$C_{30}H_{44}ON_2$	WD	—	403
$C_{32}H_{32}O_5N_4$	2-Desethyl-4-acetylrhodoporphyrin	Normal	WD	—	404

C_{33}–C_{37}

$C_{33}H_{50}O_5$	Methyl $\Delta^{12,13}$-2-acetoxy-19-keto-28-oleanenate	None	?	—	390
	Methyl acetylketoechinocystate	$C_{29}H_{48}O$	WD	—	389
$C_{33}H_{36}O_2N_4$	Desoxophylloerythrin	None	WD	—	405
$C_{33}H_{34}O_3N_4$	Phylloerythrin	Normal	WD, WS	45A, —	405
	Pyrropheophorbide (a)	Normal ‡	WD	—	406
	Pyrropheophorbide (b)	Normal	WD	28A	407
$C_{33}H_{36}O_5N_4$	Rhodin l monomethyl ester	§	WD	—	408
	An isomer of rhodin l methyl ester	§	WD	—	408
$C_{34}H_{52}O_5$	Diacetylhederaldehyde	Hederadiol ‖	WS	34B	409
	Diacetylechinocystaldehyde	$C_{30}H_{50}O_2$ ¶	WD	56A (cr.)	410
$C_{34}H_{50}O_7$	Diacetylquillaic acid lactone	Desoxyquillaic acid lactone	WD	70A	411
$C_{34}H_{36}O_3N_4$	Pyrropheophorbide (b) methyl ester	Normal **	WD	—	412
$C_{34}H_{38}O_3N_4$	Mesopyrropheophorbide (a) methyl ester	Normal	WD	—	412
$C_{34}H_{36}O_5N_4$	Oxorhodoporphyrin dimethyl ester	Rhodoporphyrin	WD	—	404
$C_{36}H_{36}O_6N_4$	Isopheoporphyrin (a₆) methyl ester	Desoxophylloerythrin	WD	—	413
$C_{36}H_{38}O_7N_4$	Purpurine-7 trimethyl ester	Mesorhodochlorine dimethyl ester	WD	Poor	406
$C_{37}H_{53}O_3N$	Betulinone phenylcarbamate	2-Desoxybetulin	WD	46A	380

* References 86a–413 are listed on pp. 416–422.
† There was also formed some $C_{32}H_{52}O_2$.
‡ There was also formed some $C_{33}H_{38}O_2N_4$.
§ There were formed pyrroporphyrin and rhodoporphyrin.
‖ There was also formed 67% of nor-β-amyrin.
¶ A little of the carbinol $C_{30}H_{50}O_3$ was also formed.
** There was also formed some $C_{34}H_{40}O_2N_4$.

REFERENCES TO TABLES

[86a] Wolff and Thielepape, *Ann.*, **420**, 275 (1920).

[87] Filipov, *J. Russ. Phys. Chem. Soc.*, **46**, 1141 (1914) [*C. A.*, **9**, 1904 (1915)].

[88] Rozanov, *J. Russ. Phys. Chem. Soc.*, **48**, 168 (1916) [*C. A.*, **11**, 454 (1917)].

[89] Philipov, *J. prakt. Chem.*, **93**, 162 (1916).

[90] Kishner, *J. Russ. Phys. Chem. Soc.*, **43**, 1563 (1911) [*C. A.*, **6**, 1430 (1912)].

[91] Kishner, *J. Gen. Chem. U.S.S.R.*, **1**, 1212 (1931) [*C. A.*, **26**, 5299 (1932)].

[92] Gilman and Burtner, *J. Am. Chem. Soc.*, **55**, 2903 (1933).

[93] Kishner, *J. Russ. Phys. Chem. Soc.*, **45**, 973 (1913) [*C. A.*, **7**, 3965 (1913)].

[94] Fischer, Beller, and Stern, *Ber.*, **61**, 1074 (1928).

[95] Kishner, *J. Russ. Phys. Chem. Soc.*, **44**, 165 (1912) [*C. A.*, **6**, 1431 (1912)].

[96] Kishner, *J. Russ. Phys. Chem. Soc.*, **47**, 1111 (1915) [*C. A.*, **9**, 3051 (1915)].

[97] Reichstein and Grüssner, *Helv. Chim. Acta*, **16**, 28 (1933).

[97a] Thiele and Barlow, *Ann.*, **302**, 311 (1898).

[98] Reichstein, *Ber.*, **63**, 749 (1930).

[99] Siedel, *Z. physiol. Chem.*, **231**, 167 (1935).

[100] de Jong, *Rec. trav. chim.*, **48**, 1029 (1929).

[100a] Kishner, *J. Russ. Phys. Chem. Soc.*, **45**, 987 (1913) [*C. A.*, **7**, 3965 (1913)].

[101] Reichstein, Zschokke, and Syz, *Helv. Chim. Acta*, **15**, 1112 (1932).

[102] Shuikin, Shemastina, and Cherkasova, *J. Gen. Chem. U.S.S.R.*, **8**, 674 (1938) [*C. A.*, **33**, 1316 (1939)].

[103] Votocek and Kroslak, *Collection Czechoslov. Chem. Commun.*, **11**, 47 (1939) [*C. A.*, **33**, 4983 (1939)].

[104] Woodward, Eisner, and Haines, *J. Am. Chem. Soc.*, **66**, 911 (1944).

[105] Fischer, Sturm, and Friedrich, *Ann.*, **461**, 244 (1928).

[106] Prelog, Moor, and Führer, *Helv. Chim. Acta*, **26**, 846 (1943).

[107] Zelinsky, Kazansky, and Plate, *Ber.*, **66**, 1415 (1933).

[108] Alder, Stein, Buddenbrock, Eckardt, Frercks, and St. Schneider, *Ann.*, **514**, 1 (1934).

[109] Alder and Windemuth, *Ber.*, **71**, 2404 (1938).

[110] Kishner and Losik, *Bull. acad. sci. U.S.S.R.*, **1941**, 49 [*C. A.*, **37**, 2728 (1943)].

[111] Zelinsky and Freimann, *Ber.*, **63**, 1485 (1930).

[112] Turova-Pollak and Novitskii, *J. Gen. Chem. U.S.S.R.*, **14**, 337 (1944) [*C. A.*, **39**, 4060 (1945)].

[113] Kishner, *Bull. soc. chim. France*, (4) **45**, 767 (1929).

[114] Bartlett and Woods, *J. Am. Chem. Soc.*, **62**, 2933 (1940).

[115] Diels, Blanchard, and Heyden, *Ber.*, **47**, 2355 (1914).

[116] Rabe and Jantzen, *Ber.*, **54**, 925 (1921).

[117] Fischer and Ammann, *Ber.*, **56**, 2319 (1923).

[118] Piloty and Blömer, *Ber.*, **45**, 3749 (1912).

[119] Fischer and Zerweck, *Ber.*, **56**, 519 (1922).

[120] Fischer and Walach, *Ann.*, **450**, 109 (1926).

[121] Fischer, Baumann, and Riedl, *Ann.*, **475**, 205 (1929).

[122] Fischer and Höfelmann, *Z. physiol. Chem.*, **251**, 187 (1938).

[123] Diels and Schrum, *Ann.*, **530**, 68 (1937).

[124] Hess and Eichel, *Ber.*, **50**, 1192 (1917).

[125] Hess, *Ber.*, **52**, 1622 (1919).

[126] Fischer and Rothemund, *Ber.*, **63**, 2249 (1930).

[127] Steinkopf, Frömmel, and Leo, *Ann.*, **546**, 199 (1941).

[128] Kishner, *J. Russ. Phys. Chem. Soc.*, **45**, 949 (1913) [*C. A.*, **7**, 3964 (1913)].

[129] Schmidt and Schoeller, *Ber.*, **74**, 258 (1941).

[130] Rinkes, *Rec. trav. chim.*, **64**, 205 (1945).

[131] Kasansky and Plate, *Ber.*, **68**, 1259 (1935).

[132] Nametkin and Khukhrikova, *J. Russ. Phys. Chem. Soc.*, **47**, 425 (1915) [*C. A.*, **10**, 46 (1916)].

[133] Komppa and Hasselstrom, *Ann.*, **496**, 164 (1932).

[134] Nametkin and Khukhrikova, *Ann.*, **438**, 185 (1924).

[135] Nametkin and Kagan, *J. Gen. Chem. U.S.S.R.*, **16**, 885 (1946) [*C. A.*, **41**, 2019 (1947)].

[136] Kishner, *J. Russ. Phys. Chem. Soc.*, **45**, 957 (1913) [*C. A.*, **7**, 3965 (1913)].

[137] Zelinsky and Elagina, *Compt. rend. acad. sci. U.S.S.R.*, **49**, 568 (1945) [*C. A.*, **40**, 6058 (1946)].

[138] Semmler and Feldstein, *Ber.*, **47**, 384 (1914).

[139] Kasansky, *Ber.*, **62**, 2205 (1929).

[140] Alder and Schmidt, *Ber.*, **76**, 183 (1943).

[141] Appel, *Z. physiol. Chem.*, **218**, 202 (1933).

[142] Colacicchi, *Atti accad. Lincei*, **21**, I, 489 (1912) [*C. A.*, **7**, 1182 (1913)].

[143] Fischer and Schubert, *Ber.*, **56**, 1202 (1923).

[144] Fischer and Walach, *Ann.*, **447**, 38 (1926)

[145] Fischer and Bäumler, *Ann.*, **468**, 58 (1928).

[146] Clemo, Morgan, and Raper, *J. Chem. Soc.*, **1935**, 1743.

[147] Clemo, Metcalfe, and Raper, *J. Chem. Soc.*, **1936**, 1429.

[148] Prelog and Komzak, *Ber.*, **74**, 1705 (1941).

[149] Hess and Eichel, *Ber.*, **50**, 1386 (1917).

[150] Hess and Grau, *Ann.*, **441**, 101 (1925).

[151] Fischer and Lamatsch, *Ann.*, **462**, 240 (1928).

[152] Fischer and Nüssler, *Ann.*, **491**, 162 (1931).

[153] Fischer and Wiedemann, *Z. physiol. Chem.*, **155**, 52 (1926).

[154] Haines, Eisner, and Woodward, *J. Am. Chem. Soc.*, **67**, 1258 (1945).

[155] Davidson and Feldman, *J. Am. Chem. Soc.*, **66**, 488 (1944).

[156] Bredt and Holz, *J. prakt. Chem.*, **95**, 133 (1917).

[157] Lipp, *Ber.*, **53**, 769 (1920).

[158] Ruzicka and Liebl, *Helv. Chim. Acta*, **9**, 140 (1926).

[159] Zelinsky and Shuikin, *J. Russ. Phys. Chem. Soc.*, **62**, 1343 (1930) [*C. A.*, **25**, 2420 (1931)].

[160] Nametkin and Brüssoff, *J. prakt. Chem.*, **135**, 155 (1932).

[161] Asahina and Tukamoto, *Ber.*, **70**, 584 (1937).

[162] Tukamoto, *J. Pharm. Soc. Japan*, **59**, 149 (1939) [*C. A.*, **33**, 4223 (1939)].

[163] Naves, *Helv. Chim. Acta*, **25**, 732 (1942).

[164] Naves and Papazian, *Helv. Chim. Acta*, **25**, 984 (1942).

[165] Nametkin, Dobrovolskaya, and Oparina, *J. Russ. Phys. Chem. Soc.*, **47**, 409 (1915) [*C. A.*, **10**, 45 (1916)].

[166] Alder and Windemuth, *Ann.*, **543**, 41 (1939).

[167] Guha and Krishnamurthy, *Ber.*, **70**, 2112 (1937).

[168] Nametkin, *J. Russ. Phys. Chem. Soc.*, **47**, 1590 (1915) [*C. A.*, **10**, 2894 (1916)].

[169] Kishner, *J. Russ. Phys. Chem. Soc.*, **43**, 951 (1911) [*C. A.*, **6**, 479 (1912)].

[170] Kishner, *J. Russ. Phys. Chem. Soc.*, **45**, 1779 (1913) [*C. A.*, **8**, 911 (1914)].

[171] Kishner, *J. Russ. Phys. Chem. Soc.*, **43**, 1554 (1911) [*C. A.*, **6**, 1430 (1912)].

[172] Nametkin and Jarzev, *Ber.*, **56**, 832 (1923).

[173] Schmidt, *Ber. Schimmel & Co. Akt. Ges.*, **1941**, 50 [*C. A.*, **37**, 4380 (1943)].

[174] Nametkin and Brüssoff, *Ann.*, **432**, 207 (1923).

[175] Nametkin and Brüssoff, *Ann.*, **459**, 144 (1927).

[176] Nametkin and Brüssoff, *J. Russ. Phys. Chem. Soc.*, **55**, 525 (1924) [*C. A.*, **19**, 2945 (1925)].

[177] Hückel, *Ber.*, **58**, 1449 (1925).

[178] Zelinsky and Shuikin, *Ber.*, **62**, 2180 (1929).

[179] Bogert, Hasselstrom, and Firmenich, *Am. Perfumer*, **26**, 377 (1931) [*C. A.*, **26**, 448 (1932)].

[180] Komppa, *Ann. Acad. Sci. Fennicae*, **A59**, No. 1 (1943) [*C. A.*, **41**, 426 (1947)].

[181] Bredt and Goeb, *J. prakt. Chem.*, [2] **101**, 273 (1920).

[181a] Asahina and Ishidate, *Ber.*, **67**, 71 (1934).

[182] Miyake and Watanabe, *Proc. Imp. Acad. Tokyo*, **11**, 322 (1935) [*C. A.*, **30**, 2949 (1936)].

[183] Asahina, Ishidate, and Sano, *Ber.*, **67**, 1202 (1934).
[184] Wedekind, *Ber.*, **57**, 664 (1924).
[185] Hasselstrom, *Ann. Acad. Sci. Fennicae*, **A30**, No. 12 (1930) [*C. A.*, **25**, 3640 (1931)].
[186] Hasselstrom, *J. Am. Chem. Soc.*, **53**, 1097 (1931).
[187] Komppa and Beckmann, *Ber.*, **69**, 2783 (1936).
[188] Soffer, unpublished results.
[189] Reichstein and Reichstein, *Helv. Chim. Acta*, **13**, 1275 (1930).
[190] Asahina and Yasue, *Ber.*, **69**, 2327 (1936).
[191] Fischer and Neber, *Ann.*, **496**, 1 (1932).
[192] Fischer, Weiss, and Schubert, *Ber.*, **56**, 1194 (1923).
[193] Fager, *J. Am. Chem. Soc.*, **67**, 2217 (1945).
[194] Nametkin and Brüssoff, *J. Russ. Phys. Chem. Soc.*, **62**, 341 (1930) [*C. A.*, **24**, 4017 (1930)].
[194a] Hunsdiecker, *Ber.*, **75**, 447 (1942).
[195] Rabe and Appuhn, *Ber.*, **76**, 982 (1943).
[196] Hasselstrom and Hampton, *J. Am. Chem. Soc.*, **61**, 3445 (1939).
[197] Kawai, Sugiyama, Nakamura, and Yoshimura, *Ber.*, **72**, 367 (1939).
[198] Nenitzescu, *Bul. Soc. Chim. România*, **10**, 141 (1928) [*C. A.*, **23**, 2715 (1929)].
[199] Fischer and Schubert, *Ber.*, **57**, 610 (1924).
[200] Fischer and Kutscher, *Ann.*, **481**, 193 (1930).
[201] Fischer and Klarer, *Ann.*, **450**, 181 (1926).
[202] Fischer and Stangler, *Ann.*, **459**, 53 (1927).
[203] Fischer and Pützer, *Ber.*, **61**, 1068 (1928).
[204] Alder and Windemuth, *Ber.*, **71**, 2409 (1938).
[205] Zelinsky, Shuikin, and Fateev, *J. Gen. Chem. U.S.S.R.*, **2**, 671 (1932) [*C. A.*, **27**, 2430 (1933)].
[206] Schönberg, *Ber.*, **54**, 2838 (1921).
[207] Cruickshank and Robinson, *J. Chem. Soc.*, **1938**, 2064.
[208] Asahina, Ishidate, and Sano, *Ber.*, **69**, 343 (1936).
[209] Nenitzescu, Cioranescu, and Przemetzky, *Ber.*, **73**, 313 (1940).
[210] Dutcher and Wintersteiner, *J. Biol. Chem.*, **155**, 359 (1944).
[211] Wolff, *Ann.*, **394**, 68 (1912).
[212] Fischer and Weichmann, *Ann.*, **492**, 35 (1931).
[213] Fischer, Goldschmidt, and Nüssler, *Ann.*, **486**, 1 (1931).
[214] Corwin and Quattlebaum, *J. Am. Chem. Soc.*, **58**, 1081 (1936).
[215] Fischer and Halbig, *Ann.*, **447**, 123 (1926).
[216] Fieser and Jones, *J. Am. Chem. Soc.*, **64**, 1666 (1942).
[217] McQuillin and Robinson, *J. Chem. Soc.*, **1941**, 586.
[218] Kishner, *J. Russ. Phys. Chem. Soc.*, **43**, 1398 (1911) [*C. A.*, **6**, 735 (1912)].
[219] Nametkin and Schawrigin, *Ann.*, **516**, 199 (1935).
[220] Cason, *J. Am. Chem. Soc.*, **63**, 828 (1941).
[221] Clemo, Cook, and Raper, *J. Chem. Soc.*, **1938**, 1318.
[222] Anker, Cook, and Heilbron, *J. Chem. Soc.*, **1945**, 917.
[223] Goulden and Kon, *J. Chem. Soc.*, **1945**, 930.
[224] Fischer and Klarer, *Ann.*, **447**, 48 (1926).
[225] Fischer and Orth, *Ann.*, **502**, 237 (1933).
[226] Fischer and Bertl, *Z. physiol. Chem.*, **229**, 37 (1934).
[227] Fischer, Neumann, and Hirschbeck, *Z. physiol. Chem.*, **279**, 1 (1943).
[228] Grummitt and Jenkins, *J. Am. Chem. Soc.*, **68**, 914 (1946).
[229] Ruzicka, van der Sluys-Veer, and Jeger, *Helv. Chim. Acta*, **26**, 280 (1943).
[230] Borsche and Hahn, *Ann.*, **537**, 219 (1939).
[231] Lock and Gergely, *Ber.*, **77**, 461 (1944).
[232] Fieser and Hartwell, *J. Am. Chem. Soc.*, **60**, 2555 (1938).
[232a] Bergmann and Bergmann, *J. Chem. Soc.*, **1939**, 1021.
[233] Kishner, *J. Russ. Phys. Chem. Soc.*, **47**, 1102 (1915) [*C. A.*, **9**, 3051 (1915)].
[234] Bachmann and Morin, *J. Am. Chem. Soc.*, **66**, 553 (1944).

[235] Ghosh, *Science and Culture*, **3**, 120 (1937) [*C. A.*, **32**, 145 (1938)].
[236] Bachmann and Thomas, *J. Am. Chem. Soc.*, **63**, 598 (1941).
[237] Semmler and Jakubowicz, *Ber.*, **47**, 1141 (1914).
[238] Blumann and Schulz, *Ber.*, **64**, 1540 (1931).
[239] Bradfield, Hegde, Rao, Simonsen, and Gillam, *J. Chem. Soc.*, **1936**, 667.
[240] Naves and Perrottet, *Helv. Chim. Acta*, **24**, 3 (1941).
[241] St. Pfau and Plattner, *Helv. Chim. Acta*, **22**, 640 (1939).
[242] van Veen, *Rec. trav. chim.*, **58**, 691 (1939).
[242a] Bachmann and Horton, *J. Am. Chem. Soc.*, **69**, 58 (1947).
[243] King and Robinson, *J. Chem. Soc.*, **1941**, 465.
[244] Blum-Bergmann, *Ber.*, **65**, 109 (1932).
[245] Fieser and Peters, *J. Am. Chem. Soc.*, **54**, 4373 (1932).
[246] Nametkin, Kichkina, and Kursanov, *J. Russ. Phys. Chem. Soc.*, **61**, 1065 (1929) [*C. A.*, **24**, 841 (1930)].
[246a] Boekelheide, *J. Am. Chem. Soc.*, **69**, 790 (1947).
[247] Adams, Loewe, Jelinek, and Wolff, *J. Am. Chem. Soc.*, **63**, 1971 (1941).
[247a] Cason, *J. Am. Chem. Soc.*, **69**, 1548 (1947).
[248] Borsche and Sinn, *Ann.*, **538**, 283 (1939).
[249] Borrows, Holland, and Kenyon, *J. Chem. Soc.*, **1946**, 1083.
[250] Kishner, *J. Russ. Phys. Chem. Soc.*, **47**, 1819 (1915) [*C. A.*, **10**, 1338 (1916)].
[250a] Butenandt, Dannenberg, and von Dresler, *Z. Naturforsch.*, **1**, 222 (1946) [*C. A.*, **41**, 5888 (1947)].
[251] Ruzicka and St. Kaufmann, *Helv. Chim. Acta*, **24**, 939 (1941).
[252] Ruzicka, Schinz, and Seidel, *Helv. Chim. Acta*, **10**, 695 (1927).
[253] Dansi and Sempronj, *Gazz. chim. ital.*, **66**, 182 (1936) [*C. A.*, **31**, 1022 (1937)].
[253a] Butenandt, Dannenberg, and von Dresler, *Z. Naturforsch.*, **1**, 151 (1946) [*C. A.*, **41**, 5887 (1947)].
[254] Adams, Loewe, Smith, and McPhee, *J. Am. Chem. Soc.*, **64**, 694 (1942).
[255] Borsche and Vorback, *Ann.*, **537**, 22 (1938).
[256] Prelog, Seiwerth, Hahn, and Cerkovnikov, *Ber.*, **72**, 1325 (1939).
[257] Rabe and Riza, *Ann.*, **496**, 151 (1932).
[258] Fischer and Orth, *Ann.*, **489**, 62 (1931).
[259] Cook and Hewett, *J. Chem. Soc.*, **1934**, 365.
[260] Hewett, *J. Chem. Soc.*, **1936**, 596.
[261] Wilds, Beck, and Johnson, *J. Am. Chem. Soc.*, **68**, 2161 (1946).
[262] Hewett, *J. Chem. Soc.*, **1940**, 293.
[263] Peak and Robinson, *J. Chem. Soc.*, **1936**, 759.
[264] Peak and Robinson, *J. Chem. Soc.*, **1937**, 1581.
[265] Ramage, *J. Chem. Soc.*, **1938**, 397.
[266] Butenandt, Störmer, and Westphal, *Z. physiol. Chem.*, **208**, 149 (1932).
[267] Cook and Girard, *Nature*, **133**, 377 (1934).
[268] Pearlman and Wintersteiner, *J. Biol. Chem.*, **130**, 35 (1939).
[269] Butenandt, Wolff, and Karlson, *Ber.*, **74**, 1308 (1941).
[270] Campbell and Todd, *J. Am. Chem. Soc.*, **64**, 928 (1942).
[271] Bergmann and Blum-Bergmann, *J. Am. Chem. Soc.*, **59**, 1441 (1937).
[272] Cook, Hewett, and Robinson, *J. Chem. Soc.*, **1939**, 168.
[273] Soffer, Straus, Trail, and Sherk, *J. Am. Chem. Soc.*, **69**, 1684 (1947).
[274] Perkins and Cruz, *J. Am. Chem. Soc.*, **49**, 1070 (1927).
[275] Birch and Robinson, *J. Chem. Soc.*, **1942**, 488.
[276] Gogte, *Proc. Indian Acad. Sci.*, **16A**, 240 (1942) [*C. A.*, **37**, 4053 (1943)].
[277] Small and Meitzner, *J. Am. Chem. Soc.*, **55**, 4602 (1933).
[278] Speyer and Sarre, *Ber.*, **57**, 1422 (1924).
[279] Everett and Hewett, *J. Chem. Soc.*, **1940**, 1159.
[280] Fieser and Joshel, *J. Am. Chem. Soc.*, **62**, 1211 (1940).
[281] France, Maitland, and Tucker, *J. Chem. Soc.*, **1937**, 1739.
[281a] Heer and Miescher, *Helv. Chim. Acta*, **30**, 777 (1947).

[282] Prelog, Ruzicka, and Wieland, *Helv. Chim. Acta*, **27**, 66 (1944).

[283] Butenandt and Dannenbaum, *Z. physiol. Chem.*, **229**, 192 (1934).

[284] Yun-Hsi Wu, *J. Am. Chem. Soc.*, **66**, 1778 (1944).

[285] Cohen, Cook, Hewett, and Girard, *J. Chem. Soc.*, **1934**, 653.

[286] Wettstein, Fritzsche, Hunziker, and Miescher, *Helv. Chim. Acta*, **24**, 332E (1941).

[287] Wettstein and Miescher, *Helv. Chim. Acta*, **25**, 718 (1942).

[288] Butenandt and Suranyi, *Ber.*, **75**, 591 (1942).

[289] Milas and Milone, *J. Am. Chem. Soc.*, **68**, 738 (1946).

[290] Ruzicka, Prelog, and Meister, *Helv. Chim. Acta*, **28**, 1651 (1945).

[291] Cook and Haslewood, *J. Chem. Soc.*, **1934**, 428.

[292] Ruzicka, Sternbach, and Jeger, *Helv. Chim. Acta*, **24**, 504 (1941).

[293] Moureu, Dufraisse, and Gagnon, *Compt. rend.*, **189**, 217 (1929).

[294] Bogert and Hasselstrom, *J. Am. Chem. Soc.*, **53**, 3462 (1931).

[294a] Jeger, Dürst, and Büchi, *Helv. Chim. Acta*, **30**, 1853 (1947).

[295] Ruzicka, Waldmann, Meier, and Hösli, *Helv. Chim. Acta*, **16**, 169 (1933).

[296] Hosking and Brandt, *Ber.*, **68**, 286 (1935).

[297] Heer and Miescher, *Helv. Chim. Acta*, **29**, 1895 (1946).

[298] Ruzicka, Dalma, and Scott, *Helv. Chim. Acta*, **24**, 179E (1941).

[298a] Gallagher, *J. Biol. Chem.*, **165**, 197 (1946).

[299] Cook and Preston, *J. Chem. Soc.*, **1944**, 553.

[300] Martin, *J. Chem. Soc.*, **1941**, 679.

[300a] Martin, *Helv. Chim. Acta*, **30**, 620 (1947).

[301] Fieser and Hershberg, *J. Am. Chem. Soc.*, **60**, 2542 (1938).

[302] Ruzicka, Goldberg, and Hardegger, *Helv. Chim. Acta*, **22**, 1294 (1939).

[303] Shoppee and Prins, *Helv. Chim. Acta*, **26**, 185 (1943).

[304] Huzii and Tikamori, *J. Pharm. Soc. Japan*, **59**, 116 (1939) [*C. A.*, **33**, 4592 (1939)].

[305] Shoppee, *Helv. Chim. Acta*, **27**, 8 (1944).

[306] Shoppee, *Helv. Chim. Acta*, **27**, 246 (1944).

[307] Marker and Lawson, *J. Am. Chem. Soc.*, **61**, 586 (1939).

[308] Raoul and Meunier, *Compt. rend.*, **207**, 681 (1938).

[308a] Heard and McKay, *J. Biol. Chem.*, **165**, 677 (1946).

[309] von Euw and Reichstein, *Helv. Chim. Acta*, **27**, 1851 (1944).

[309a] Heer and Miescher, *Helv. Chim. Acta*, **30**, 550 (1947).

[309b] Lardon, *Helv. Chim. Acta*, **30**, 597 (1947).

[310] Ross, *J. Chem. Soc.*, **1945**, 25.

[311] Plattner, Bucher, and Hardegger, *Helv. Chim. Acta*, **27**, 1177 (1944).

[312] Bachmann and Carmack, *J. Am. Chem. Soc.*, **63**, 1685 (1941).

[313] Bartlett and Jones, *J. Am. Chem. Soc.*, **64**, 1837 (1942).

[314] Adelson and Bogert, *J. Am. Chem. Soc.*, **59**, 1776 (1937).

[314a] Heer and Miescher, *Helv. Chim. Acta*, **30**, 786 (1947).

[315] Wieland, Dane, and Scholz, *Z. physiol. Chem.*, **211**, 261 (1932).

[316] Ruzicka, Goldberg, and Hardegger, *Helv. Chim. Acta*, **25**, 1680 (1942).

[317] Odell and Marrian, *J. Biol. Chem.*, **125**, 333 (1938).

[318] Schwenk, Riegel, Moffett, and Stahl, *J. Am. Chem. Soc.*, **65**, 549 (1943).

[319] Reich, *Helv. Chim. Acta*, **28**, 863 (1945).

[320] Bergström, *Arkiv Kemi, Mineral. Geol.*, **14B**, No. 6 (1940) [*C. A.*, **34**, 7926 (1940)].

[321] Wieland and Jacobi, *Z. physiol. Chem.*, **148**, 232 (1925).

[322] Chakravorty and Wallis, *J. Am. Chem. Soc.*, **62**, 318 (1940).

[323] Seebeck and Reichstein, *Helv. Chim. Acta*, **26**, 536 (1943).

[324] Hicks, Berg, and Wallis, *J. Biol. Chem.*, **162**, 633 (1946).

[325] Wieland, Dane, and Martius, *Z. physiol. Chem.*, **215**, 15 (1933).

[326] Hoehn, Linsk, and Moffett, *J. Am. Chem. Soc.*, **68**, 1855 (1946).

[327] Marker and Lawson, *J. Am. Chem. Soc.*, **60**, 1334 (1938).

[328] Meystre and Miescher, *Helv. Chim. Acta*, **29**, 33 (1946).

[329] Marker, Shabica, Jones, Crooks, and Wittbecker, *J. Am. Chem. Soc.*, **64**, 1228 (1942).

[330] Kawai, *Z. physiol. Chem.*, **214**, 71 (1933).

[331] Longwell and Wintersteiner, *J. Am. Chem. Soc.*, **62**, 200 (1940).
[332] Gallagher and Hollander, *J. Biol. Chem.*, **162**, 533 (1946).
[333] Gallagher and Long, *J. Biol. Chem.*, **162**, 521 (1946).
[334] Gallagher, *J. Biol. Chem.*, **162**, 539 (1946).
[335] Wintersteiner, Moore, and Reinhardt, *J. Biol. Chem.*, **162**, 707 (1946).
[336] Haslewood, *Biochem. J.*, **38**, 108 (1944).
[337] Asahina and Nonomura, *Ber.*, **68**, 1698 (1935).
[338] Windaus, *Ann.*, **447**, 233 (1926).
[338a] Alther and Reichstein, *Helv. Chim. Acta*, **26**, 492 (1943).
[338b] Kuwada and Morimoto, *Bull. Chem. Soc. Japan*, **17**, 147 (1942) [*C. A.*, **41**, 4505 (1947)].
[339] Suszko and Schillak, *Roczniki Chem.*, **14**, 1216 (1934) [*C. A.*, **29**, 6231 (1935)].
[340] Lettré, *Z. physiol. Chem.*, **221**, 73 (1933).
[341] Windaus and Nielke, *Ann.*, **536**, 116 (1938).
[342] Whitmore, Herr, Clarke, Rowland, and Schiessler, *J. Am. Chem. Soc.*, **67**, 2059 (1945).
[343] Reindel and Niedorländer, *Ann.*, **522**, 218 (1936).
[344] Wieland and Kapitel, *Z. physiol. Chem.*, **212**, 269 (1932).
[345] Eck and Hollingsworth, *J. Am. Chem. Soc.*, **63**, 107 (1941).
[346] Blunschy, Hardegger, and Simon, *Helv. Chim. Acta*, **29**, 199 (1946).
[347] Butenandt and Ruhenstroth-Bauer, *Ber.*, **77**, 397 (1944).
[348] Stavely and Bergmann, *J. Org. Chem.*, **1**, 567 (1937).
[349] Ruzicka, Plattner, and Furrer, *Helv. Chim. Acta*, **27**, 727 (1944).
[350] Stange, *Z. physiol. Chem.*, **223**, 245 (1934).
[351] Marker, Turner, and Ulshafer, *J. Am. Chem. Soc.*, **62**, 3009 (1940).
[351a] Marker et al., *J. Am. Chem. Soc.*, **69**, 2167 (1947).
[352] Marker and Rohrmann, *J. Am. Chem. Soc.*, **61**, 1284 (1939).
[353] Grand and Reichstein, *Helv. Chim. Acta*, **28**, 344 (1945).
[354] Alther and Reichstein, *Helv. Chim. Acta*, **25**, 805 (1942).
[355] Sorkin and Reichstein, *Helv. Chim. Acta*, **26**, 2097 (1943).
[356] Noller and Lieberman, *J. Am. Chem. Soc.*, **63**, 2131 (1941).
[357] Tschesche, *Ber.*, **68**, 1090 (1935).
[358] Hoehn and Linsk, *J. Am. Chem. Soc.*, **67**, 312 (1945).
[359] Isaka, *Z. physiol. Chem.*, **266**, 117 (1940).
[360] Bilham and Kon, *J. Chem. Soc.*, **1940**, 1469.
[361] Ruzicka, Jeger, and Ingold, *Helv. Chim. Acta*, **27**, 1859 (1944).
[362] Marker, Kamm, Fleming, Popkin, and Wittle, *J. Am. Chem. Soc.*, **59**, 619 (1937).
[363] Marker and Turner, *J. Am. Chem. Soc.*, **63**, 767 (1941).
[364] Gallagher and Long, *J. Biol. Chem.*, **147**, 131 (1943).
[365] Plattner and Heusser, *Helv. Chim. Acta*, **27**, 748 (1944).
[366] Long and Gallagher, *J. Biol. Chem.*, **162**, 511 (1946).
[367] Wintersteiner and Moore, *J. Biol. Chem.*, **162**, 725 (1946).
[368] Ruzicka, Denss, and Jeger, *Helv. Chim. Acta*, **29**, 204 (1946).
[369] Ruzicka, Müller, and Schellenberg, *Helv. Chim. Acta*, **22**, 758 (1939).
[370] Ruzicka, Schellenberg, and Goldberg, *Helv. Chim. Acta*, **20**, 791 (1937).
[371] Ruzicka and Rosenkranz, *Helv. Chim. Acta*, **23**, 1311 (1940).
[372] Ruzicka, Rey, and Muhr, *Helv. Chim. Acta*, **27**, 472 (1944).
[372a] Jeger, Krüsi, and Ruzicka, *Helv. Chim. Acta*, **30**, 1048 (1947).
[373] Wieland, Pasedach, and Ballauf, *Ann.*, **529**, 68 (1937).
[374] Nath, *Z. physiol. Chem.*, **247**, 9 (1937).
[375] Ruzicka and Jeger, *Helv. Chim. Acta*, **24**, 1178 (1941).
[376] Ruzicka, Denss, and Jeger, *Helv. Chim. Acta*, **28**, 759 (1945).
[377] Ruzicka, Rey, Spillmann, and Baumgartner, *Helv. Chim. Acta*, **26**, 1659 (1943).
[378] Ruzicka, Jeger, and Ringnes, *Helv. Chim. Acta*, **27**, 972 (1944).
[379] Ruzicka and Rey, *Helv. Chim. Acta*, **24**, 529 (1941).
[380] Ruzicka and Heineman, *Helv. Chim. Acta*, **23**, 1512 (1940).
[381] Jeger, Montavon, and Ruzicka, *Helv. Chim. Acta*, **29**, 1124 (1946).

[382] Ruzicka and Marxer, *Helv. Chim. Acta*, **25**, 1561 (1942).

[383] Kon and Soper, *J. Chem. Soc.*, **1940**, 1335.

[384] Ruzicka, Rey, and Spillmann, *Helv. Chim. Acta*, **25**, 1375 (1942).

[385] Ruzicka and Häusermann, *Helv. Chim. Acta*, **25**, 439 (1942).

[386] Ruzicka, Jeger, Grob, and Hösli, *Helv. Chim. Acta*, **26**, 2283 (1943).

[387] Jeger, Norymberski, and Ruzicka, *Helv. Chim. Acta*, **27**, 1532 (1944).

[388] Jacobs and Fleck, *J. Biol. Chem.*, **96**, 341 (1932).

[389] Harris and Noller, *J. Am. Chem. Soc.*, **66**, 1005 (1944).

[390] Ruzicka, Grob, Egli, and Jeger, *Helv. Chim. Acta*, **26**, 1218 (1943).

[391] Elliott, Kon, and Soper, *J. Chem. Soc.*, **1940**, 612.

[392] Ruzicka and Schellenberg, *Helv. Chim. Acta*, **20**, 1553 (1937).

[393] Goodson, *J. Chem. Soc.*, **1938**, 999.

[394] Ruzicka and Marxer, *Helv. Chim. Acta*, **22**, 195 (1939).

[395] Ruzicka and Wirz, *Helv. Chim. Acta*, **23**, 132 (1940).

[396] Ruzicka and Wirz, *Helv. Chim. Acta*, **24**, 248 (1941).

[397] Ruzicka and Wirz, *Helv. Chim. Acta*, **22**, 948 (1939).

[398] Ruzicka and Brenner, *Helv. Chim. Acta*, **22**, 1523 (1939).

[399] Ruzicka, Jeger, Redel, and Volli, *Helv. Chim. Acta*, **28**, 199 (1945).

[400] Ruzicka and Jeger, *Helv. Chim. Acta*, **24**, 1236 (1941).

[401] Hoehn and Mason, *J. Am. Chem. Soc.*, **62**, 569 (1940).

[402] Ruzicka and Giacomello, *Helv. Chim. Acta*, **19**, 1136 (1936).

[403] Ruzicka and Jeger, *Helv. Chim. Acta*, **25**, 1409 (1942).

[404] Fischer and Krauss, *Ann.*, **521**, 261 (1936).

[405] Fischer, Moldenhauer, and Süs, *Ann.*, **485**, 1 (1931).

[406] Fischer and Gibian, *Ann.*, **550**, 208 (1942).

[407] Fischer, Lakatos, and Schnell, *Ann.*, **509**, 201 (1934).

[408] Conant, Dietz, and Werner, *J. Am. Chem. Soc.*, **53**, 4436 (1931).

[409] Ruzicka and Marxer, *Helv. Chim. Acta*, **23**, 144 (1940).

[410] Jeger, Nisoli, and Ruzicka, *Helv. Chim. Acta*, **29**, 1183 (1946).

[411] Bilham and Kon, *J. Chem. Soc.*, **1941**, 552.

[412] Fischer and Gibian, *Ann.*, **552**, 153 (1942).

[413] Fischer and Riedmair, *Ann.*, **505**, 87 (1933).

INDEX

Numbers in **bold-face** type refer to experimental procedures

Time for Bed

stars

slippers

comb

mirror

pillow

bed

bathtub

toothbrush

soap

sponge

What time does Elephant go to bed?

Christmas Time

Christmas tree

holly

lights

presents

tinsel

stocking

card

mistletoe

carol singer

angel

Who is dressed as
Santa Claus?

Learn and Play

paint brushes

easel

picture

blackboard

scissors

paints

pencils

clock

chalk

paper

What is Elephant painting?

Down by the River

fish

jar

rabbit

tadpole

bees

fishing rod

windmill

net

caterpillar

butterfly

How many bees are there?

Out in the Snow

ice skates

snowman

skis

gloves

scarf

toboggan

snowballs

robin

icicles

hat

Who is skating?

At the Shops

sweater

shoes

jeans

bag

shirt

socks

money

cap

tie

skirt

What is Elephant buying?

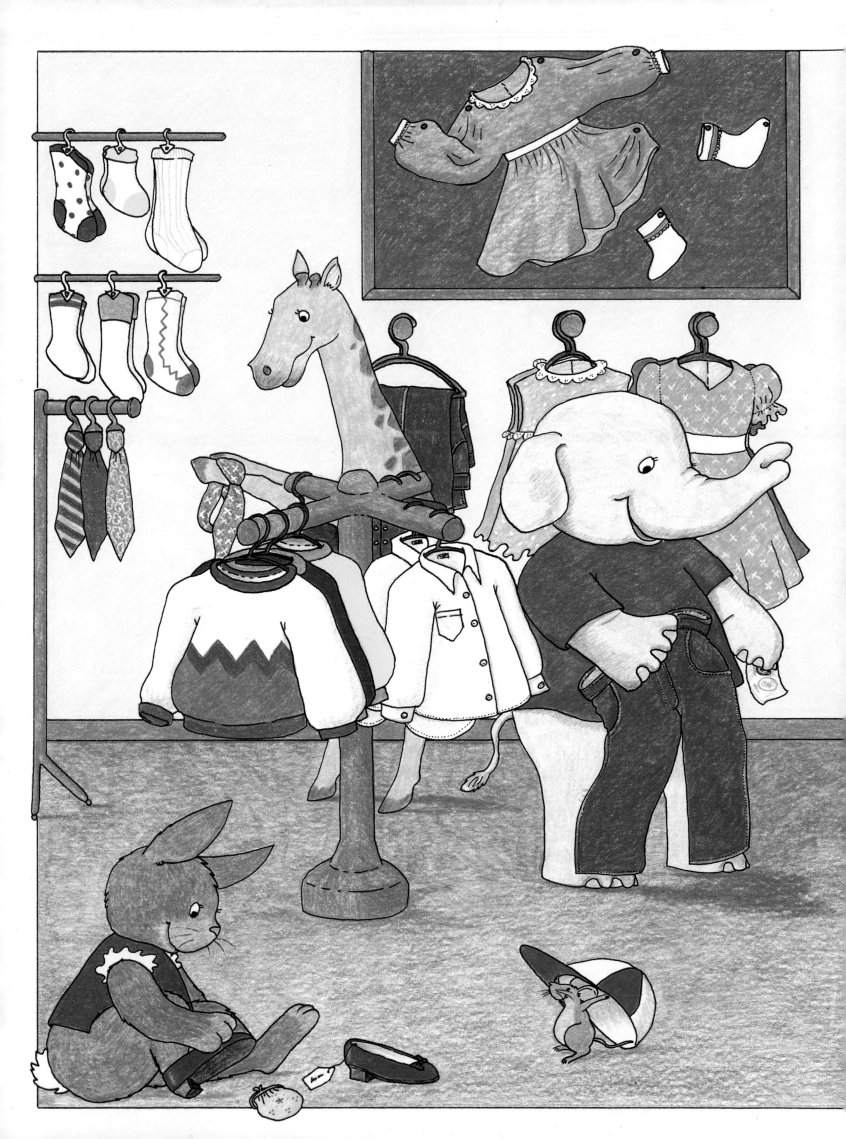

Fruit Picking

basket

pear

strawberry

ladder

gate

raspberry

plum

apple

tree

squirrel

How many baskets are there?

On the Farm

tractor

pig

chick

horse

goat

scarecrow

lamb

cow

duck

pond

What noises do the animals make?

Working Outside

hammer

window

toolbox

hammock

nail

garage

paint

broom

fence

car

How many windows
are there?

A Rainy Day

puddle

umbrella

boots

raincoat

rainbow

rain hat

frog

boat

bridge

cloud

Who is jumping in
the puddles?

Happy Birthday, Elephant

cake

candle

balloon

present

straw

party hat

camera

blindfold

cookie

sandwich

How old is Elephant?

Cooking in the Kitchen

stove

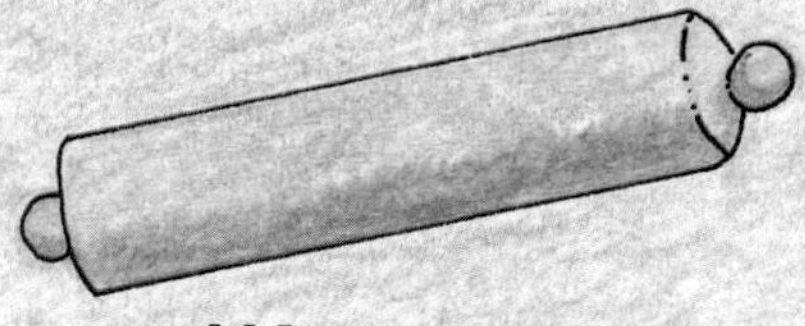

rolling pin

flour

apron

butter

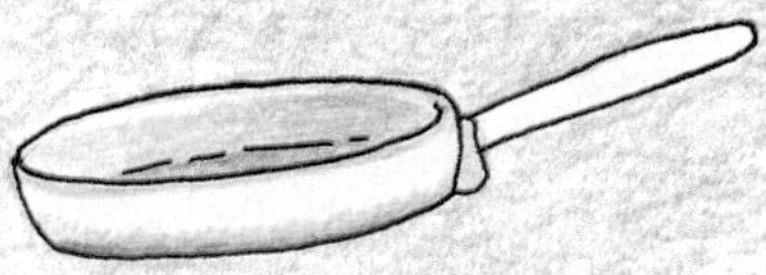

frying pan

mixing bowl

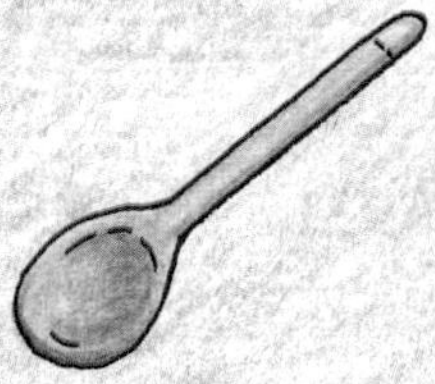

wooden spoon

eggs

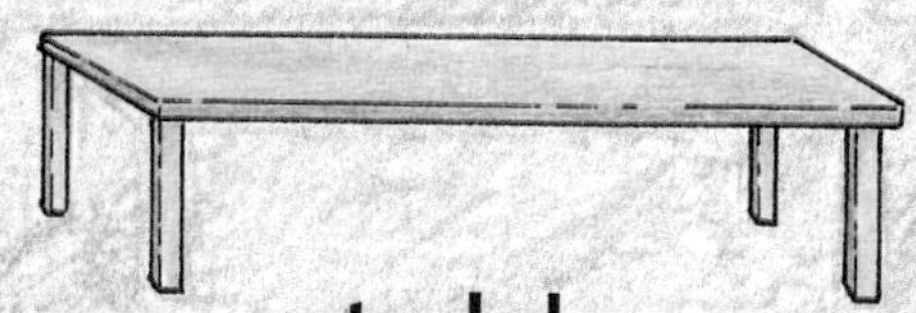

table

How many blue cups can you see?

Playing in a Band

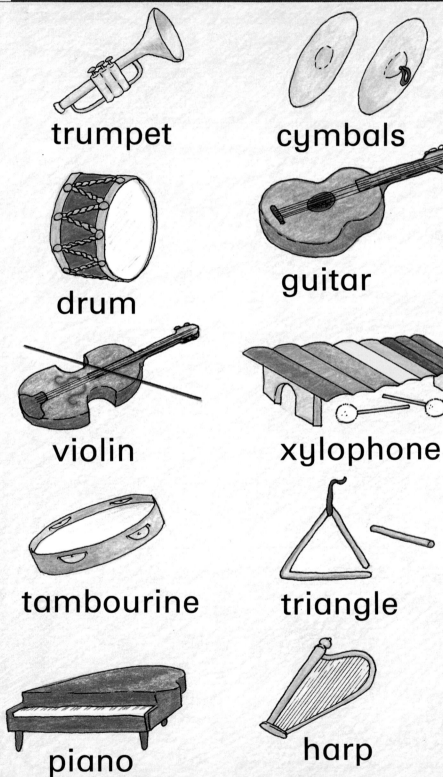

trumpet

cymbals

drum

guitar

violin

xylophone

tambourine

triangle

piano

harp

How do you play the different instruments?

A Visit to the Toyshop

jack-in-the-box

doll

teddy bear

train

jig-saw puzzle

car

drum

book

plane

blocks

How many blocks are there?

The Animals' Fancy Dress

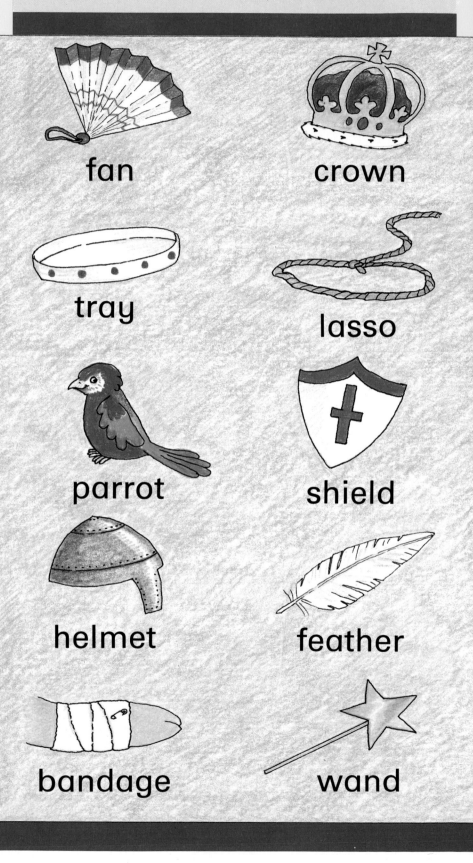

fan

crown

tray

lasso

parrot

shield

helmet

feather

bandage

wand

Who is dressed as a king?

Playing Games

tennis racquet

yo-yo

hoop

marbles

dominoes

hopscotch

roller skates

basket ball

shuttlecock

bicycle

How many balls are there?

In the Garden

watering can

sprinkler

cabbage

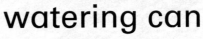

flowerpot

flower

wheelbarrow

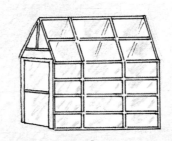
greenhouse

carrot

shed

bush

What is Elephant planting?

At the Circus

juggler

acrobat

clown

tightrope

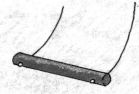
trapeze

ringmaster

popcorn

ring

stilts

pie

Who is throwing the custard pie?

In the Park

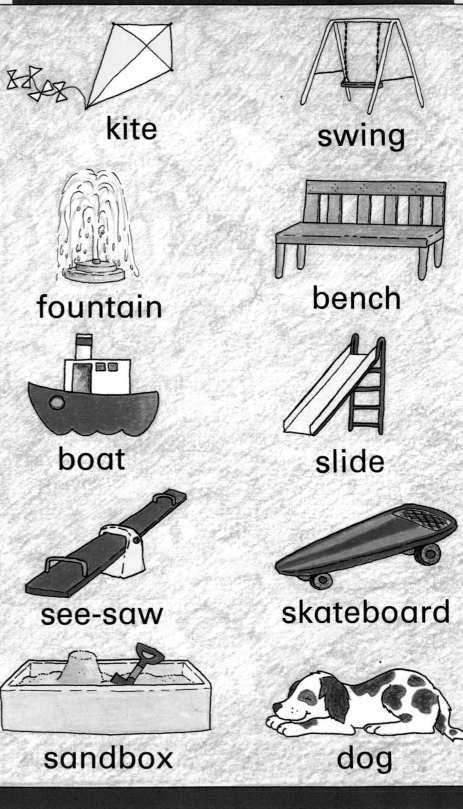

kite

swing

fountain

bench

boat

slide

see-saw

skateboard

sandbox

dog

Where is the boat?

On the Beach

bucket

sandcastle

flag

ice cream

beach ball

seagull

ship

starfish

towel

crab

How many shells
can you find?

The Elephant's Find and Say

Brimax Books Newmarket England

Illustrated by Lesley Blackman

Edited and compiled by Deborah Campbell-Todd
Cover design by Oxprint Ltd

ISBN 0 86112 744 7
© Brimax Books Ltd 1991. All rights reserved.
Published by Brimax Books Ltd, Newmarket, England 1991.
Third printing 1991.
Printed in Portugal